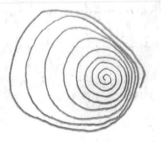

HOLT
ALGEBRA 1

Eugene D. Nichols
Mervine L. Edwards
E. Henry Garland
Sylvia A. Hoffman
Albert Mamary
William F. Palmer

Holt, Rinehart and Winston, Inc.
Harcourt Brace Jovanovich, Inc.

Orlando • Austin • San Diego • Chicago • Dallas • Toronto

About the Authors

Eugene D. Nichols
Distinguished Professor of Mathematics Education
Florida State University
Tallahassee, Florida

Mervine L. Edwards
Chairman, Department of Mathematics
Shore Regional High School
West Long Branch, New Jersey

E. Henry Garland
Head of Mathematics Department
Developmental Research School
DRS Professor
Florida State University
Tallahassee, Florida

Sylvia A. Hoffman
Resource Consultant in Mathematics
Illinois State Board of Education
State of Illinois

Albert Mamary
Superintendent of Schools for Instruction
Johnson City Central School District
Johnson City, New York

William F. Palmer
Professor of Education and Director
Center for Mathematics and Science Education
Catawba College
Salisbury, North Carolina

123456   036   98765432   ISBN 0-03-005419-2

Acknowledgments

Reviewers

Jeanette Gann
Mathematics Supervisor
High Point Schools
High Point, North Carolina

Patrice Gossard, Ph.D.
Mathematics Teacher
Cobb County School District
Marietta, Georgia

Linda Harvey
Mathematics Teacher
Reagan High School
Austin, Texas

Gerald Lee
Chairman, Mathematics Department
McArthur High School
Lawton, Oklahoma

Janet Page
Mathematics Teacher
Hoffman Estates High School
Hoffman Estates, Illinois

Photo Credits

Illustration

Chapter Contents

1 Introduction to Algebra   xiv

1.1	Algebraic Expressions	1
1.2	Grouping Symbols	5
1.3	Exponents	9
1.4	Formulas from Geometry	13
1.5	The Commutative and Associative Properties	17
1.6	The Distributive Property	22
1.7	Combining Like Terms	26
1.8	Solution Sets of Sentences	30

Special Features

Focus on Reading 11, 33
Application: Temperature Humidity Index 8
Application: Heat Transfer 21
Application: Costs and Profit 29
Problem Solving Strategies: Understanding
   the Problem 35
Using the Calculator 8, 10, 14

Review and Testing

Mixed Review 8, 12, 21, 25, 29, 34
Midchapter Review 16
Chapter 1 Review 36
Chapter 1 Test 38
College Prep Test 39

v

2 Operations with Real Numbers   40

2.1	The Set of Real Numbers	41
2.2	Opposites and Absolute Value	45
2.3	Addition on a Number Line	49
2.4	Adding Real Numbers	53
2.5	Subtraction of Real Numbers	57
2.6	Multiplication of Real Numbers	62
2.7	Division of Real Numbers	67
2.8	Mixed Operations	72
2.9	Like Terms: Real Number Coefficients	75
2.10	Removing Parentheses: Negative Factors	79

Special Features

Focus on Reading **64, 73**
Application: Windchill **61**
Application: Automobile Rental Rates **66**
Using the Calculator **54, 68, 71**
Brainteaser **78**

Review and Testing

Mixed Review **44, 48, 52, 56, 66, 71, 74, 78, 81**
Midchapter Review **60**
Chapter 2 Review **82**
Chapter 2 Test **84**
College Prep Test **85**
Cumulative Review: Chapters 1–2 . . . . **86**

3 Solving Equations   88

3.1	Solving Equations by Adding or Subtracting	89
3.2	Solving Equations by Multiplying or Dividing	94
3.3	Using Two Properties of Equality	98
3.4	Equations with the Variable on Both Sides	102
3.5	Equations with Parentheses	106
3.6	Problem Solving: Using Formulas	110
3.7	Proving Statements	115

Special Features

Focus on Reading **104**
Application: Mathematics in Typing **93**
Application: Thunder and Lightning **109**
Application: The Shock Wave **114**
Problem Solving Strategies: Developing a Plan **101**

Review and Testing

Mixed Review **93, 97, 105, 108, 113, 118**
Midchapter Review **100**
Mixed Problem Solving **119**
Chapter 3 Review **120**
Chapter 3 Test **122**
College Prep Test **123**

4 Applying Equations — 124

4.1 Translating English to Algebra 125
4.2 Problem Solving: Two or More Numbers 129
4.3 Problem Solving: Consecutive Integer Problems 135
4.4 Problem Solving: Perimeter and Angle Measure 139
4.5 Equations with Fractions 144
4.6 Equations with Decimals 147
4.7 Percent Problems 150
4.8 Problem Solving: Using Percent 154

Special Features
Focus on Reading 137
Application: Gear Depths 143
Problem Solving Strategies: Carrying Out the Plan 157
Using the Calculator 151
Brainteaser 150

Review and Testing
Mixed Review 128, 134, 138, 146, 149, 153, 156
Midchapter Review 143
Chapter 4 Review 158
Chapter 4 Test 160
College Prep Test 161
Cumulative Review: Chapters 1–4 162

5 Inequalities and Absolute Value — 164

5.1 The Addition and Subtraction Properties
    of Inequality 165
5.2 The Multiplication and Division Properties
    of Inequality 170
5.3 Conjunctions and Disjunctions 175
5.4 Combining Inequalities 179
5.5 Problem Solving: Using Inequalities 186
5.6 Equations with Absolute Value 190
5.7 Inequalities with Absolute Value 192

Special Features
Focus on Reading 182
Application: Triangle Inequality 189
Problem Solving Strategies: Looking Back 185
Brainteaser 184

Review and Testing
Mixed Review 169, 174, 178, 189, 191, 194
Midchapter Review 184
Mixed Problem Solving 195
Chapter 5 Review 196
Chapter 5 Test 198
College Prep Test 199

6 Powers and Polynomials 200

6.1	Multiplying Monomials	201
6.2	Powers of Monomials	204
6.3	Dividing Monomials	207
6.4	Negative Exponents	210
6.5	Scientific Notation	214
6.6	Simplifying Polynomials	218
6.7	Addition and Subtraction of Polynomials	222
6.8	Multiplying a Polynomial by a Monomial	226
6.9	Multiplying Binomials	229
6.10	Special Products	232

Special Features

Focus on Reading 220, 230, 234
Application: The Earth's Hydrosphere 217
Application: Compound Interest 225
Using the Calculator 215, 217, 225
Brainteaser 235

Review and Testing

Mixed Review 203, 206, 209, 213, 216, 225, 228, 231, 235
Midchapter Review 221
Chapter 6 Review 236
Chapter 6 Test 238
College Prep Test 239
Cumulative Review: Chapters 1–6 240

7 Factoring Polynomials 242

7.1	Introduction to Factoring	243
7.2	Greatest Common Monomial Factor	248
7.3	Factoring Trinomials: $x^2 + bx + c$	252
7.4	Factoring Trinomials: $ax^2 + bx + c$	256
7.5	Two Special Cases of Factoring	259
7.6	Combined Types of Factoring	263
7.7	Solving Quadratic Equations by Factoring	267
7.8	Standard Form of a Quadratic Equation	272
7.9	Problem Solving: Using Quadratic Equations	277

Special Features

Focus on Reading 264, 269
Application: Gas Mileage 255
Application: Commission Sales 266
Application: Boiling Point of Water 271
Problem Solving Strategies: Organizing the Possibilities 282
Using the Calculator 244
Brainteaser 251, 276

Review and Testing

Mixed Review 247, 251, 255, 258, 266, 270, 276, 281
Midchapter Review 262
Mixed Problem Solving 283

Chapter 7 Review...................................284
Chapter 7 Test....................................286
College Prep Test.................................287

8 Rational Expressions 288

8.1 Simplifying Rational Expressions................................289
8.2 Simplifying Rational Expressions: Convenient Form..............294
8.3 Multiplying Rational Expressions................................297
8.4 Dividing Rational Expressions...................................302
8.5 Adding and Subtracting: Like Denominators.....................306
8.6 Adding and Subtracting: Unlike Denominators...................311
8.7 Adding and Subtracting: Polynomial Denominators..............316
8.8 Dividing Polynomials...320
8.9 Complex Rational Expressions.................................325

Special Features
Focus on Reading...295, 313
Problem Solving Strategies: Testing Conditions.....................324

Review and Testing
Mixed Review.....................293, 296, 301, 305, 315, 319, 323, 329
Midchapter Review...310
Chapter 8 Review..330
Chapter 8 Test..332
College Prep Test...333
Cumulative Review: Chapters 1–8..................................334

9 Applying Rational Expressions 336

9.1 Rational Equations..337
9.2 Ratios and Proportions......................................343
9.3 Literal Equations...349
9.4 Problem Solving: Motion Problems.............................354
9.5 Problem Solving: Work Problems...............................359
9.6 Dimensional Analysis..364

Special Features
Focus on Reading..346
Application: Direct Variation......................................348
Using the Calculator..345, 350
Brainteaser...353

Review and Testing
Mixed Review..............................342, 348, 358, 363, 366
Midchapter Review...353
Mixed Problem Solving...367
Chapter 9 Review..368
Chapter 9 Test..370
College Prep Test...371

ix

10 Relations, Functions, and Variations 372

10.1	Coordinates of Points in a Plane	373
10.2	Relations and Functions	378
10.3	Values of a Function	382
10.4	Equations with Two Variables	386
10.5	Graphing Linear Equations	392
10.6	Direct Variation	397
10.7	Inverse Variation	401

Special Features

Focus on Reading 375, 395, 399
Application: Fixed and Variable Costs 391
Problem Solving Strategies: Making a Graph 390
Problem Solving Strategies: Restating the Problem 405
Using the Calculator 381

Review and Testing

Mixed Review 377, 381, 385, 396, 400, 404
Midchapter Review 389
Chapter 10 Review 406
Chapter 10 Test 408
College Prep Test 409
Cumulative Review: Chapters 1–10 410

11 Analytic Geometry 412

11.1	Slope of a Line	413
11.2	Equation of a Line: Point–Slope Form	418
11.3	Equation of a Line: Slope–Intercept Form	424
11.4	Line Relationships	429
11.5	Graphing Linear Inequalities	433

Special Features

Application: Termperature and Altitude 423
Problem Solving Strategies: Using Logical Reasoning 438

Review and Testing

Mixed Review 417, 422, 432, 437
Midchapter Review 428
Mixed Problem Solving 439
Chapter 11 Review 440
Chapter 11 Test 442
College Prep Test 443

12 Systems of Linear Equations — 444

12.1	Systems of Equations—Graphing	445
12.2	The Substitution Method	452
12.3	Problem Solving: Using Two Variables	456
12.4	The Addition Method	460
12.5	The Multiplication with Addition Method	464
12.6	Problem Solving: Digit Problems	468
12.7	Problem Solving: Age Problems	472
12.8	Problem Solving: Coin and Mixture Problems	475
12.9	Problem Solving: Motion Problems	479
12.10	Systems of Inequalities	483

Special Features

Focus on Reading 465
Application: Linear Programming 486
Problem Solving Strategies: Working Backwards 451

Review and Testing

Mixed Review **450, 455, 459, 463, 471, 474, 478, 482, 485**
Midchapter Review 467
Chapter 12 Review 488
Chapter 12 Test 490
College Prep Test 491
Cumulative Review: Chapters 1–12 492

13 Radicals — 494

13.1	Rational Numbers and Irrational Numbers	495
13.2	Square Roots	500
13.3	Approximating Square Roots	504
13.4	The Pythagorean Theorem	508
13.5	Simplifying Radicals	513
13.6	Adding and Subtracting Radicals	516
13.7	Multiplying Radicals	519
13.8	Dividing Radicals	522
13.9	Radical Equations	526

Special Features

Focus on Reading 502
Application: Using Formulas 507
Using the Calculator 501

Review and Testing

Mixed Review **499, 503, 507, 512, 518, 521, 525, 528**
Midchapter Review 515
Mixed Problem Solving 529
Chapter 13 Review 530
Chapter 13 Test 532
College Prep Test 533

14 Quadratic Equations and Functions   534

14.1 The Square Root Property 535
14.2 Completing the Square 539
14.3 The Quadratic Formula 543
14.4 Choosing a Method of Solution 548
14.5 Problem Solving: Quadratic Equations and Geometry 553
14.6 Quadratic Functions 558
14.7 Quadratic Functions and the Discriminant 564

Special Features
Focus on Reading 550
Application: Stopping Distance for a Car 552
Problem Solving Strategies: Checking Assumptions 557
Using the Calculator 554
Brainteaser 567

Review and Testing
Mixed Review 538, 542, 547, 556, 563, 567
Midchapter Review 552
Chapter 14 Review 568
Chapter 14 Test 570
College Prep Test 571
Cumulative Review 572

15 Trigonometry   574

15.1 Similar Triangles 575
15.2 Trigonometric Ratios 579
15.3 Trigonometric Tables 583
15.4 Right-Triangle Solutions 586
15.5 Problem Solving: Applying Trigonometry 590

Special Features
Focus on Reading 576
Brainteaser 589

Review and Testing
Mixed Review 578, 582, 589, 592
Midchapter Review 585
Mixed Problem Solving 593
Chapter 15 Review 594
Chapter 15 Test 596
College Prep Test 597

16 Probability and Statistics 598

16.1	Probability of an Event	599
16.2	Probability: Compound Events	603
16.3	Mean, Median, and Mode	608
16.4	Statistical Graphs	614
16.5	Range and Standard Deviation	619

Special Features

Focus on Reading	611
Brainteaser	607

Review and Testing

Mixed Review	602, 607, 618, 621
Midchapter Review	613
Chapter 16 Review	622
Chapter 16 Test	624
College Prep Test	625
Cumulative Review: Chapters 1–16	626

Computer Investigations: Algebra 1	628
Table of Roots and Powers	642
Table of Trigonometric Ratios	643
Glossary	644
Selected Answers to Written Exercises	650
Index	680

1 INTRODUCTION TO ALGEBRA

In very dry forest areas, fire spotters of the U.S. Forest
Service watch for smoke from towers high above the trees.
Using this firefinder table, they can relay the exact direction
to the nearest firefighting unit.

1.1 Algebraic Expressions

To evaluate algebraic expressions for given values of the variables
To write algebraic expressions for word descriptions

The study of algebra involves numbers and operations. A **numerical expression** contains one or more numbers and may also contain one or more operations. The following are examples of numerical expressions.

$$12 \qquad 7.6 \qquad 5 + 9 \qquad 14 - 7 \times 2$$

In algebra, letters are often used to represent numbers. For example, when you buy movie tickets at $5 per ticket, the cost depends on the number of tickets you buy.

Number of tickets bought	Cost in dollars
1	5×1, or 5
2	5×2, or 10
3	5×3, or 15
4	5×4, or 20
5	5×5, or 25
⋮	⋮
n	$5 \times n$

In the chart above, the letter n is a *variable* that represents the number of tickets. A **variable** is a symbol that represents two or more numbers.

An **algebraic expression** contains one or more variables and usually one or more operations. It may also contain numbers. The algebraic expression $5 \times n$ can be written in several other ways:

$$5 \cdot n \qquad 5(n) \qquad (5)n \qquad 5n$$

To **evaluate an expression**, replace each variable with a number and find the numerical value. To evaluate $5n$ for $n = 6$, substitute 6 for n. The result is

$$5n = 5(6)$$
$$= 30$$

Thus, the value of $5n$ is 30 for $n = 6$.

EXAMPLE 1   Evaluate $2xy$ for $x = 4$ and $y = 3$.

Solution $2 \cdot x \cdot y$ ⟵ The expression $2xy$ means $2 \cdot x \cdot y$.
$2 \cdot 4 \cdot 3$ ⟵ Substitute 4 for x and 3 for y.

$\underbrace{8 \quad \cdot 3}$

24

TRY THIS   **1.** Evaluate $3mn$ for $m = \frac{2}{3}$ and $n = \frac{1}{2}$.

The chart below shows algebraic expressions with the variable x.

Algebraic expression	English expressions	Value for $x = 9$
$x + 28$	x plus 28 28 added to x x increased by 28 28 more than x the *sum* of x and 28	$x + 28$ $9 + 28$ 37
$42 - x$	42 minus x x subtracted from 42 x less than 42 the *difference*, 　42 decreased by x	$42 - x$ $42 - 9$ 33
$16 \cdot x$, or $16x$	16 times x 16 multiplied by x the *product* of 16 and x	$16x$ $16 \cdot 9$ 144
$18 \div x$, or $\dfrac{18}{x}$	18 divided by x the *quotient*, 　$18 \div x$	$18 \div x$ $18 \div 9$ 2

Compare: x *decreased by* 16 and x *less than* 16

$x - 16$ $16 - x$

EXAMPLE 2   Evaluate $\dfrac{x}{y}$ for $x = 12.8$ and $y = 4$.

Solution $\dfrac{x}{y} = \dfrac{12.8}{4} = 3.2$ ⟵ Substitute 12.8 for x and 4 for y.

Thus, $\dfrac{x}{y} = 3.2$ for $x = 12.8$ and $y = 4$.

TRY THIS   **2.** Evaluate $\dfrac{2a}{b}$ for $a = 3.9$ and $b = 6$.

Algebraic expressions can represent word descriptions.

EXAMPLE 3 Write an algebraic expression for each word description.
  a. the cost in cents of p pounds of tomatoes at 79¢ per pound
  b. y years less than x years
  c. $\frac{3}{4}$ the number of students s
  d. twice the number of people p
  e. the cost of one pencil, in dollars, if n pencils cost $1.46

Solutions a. $79p$ b. $x - y$ c. $\frac{3}{4}s$ d. $2p$ e. $\frac{1.46}{n}$

TRY THIS 3. Write an algebraic expression for x dollars more than ten dollars.

Classroom Exercises

Give the meaning for each expression.

1. $x + 4$ **2.** $5 - y$ **3.** $6b$ **4.** $\frac{a}{7}$ **5.** cd **6.** $3 \cdot y$

Evaluate.

7. $3x$ for $x = 12$ **8.** $5y$ for $y = 9$ **9.** $a + 6$ for $a = 13$
10. $7 + z$ for $z = 17$ **11.** $q - 5$ for $q = 23$ **12.** $21 - r$ for $r = 6$
13. $\frac{x}{3}$ for $x = 18$ **14.** $\frac{21}{y}$ for $y = 7$ **15.** $p + q$ for $p = 9$ and $q = 3$
16. $-10a$ for $a = \frac{2}{5}$ **17.** $30 - t$ for $t = 2.3$ **18.** pq for $p = 10$ and $q = -3.4$

Written Exercises

Evaluate.

1. $7p$ for $p = 9$ **2.** $x + y$ for $x = 12$ and $y = 9$
3. $\frac{16}{y}$ for $y = 2$ **4.** $\frac{x}{9}$ for $x = 63$
5. $a + b$ for $a = 7$ and $b = 13$ **6.** $8z$ for $z = 15$
7. $c - d$ for $c = 18$ and $d = 3$ **8.** mn for $m = 3$ and $n = 15$
9. $3rs$ for $r = 2$ and $s = 7$ **10.** $p - q$ for $p = 28$ and $q = 14$
11. $\frac{a}{b}$ for $a = 52$ and $b = 13$ **12.** $\frac{c}{d}$ for $c = 48$ and $d = 3$

Write an algebraic expression for each word description.

13. the cost, in dollars, of y pounds of peaches at 89¢ per pound
14. $45 decreased by the amount spent, s, in dollars

15. the total number of weeks y in x days

16. the cost, in dollars, of each sticker if n stickers cost $1.35

17. the number of sunny days s subtracted from 365

18. the cost, in cents, of 5 pounds of beans at c cents per pound

19. $\frac{2}{3}$ of the number of girls g

20. 5 less than the number of boys b in the class

21. 3 more than the number of cars c in the parking lot

22. twice the number of record albums r

23. $\frac{3}{4}$ of the number of seats s

24. $1\frac{1}{2}$ times the regular pay rate r

25. $\frac{1}{3}$ the length b of a bat

26. x inches less than 8 inches

27. two-tenths of the population p

28. 5 times the number of books b

Evaluate.

29. $x + 8$ for $x = 22.7$

30. $24.3 - n$ for $n = 9.7$

31. $n - 2.4$ for $n = 33$

32. $n \div 36$ for $n = 7.2$

33. $x + \frac{1}{2}$ for $x = 2\frac{1}{2}$

34. $y - \frac{1}{4}$ for $y = 5\frac{3}{4}$

35. $\frac{3.6}{p}$ for $p = 3$

36. $1.2w$ for $w = 8$

37. ab for $a = 0.4$ and $b = 13$

38. $b - a$ for $a = 8$ and $b = 13.6$

39. $\frac{m}{n}$ for $m = 54$ and $n = 0.6$

40. $\frac{3}{5}y$ for $y = \frac{2}{3}$

41. $\frac{m}{n}$ for $m = 3.51$ and $n = 100$

42. $x - y$ for $x = 0.54$ and $y = 0.37$

43. $\frac{x}{3.2}$ for $x = 13.12$

44. $\frac{23.22}{m}$ for $m = 4.3$

45. xy for $x = \frac{1}{3}$ and $y = 2\frac{1}{4}$

46. $a + b$ for $a = 1.25$ and $b = 1.5$

47. $c - d$ for $c = \frac{3}{5}$ and $d = \frac{1}{4}$

48. rs for $r = \frac{3}{8}$ and $s = 1\frac{1}{3}$

49. $\frac{m}{n}$ for $m = 6.2$ and $n = 0.4$

50. $\frac{a}{b}$ for $a = \frac{2}{3}$ and $b = \frac{3}{9}$

Write an algebraic expression for each word description.

51. A number x is 4 less than another number. Write an algebraic expression for the larger number.

52. Jim's height h is twice Bill's height. Write an algebraic expression for Bill's height.

53. The number of dollars d in Carey's bank is one-third the number of dollars in Jane's bank. Write an algebraic expression for the number of dollars in Jane's bank.

54. The number of fans f is 18 more than the number of players. Write an algebraic expression for the number of players.

1.2 Grouping Symbols

To simplify numerical expressions by using the rules for order of operations

To evaluate algebraic expressions

To **simplify an expression** such as $4 + 5 + 8$, complete the addition and write the sum 17. Examine how $36 - 5 \cdot 4$ might be simplified.

Multiply first; then subtract.

$$36 - 5 \cdot 4$$
$$36 - \quad 20$$
$$16 \longleftarrow \text{Correct}$$

Subtract first; then multiply.

$$36 - 5 \cdot 4$$
$$31 \quad \cdot 4$$
$$124 \quad \longleftarrow \text{Incorrect}$$

It would be confusing for a numerical expression to name more than one number. So the following order of operations is agreed upon.

Order of Operations
1. Do all multiplications and divisions in order from left to right.
2. Do all additions and subtractions in order from left to right.

EXAMPLE 1   Simplify: **a.** $16 + 8 \cdot 9$ **b.** $18 - 8 \div 4$

Solutions

a. Multiply first; then add.
$$16 + 8 \cdot 9$$
$$16 + \quad 72$$
$$88$$

b. Divide first; then subtract.
$$18 - 8 \div 4$$
$$18 - \quad 2$$
$$16$$

TRY THIS   Simplify: **1.** $24 - 6 \div 3$ **2.** $12 + 4 \cdot 3$

Parentheses ( ) and brackets [ ] are called *grouping symbols*. Do operations within grouping symbols first. A multiplication symbol may be omitted when it occurs next to a grouping symbol. For example,

$$3 \cdot (5 + 2) = 3(5 + 2) = 3(7).$$

If there is more than one set of grouping symbols, operate within the innermost symbols first.

$$5[8 + (7 - 3)] = 5[8 + 4] = 60$$

EXAMPLE 2 Simplify.

    a. $11 + 21 \div (16 - 9)$ **b.** $18 - 6[4 \div (9 - 7)]$

Solutions **a.** $11 + 21 \div \underbrace{(16 - 9)}$ **b.** $18 - 6[4 \div \underbrace{(9 - 7)}]$

               $11 + \underbrace{21 \div \quad 7}$ $18 - \underbrace{6[4 \div 2]}$

               $\underbrace{11 + \quad 3}$ $18 - \underbrace{6[2]}$

                  14 $\underbrace{18 - 12}$

                                                 6

EXAMPLE 3 Evaluate $11 - 8x$ for $x = \frac{3}{4}$.

Solution $11 - 8x = 11 - \underbrace{8 \cdot \frac{3}{4}}$ $\longleftarrow$ $8 \cdot \frac{3}{4} = \frac{\overset{2}{\cancel{8}}}{1} \cdot \frac{3}{\underset{1}{\cancel{4}}} = \frac{6}{1} = 6$

             $= \underbrace{11 - \quad 6}$

             $= \quad\quad 5$

TRY THIS

3. Simplify $15 - 2[3(7 - 5)]$.

4. Evaluate $20 - 2y$ for $y = 4.5$.

A fraction bar is also a grouping symbol. Perform operations within the numerator and the denominator before simplifying further.

EXAMPLE 4 Simplify $\dfrac{2(13 - 7)}{15 - 6 \cdot 2}$.

Solution $\dfrac{2(13 - 7)}{15 - 6 \cdot 2} = \dfrac{2 \cdot 6}{15 - 12} = \dfrac{12}{3}$, or 4

EXAMPLE 5 Evaluate $x + 5(8 - y)$ for $x = 9$ and $y = 3$.

Solution $x + 5(8 - y) = 9 + 5(8 - 3)$

                    $= 9 + 5 \cdot 5$

                    $= 9 + 25 = 34$

TRY THIS

5. Simplify $\dfrac{3(15 - 7)}{12 - 3 \cdot 2}$.

6. Evaluate $3(x + 5) - y$ for $x = 2$ and $y = 4$.

Classroom Exercises

What is the first operation to perform in simplifying each expression?

1. $6 \cdot 8 - 5$ **2.** $4 + 3 \cdot 9$ **3.** $7 - 8 \div 2$ **4.** $\dfrac{16}{5 + 3}$

Simplify.

5. $14 - 5 \cdot 2$ **6.** $(14 - 5) \cdot 2$ **7.** $12 + 6 \div 3$ **8.** $(12 + 6) \div 3$

Evaluate.

9. $5 + 2x$ for $x = 3$

10. $14 \div c - 3$ for $c = 2$

11. $7 - (8 - a)$ for $a = 6$

12. $x \div (9 - 7)$ for $x = 4$

Written Exercises

Simplify.

1. $15 \cdot 7 + 9$ **2.** $15 + 7 \cdot 9$ **3.** $20 - 4 \cdot 3$

4. $24 \div 3 + 5$ **5.** $18 - 2 \cdot 9$ **6.** $24 - 48 \div 2$

7. $43 + 140 \div 70$ **8.** $24 \div 8 \cdot 2$ **9.** $24 \div 12 + 8 - 6$

10. $17 - 4 + 2 \cdot 8$ **11.** $12 + 13 - (12 + 4)$ **12.** $12 + (13 - 12) + 4$

13. $(12 + 13) - (12 + 4)$ **14.** $12 - (13 - 12 + 4)$ **15.** $12 - (13 - 12 \div 4)$

16. $12 + 3(4 \cdot 5)$ **17.** $12 - (15 \div 3)$ **18.** $12 - 2(15 \div 3)$

19. $\dfrac{18 - 12}{13 - 7}$ **20.** $\dfrac{18 - 7 \cdot 2}{3 - 1}$ **21.** $\dfrac{3(10 - 4)}{15 - 3 \cdot 3}$

Evaluate.

22. $16 - 3x$ for $x = 4$

23. $12x + 9$ for $x = 3$

24. $2a - 6 \div 2$ for $a = 8$

25. $14 + y \div 5$ for $y = 30$

26. $17 - 18 \div x$ for $x = 6$

27. $5a + 3 \cdot 4$ for $a = 2$

28. $15 - 9d$ for $d = \dfrac{2}{3}$

29. $4y + 2 \cdot 7$ for $y = 3.5$

Simplify.

30. $4.2 + 3.1 \times 4$

31. $5.8 - 2.1 \div 7$

32. $8.4 \div (6.3 \div 3)$

33. $8.1 - 2(4.3 - 1)$

34. $\dfrac{4.02 + 3.21}{3}$

35. $10(5.2 - 1.4)$

36. $9 - 2(4.9 - 3.2)$

37. $5[8 - (6.2 + 1.8)]$

Evaluate.

38. $a + 2(b - 4)$ for $a = 5$ and $b = 9$

39. $x - 4(5 - y)$ for $x = 20$ and $y = 3$

40. $m(n + 1) - (m + 1)$ for $m = 5$ and $n = 2$

41. $c + 2[d + d(c - 1)]$ for $c = 4$ and $d = 2$

42. $x - (y - 1)$ for $x = 20$ and $y = 3$

43. $(x + 2) - (y + 3)$ for $x = 7$ and $y = 2$

44. Write an explanation of the need for an agreement on the order of operations.

Write an algebraic expression for each word description.

45. the amount, in dollars, that will remain if you have $360 now and you spend $8 a week for w weeks

46. the repair bill, in dollars, for x hours if a man charges a base fee of $25 plus $15 per hour

47. the total cost, in cents, of p pencils at 10¢ each and t tablets at 65¢ each

48. 10 lb less than twice the weight y of a package

49. After you enter 10 $\boxed{+}$ 2 $\boxed{\times}$ 3 $\boxed{=}$, some calculators display 36 and others display 16. Explain why.

Mixed Review

Evaluate.   *1.1*

1. $15 - y$ for $y = 8$

2. $3x$ for $x = 2.1$

3. $4d$ for $d = \frac{3}{4}$

4. $\frac{21}{c}$ for $c = 3$

5. $\frac{a}{b}$ for $a = 28, b = 7$

6. $\frac{m}{n}$ for $m = 28, n = 0.8$

7. Write an algebraic expression for the cost, in dollars, of p pounds of grapes at $1.09 per pound.

Application: *Temperature Humidity Index (THI)*

Weather forecasters sometimes report a Temperature Humidity Index, (THI). The THI is a number that measures the degree of discomfort you may feel because of the amount of water vapor in the air. The higher the index, the greater the discomfort. You can find the THI by using the formula, THI $= 0.4(t + s) + 15$, where t is the temperature of the air and s is the temperature of a thermometer with a moistened cloth on its bulb.

For example, if $t = 84$ and $s = 71$,

$$\text{THI} = 0.4(84 + 71) + 15 = 0.4(155) + 15 = 77.$$

Find the THI for each pair of Fahrenheit temperatures.

1. $t = 80, s = 65$

2. $t = 86, s = 74$

3. $t = 100, s = 81$

1.3 Exponents

Objectives

To simplify expressions containing exponents
To evaluate expressions containing exponents

If a car is going 40 mi/h on dry concrete, it takes about 60 ft to stop after the brakes are applied. If it is going 55 mi/h, the braking distance is about twice as long. The braking distance can be estimated by using the *formula* $d = 0.04 \times s \times s$. A simpler way to write this formula uses *exponents*: $d = 0.04s^2$.

In the product $7 \cdot 3$, 7 and 3 are *factors*. The product $5 \cdot 5 \cdot 5$ consists of the factor 5 used three times. Another way to write $5 \cdot 5 \cdot 5$ is to use an exponent. The *exponent* indicates the number of times the *base* is used as a factor.

$$\text{base} \longrightarrow 5^3 \longleftarrow \text{exponent}$$

5^3 is read *5 to the third power* or *5 cubed*. Other expressions containing exponents are shown in the table.

Exponential expression	English expression	Base	Exponent	Meaning
7^2	7 to the second power, or 7 squared	7	2	$7 \cdot 7$, or 49
4^3	4 to the third power, or 4 cubed	4	3	$4 \cdot 4 \cdot 4$, or 64
6^1	6 to the first power	6	1	6
x^5	x to the fifth power	x	5	$x \cdot x \cdot x \cdot x \cdot x$

The rules for simplifying an expression can be extended to include expressions containing exponents.

Order of Operations
1. Operate within grouping symbols first. Work from the inside to the outside.
2. Simplify powers.
3. Multiply and divide from left to right.
4. Add and subtract from left to right.

EXAMPLE 1 Simplify: **a.** $6 \cdot 5^2$ **b.** $4^2 \cdot 1^3 + 8$

Solutions **a.** $6 \cdot 5^2$ **b.** $4^2 \cdot 1^3 + 8$
$\quad\quad\quad\quad 6 \cdot 5 \cdot 5$ $4 \cdot 4 \cdot 1 \cdot 1 \cdot 1 + 8$
$\quad\quad\quad\quad 6 \cdot 25$ $16 + 8$
$\quad\quad\quad\quad 150$ 24

EXAMPLE 2 Simplify: $\dfrac{2^3 + 4^2}{(5 - 3)^2}$

Solution $\dfrac{2^3 + 4^2}{(5 - 3)^2} = \dfrac{2 \cdot 2 \cdot 2 + 4 \cdot 4}{(2)^2} = \dfrac{8 + 16}{2 \cdot 2} = \dfrac{24}{4} = 6$

TRY THIS Simplify: **1.** $2^4 \cdot 4$ **2.** $\dfrac{3^3 + 1}{(3 - 1)^2}$

Example 3 shows that $4x^3$ and $(4x)^3$ do not mean the same thing.

EXAMPLE 3 Evaluate: **a.** $4x^3$ for $x = 2$ **b.** $(4x)^3$ for $x = 2$

Solutions **a.** $4x^3 = 4 \cdot 2^3$ **b.** $(4x)^3 = (4 \cdot 2)^3$
$\quad\quad\quad\quad\quad = 4 \cdot 2 \cdot 2 \cdot 2$ $= 8^3$
$\quad\quad\quad\quad\quad = 32$ $= 8 \cdot 8 \cdot 8 = 512$

EXAMPLE 4 Evaluate $3x^2 - 2x + 1$ for $x = 4$.

Solution $3x^2 - 2x + 1 = 3 \cdot 4^2 - 2 \cdot 4 + 1$
$\quad\quad\quad\quad\quad\quad\quad\quad = 3 \cdot 16 - 8 + 1$
$\quad\quad\quad\quad\quad\quad\quad\quad = 48 - 8 + 1$
$\quad\quad\quad\quad\quad\quad\quad\quad = 40 + 1 = 41$

EXAMPLE 5 The distance an object falls if dropped from any height is found by the formula $d = 5t^2$, where d is the distance in meters (m) and t is the time in seconds. Find d if $t = 5.2$ seconds. Round the answer to the nearest whole number.

Solution Substitute 5.2 for t and evaluate.   **Calculator Steps:**
$d = 5t^2 = 5 \times (5.2)^2 = 5 \times 5.2 \times 5.2$ $5 \boxed{\times} 5.2 \boxed{x^2} \boxed{=} 135.2$
$\quad\quad\quad\quad\quad\quad\quad = 135.2$

Thus, the distance is about 135 m

TRY THIS **3.** Evaluate $2x^2 - x + 3$ **4.** Evaluate $d = 5t^2$
for $x = 3$.   for $t = 0.3$.

Use one of the words at the right to complete each sentence.

1. In x^3, x is the ___ .
2. In y^4, 4 is the ___ .
3. 5^4 means 5 to the fourth ___ .
4. In 6^5, 6 is used as a(n) ___ 5 times.
5. $7y^3$ means the ___ of 7 and y cubed.
6. $4z^2$ means 4 times z ___ .

a. product
b. squared
c. exponent
d. factor
e. base
f. power

Classroom Exercises

Use exponents to rewrite the expressions in Exercises 1–6.

1. $5 \times 5 \times 5$
2. $3 \cdot 3 \cdot 2 \cdot 2 \cdot 2$
3. $x \cdot x \cdot x \cdot y$
4. $x \cdot x + 1$
5. $a \cdot a - b \cdot b + c \cdot c$
6. $\dfrac{3 \cdot c \cdot c + 2 \cdot d \cdot d}{c \cdot c - d \cdot d \cdot d}$

Simplify.

7. 6^2
8. 10^3
9. 2^4
10. $3^3 - 2$
11. $2 \cdot 5^2$
12. $7^2 + 1$
13. $6 \cdot 5^2$
14. $100^2 + 3$

Written Exercises

Simplify.

1. 3^4
2. 2^6
3. 10^5
4. $5 \cdot 2^3$
5. $3^2 \cdot 6$
6. $(5 \cdot 2)^3$
7. $5^3 \cdot 2^3$
8. $4 \cdot 10^3$
9. $3 + 7^2$
10. $(3 + 7)^2$
11. $(45 - 5)^2$
12. $45 - 5^2$
13. $(5 \cdot 4)^2$
14. $5 \cdot 10^3$
15. $5^2 - 4^2$
16. $(5 - 4)^7$
17. $2^6 + 2^4 + 2^2$
18. $3^5 - 3^4 + 3^3 - 3^2$
19. $9^2 - 3 \cdot 5$
20. $6^2 + 2 \cdot 3^2$
21. 4.6×10^3
22. 10.3×2^3
23. $(1^3 + 2^2 + 3) \div 4$
24. $(4^3 \div 2^5) + 5$
25. $8^2 \div (3^2 - 1^2)$
26. $5^3 - 3 \cdot 5^2 + 2 \cdot 5$
27. $(2^5 - 3^3)^2 - 5^2$
28. $4^2 + 8(16 - 3^2)$
29. $\dfrac{8^2 - 6^2}{10 - 6}$
30. $\dfrac{4^3 - 2}{4^2 + 15}$
31. $\dfrac{10^2 - 5^2}{(9 - 4)^2}$

Use the formula $d = 5t^2$ to find d for each value of t. Round your answer to the nearest meter.

32. $t = 0$
33. $t = 1$
34. $t = 10$
35. $t = 6$
36. $t = 0.5$
37. $t = 1.5$

Evaluate.

38. $3x^2 - 2x$ for $x = 4$

39. $x^2 - 2x + 1$ for $x = 4$

40. $x^2 + 2x + 1$ for $x = 3$

41. $m^2 - m - 6$ for $m = 4$

42. $3y^2 + y$ for $y = 4$

43. $(3 \cdot y)^2 + y$ for $y = 4$

44. $36 + 3n - n^2$ for $n = 2$

45. $x^3 + x^2 - 6x$ for $x = 2$

46. $(x^2 - y^2)^3$ for $x = 3$ and $y = 2$

47. $a(ab)^2 - a^3$ for $a = 3$ and $b = 4$

48. $\dfrac{m^2 - n^2}{(m - n)^2}$ for $m = 5$ and $n = 4$

49. $\dfrac{x^2 + 2xy + y^2}{(x + y)^2}$ for $x = 3$ and $y = 4$

50. Explain in writing why $2x^3$ is not equivalent to $(2x)^3$.

The braking distance of a car can be estimated by the formula $d = 0.04s^2$, where d is the braking distance in feet and s is the speed in miles per hour. Find d for each value of s.

51. $s = 50$
52. $s = 10$
53. $s = 20$
54. $s = 30$

55. $s = 40$
56. $s = 90$
57. $s = 70$
58. $s = 80$

Solve each problem. Round your answer to the nearest whole number. (Ex. 59–62)

59. Use the formula $A = 3.14r^2$ to find A for $r = 2.1$.

60. Use the formula $V = 4.19r^3$ to find V for $r = 2.1$.

Use the formula $l = ar^{n-1}$ to find l for the given values of a, r, and n.

61. $a = 2$, $r = 3$, and $n = 5$

62. $a = 1.6$, $r = 2.1$, and $n = 3$

Use the formula $y = \left(\dfrac{1}{a}\right)^{kt}$ to find y for the given values of a, k, and t.

63. $a = 2$, $k = 3$, and $t = 2$

64. $a = 2.5$, $k = 3$, and $t = 1$

Mixed Review

Simplify *1.2*

1. $15 + 5 \cdot 7 + 14 \cdot 2$

2. $7(8 - 3) - 15 \div 5$

3. $\dfrac{8 + 4 \cdot 3}{7 - 3}$

4. $\dfrac{9 \cdot 3 + 4 \cdot 7}{4 \cdot 17 - 3 \cdot 19}$

Evaluate. *1.2, 1.3*

5. $3r^2 - 5$ for $r = 3$

6. $(x - 5)(9 + y)$ for $x = 12$ and $y = 2$

1.4 Formulas from Geometry

To use perimeter, area, and volume formulas

The distance around a rectangle is called its **perimeter.** The formula for the perimeter of a rectangle is

$$p = 2l + 2w$$

where p is the perimeter, l is the length, and w is the width.

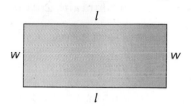

EXAMPLE 1   Find the perimeter of a rectangle with length 13.5 ft and width 2.7 ft.

Solution   Evaluate the formula $p = 2l + 2w$ for $l = 13.5$ and $w = 2.7$.

$$p = 2l + 2w$$
$$= 2(13.5) + 2(2.7) \quad \longleftarrow \quad l = 13.5 \text{ and } w = 2.7$$
$$= 27 + 5.4$$
$$= 32.4$$

Thus, the perimeter is 32.4 feet.

Calculator Steps:

2 ⨯ 13.5 + 2 ⨯ 2.7 = 32.4

TRY THIS   1. Find the perimeter of a rectangle with length 6.8 yd and width 2.3 yd.

The **area** of a geometric figure is the number of square units it contains. Area is measured in *square units,* such as square centimeters (cm^2), square meters (m^2), or square inches ($in.^2$). Two area formulas are shown below.

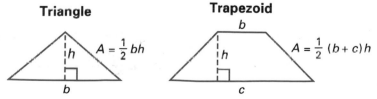

Triangle $A = \frac{1}{2}bh$

Trapezoid $A = \frac{1}{2}(b + c)h$

For the two figures above, the *height* or *altitude* is h. For the triangle, the *base* is b. For the trapezoid, the *bases* are b and c.

EXAMPLE 2   Find the area of a trapezoid with $b = 5$ in., $c = 7$ in., and $h = 9$ in.

Solution $A = \frac{1}{2}(b + c)h = \frac{1}{2}(5 + 7)(9) = \frac{1}{2} \cdot 12 \cdot 9 = 6 \cdot 9 = 54$

Thus, the area is 54 in^2.

TRY THIS   2. Find the area of a triangle with $b = 2$ ft and $h = 7.8$ ft.

The **volume** of a solid figure is the number of cubic units it contains. The formula for the volume of a *rectangular solid* is $V = lwh$, where l is the length, w is the width, and h is the height of the solid. Volume is measured in *cubic units*, such as cubic centimeters (cm^3), cubic meters (m^3), or cubic inches (in.^{3}).

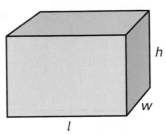

EXAMPLE 3   Use the formula $V = lwh$ to find the volume of a rectangular solid if $l = 4.2$ cm, $w = 3.5$ cm, and $h = 6.7$ cm. Round your answer to the nearest whole number.

Solution $V = lwh$
$= (4.2)(3.5)(6.7)$
$= (14.7)(6.7)$
$= 98.49$ **Calculator Steps:** 4.2 $\boxed{\times}$ 3.5 $\boxed{\times}$ 6.7 $\boxed{=}$

Thus, the volume is about 98 cm^3.

TRY THIS   3. Find the volume of a rectangular solid where $l = 9$ m, $w = 2.4$ m, and $h = 4.8$ m.

Classroom Exercises

Give a formula for each of the following.

1. area of a square with side s

2. perimeter of a square with side s

3. area of a rectangle of length l and width w

4. perimeter of a rectangle of length l and width w

5. area of a triangle with base b and height h

6. area of a trapezoid of height h with bases of length b and c

7. Use $p = 4s$ to find the perimeter p of a square where $s = 7$ in.

8. Use $V = e^3$ to find the volume V of a cube where $e = 3$ cm.

Written Exercises

Use $p = 4s$ to find the perimeter p of each square where s is given.

1. $s = 9$ ft　　　　　　**2.** $s = 15$ in.　　　　　　**3.** $s = 5.2$ cm

Use the formula $p = 2l + 2w$ to find the perimeter p of each rectangle where l and w are given.

4. $l = 8$ yd, $w = 3$ yd　　**5.** $l = 12$ ft, $w = 9$ ft　　**6.** $l = 6.2$ m, $w = 5.8$ m

Use $A = s^2$ to find the area A of each square where s is given.

7. $s = 8$ yd　　　　　　**8.** $s = 3.20$ cm　　　　　**9.** $s = \frac{1}{2}$ in.

Use the formula $A = lw$ to find the area A of each rectangle where l and w are given.

10. $l = 6$ in., $w = 5$ in.　　**11.** $l = 16$ m, $w = 11$ m　　**12.** $l = 6.80$ cm, $w = 2.40$ cm

Use the formula $A = \frac{1}{2}bh$ to find the area A of each triangle where b and h are given. Round your answer to the nearest whole number.

13. $b = 5$ ft, $h = 4$ ft　　**14.** $b = 9$ yd, $h = 5$ yd　　**15.** $b = 9.8$ cm, $h = 5$ cm

Use the formula $V = lwh$ to find the volume V of each rectangular solid where l, w, and h are given.

16. $l = 5$ in., $w = 3$ in., and $h = 6$ in.　　**17.** $l = 7$ ft, $w = 4$ ft, and $h = 2$ ft

Use the formula $A = \frac{1}{2}(b + c)h$ to find the area A of each trapezoid where b, c, and h are given.

18. $b - 6$ ft, $c = 8$ ft, and $h = 4$ ft　　**19.** $b = 6$ m, $c = 14$m, and $h = 6$ m

Use the formula $V = e^3$ to find the volume V of a cube where e, the length of an edge, is given.

20. $e = 5$ cm　　　　　　　　　　**21.** $e = 7$ ft
22. $e = 9$ m　　　　　　　　　　**23.** $e = 0.8$ cm

In Exercises 24–44, round your answer to the nearest whole number.

24. Find the perimeter and area of a square with each side 6.5 cm.
25. Find the perimeter and area of a rectangle with length 16.3 m and width 8.4 m.
26. Find the area of a triangle with base 7.5 cm and altitude 6.2 cm.
27. Find the area of a trapezoid with bases 3.7 m and 5.9 m and altitude 4.2 m.

The circumference of a circle is the distance around it. Use the formula $C = 2\pi r$ to find the circumference C of each circle where r, the length of a radius, is given. Use 3.14 for π. Round answers to the nearest whole number.

28. $r = 4\,\text{m}$ **29.** $r = 9\,\text{in.}$ **30.** $r = 1.6\,\text{cm}$

31. $r = 3\,\text{yd}$ **32.** $r = 6\,\text{ft}$ **33.** $r = 10\,\text{in.}$

Use the formula $A = \pi r^2$ to find the area A of each circle where r is given. Use 3.14 for π. Round answers to the nearest square unit.

34. $r = 7.0\,\text{m}$ **35.** $r = 9.0\,\text{in.}$ **36.** $r = 5.2\,\text{cm}$

37. $r = 2.0\,\text{yd}$ **38.** $r = 6.0\,\text{in.}$ **39.** $r = 12\,\text{ft}$

40. In a regular pentagon, all five sides are the same length. Write a formula for the perimeter p of a regular pentagon with s the length of each side. Use it to find the perimeter of a regular pentagon with each side 6.2 cm.

41. If each side of a square is doubled in length, what will happen to its perimeter?

42. If each side of a square is doubled in length, what will happen to its area?

43. If each edge of a cube is doubled in length, what will happen to its volume?

44. If the radius of a circle is doubled in length, what will happen to its area?

Midchapter Review

Simplify.   *1.2, 1.3*

1. $7 \cdot 5 - 18$ **2.** $8 + 2 \cdot 7$ **3.** $3(4 + 5)$ **4.** $\dfrac{5 + 4}{3 - 2}$

Evaluate.   *1.1–1.3*

5. $4x$ for $x = 7$ **6.** $5y^3$ for $y = 2$

7. $a + 2b$ for $a = 2$ and $b = 4$ **8.** $(a + 2)b$ for $a = 2$ and $b = 4$

Write an algebraic expression for each word description.   *1.1*

9. 7 more than x **10.** 6 less than the number n

11. the cost, in cents, of y note pads at 79¢ per pad   **12.** $\frac{4}{5}$ of the population p

Find the perimeter and the area of each rectangle with the given dimensions.   *1.4*

13. $l = 4\,\text{in.}, w = 7\,\text{in.}$ **14.** $l = 2.3\,\text{cm}, w = 6.0\,\text{cm}$

1.5 The Commutative and Associative Properties

Objectives   To determine which property is illustrated by a mathematical sentence

To simplify expressions by using the Commutative and Associative Properties

Suppose you want to calculate $4 \cdot 39 \cdot 25$ mentally. Multiplying 4 by 25 first makes the mental calculation easier. You can multiply any two numbers first because of some properties of multiplication. These properties and others have been given special names. The reason for giving them names is to make it easier to refer to them.

Property	Meaning of property with examples
Commutative Property of Addition For all numbers a and b, $a + b = b + a$.	The order in which two numbers are added does not affect the sum. $6 + 8 = 8 + 6$ $42.7 + 3.1 = 3.1 + 42.7$ $7\frac{1}{2} + 5\frac{1}{4} = 5\frac{1}{4} + 7\frac{1}{2}$
Commutative Property of Multiplication For all numbers a and b, $a \cdot b = b \cdot a$.	The order in which two factors are multiplied does not affect the product. $9 \cdot 7 = 7 \cdot 9$ $\frac{1}{2} \cdot \frac{3}{4} = \frac{3}{4} \cdot \frac{1}{2}$ $12(0.25) = (0.25)12$
Associative Property of Addition For all numbers a, b, and c, $(a + b) + c = a + (b + c)$.	The sum of three numbers is the same no matter how you group the numbers. $(6 + 3) + 8 = 6 + (3 + 8)$ $(2 + 9.3) + 0.7 = 2 + (9.3 + 0.7)$ $\left(3 + \frac{1}{2}\right) + 0.5 = 3 + \left(\frac{1}{2} + 0.5\right)$
Associative Property of Multiplication For all numbers a, b, and c, $(a \cdot b) \cdot c = a \cdot (b \cdot c)$.	The product of three factors is the same no matter how you group the factors. $(3 \cdot 7) \cdot 10 = 3 \cdot (7 \cdot 10)$ $\left(3 \cdot 22\frac{1}{2}\right) \cdot 2 = 3 \cdot \left(22\frac{1}{2} \cdot 2\right)$ $[2(0.125)]8 = 2[(0.125)8]$

From the associative properties, it follows that $a + b + c$ names just one number and abc names just one number.

EXAMPLE 1 Which property of multiplication is illustrated?

a. $(4 \cdot 39) \cdot 25 = 4 \cdot (39 \cdot 25)$ Associative Property of Multiplication

b. $4 \cdot (39 \cdot 25) = 4 \cdot (25 \cdot 39)$ Commutative Property of Multiplication

c. $4 \cdot (25 \cdot 39) = (4 \cdot 25) \cdot 39$ Associative Property of Multiplication

TRY THIS **1.** Name the property: $(4 + 25) + 39 = (25 + 4) + 39$

You can use the commutative and associative properties together.

EXAMPLE 2 Simplify $4 \cdot 39 \cdot 25$ mentally. Explain your thinking.

Solution You can multiply 4 by 25 first because of the Commutative and Associative Properties of Multiplication, as shown in Example 1 above.

$$4 \cdot 39 \cdot 25 = \underbrace{4 \cdot 25} \cdot 39$$
$$= 100 \cdot 39$$
$$= 3,900$$

EXAMPLE 3 Which property is illustrated?

a. $(x + 5) + 2 = x + (5 + 2)$ Associative Property of Addition

b. $(5p) \cdot 3 = 3 \cdot (5p)$ Commutative Property of Multiplication

c. $(7 \cdot x) \cdot y = 7 \cdot (x \cdot y)$ Associative Property of Multiplication

d. $7t + 9y = 9y + 7t$ Commutative Property of Addition

TRY THIS **2.** Name the property: $(5 + a) + 3 = 3 + (5 + a)$

The commutative and associative properties can be used to simplify algebraic expressions, as shown in the next examples. When you actually do such simplifications, you need not write the property.

EXAMPLE 4 Simplify $\frac{2}{3}(12c)$.

Solution $\frac{2}{3}(12c) = \left(\frac{2}{3} \cdot 12\right)c$ ⟵ Associative Property of Multiplication

$$= 8c \quad \longleftarrow \quad \frac{2}{\underset{1}{\cancel{3}}} \cdot \frac{\overset{4}{\cancel{12}}}{1} =$$

TRY THIS Simplify   **3.** $5\left(\frac{2}{5}a\right)$ **4.** $\frac{1}{2}(2b)$

Example 4 shows that when you simplify $\frac{2}{3}(12c)$, you get $8c$. This means that $\frac{2}{3}(12c) = 8c$ is true for every number c. Two algebraic expressions are said to be **equivalent** if they name the same number for all values of their variables for which the expressions have meaning.

The two expressions $\frac{2}{3}(12c)$ and $8c$ are *equivalent*.

EXAMPLE 5	Simplify $(7x)5$.
Solution	$(7x)5 = 5(7x)$ ←—— Commutative Property of Multiplication
	$= (5 \cdot 7)x$ ←—— Associative Property of Multiplication
	$= 35x$

TRY THIS   Simplify: **5.** $(3a)\frac{2}{3}$ **6.** $(0.5b)6.2$

Classroom Exercises

Which property is described?

1. When multiplying two numbers, you may interchange the numbers without changing the result.

2. When adding three numbers, you get the same result whether you add the third to the sum of the first two or add the first to the sum of the last two.

Which property is illustrated?

3. $8 \cdot 4 = 4 \cdot 8$ **4.** $a + b = b + a$ **5.** $(7 + 6) + 9 = 7 + (6 + 9)$

6. $19 + 45 = 45 + 19$ **7.** $(3b) \cdot 2 = 2 \cdot (3b)$ **8.** $(x \cdot 3) \cdot 2 = x \cdot (3 \cdot 2)$

Simplify mentally. Explain your thinking.

9. $199 + 47 + 1$ **10.** $25 \cdot 59 \cdot 4$ **11.** $25 + 20.9 + 75$

12. $\frac{1}{3} \cdot 37 \cdot 3$ **13.** $\frac{1}{2} + 3\frac{7}{8} + \frac{1}{2}$ **14.** $99 + 197 + 1 + 3$

Simplify.

15. $3(5a)$ **16.** $(4x)2$ **17.** $7(6m)$

18. Show that $6(3a)$ is equivalent to $2(9a)$.

19. Which expressions are equivalent?

   a. $\left(\frac{1}{3} \cdot 3\right)c$ and $c + \left(\frac{1}{3} \cdot 3\right)$ **b.** $(10t)\frac{2}{5}$ and $\frac{1}{8}(32t)$

   c. $3 + (a + 1)$ and $(a + 1) + 3$ **d.** $3 \cdot (24 \cdot r)$ and $(3 \cdot 24) \cdot r$

Written Exercises

Which property is illustrated?

1. $49 + 73 = 73 + 49$

2. $(2 + 9) + 3 = 2 + (9 + 3)$

3. $(3 \cdot 7)8 = 3(7 \cdot 8)$

4. $(7k)5 = 5(7k)$

Simplify mentally. Explain your thinking.

5. $299 + 73 + 1$
6. $25 \cdot 73 \cdot 4$
7. $15 \cdot 7 \cdot 2$
8. $57 + 29 + 3$

9. $50 \cdot 14 \cdot 2$
10. $18 + 42 + 2$
11. $20 \cdot 43 \cdot 5$
12. $4 \cdot 23 \cdot 5$

13. $\frac{1}{4} + 18 + \frac{3}{4}$
14. $\frac{1}{2} \cdot 317 \cdot 2$
15. $\frac{2}{3} \cdot 17 \cdot 3$
16. $\frac{3}{5} + 23\frac{1}{2} + \frac{2}{5}$

Simplify.

17. $8(4m)$
18. $3(7b)$
19. $(5k)3$
20. $(8m)9$

21. $6(7y)$
22. $14(3p)$
23. $16(4d)$
24. $(9x)7$

Which property is illustrated?

25. $(3 + 5a) + 4a = 3 + (5a + 4a)$
26. $7(3a) = (7 \cdot 3)a$

27. $5m + 3m^2 = 3m^2 + 5m$
28. $(3k)(7b) = (7b)(3k)$

Simplify mentally. Explain your thinking.

29. $299 + 57 + 3 + 1$
30. $2 + 175 + 138 + 5$
31. $688 + 289 + 12 + 11$

32. $0.07 + 0.18 + 0.93$
33. $(0.5) \cdot 27 \cdot 2$
34. $5 \cdot 23 \cdot 4 \cdot 5$

35. $2\frac{3}{7} + 399 + 3\frac{4}{7} + 1$
36. $\frac{1}{3}(22.5) \cdot 6$
37. $\frac{1}{2} \cdot 25 \cdot 12 \cdot 4$

Simplify.

38. $3(5k)4$
39. $8y(4)3$
40. $7(3a)6$

41. $2 \cdot 13 \cdot 50g$
42. $5t(9.3)20$
43. $25 \cdot \frac{3}{5}b \cdot 4$

44. Show that $4(5a)$ is equivalent to $2(10a)$.

45. Is there a number x for which $6(3x) = 18x$ is not true? Why?

46. Write an explanation of the difference between the commutative and associative properties of addition.

47. Is division of nonzero numbers commutative? That is, is "$a \div b = b \div a$" true for all nonzero numbers a and b? If not, give an example to show that it is not.

48. Is division of nonzero numbers associative? That is, is "$(a \div b) \div c = a \div (b \div c)$" true for all nonzero numbers a, b, and c? If not, give an example to show that it is not.

Mixed Review

Evaluate. *1.2, 1.3*

1. $14 - 6x$ for $x = \frac{2}{3}$ **2.** $x^2 - 4x$ for $x = 6$ **3.** $(x - 4)x$ for $x = 6$

4. Write an algebraic expression for the cost, in cents, of one pencil if k pencils cost \$1.20. *1.1*

5. Use the formula $A = \frac{1}{2}(b + c)h$ to find the area of a trapezoid for $b = 6$ cm, $c = 10$ cm, and $h = 4$ cm. *1.4*

Application: *Heat Transfer*

When the temperature outside your house is colder than it is inside, heat will escape through the windows. The rate of heat transfer is measured in British Thermal Units, or BTUs, per hour. One BTU is the amount of heat needed to raise the temperature of one pound of water one degree Fahrenheit. The formula for the rate of heat transfer through glass is

$$H = \frac{A \times T}{R}.$$

In this formula, H is the rate of heat transfer in BTUs, A is the window area in square feet, T is the difference in inside and outside temperatures in degrees Fahrenheit, and R is the thermal resistance. Thermal resistance is a measure of a material's resistance to the flow of heat through it. The R value for a single-pane window is 0.88. If a storm window is added, the R value of the double-pane window is 1.79.

To calculate H for a single-pane window 2 ft by 3 ft when the inside temperature is 72° and the outside temperature is 30°, begin by writing the formula. Then substitute the values you know.

$$H = \frac{A \times T}{R}$$

$$H = \frac{(2 \cdot 3) \cdot (72 - 30)}{0.88} \quad \longleftarrow \text{ Simplify. Use a calculator.}$$

$$H = 290 \text{ BTU/h (nearest 10 BTUs)}$$

Solve each problem. Round your answers to the nearest 10 BTUs.

1. Calculate H for the same conditions if the single-pane window is replaced by a double-pane window.

2. Suppose that in Exercise 1 the inside temperature is lowered to 70°. How many BTUs would be saved in 1 hour? How many in a day (24 h)?

1.6 The Distributive Property

Objective　　To rewrite expressions by using the Distributive Property

How do you find the area of the swimming pool at the right? Compare the following two methods.

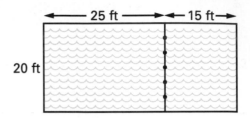

Method 1
Multiply the total length by the width.
20(25 + 15)

20 · 40
800

Method 2
Add the areas of the two small rectangles.
20 · 25 + 20 · 15

500 + 300
800

So the area of the pool is 800 square feet (800 ft²).

Notice that 20(25 + 15) = 20 · 25 + 20 · 15. This illustrates that multiplication is *distributive* over addition.

Property	Meaning of Property with Examples
Distributive Property of Multiplication over Addition For all numbers a, b, and c, $a(b + c) = ab + ac$ and $(b + c)a = ba + ca$.	To multiply a sum by a factor, you can multiply each addend by the factor and then add the products. $8(300 + 2) = 8 \cdot 300 + 8 \cdot 2$ $(3 + 0.2)4 = 3 \cdot 4 + (0.2)4$ $5\left(4 + \frac{1}{2}\right) = 5 \cdot 4 + 5 \cdot \frac{1}{2}$

This property can help you do mental calculations.

EXAMPLE 1　　Compute 8 · 52 mentally. Explain your thinking.

Solution　　Think:　52 = 50 + 2

Thus, 8 · 52 = 8(50 + 2)

= 8 · 50 + 8 · 2　　←　Distributive Property of Multiplication over Addition

= 400 + 16 = 416

TRY THIS　　1. Compute mentally:　5 · 308

The Distributive Property of Multiplication over Addition can also be used in reverse to rewrite $7 \cdot 9 + 7 \cdot 5$.

$$7 \cdot 9 + 7 \cdot 5 = 7(9 + 5)$$

EXAMPLE 2 Rewrite by using the Distributive Property of Multiplication over Addition. Then simplify.

a. $7(8 + 5)$ **b.** $6 \cdot 4 + 6 \cdot 3$

Solutions
a. $7(8 + 5) = 7 \cdot 8 + 7 \cdot 5$
$= 56 + 35$
$= 91$

b. $6 \cdot 4 + 6 \cdot 3 = 6(4 + 3)$
$= 6 \cdot 7$
$= 42$

TRY THIS Use the Distributive Property of Multiplication over Addition to rewrite each expression. Then simplify.

2. $4(7 + 3)$ **3.** $5 \cdot 9 + 5 \cdot 1$

The Distributive Property of Multiplication over Addition works with any number of addends.

EXAMPLE 3 Rewrite by using the Distributive Property of Multiplication over Addition. Then simplify.

a. $\frac{1}{3}(15 + 9 + 3)$ **b.** $6 \cdot 7 + 1 \cdot 7 + 4 \cdot 7$

Solutions
a. $\frac{1}{3}(15 + 9 + 3)$

$\frac{1}{3} \cdot 15 + \frac{1}{3} \cdot 9 + \frac{1}{3} \cdot 3$

$5 + 3 + 1$

9

b. $6 \cdot 7 + 1 \cdot 7 + 4 \cdot 7$
$(6 + 1 + 4)7$
$11 \cdot 7$
77

TRY THIS Use the Distributive Property of Multiplication over Addition to rewrite each expression. Then simplify.

4. $1.2(10 + 5 + 1)$ **5.** $7 \cdot \frac{1}{2} + 4 \cdot \frac{1}{2} + 9 \cdot \frac{1}{2}$

Multiplication is also distributive over subtraction. For example, $2(9 - 4) = 2 \cdot 9 - 2 \cdot 4$, as shown below.

$$2(9 - 4) \stackrel{?}{=} 2 \cdot 9 - 2 \cdot 4$$
$$2 \cdot 5 \stackrel{?}{=} 18 - 8$$
$$10 = 10 \quad \text{True}$$

The Distributive Property of Multiplication over Addition and the Distributive Property of Multiplication over Subtraction are often referred to simply as the **Distributive Property**.

EXAMPLE 4   Rewrite by using the Distributive Property. Then simplify.

   a. $5(6a - 8)$ **b.** $(12a + 9)\frac{2}{3}$

Solutions   **a.** $5(6a - 8) = 5 \cdot 6a - 5 \cdot 8$ **b.** $(12a + 9)\frac{2}{3} = 12a \cdot \frac{2}{3} + 9 \cdot \frac{2}{3}$
                   $= 30a - 40$ $= 8a + 6$

TRY THIS   Rewrite by using the Distributive Property. Then simplify.

   6. $2(3c - 5)$ **7.** $(4b - 2)3$

You need to be able to distinguish the Commutative, Associative, and Distributive Properties in order to use them correctly.

EXAMPLE 5   Which property is illustrated?

   a. $7(4 \cdot 6) = (7 \cdot 4)6$ Associative Property of Multiplication
   b. $2(1 + 5) = 2(5 + 1)$ Commutative Property of Addition
   c. $(a + 5) + 2 = a + (5 + 2)$ Associative Property of Addition
   d. $8 \cdot 15 + 8 \cdot 5 = 8(15 + 5)$ Distributive Property
   e. $(x + 2)4 = 4(x + 2)$ Commutative Property of Multiplication

TRY THIS   **8.** Which property is illustrated? $(3 + 4) + 6 = 6 + (3 + 4)$

Classroom Exercises

Rewrite by using the Distributive Property.

   1. $8(4 + 5)$ **2.** $(6 - 2)9$ **3.** $5 \cdot 6 - 5 \cdot 3$ **4.** $4(2a + 5)$

Rewrite by using the Distributive Property. Then simplify.

   5. $10 \cdot 3 - 6 \cdot 3$ **6.** $7 \cdot 4 + 13 \cdot 4$ **7.** $6(5x - 2)$ **8.** $(4y + 5)2$

Written Exercises

Rewrite by using the Distributive Property. Then simplify.

   1. $8(7 + 6)$ **2.** $6(5 - 3)$ **3.** $(4 + 8)3$
   4. $(12 - 4)2$ **5.** $\frac{1}{2}(8 + 4 + 2)$ **6.** $\frac{2}{3}(9 - 6)$
   7. $\frac{1}{4}(28 - 16)$ **8.** $(10 + 5 + 15)\frac{1}{5}$ **9.** $8 \cdot 7 + 8 \cdot 3$
   10. $6 \cdot 4 - 6 \cdot 2$ **11.** $8 \cdot 4 + 12 \cdot 4$ **12.** $9 \cdot 3 - 7 \cdot 3$
   13. $4 \cdot 7 + 5 \cdot 7 + 8 \cdot 7$ **14.** $6 \cdot 9 + 7 \cdot 9 + 5 \cdot 9$

15. $4(3a - 9)$ **16.** $4(5b + 3)$ **17.** $(x - 5)4$ **18.** $(3k + 7)6$

19. $\frac{3}{4}(8x + 12)$ **20.** $(10y - 15)\frac{1}{5}$ **21.** $\frac{2}{3}(6x + 12)$ **22.** $(14y - 21)\frac{3}{7}$

23. $1.5(2x + 3)$ **24.** $(2x - 1.6)4$ **25.** $3(4.1x - 6)$

26. $3(2a + 4b + 6)$ **27.** $(4c - 2b + 1)1.5$ **28.** $2(3a + 6x - 1.3d)$

Compute mentally. Explain your thinking.

29. $6 \cdot 43$ **30.** $5 \cdot 307$ **31.** $7 \cdot 49$

32. $4 \cdot 598$ **33.** $49 \cdot 3 + 49 \cdot 7$ **34.** $96 \cdot 294 + 4 \cdot 294$

35. $\frac{1}{2} \cdot 47 + \frac{1}{2} \cdot 3$ **36.** $40 \cdot 52 - 40 \cdot 2$ **37.** $15 \cdot \frac{3}{4} + 5 \cdot \frac{3}{4}$

38. Show that $3(4y + 5) = 12y + 15$ for at least 4 values of y.

39. Show that $4(2b - 6) = 8b - 24$ for at least 4 values of b.

Which property is illustrated?

40. $17\frac{1}{2} \cdot 32 = 32 \cdot 17\frac{1}{2}$ **41.** $13 \cdot 21 + 13 \cdot 9 = 13(21 + 9)$

42. $14 + (9 + 6) = (14 + 9) + 6$ **43.** $14 + (9 + 6) = 14 + (6 + 9)$

44. $6(5.7 + 9) = 6(5.7) + 6(9)$ **45.** $7(5 \cdot 2\frac{1}{2}) = (7 \cdot 5)2\frac{1}{2}$

46. $6(x + y) = 6x + 6y$ **47.** $4(5x) = (4 \cdot 5)x$

48. $(4a)(b + c) = (b + c)(4a)$ **49.** $(4a)(b + c) = 4ab + 4ac$

50. Is it true that $(a + b) \div c = (a \div c) + (b \div c)$ for all nonzero numbers a, b, and c? If not, give an example to show that it is not.

51. Is it true that $c \div (a + b) = (c \div a) + (c \div b)$ for all nonzero numbers a, b, and c? If not, give an example to show that it is not.

52. Is it true that $(a + b)^2 = a^2 + b^2$ for all numbers a and b?

53. Is it true that $(a \cdot b)^2 = a^2 \cdot b^2$ for all numbers a and b?

Mixed Review

Evaluate.   *1.1–1.3*

1. $y - x$ for $x = 4.1$ and $y = 7$

2. $c - (d + 1)$ for $c = 9$ and $d = 6$

3. $x^2 - 5x$ for $x = 9$

4. $\dfrac{x^2 + y^2}{(x + y)^2}$ for $x = 2$ and $y = 4$

5. Find the perimeter and the area of a square with sides of length 2.1 cm.   *1.4*

6. Use the formula $A = \frac{1}{2}bh$ to find the area of a triangle with base 3 cm and height 5.4 cm.   *1.4*

1.7 Combining Like Terms

Objective	To simplify expressions by combining like terms

The expression $7x + 13xy^2 + 18$ has three *terms*, $7x$, $13xy^2$, and 18. The parts of an expression connected by addition or subtraction are called **terms** of the expression. The term 18, with no variable, is called a *constant term*, or **constant**.

Like terms have the same variables and the corresponding variables have the same exponents. Also, all constant terms are like terms.

Like terms	**Unlike terms**
$6x$ and $4x$	$5x$ and $5y$
$7a^2b$ and $\frac{1}{2}a^2b$	$8t$ and 8
3 and 2.7	$3m^2n$ and $2mn$

In the term $7x$, 7 is the *numerical coefficient* of x. The numerical coefficient of a term is usually called simply the **coefficient** of the term. For example, the numerical coefficient of the term $13xy^2$ is 13.

You can use the Distributive Property to simplify expressions with like terms. For example, $3t + 7t + 5t = (3 + 7 + 5)t$, or $15t$. You can combine like terms by adding or subtracting coefficients in one step.

EXAMPLE 1	Simplify.
	a. $8y - 3y$ **b.** $6x + 4x + 5x$
Plan	Combine like terms.
Solutions	**a.** $8y - 3y = 5y$ **b.** $6x + 4x + 5x = 15x$

TRY THIS　　**1.** Simplify $5b - 2b + 3b$.

Remember, only like terms can be combined. Thus, to simplify the expression $9a + 4b + 3a + 5$:

1. Rearrange the terms so that $9a + 4b + 3a + 5$
   like terms are grouped together. $(9a + 3a) + 4b + 5$
2. Combine like terms. $12a + 4b + 5$

The expression $12a + 4b + 5$ cannot be simplified since the terms, $12a$, $4b$, and 5, are unlike.

The product of 1 and any number is that number. Therefore, 1 is called the *identity element for multiplication*, or the **multiplicative identity**.

Identity Property for Multiplication
For any number a, $1 \cdot a = a$ and $a \cdot 1 = a$.

Since $y = 1 \cdot y$, the coefficient of y is understood to be 1.

EXAMPLE 2   Simplify $8y + y - 3y$.

Plan   Rewrite y as $1 \cdot y$, or $1y$.

Solution $8y + y - 3y = 8y + 1y - 3y$
$= 6y$

TRY THIS   2. Simplify $7y - y + 2y$.

To simplify $9 + 3(4a + 2) + a$, multiply 3 and $4a + 2$ first.

EXAMPLE 3   Simplify $9 + 3(4a + 2) + a$.

Solution

Rewrite a as $1a$.	$9 + 3(4a + 2) + 1a$
Use the Distributive Property.	$9 + 3 \cdot 4a + 3 \cdot 2 + 1a$
Multiply.	$9 + 12a + 6 + 1a$
Group the like terms.	$(12a + 1a) + (9 + 6)$
Combine the like terms.	$13a + 15$

EXAMPLE 4   Simplify $2(3x + 5) + \frac{2}{3}(6x - 3)$. Then evaluate for $x = 5$.

Solution $2(3x + 5) + \frac{2}{3}(6x - 3) = 2 \cdot 3x + 2 \cdot 5 + \frac{2}{3} \cdot 6x - \frac{2}{3} \cdot 3$
$= 6x + 10 + 4x - 2$
$= (6x + 4x) + (10 - 2)$
$= 10x + 8$

Now substitute 5 for x and simplify.
$10x + 8 = 10 \cdot 5 + 8$
$= 50 + 8$
$= 58$

TRY THIS   3. Simplify $(4.5x - 8)2 + x$. Then evaluate for $x = 2$.

Classroom Exercises

Identify the like terms. Give the coefficient of each variable term.

1. $3x + 5x + 7$ **2.** $y + 4 + 7y$ **3.** $8m + 4 + m$

Simplify, if possible.

4. $13y - 6y$ **5.** $8x + 4x + x$ **6.** $7 + 4y + y$

7. $3k + 5 + k + 2$ **8.** $x + 5 + 2x - 4$ **9.** $3a + 2 + a$

10. $3x + 7$ **11.** $b + 7 + 4b + 1$ **12.** $2(3a + 1) + 4$

13. $3(4a + 5) + 1$ **14.** $5(a + 3) + 4$ **15.** $7x + 3(4 - 2x)$

Written Exercises

Simplify, if possible.

1. $7m - 2m$ **2.** $4k + 5k$ **3.** $2 + 5u$

4. $b + 3b$ **5.** $7x + 5x - 2x$ **6.** $3a + 5a + 2a$

7. $3a + 4a + 7$ **8.** $6m + 2 + 5m$ **9.** $7y + y + 4y$

10. $3 + 5 + m$ **11.** $a + 5a + 9a$ **12.** $4 + 5x + 3y$

13. $7 + a + 13 + 6a$ **14.** $5m + 13 + m + 4$ **15.** $2x + 7y + 9x + 3y$

16. $t + 7g + t + 8g$ **17.** $3m + 4(2m + 3) - 6$ **18.** $3(4x + 5) + x$

19. $3x + 4(6 + 2x) + 5x$ **20.** $9 + 2(3m + 4) - m$ **21.** $y + 4(2y + 3) + 2$

22. $\frac{2}{3}(6y + 9) + 5y - 2$ **23.** $\frac{1}{2}(2b + 8) + b + 1$ **24.** $\frac{2}{3}(9 + 12x) + x$

25. $\frac{1}{4}(8x - 4) - 5x$ **26.** $(9x - 12)\frac{2}{3} - 8$ **27.** $15 + \frac{3}{5}(5x - 10)$

28. $2\frac{1}{2}m + 3m + 1\frac{1}{2}m$ **29.** $8\frac{3}{5}c + 1\frac{1}{5}c - 2\frac{3}{5}c$ **30.** $7\frac{1}{6}p - 2\frac{5}{6}p + 3\frac{1}{6}p$

31. $8\frac{3}{4}m + 6 + 5\frac{1}{2}m + 4\frac{1}{4}$ **32.** $7\frac{5}{6}a + 9\frac{1}{4} + 2\frac{2}{3}a + 3\frac{1}{2}$

33. $4(3x + 8) + 4(2x - 3)$ **34.** $5(3x + 4) + 2(7x + 2)$

35. $6(x + 4) + 3(2x + 6)$ **36.** $7(3a + 5) - 4a + 2(3a - 5)$

37. $\frac{1}{2}(4x + 10) + \frac{2}{3}(9x + 6)$ **38.** $\frac{2}{5}(5v + 10) + \frac{3}{4}(12 + 8v)$

39. $\frac{1}{2}(2a + 12) + \frac{3}{7}(7a + 14)$ **40.** $\frac{3}{4}(16m + 20) + \frac{1}{6}(12 + 24m)$

Simplify. Then evaluate for the given value of the variable.

41. $5(2a + 3) + 4(3a + 1)$ for $a = 5$ **42.** $4(6 + 3x) + \frac{3}{4}(8x + 12)$ for $x = 3$

43. $5(3b + 5) + \frac{3}{5}(10b + 25)$ for $b = 4$ **44.** $\frac{2}{3}(6 + 12p) + \frac{1}{2}(2p - 4)$ for $p = 6$

45. $13y + \frac{1}{4}(8y + 12) + 3 + 7y + \frac{3}{7}(28 + 7y)$ for $y = 9$

Simplify.

46. $3a + 2[41 + 5(4a + 6)]$

47. $3(2x + 3) + 7[12 + 4(7x + 2)]$

48. $2(6y + 4) + 3[8 + 2(5y + 1)]$

49. $k + 6[3k + 5 + 5(3 + 7k)]$

50. Find the perimeter of the figure in terms of x. Simplify the result.

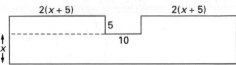

Mixed Review

Evaluate for the given value of the variable.   *1.2, 1.3*

1. $7 - 12x$ for $x = \frac{1}{4}$

2. $3x^2$ for $x = 4$

3. $2x^2 + 5x$ for $x = 2$

Which property is illustrated?   *1.5, 1.6*

4. $a + b = b + a$

5. $(x + y) + z = x + (y + z)$

6. $a(b + c) = ab + ac$

7. Find the perimeter and area of a rectangle with length 14 cm and width 12 cm.   *1.4*

Application: *Costs and Profit*

In business, accounting, and many other fields, formulas are frequently used to make predictions about costs or profit.

Solve each problem.

1. The manager of a restaurant figures the cost of making coffee is
$$m = 0.049x,$$
where m is the cost of making x cups. Find the cost of making 600 cups of coffee.

2. Mr. Irvington owns and operates Appealing Apple Pies. A consultant gave him the following formula to analyze his profits
$$p = 2x - 0.01x^2$$
where p is the profit and x is the number of pies baked. Find the profit on 60 pies.

3. The following formula is used by some taxi companies to figure how much to charge for a ride,
$$C = f + rd,$$
where C is the charge for the ride, f is a fixed charge, r is the rate per tenth of a mile, and d is the distance of the ride in tenths of a mile. Find the charge if f is $1.10, r is $0.10, and the ride is 25 tenths of a mile.

1.8 Solution Sets of Sentences

Objectives   To determine whether a sentence with no variables is true or false
To find the solution set of an open sentence

A balance scale can be used to
compare the weights of two objects.
The result can be written using an
inequality symbol.

$4 < 8$ $8 > 4$ $4 \neq 8$

4 is less than 8.   8 is greater than 4.   4 is not equal to 8.

On a horizontal number line, the smaller of two numbers is at the left
of the larger number. Thus, 4 is at the left of 8 because $4 < 8$.

Equations and inequalities are two types of *mathematical sentences*. An
equation consists of two expressions with an equals sign between them.
An **inequality** consists of two expressions with an inequality symbol
such as $<$, $>$, or $\neq$ between them. A mathematical sentence can be true
or false.

EXAMPLE 1   True or false?

a. $8(7 - 4) = 23$ **b.** $26 - 7 \cdot 3 > 2 \cdot 6 - 8$

Solutions   **a.** $8(7 - 4) = 23$ **b.** $26 - 7 \cdot 3 > 2 \cdot 6 - 8$
$8 \cdot 3 \overset{?}{=} 23$ $26 - 21 \overset{?}{=} 12 - 8$
$24 \neq 23$ False $5 > 4$ True

TRY THIS   True or false?   **1.** $(7 + 5)6 = 37$
2. $8 \cdot 4 < 2 \cdot 16$

The mathematical sentence $6x + 5 = 17$ contains a variable and is
called an **open sentence**. An *open sentence* is neither true nor false until
the variable or variables are replaced with numbers. The set of numbers
that can replace a variable is called the **replacement set** for the variable.

The **solution set** of an open sentence is the set of numbers from the given replacement set that makes the sentence true.

You can use braces, { }, to indicate a set. In Example 2, {0, 1, 2} is the set with members 0, 1, and 2.

EXAMPLE 2

Find the solution set of $6x + 5 = 17$. The replacement set for x is {0, 1, 2, 3}.

Plan

Replace x with each number in the replacement set.

Solution

Replace x with 0.

$$6x + 5 = 17$$
$$6 \cdot 0 + 5 \stackrel{?}{=} 17$$
$$5 \stackrel{?}{=} 17$$
$$5 \neq 17 \text{ False}$$

Replace x with 1.

$$6x + 5 = 17$$
$$6 \cdot 1 + 5 \stackrel{?}{=} 17$$
$$11 \stackrel{?}{=} 17$$
$$11 \neq 17 \text{ False}$$

Replace x with 2.

$$6x + 5 = 17$$
$$6 \cdot 2 + 5 \stackrel{?}{=} 17$$
$$12 + 5 \stackrel{?}{=} 17$$
$$17 \stackrel{?}{=} 17$$
$$17 = 17 \text{ True}$$

Replace x with 3.

$$6x + 5 = 17$$
$$6 \cdot 3 + 5 \stackrel{?}{=} 17$$
$$18 + 5 \stackrel{?}{=} 17$$
$$23 \stackrel{?}{=} 17$$
$$23 \neq 17 \text{ False}$$

Thus, the solution set is {2}.

EXAMPLE 3

Find the solution set of $2x > x + 5$. The replacement set is {2, 4, 6}.

Solution

Replace x with 2.

$$2x > x + 5$$
$$2 \cdot 2 \stackrel{?}{>} 2 + 5$$
$$4 \stackrel{?}{>} 7$$
$$4 \not> 7 \text{ False}$$

Replace x with 4.

$$2x > x + 5$$
$$2 \cdot 4 \stackrel{?}{>} 4 + 5$$
$$8 \stackrel{?}{>} 9$$
$$8 \not> 9 \text{ False}$$

Replace x with 6.

$$2x > x + 5$$
$$2 \cdot 6 \stackrel{?}{>} 6 + 5$$
$$12 \stackrel{?}{>} 11$$
$$12 > 11 \text{ True}$$

Thus, the solution set is {6}.

TRY THIS

3. Find the solution set of $2x - 3 < x + 5$. The replacement set for x is {7, 8, 9}.

The set containing no members is called the **empty set**, or the **null set**, and is written $\emptyset$. If no number in the replacement set makes an open sentence true, then the solution set of the sentence is the empty set, $\emptyset$.

EXAMPLE 4   Find the solution set of $1.2x + 3x = 4.1x$. The replacement set is $\{2, 5\}$.

Solution   Replace x with 2.   Replace x with 5.

$$1.2x + 3x = 4.1x \qquad\qquad 1.2x + 3x = 4.1x$$
$$1.2(2) + 3(2) \overset{?}{=} 4.1(2) \qquad 1.2(5) + 3(5) \overset{?}{=} 4.1(5)$$
$$2.4 + 6 \overset{?}{=} 8.2 \qquad\qquad 6 + 15 \overset{?}{=} 20.5$$
$$8.4 \overset{?}{=} 8.2 \qquad\qquad\qquad 21 \overset{?}{=} 20.5$$
$$8.4 \neq 8.2 \quad \text{False} \qquad\qquad 21 \neq 20.5 \quad \text{False}$$

Thus, the solution set is $\varnothing$.

EXAMPLE 5   Find the solution set of $2x + 1 > 3x + 1$. The replacement set is $\{0, 1, 2, 3, 4\}$.

Solution   Replace x with 0. The result is $1 > 1$ (false). Replacing x with numbers greater than 1 will also result in a false sentence. Thus, the solution set is $\varnothing$.

TRY THIS   4. Find the solution set of $3x + x \neq 4x$. The replacement set is $\{3, 4, 5, 6, 7\}$.

Sometimes open sentences involve exponents.

EXAMPLE 6   Find the solution set of $3x^2 + 2x > 7$. The replacement set is $\{0, 1, 3, 5\}$.

Solution   Replace x with 0.   Replace x with 1.

$$3x^2 + 2x > 7 \qquad\qquad 3x^2 + 2x > 7$$
$$3 \cdot 0^2 + 2 \cdot 0 \overset{?}{>} 7 \qquad 3 \cdot 1^2 + 2 \cdot 1 \overset{?}{>} 7$$
$$3 \cdot 0 + 0 \overset{?}{>} 7 \qquad\qquad 3 \cdot 1 + 2 \overset{?}{>} 7$$
$$0 + 0 \overset{?}{>} 7 \qquad\qquad 3 + 2 \overset{?}{>} 7$$
$$0 \not> 7 \quad \text{False} \qquad\qquad 5 \not> 7 \quad \text{False}$$

Replace x with 3.   Replace x with 5.

$$3x^2 + 2x > 7 \qquad\qquad 3x^2 + 2x > 7$$
$$3 \cdot 3^2 + 2 \cdot 3 \overset{?}{>} 7 \qquad 3 \cdot 5^2 + 2 \cdot 5 \overset{?}{>} 7$$
$$3 \cdot 9 + 6 \overset{?}{>} 7 \qquad\qquad 3 \cdot 25 + 10 \overset{?}{>} 7$$
$$33 > 7 \quad \text{True} \qquad\qquad 85 > 7 \quad \text{True}$$

Thus, the solution set is $\{3, 5\}$.

TRY THIS   5. Find the solution of $x^2 + 1 > (x + 1)^2 - 1$. The replacement set is $\{0, 1, 2, 3\}$.

Focus on Reading

Match each term at the left with the appropriate definition at the right.

1. solution set
2. replacement set
3. open sentence
4. empty set
5. inequality
6. equation

a. the set of numbers that can replace the variable in an open sentence

b. a sentence that states that two expressions name the same number

c. the set containing no members

d. the set of numbers from the given replacement set that makes an open sentence true

e. a sentence containing one or more variables

f. a sentence containing $\neq$, $>$, or $<$

Classroom Exercises

True or false?

1. $5 > 4$
2. $8 + 2 > 13$
3. $3 + 2 \neq 5$
4. $7 < 4 + 6$
5. $4 \cdot 4 < 5$
6. $3^2 \neq 6$
7. $7 > 5 + 6$
8. $2(3 + 5) > 13$

Tell whether the given number is a solution of the open sentence.

9. $15 = x + 7$; 8
10. $14 + y > 16$; 12
11. $a \neq 5.9$; 5.9
12. $x - 5 < 2$; 10
13. $16 - x > 8$; 8
14. $2c - 6 > 1$; 4
15. $x^2 > x$; 2
16. $x^2 > x; \frac{1}{2}$
17. $x > x$; 2.7

Written Exercises

True or False?

1. $83 + 0 = 83$
2. $23 \cdot 1 < 23$
3. $18 + 5 < 5 + 18$
4. $6(4 + 3) < 90$
5. $20 - 6 < 4(3 + 2)$
6. $10(3 + 8) = 30 + 80$
7. $3(10 - 3) \neq 4(7 - 1)$
8. $32 - 4 \cdot 6 < 12 + 5$
9. $24 - 5 \cdot 3 > 10 - 3$

Find the solution set. The replacement set is {0, 1, 2, 3}.

10. $3x + 1 > 5$
11. $4x + 1 < 22$
12. $3x + 4 = 4$
13. $3x + 5 = x + 8$
14. $\frac{x + 3}{2} = 2$
15. $\frac{3x + 2}{4} \neq 2$

Find the solution set. The replacement set is {1, 3, 5}.

16. $3x + 2 = x + 8$
17. $2x - 2 = x + 3$
18. $3(x + 1) = 3x + 3$
19. $2x > x + 1$
20. $5x - 5 < 4x$
21. $4(x + 2) > 3(x + 5)$

Find the solution set. The replacement set is $\{0, 5, 10\}$.

22. $1.1x = x + 0.5$

23. $0.4x = 0.2x + 0.5 + 0.1x$

24. $x^2 - 3x < 10$

25. $x^2 + 4x = 45$

26. $x^2 - 5x < 100$

27. $x^2 + 7x = 3x + 45$

28. $\dfrac{3x}{4} + x = \dfrac{x + 5}{2} + x$

29. $\dfrac{1}{2}(x + 2) < 2x + 1 + \dfrac{1}{2}x$

30. $0.15x > 0.2 + 0.1 + 0.1x$

31. $1.6x < x + 1 + 0.5x$

32. $x < x^2$

33. $x^2 + 4x = 8x + 5$

An open sentence can contain more than one variable. For each sentence, tell whether it is true for all numbers. If not, give an example showing it is not.

34. $x + y = y + x$ **35.** $x - y = y - x$ **36.** $x + y - y = x$ **37.** $x^2 > x$

38. $x(y - z) = xy - xz$ **39.** $x \cdot x < x^2 + 1$

Find the solution set. The replacement set is $\{1, 2, 3, 4\}$.

40. $x + 3[4 + 2(5x + 1)] = 30x + 19$

41. $\dfrac{x^2 + 7x}{2x + 5} = \dfrac{1}{2}x + 1$

42. $2x + 3x + 4x = x + 8x$

43. $x + 3x + 4x = x + 8x$

Mixed Review

Write an algebraic expression for each word description.   *1.1, 1.2*

1. 19 less than x

2. $\dfrac{1}{4}$ of the number n of students enrolled

3. the total bill for x hours if a person charges \$12 per hour.

Simplify.   *1.3, 1.5–1.7*

4. $3(2y)4$ **5.** $2 \cdot 4^2$ **6.** $2(3x + 7)$ **7.** $3a + 4(2a + 5) + a$

For Exercises 8–9, refer to the rectangle below.   *1.4*

8. What is the perimeter?

9. What is the area?

4 cm

6 cm

10. Find the perimeter and the area of a square with a side of 3.2 cm.

11. Find the area of a trapezoid with bases 3.5 cm and 2.7 m and an altitude of 4.6 m.

Problem Solving Strategies

Understanding the Problem

Everyone solves problems every day,—which shirt to wear, scheduling time for homework assignments and for TV, budgeting money for a class trip, and so on. Whether in personal life, at school, or on the job, you can often solve problems that appear difficult at first glance by using a series of steps. Here is a four-step process that many people have found useful for solving problems.

To Solve a Problem
1. Understand the Problem
2. Develop a Plan
3. Carry Out the Plan
4. Look Back

To understand a problem (Step 1), do these things.
a. Read the problem carefully. Make a list of all new words.
b. Look up the meaning of the words that are new to you.
c. Decide what given information is needed to solve the problem, and what is not needed.
d. Identify what you are asked to find. Identify the units (if any) that you will need to write the answer.

Exercises

Follow the steps (a–d) to understand the problem.
(a) List the information you need to solve the problem; (b) write the words from the problem that tell you what you are looking for, and (c) without solving the problem, write the unit for the answer.

1. Five people are planning a 123-mile trip to the beach. They estimate that the total cost will be $285. About how much is each person's share?

2. Raysa has saved $17 for a new bicycle seat. She needs about $50 more to cover the cost and the sales tax. If Raysa earns money by mowing lawns at $10 each, how many more lawns does she need to mow to earn the amount she needs?

3. For a science club experiment, Ed, Carla, and Ramon are counting the minutes that a hamster spends on its exercise wheel during three 12-hour days. The wheel has a diameter of 5 in. If each student shares the observation time for the experiment equally, how many hours must Ed observe the experiment?

Chapter 1 Review

Key Terms

algebraic expression   (p. 1)
area   (p. 13)
Associative Properties   (p. 17)
coefficient   (p. 26)
Commutative Properties   (p. 17)
Distributive Property   (p. 22)
empty set   (p. 31)
equation   (p. 30)
equivalent expressions   (p. 19)
evaluate   (p. 1)
exponent   (p. 9)
factors   (p. 9)
formula   (p. 9)
grouping symbols   (p. 5)

Identity Property for Multiplication   (p. 27)
inequality   (p. 30)
like terms   (p. 26)
mathematical sentence   (p. 30)
multiplicative identity   (p. 27)
numerical expression   (p. 1)
open sentence   (p. 30)
perimeter   (p. 13)
power   (p. 9)
replacement set   (p. 30)
solution set   (p. 31)
term   (p. 26)
variable   (p. 1)
volume   (p. 14)

Key Ideas and Review Exercises

1.1   To evaluate an algebraic expression, replace the variables with the numbers that are given and then simplify.

Evaluate.

1. $7x$ for $x = 9$

2. $a - b$ for $a = 11$ and $b = 7$

Write an algebraic expression for each word description.

3. 31 decreased by the number of cloudy days c

4. the cost, in dollars, of one bracelet if n bracelets cost $6

1.2–1.4   To simplify a numerical expression:
1. Operate within grouping symbols. Begin with the innermost symbols.
2. Simplify powers.
3. Multiply or divide from left to right.
4. Add or subtract from left to right.

Simplify.

5. $30 + 5 \cdot 4$

6. $4 + 6^2$

7. $(3 \cdot 5)^2$

8. $3 \cdot 5^2$

9. $35 \div 7 + 8$

10. $6 + [13 - (18 - 9)]$

Evaluate.

11. $x^3 - x^2 + 3x$ for $x = 2$

12. $\dfrac{x^2 + y^2}{x - y}$ for $x = 4$ and $y = 3$

Use the formula $p = 2l + 2w$ to find the perimeter of each rectangle with the given dimensions.

13. $l = 9$ in. and $w = 7$ in.

14. $l = 5.8$ cm and $w = 3.9$ cm

1.5   For all numbers a, b, and c,
   $a + b = b + a$ and $a \cdot b = b \cdot a$ (Commutative Properties)
   $(a + b) + c = a + (b + c)$ and $(a \cdot b)c = a(b \cdot c)$ (Associative Properties)

Which property is illustrated?

15. $65 + 43 = 43 + 65$

16. $(3a)2 = 2(3a)$

Simplify.

1.7   To simplify the expression $a + 3(2a - 4)$, first use the Distributive Property.

1.6   For all numbers a, b, and c, the Distributive Property states:
   $a(b + c) = ab + ac$ $(b + c)a = ba + ca$
   $a(b - c) = ab - ac$ $(b - c)a = ba - ca$

Rewrite by using the Distributive Property. Then simplify.

17. $5(7 + 2)$

18. $8 \cdot 5 + 8 \cdot 7$

19. $4(7a - 3)$

20. $6x + 5x + 7x$

1.7   To combine like terms, use the Distributive Property. To simplify the expression $a + 3(2a - 4)$, first multiply 3 by $2a - 4$.

Simplify. (Exercises 25–27)

21. $7y - 4y$

22. $17 + 4(6x - 2) + x$

23. Simplify $4(2p + 5) + (6p + 12)\frac{2}{3}$. Then evaluate for $p = 2$.

1.8   The solution set of an open sentence is the set of numbers from the replacement set that makes the sentence true.

Find the solution set. The replacement set is $\{1, 3, 5\}$.

24. $4x - 3 = 17$

25. $7 + 4y < 6$

26. $2x + 8 > 3x$

27. $x^2 + 4x > 12$

28. Explain in your own words the meaning of the symbols $>$ and $<$. Show how $a > b$ can be read in two different ways. Can you use the shape of the inequality symbol to describe a way to remember which number is larger?

Chapter 1 Test

Evaluate.

1. $6s$ for $s = 12$ *72*

2. $x^2 + 2x + 5$ for $x = 4$ *29*

3. $\dfrac{4.5}{c}$ for $c = 3$ *1.5*

4. $x^3(x + y)$ for $x = 3$ and $y = 7$ *270*

Write an algebraic expression for each word description.

5. the cost, in cents, of p pencils if each pencil costs 39¢ *39p*

6. 6 less than Julio's age j *j − 6*

Simplify.

7. $20 - 5 \cdot 3$ *5*

8. $3 \cdot 2^3$ *24*

9. $(3 \cdot 2)^3$ *216*

10. $10 + 2(7 - 4)$ *16*

11. Use the formula $A = lw$ to find the area of a rectangle of length 11.5 cm and width 6.2 cm. *71.3 cm²*

Which property is illustrated?

12. $5(7 + 2) = 5 \cdot 7 + 5 \cdot 2$ *Dis.*

13. $3 \cdot 10 = 10 \cdot 3$ *Comm. for ×*

14. $(4 + 5) + 1 = 4 + (5 + 1)$ *Assoc for +*

15. $(3 + 9) + 7 = (9 + 3) + 7$ *Comm. for +*

Rewrite by using the Distributive Property. Then simplify.

16. $7(10 - 6)$ *7·10 − 7·6 = 28*

17. $5 \cdot 7 + 5 \cdot 9 + 5 \cdot 3$ *5(7+9+3)=95*

18. $4(9x - 5)$ *4·9x − 4·5 = 36x − 20*

19. $(20a + 15)\dfrac{3}{5}$ *20a·3/5 + 15·3/5 = 12a + 9*

Simplify.

20. $(7m)4$ *28m*

21. $9(21y)$ *189y*

22. $7(2x)3$ *42x*

23. $16 \cdot \dfrac{3}{4}k \cdot 2$ *24k*

24. $5x + x + 7x$ *13x*

25. $8m - 2m$ *6m*

26. $6x + 3 + x + 2$ *7y+5*

27. $8 + 2(3x + 2) + x$ *7x+12*

28. Simplify $5(2y + 4) + (4y + 8)\dfrac{3}{4}$. Then evaluate for $y = 5$. *13y + 26 = 91) after plug*

Find the solution set. The replacement set is {1, 2, 3}.

29. $3x + 8 = 17$ *3*

30. $4y - 1 > 3y$ *2,3*

31. $5x + 6 \neq 7x + 2$ *1,3*

32. $x^2 + 4x < 10x + 1$ *1,2,3*

33. Simplify $(5 + 3x)2 + 3[9 + 5(2x + 1)]$ *36x +52*

34. Use the formula $V = \dfrac{\pi r^2 h}{3}$ to find V for $r = 10$ cm and $h = 5$ cm.

    Use 3.14 for π. Round your answer to the nearest whole number.

College Prep Test

Choose the best answer to each question or problem.

1. If $r = 3.8$ and $s = 1.9$, then $r \div s$ is __?__.
   (A) $\frac{1}{2}$ (B) $\frac{1}{20}$ (C) 2
   (D) 20   (E) None of these

2. If each apple costs c cents, what is the cost in dollars for a dozen apples?
   (A) $\frac{c}{100}$ (B) $\frac{c}{12}$ (C) $12c$
   (D) $\frac{12}{c}$ (E) $\frac{12c}{100}$

3. If change for a dollar consists of some quarters and some nickels, what is the least number of coins possible?
   (A) 4   (B) 6   (C) 8
   (D) 12   (E) 20

4. $(9x)^3$ and $9x^3$ have the same value if x is equal to __?__.
   (A) 0   (B) 1   (C) 0 or 1
   (D) 9   (E) None of these

5. How many numbers between 300 and 600 begin or end with 5?
   (A) 100   (B) 120   (C) 130
   (D) 140   (E) 200

6. Find the next number in the sequence 1, 2, 3, 5, 8, 13, __?__.
   (A) 15   (B) 18   (C) 20
   (D) 21   (E) 25

7. Thirty-cent cans of fruit juice can be bought for $3.12 per dozen. What would be the total savings on 48 cans of juice?
   (A) $1.20   (B) $1.44
   (C) $1.92   (D) $2.40
   (E) $2.88

8. The value of $\frac{5}{x}$ is greatest if x equals __?__.
   (A) $\frac{1}{5}$ (B) $\frac{1}{2}$ (C) 1
   (D) 2   (E) 5

9.

   If each side of the square is multiplied by 3, then the area will be __?__.
   (A) unchanged
   (B) tripled
   (C) multiplied by 6
   (D) multiplied by 9
   (E) multiplied by 12

10. A taxi meter registers $1.25 for the first $\frac{1}{6}$ mile and 10¢ for each additional $\frac{1}{6}$ mile. If the meter registers $3.25, how many miles was the trip?
    (A) $2\frac{5}{6}$ (B) $3\frac{1}{6}$ (C) $3\frac{1}{4}$
    (D) $3\frac{1}{3}$ (E) $3\frac{1}{2}$

11. An algebraic expression for y in. less than 5 ft is __?__.
    (A) $60 - y$ (B) $y - 5$
    (C) $5 - y$ (D) $y + 5$
    (E) $12y - 5$

12. If a number between 1 and 2 is squared, the result is a number between __?__.
    (A) 0 and 1   (B) 2 and 3
    (C) 2 and 4   (D) 1 and 4
    (E) None of these

13. If the postage rate is 25¢ for the first ounce and 20¢ for each additional ounce, then the weight of a package costing $2.45 is __?__.
    (A) 8 oz   (B) 9 oz   (C) 10 oz
    (D) 11 oz   (E) 12 oz

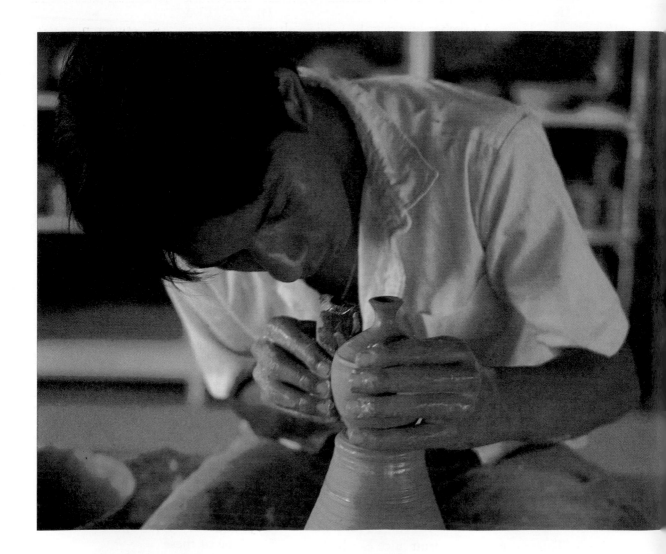

To turn mud into beautiful ceramics, potters make use of many formulas. They mix clay in different proportions, create glazes that melt into various colors, and fire the dried pieces to precise temperatures.

2.1 The Set of Real Numbers

To graph a point on a number line, given the coordinate of the point
To use real numbers to describe real-life situations
To compare real numbers

A number line may be used to show the relationships between numbers. A starting point, labeled 0, is called the *origin*. Numbers to the right of 0 are *positive*, and numbers to the left of 0 are *negative*. Zero is neither positive nor negative.

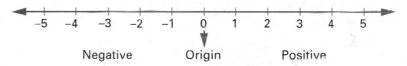

Different sets of numbers can be represented by listing their members. The three dots at the end of each list means *go on forever*.

Natural or **counting numbers:** $N = 1, 2, 3, 4, \cdots$
Whole Numbers: $W = 0, 1, 2, 3, 4, \cdots$
Integers: $I = \cdots -3, -2, -1, 0, 1, 2, 3, 4, \cdots$

The positive integers, 1, 2, 3, . . . are read as positive 1, positive 2, positive 3, and so on. The negative integers $-1, -2, -3, \ldots$ are read as negative 1, negative 2, negative 3, and so on.

These sets can be graphed on a number line. The shaded arrows mean that the graph goes on forever.

Graph of N: Natural numbers

Graph of W: Whole numbers

Graph of I: Integers

On a number line, the number that corresponds to a point is called the *coordinate* of the point. The point is called the *graph* of the number. In the graph of the integers above, point A is the graph of the number 3. The coordinate of point A is 3.

There are numbers on the number line that are not integers.
Numbers like $\frac{2}{5}$, $\frac{15}{4}$, $-\frac{1}{2}$, and 3 $\left(\text{or } \frac{3}{1}\right)$ are called *rational numbers*.

On the graph below, the coordinate of point D is 0.423. The graph of $-1\frac{2}{3}$ is B.

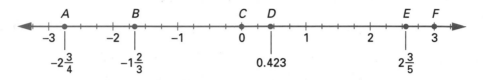

EXAMPLE 1 Give the coordinates of A, C, and E on the graph above.

Solution $-2\frac{3}{4}$ is the coordinate of A; 0 is the coordinate of C; $2\frac{3}{5}$ is the coordinate of E.

EXAMPLE 2 Graph the points with coordinates -4, -2.6, and $3\frac{3}{4}$ on a number line. Label the points A, B, and C.

Solution

Point A is the graph of -4. Point B is the graph of -2.6.
Point C is the graph of $3\frac{3}{4}$.

TRY THIS 1. Give the coordinate of F on the first number line above.

Any number that is positive, negative, or zero is called a **real number.** Real numbers are often used to represent real-life situations.

EXAMPLE 3 Write a real number to represent each situation.
a. 25° above zero   25
b. a loss of 5 yd in football -5
c. withdrawal of $400.25 from a checking account -400.25
d. a gain of $1\frac{3}{8}$ on the stock market $+1\frac{3}{8}$

TRY THIS 2. Write a real number to represent a temperature drop of four degrees.

Numbers on a horizontal number line increase from left to right.

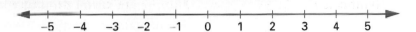

Therefore, $-4 < 3$ *or* $3 > -4$.

EXAMPLE 4   Use $<$ or $>$ to make a true statement.

  a. -5 ___ -2 **b.** $4\frac{1}{2}$ ___ -6 **c.** -5.3 ___ -5.4

Solutions   **a.** -5 is to the *left* of -2. Thus, $-5 < -2$.
  b. $4\frac{1}{2}$ is to the *right* of -6. Thus, $4\frac{1}{2} > -6$.
  c. -5.3 is to the *right* of -5.4. Thus, $-5.3 > -5.4$.

TRY THIS   **3.** Use $<$ or $>$ to make a true statement: 2.25 _?_ -2.35.

Classroom Exercises

Give the approximate coordinate of each point graphed below.

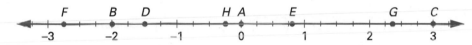

1. A   **2.** B   **3.** C   **4.** D   **5.** E   **6.** F   **7.** G   **8.** H

Use $<$ or $>$ to make each statement true.

9. 1 _?_ 4 **10.** 2 _?_ -3 **11.** -3.7 _?_ -3.6 **12.** $2\frac{1}{3}$ _?_ $-3\frac{2}{3}$

Written Exercises

Give the approximate coordinate of each point graphed below.

1. A   **2.** B   **3.** C   **4.** D   **5.** E   **6.** F   **7.** G   **8.** H

On a number line, graph each point whose coordinate is given.

9. A: -1 **10.** B: 4 **11.** C: 1.5 **12.** D: -2.1
13. E: $1\frac{2}{5}$ **14.** F: -4.7 **15.** G: $2\frac{3}{4}$ **16.** H: $-3\frac{2}{3}$

Write a real number to represent each situation.

17. a gain of 20 yd

18. a temperature drop of 6°

19. 8 wins

20. no gain, no loss

21. 3 below par

22. a deposit of $136.52

23. a weight loss of $3\frac{1}{2}$ pounds

24. a loss of $2\frac{3}{8}$ points

25. a profit of $236.25

26. a withdrawal of $9.42

27. 4.2 km below sea level

28. a weight gain of 2.1 kg

Use < or > to make each sentence true.

29. 7 ___ 3

30. 0 ___ 5

31. -2 ___ 1

32. 4 ___ -4

33. -8 ___ -6

34. 2 ___ -6

35. -7 ___ -9

36. -3 ___ 0

37. $2\frac{1}{2}$ ___ 3

38. $-4\frac{1}{4}$ ___ -4

39. $3\frac{1}{3}$ ___ 3

40. $-8\frac{3}{4}$ ___ $8\frac{3}{4}$

41. 0.2 ___ 0.1

42. -0.6 ___ 0.6

43. -2.4 ___ -2.3

44. -6.1 ___ 0

45. $\frac{1}{2}$ ___ $\frac{1}{3}$

46. $-\frac{1}{5}$ ___ $-\frac{1}{4}$

47. $\frac{2}{3}$ ___ $-1\frac{1}{3}$

48. $\frac{3}{4}$ ___ $\frac{1}{2}$

49. 4.62 ___ 4.6

50. -3.81 ___ 3.81

51. 7.94 ___ 7.95

52. -8.3 ___ -8.31

53. 3.6 ___ $3\frac{1}{2}$

54. 5.4 ___ $-5\frac{1}{2}$

55. 6.7 ___ $6\frac{3}{4}$

56. -8.2 ___ $-8\frac{1}{4}$

True or false?

57. 0 is an integer.

58. Every integer is a real number.

59. Every real number is an integer.

60. $-6\frac{1}{2}$ is not an integer.

61. 0 is not positive or negative.

62. -6 is less than $-6\frac{1}{2}$.

63. Every negative integer is less than every positive integer.

64. On a number line, -2 lies to the right of $-3\frac{1}{2}$.

65. On a number line, x and $-x$ are each the same distance from 0.

66. For all real numbers x and y, if $x < y$, then $y > x$.

67. For all real numbers x and y, if $x > 0$ and $y < 0$, then $x < y$.

68. For all real numbers x, y, and z, if $x < y$ and $y < z$, then $x < z$.

Mixed Review

Simplify. *1.2, 1.3*

1. $19 - 3 \cdot 6$

2. $(19 - 3)6$

3. $2 \cdot 4^2$

4. $(2 \cdot 4)^2$

Find the solution set. The replacement set is {0, 1, 2, 3}. *1.8*

5. $x + 2 < 4$

6. $2x + 3 = 4$

7. $4(y + 2) = 4y + 8$

8. Use the formula $A = \frac{1}{2}(b + c)h$ to find the area of a trapezoid with $b = 10$ cm, $c = 6$ cm, and $h = 4$ cm. *1.4*

2.2 Opposites and Absolute Value

Objective   To simplify expressions involving opposites and absolute values

In football, a 2-yd gain is represented by the number 2. The opposite of a 2-yd gain is a 2-yd loss, which is represented by the number -2. The numbers 2 and -2 are called **opposites**. On a number line they are the same distance from 0, and they lie on opposite sides of 0. Every real number has an opposite.

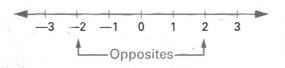

The opposite of 2 is -2.
The opposite of -2 is 2.
The opposite of 0 is 0.

So far, a dash has been used to indicate a negative number. Since -5 is the opposite of 5, a dash can also mean *the opposite of*. For example, -5 means *negative 5* or *the opposite of 5*.

You can indicate the opposite of a negative number also. For example, $-(-4)$ means *the opposite of* -4. Note that $-(-4) = 4$. This is read: *The opposite of negative 4 is 4.*

For any real number a, $-a$ means the opposite of a, and $-(-a) = a$.

EXAMPLE 1   Simplify each of the following expressions.

Expression	Meaning	Value
a. $-\left(-\frac{1}{2}\right)$	the opposite of negative $\frac{1}{2}$	$\frac{1}{2}$
b. -0	the opposite of 0	0
c. $-(7.8 - 3.2)$	the opposite of the difference: $7.8 - 3.2 = 4.6$	-4.6

TRY THIS   1. Simplify $-(6.9 - 4.7)$.

The distance between 4 and 0 on the number line is 4 units. The distance between −4 and 0 is also 4 units.

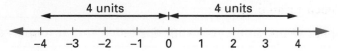

4 units   4 units

The distance of each number from zero is its *absolute value*.

The absolute value of 4 is equal to 4.

$$|4| = 4$$

The absolute value of −4 is equal to 4.

$$|-4| = 4$$

Definition

The **absolute value** of a real number x is the distance between x and 0 on a number line. The symbol $|x|$ means the absolute value of x.

$|x| = x$, if $x \geq 0$ ($\geq$ means *is greater than or equal to*.)
$|x| = -x$, if $x < 0$

In general, if x is a positive number or zero, $|x| = x$. If x is a negative number, $|x| = -x$. In this case, $-x$ is positive.

EXAMPLE 2   Simplify.
a. $|7|$ b. $|-2.3|$ c. $|0|$ d. $|8 + 3|$

Solutions   a. $|7| = 7$ b. $|-2.3| = 2.3$ c. $|0| = 0$ d. $|8 + 3| = |11| = 11$

EXAMPLE 3   Simplify. First rewrite the expressions without absolute value symbols.
a. $-|-4|$ b. $|-8| + |5|$ c. $-|13 - 7|$

Solutions   a. $-|-4| = -(4)$ b. $|-8| + |5| = 8 + 5$ c. $-|13 - 7| = -(6)$
              $= -4$ $= 13$ $= -6$

EXAMPLE 4   Compare. Use $>$, $<$, or $=$.
a. $|2.5| \underline{\ ?\ } |-2.5|$ b. $|-6| \underline{\ ?\ } -|-9|$ c. $-(-5) \underline{\ ?\ } -|-5|$

Solutions   a. $|2.5| \underline{\ ?\ } |-2.5|$ b. $|-6| \underline{\ ?\ } -|-9|$ c. $-(-5) \underline{\ ?\ } -|-5|$
              $2.5 \underline{\ ?\ } 2.5$ $6 \underline{\ ?\ } -(9)$ $5 \underline{\ ?\ } -(5)$
              $2.5 = 2.5$ $6 > -9$ $5 > -5$

TRY THIS   Simplify: 2. $|3| + |-2|$ 3. $-|3 - 2|$
4. Compare. Use $<$ or $>$. $-(-4) \underline{\ \ \ \ } -|6 - 2|$

Classroom Exercises

Give the opposite of each number.

1. 9   **2.** -6.4 **3.** 1.876   **4.** -0.72

Give the absolute value of each number.

5. 9   **6.** -5.2 **7.** $-\frac{3}{5}$ **8.** 5.384

Simplify.

9. $-\left(-6\frac{1}{2}\right)$ **10.** $-(7 + 9)$ **11.** $-\left(\frac{18}{6}\right)$ **12.** $-(-8.2)$

13. $|15|$ **14.** $|6 - 7|$ **15.** $|2 + 6|$ **16.** $|7| + |-8|$

Written Exercises

Give the opposite of each number.

1. 2   **2.** -5.6 **3.** 0   **4.** 40

5. -3 **6.** $-\frac{4}{5}$ **7.** 0.5   **8.** $\frac{1}{3}$

Simplify.

9. $-(-10)$ **10.** $-(-4.7)$ **11.** $-(5 - 3)$ **12.** $-(3 \cdot 8)$

13. $-(14 \div 2)$ **14.** $-(8 \cdot 0)$ **15.** $-(17 + 0)$ **16.** $-(6.8 - 4.9)$

17. $|3|$ **18.** $|-20|$ **19.** $|-1|$ **20.** $|6|$

21. $|1|$ **22.** $|-18|$ **23.** $|0.8|$ **24.** $|-1.9|$

25. $-|3|$ **26.** $-|-3|$ **27.** $|-(-3)|$ **28.** $-|-(-3)|$

29. $|8 - 5|$ **30.** $-|4 \cdot 2|$ **31.** $\left|\frac{20}{4}\right|$ **32.** $-|8 - 7|$

33. $|6 \cdot 9|$ **34.** $-|6 + 10|$ **35.** $-|30 \div 5|$ **36.** $|1| + |5|$

37. $|7| + |-4|$ **38.** $|-9| + |-1|$ **39.** $|6| + |-6|$ **40.** $|3| - |-3|$

41. $|-8| + |4|$ **42.** $|-6| + |-10|$ **43.** $|-6| \cdot |8|$ **44.** $|-4| \cdot |0|$

45. $|-9| \cdot |-2|$ **46.** $|-4| \cdot |-3|$ **47.** $|-1| \cdot |8|$ **48.** $|-38| \cdot |1|$

Write a positive number or a negative number for each phrase. Then write the opposite phrase and the corresponding opposite number.

      Example: depositing $40
      Answer: 40; withdrawing $40; -40

49. losing 5 lb   **50.** a profit of $80   **51.** temperature falling 8°

52. 5 mi/h gain in speed   **53.** 12 ft above sea level   **54.** a $15 price markdown

True or false? Justify your answer.

55. $-6 > -(2)$ **56.** $-(-4) = 4$ **57.** $-2 < |2|$ **58.** $-(3) = |-3|$

59. $|-8| = 8$ **60.** $|16.2| > 6.2$ **61.** $\left|-\frac{3}{4}\right| < \frac{1}{2}$ **62.** $|0| < -1$

63. $|-16| = |16|$ **64.** $\left|\frac{1}{2}\right| < \left|\frac{1}{4}\right|$ **65.** $|0| < |-1|$ **66.** $|9| > |-9|$

Compare. Use $>$, $<$, or $=$.

67. $-6 \underline{\quad} -(6)$ **68.** $0 \underline{\quad} -(5)$ **69.** $-8 \underline{\quad} -(-8)$ **70.** $-(3) \underline{\quad} |-3|$

71. $|5| \underline{\quad} |-5|$ **72.** $|-6| \underline{\quad} |6|$ **73.** $|-1| \underline{\quad} -(1)$ **74.** $|2| \underline{\quad} |-8|$

75. $|0| \underline{\quad} -|0|$ **76.** $\left|-\frac{1}{3}\right| \underline{\quad} \left|-\frac{1}{2}\right|$ **77.** $|6| \underline{\quad} -|-6|$ **78.** $-|-4| \underline{\quad} |4|$

79. Explain in writing why the absolute value of a number may be the same as the opposite of that number.

True or false? If false, justify your answer.

80. If x is a positive number, then $-x$ is a negative number.

81. If $-x$ is a positive number, then x is a negative number.

82. If x is a negative number, then $-(-x)$ is a positive number.

83. If x is any real number, then $|x| = x$.

84. If x is any real number, then $|x| = |-x|$.

85. There are two real numbers whose absolute value is 8.

86. If $x > 0$, then $|x| = x$.

87. If $x < 0$, then $x > -x$.

Mixed Review

Evaluate for $x = 2$, $y = 3$, and $z = 4$.   *1.1, 1.3*

1. $yz - xy$ **2.** $\dfrac{x + y + z}{x + y - z}$ **3.** xy^2 **4.** $x(7z - xy - 6)$

Which property is illustrated?   *1.5, 1.6*

5. $y(z - x) = yz - yx$ **6.** $(9y + 2z) + 6x = 6x + (9y + 2z)$

7. $(10y)z = 10(yz)$ **8.** $4x + 5x = (4 + 5)x$

Simplify.   *1.7*

9. $7x + 5x + 4x$ **10.** $7y + 4 + 3y$

11. $3k + 5b + 7k$ **12.** $5a + 4b + 7a + 9b$

2.3 Addition on a Number Line

Objective	To add real numbers using a number line

The result of two successive weight gains can be expressed as the sum of two positive numbers. Similarly, the result of two successive weight losses can be expressed as the sum of two negative numbers.

The number line can be used as a model when numbers are added.

EXAMPLE 1 Add 3 + 2.

Solution Start at 3. Move 2 units to the right. Stop at 5.

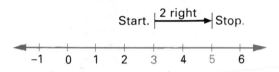

Thus, 3 + 2 = 5.

TRY THIS 1. How can you use the number line to add 2 + 4?

The sum of two negative numbers, such as −2 and −4 is written

$$-2 + (-4).$$

The parentheses are used to separate the addition symbol (+) from the negative symbol (−) that is part of the numeral, −4.

EXAMPLE 2 Add −2 + (−4).

Solution Start at −2. Move 4 units to the left. Stop at −6.

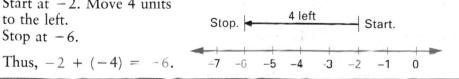

Thus, −2 + (−4) = −6.

TRY THIS 2. How can you use a number line to add −5 + (−2)?

An application of adding two negative numbers is finding a total weight loss when dieting. The result of a loss of 2 lb last week, followed by a loss of 4 lb this week, can be represented as follows.

$$-2 + (-4) = -6 \qquad \text{The total loss is 6 lb.}$$

A number line can be used to add numbers that have unlike signs.

EXAMPLE 3   Add $-4 + 3$.

Solution   Start at -4. Move 3 units to the right. Stop at -1.

Thus, $-4 + 3 = -1$.

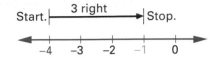

EXAMPLE 4   Add $-2 + 5$.

Solution   Start at -2. Move 5 units to the right. Stop at 3.

Thus, $-2 + 5 = 3$.

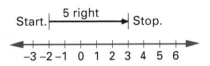

TRY THIS   Add: **3.** $2 + (-5)$ **4.** $-3 + 8$

A number line can be used to add more than two numbers. To find the sum of $(-7) + 6 + (-3)$, add $(-7) + 6$ first. Then add the result to (-3).

EXAMPLE 5   Add $-7 + 6 + (-3)$.

Solution   Start at -7. Move 6 units to the right. Then move 3 units to the left. Stop at -4.

Thus, $-7 + 6 + (-3) = -4$.

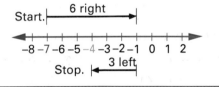

TRY THIS   **5.** Add $4 + (-7) + 3$.   **6.** Add $(-1) + 5 + (-6)$.

Adding 0 to a number on the number line is the same as moving 0 units. The sum $-3 + 0$ means to start at -3 and move 0 units. The sum $3 + 0$ means to start at 3 and move 0 units. Thus,

$$-3 + 0 = -3 \quad \text{and} \quad 3 + 0 = 3$$

The sum of any given number and 0 is equal to the given number. This illustrates the Property of Zero for Addition of real numbers. Thus, 0 is called the *identity element for addition*.

Identity Property for Addition
For all real numbers a, $a + 0 = a$ and $0 + a = a$.

Think of adding a pair of opposites, such as 5 and −5 on a number line.

Start at 5.

Then move 5 units to the left to 0.

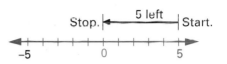

Therefore, $5 + (-5) = 0$.

Similarly, it can be shown that

$$-5 + 5 = 0.$$

Another name for opposite is *additive inverse*. Thus, the additive inverse, or opposite, of −7 is 7. The following property relates to the sum of two additive inverses.

Additive Inverse Property

For each real number a, there is exactly one real number $-a$ such that

$$a + (-a) = 0 \quad \text{and} \quad -a + a = 0.$$

Classroom Exercises

Tell how to add these numbers using a number line. Then add.

1. $5 + 6$ **2.** $-7 + (-2)$ **3.** $8 + (-10)$ **4.** $-5 + 0$

5. $4 + (-4)$ **6.** $8 + 1$ **7.** $0 + (-7)$ **8.** $10 + (-2)$

9. $7 + (-9)$ **10.** $-5 + (-4)$ **11.** $-4 + 5$ **12.** $3 + (-3)$

13. $-6 + (-1)$ **14.** $2 + (-7)$ **15.** $-8 + (-3)$ **16.** $-11 + 2$

Give the additive inverse of each number.

17. -6 **18.** -32 **19.** 24 **20.** -13 **21.** 17 **22.** 64

Written Exercises

Add.

1. $3 + 7$ **2.** $8 + 5$ **3.** $-6 + (-9)$ **4.** $-7 + (-5)$

5. $0 + (-3)$ **6.** $-4 + 0$ **7.** $7 + (-7)$ **8.** $11 + (-3)$

9. $-9 + 8$ **10.** $-1 + 9$ **11.** $-5 + (-5)$ **12.** $8 + (-12)$

13. $8 + (-8)$ **14.** $-14 + 1$ **15.** $-9 + 9$ **16.** $-14 + (-3)$

17. $-5 + 4 + (-2)$ **18.** $5 + 4 + (-2)$ **19.** $6 + (-2) + (-4)$

20. $-8 + 8 + (-1)$ **21.** $9 + 5 + (-14)$ **22.** $3 + (-3) + (-5)$

23. $-5 + (-8) + 4$ **24.** $9 + (-5) + (-2)$ **25.** $-7 + (-7) + 14$

26. $-8 + (-3) + (-2) + 4$ **27.** $12 + (-2) + (-5) + (-3)$

28. $-16 + 5 + (-7) + 16$ **29.** $-25 + 50 + 50 - 75$

30. $12 + (-14) + (-9) + 5$ **31.** $100 + (-60) + 10 + (-40)$

32. Find the additive inverse of the sum $-5 + 4$.

33. Find the value of $-7 + (-9)$.

Evaluate for the given values of the variables.

34. $x + y$, for $x = -5$ and $y = 4$

35. $-x + y$, for $x = -3$ and $y = -6$

36. For what values of a will $-a < 0$ be true?

37. Write a rule for adding two negative numbers without using a number line. Then use this rule to find the sum $-43 + (-118)$.

38. Write a rule for adding two numbers with different signs. Then use this rule to find the sum $-47 + 86$.

39. Is $|a + b| = |a| + |b|$ true for all numbers a and b? If not, give a *counterexample*. A **counterexample** is an example that shows that a statement is false.

Mixed Review

Simplify. *1.2, 1.3, 1.7*

1. $4 \cdot 3 + 18$ **2.** $8 \cdot 4^3$ **3.** $4y + 8y$ **4.** $3x + 5 + x$

5. Write an algebraic expression for 6 less than the number x of workdays in a year. *1.1*

6. Write an algebraic expression for $62 increased by d dollars saved.

7. Write an algebraic expression for the number of yards in x inches.

8. Find the perimeter of a rectangle with length 8 m and width $6\frac{1}{4}$ m. Use the formula $p = 2l + 2w$. *1.4*

9. Find the solution set of $3x + 2 = 11$. The replacement set is $\{1, 3, 7\}$. *1.8*

10. Find the solution set of $2x + 5 = 15$. The replacement set is $\{0, 2, 5\}$.

2.4 Adding Real Numbers

Objective	To add real numbers using the rules for addition

In the last lesson a number line was used to add integers. This is not very practical for finding sums of numbers such as $4\frac{1}{2} + \left(-6\frac{1}{3}\right)$.

Examine the sums below.

$$2 + 4 = 6 \qquad -3 + (-2) = -5$$
$$3 + 2 = 5 \qquad -2 + (-4) = -6$$

The sums suggest the following rule.

> To add two real numbers with the same sign:
>
> 1. Add their absolute values.
> 2. Determine the sign of the sum:
>   a. If both numbers are positive, then the sum is positive.
>   b. If both numbers are negative, then the sum is negative.

EXAMPLE 1 Add $-12 + (-19)$.

Solution

Add the absolute values.	$\lvert -12 \rvert + \lvert -19 \rvert = 12 + 19 = 31$
The sum is negative.	Thus, $-12 + (-19) = -31$.

TRY THIS Add: **1.** $-7 + (-3)$ **2.** $4 + 11$

Examine the sums below.

$$-4 + 3 = -1 \qquad -2 + 5 = 3$$

The sums suggest the following rule.

> To add two real numbers with unlike signs, if the numbers are not opposites:
>
> 3. Subtract their absolute values, the smaller from the larger.
> 4. The sign of the sum will be the same as the sign of the number with the greater absolute value.

EXAMPLE 2   Add $-16 + 12$.

Solution   The signs are unlike, and -16 has the greater absolute value.
Subtract the absolute values. $|-16| - |12| = 16 - 12 = 4$
$|-16| > |12|$; sum is negative.   Thus, $-16 + 12 = -4$.

EXAMPLE 3   Evaluate $x + y$ for $x = -4.5$ and $y = 6.3$.

Solution   The signs are unlike, and 6.3 has the greater absolute value.

Subtract the absolute values. $|6.3| - |-4.5| = 6.3 - 4.5 = 1.8$
$|6.3| > |-4.5|$; sum is positive.   Thus, $-4.5 + 6.3 = 1.8$.

TRY THIS   3. Evaluate $x + y$ for $x = 5$ and $y = -8$.

Notice that when you add two real numbers the sum is also a real number. We say that the set of real numbers is *closed* under addition.

The commutative and associative properties allow you to group numbers in any convenient way and add in any order. Adding more than two real numbers is sometimes easier when numbers with like signs are grouped together. This is shown in Example 4.

EXAMPLE 4   Add $3 + (-2) + 4 + (-6)$.

Solution

Method 1
Add the numbers in order from left to right.

$$3 + (-2) + 4 + (-6)$$
$$\underbrace{}$$
$$1 \quad + 4 + (-6)$$
$$\underbrace{}$$
$$5 \quad + (-6)$$
$$-1$$

Method 2
Group the positive numbers and the negative numbers. Then add.

$$3 + (-2) + 4 + (-6)$$
$$\underbrace{3 + 4}\; +\; \underbrace{(-2) + (-6)}$$
$$7 \quad + \quad (-8)$$
$$-1$$

Here are calculator steps for Method 1.

3 ⊞ 2 ⊞ ⊞ 4 ⊞ 6 ⊞ ⊟ -1

TRY THIS   4. Add $-3 + 5 + (-8) + 9$.

54   Chapter 2 Operations with Real Numbers

EXAMPLE 5   On Tuesday afternoon the temperature was $-3°F$. That night it dropped 8° and the next morning it rose 15°. What was the temperature on Wednesday morning?

Plan   Translate the problem into a sum of real numbers and add.

Solution

Tuesday afternoon		Tuesday night		Wednesday morning
-3	+	(-8)	+	15
	-11		+	15
		4		

Thus, the temperature was 4°F on Wednesday morning.

TRY THIS   5. Translate: Nancy is three years younger than Harry. Harry is 17. How old is Nancy?

Classroom Exercises

Add.

1. $5 + 8$
2. $-4 + (-6)$
3. $-8 + (-2)$
4. $0 + 11$
5. $-7 + 4$
6. $9 + (-10)$
7. $-8 + 3$
8. $-4 + 9$
9. $-6 + 13$
10. $8 + (-13)$
11. $-9 + (-7)$
12. $15 + (-15)$
13. $-7 + (-3)$
14. $7 + (-8)$
15. $-4 + (-5)$
16. $-13 + (-8)$

Written Exercises

Add.

1. $7 + 6$
2. $9 + 5$
3. $-4 + (-9)$
4. $-10 + (-5)$
5. $5 + (-7)$
6. $-11 + (-8)$
7. $-12 + 4$
8. $-13 + (-6)$
9. $-16 + 8$
10. $32 + (-15)$
11. $-17 + 0$
12. $23 + (-16)$
13. $4.8 + (-4.8)$
14. $-3.7 + (-2.8)$
15. $-7.4 + 3.8$
16. $2.9 + 4.7$
17. $16.2 + (-8.5)$
18. $-8.7 + 7.9$
19. $-5.4 + (-5.4)$
20. $7.3 + (-2.6)$
21. $-2.8 + 9.6 + (-1.5)$
22. $-6 + 2 + (-4)$
23. $19 + (-4) + 3$
24. $-2 + 12 + (-14)$

25. A football team had a 4-yd gain followed by a 7-yd loss. Find the resulting gain or loss.

26. The temperature was $-5°F$ at midnight. It dropped 7° by 3:00 A.M. Find the temperature at that time.

27. In one month Mike gained 3 lb. The next month he lost 5 lb. He lost 2 more pounds the third month. Find the net gain or loss.

28. A team scored 5 points. Then there was a 2-point penalty. This was followed by a 3-point score. Find the net gain or loss.

Add.

29. $-3\frac{1}{3} + \left(-3\frac{2}{3}\right)$ **30.** $7\frac{5}{6} + \left(-2\frac{1}{6}\right)$ **31.** $7 + \left(-2\frac{4}{5}\right)$

32. $-6\frac{7}{10} + \left(-8\frac{3}{5}\right)$ **33.** $8\frac{1}{6} + \left(-3\frac{1}{3}\right)$ **34.** $-5\frac{2}{3} + \left(-4\frac{1}{2}\right)$

Evaluate for $x = -8$, $y = 18$, and $z = -13$.

35. $x + 5$ **36.** $-6 + y$ **37.** $z + (-4)$ **38.** $x + 8$

39. $x + y$ **40.** $x + z$ **41.** $y + z$ **42.** $x + y + z$

43. $x + (-y)$ **44.** $-x + y$ **45.** $|x| + |y|$ **46.** $|x| + |z|$

47. Evaluate $a + b$ for $a = 7.5$ and $b = -0.9$.

48. Evaluate $a + b$ for $a = -\frac{3}{4}$ and $b = -1\frac{1}{8}$.

49. Evaluate $a + b + c$ for $a = 2.6$, $b = -1.4$, and $c = -0.7$.

50. Evaluate $a + b + c$ for $a = -\frac{2}{3}$, $b = 2\frac{1}{3}$, and $c = -\frac{5}{6}$.

51. The lowest point in Death Valley, California, is 276 ft below sea level. A hot-air balloon was floating 83 ft above this point. The balloon climbed 68 ft higher and then dropped 72 ft. Find the altitude of the balloon relative to sea level.

52. Mary took out a loan to open a small business. In the first year the business lost $1,700. In the second year the business made a profit of $2,845. In the third year the business made a profit of $3,650. When Mary paid off the loan and a total of $1,125 in interest, she had a net profit of $1,140. How much was the loan?

53. José left on a flight from London at 2:42 P.M. The flight was due to land in New York 7 h 35 min later. In New York, the time is 5 h earlier than it is in London. Give the time in New York when the plane was due to land.

54. If the balance in Bill's checking account falls below $600.00 during a month, he is charged a $7.00 service charge for that month. At the beginning of January his balance was $1,426.51. At the end of January his balance was $582.70. During January he wrote checks totaling $1,872.85. How much did he deposit during January?

Mixed Review

Compare. Use $<$, $>$, or $=$.   *2.1*

1. 2 ___ -3 **2.** -7 ___ -4

Simplify.   *2.2*

3. $-(8 - 3)$ **4.** $9 - 2$

2.5 Subtraction of Real Numbers

To subtract real numbers

To simplify and evaluate expressions involving addition and subtraction of real numbers

Consider the following examples.

$$9 - 3 = 6 \qquad 7 - 3 = 4 \qquad 3 - 3 = 0$$
$$9 + (-3) = 6 \qquad 7 + (-3) = 4 \qquad 3 + (-3) = 0$$

In all three cases, subtracting 3 and adding -3 gave the same result. Subtracting a number gives the same result as adding the opposite of that number. Thus, $1 - 3 = 1 + (-3) = -2$.

Definition

Subtraction
For all real numbers a and b, $a - b = a + (-b)$.
That is, to subtract a number, add its opposite.

EXAMPLE 1 Subtract.

a. $2 + 5$ Subtract 5 by adding -5. $2 - 5 = 2 + (-5) = -3$
b. $6 - (-9)$ Subtract -9 by adding 9. $6 - (-9) = 6 + 9 = 15$
c. $-2.3 - (-1.8)$ Subtract -1.8 by adding 1.8. $-2.3 - (-1.8) =$
                                                     $-2.3 + 1.8 = -0.5$

TRY THIS Subtract: **1.** $3 - 8$ **2.** $-7 - (-10)$

Since subtraction is defined in terms of addition, the expression $6 - 9 + 4 - 1$ can be thought of as the sum $6 + (-9) + 4 + (-1)$.

You can then use the properties of addition to group the numbers in a convenient way, as shown in Example 2.

EXAMPLE 2 Simplify $6 - 9 + 4 - 1$.

Plan Group the positive numbers and the negative numbers.

Solution
$$6 - 9 + 4 - 1 = 6 + (-9) + 4 + (-1)$$
$$= 6 + 4 + (-9) + (-1)$$
$$= \underbrace{10} + \underbrace{-10} \qquad 0$$

TRY THIS **3.** Simplify $-4 + 7 - 9 + 2$.

EXAMPLE 3   Evaluate $x + y - z$ for $x = -7$, $y = 8$, and $z = -9$.

Solution
$$x + y - z = -7 + 8 - (-9)$$
$$= -7 + \underbrace{8 + 9}_{} \quad \longleftarrow \text{ Subtracting } -9 \text{ is the same as adding } 9.$$
$$= -7 + \quad 17$$
$$= 10$$

Thus, $x + y - z = 10$ for $x = -7$, $y = 8$, and $z = -9$.

TRY THIS   4. Evaluate $x - y + z$ for $x = -2$, $y = -6$, and $z = -3$.

Subtraction of real numbers can be used to solve problems.

EXAMPLE 4   The temperature rose from $-3°F$ to $16°F$. What was the temperature change?

Solution
$$16 - (-3) = 16 + 3 \quad \longleftarrow \text{ Subtract } -3 \text{ from } 16.$$
$$= 19$$

Thus, the temperature rose $19°$.

EXAMPLE 5   An elevator on the 8th floor goes up 3 floors, then down 5 floors, then up 2 floors, and then down 7 floors. At what floor is the elevator after these moves are completed?

Solution   THINK: $8 + 3 + (-5) + 2 + (-7)$
WRITE: $8 + 3 - 5 + 2 - 7$ Then group positive and negative terms together.

$$\underbrace{-5 - 7}_{} + \underbrace{8 + 3 + 2}_{}$$
$$-12 \quad + \quad 13$$
$$1 \qquad \text{The elevator is at the first floor.}$$

TRY THIS   5. An elevator started three floors below the ground and stopped four floors above the ground. How many floors did the elevator move?

Classroom Exercises

State each subtraction problem as an equivalent addition problem. Then simplify.

1. $6 - 8$ **2.** $-3 - 9$ **3.** $4 - (-7)$ **4.** $10 - 2$

5. $16 - 20$ **6.** $-9 - (-5)$ **7.** $-8 - 6$ **8.** $7 - (-12)$

9. $-8 - (-6)$ **10.** $4 - 11$ **11.** $21 - 3$ **12.** $-6 - (-7)$

Written Exercises

Subtract.

1. $10 - 4$	**2.** $4 - 10$	**3.** $-5 - 3$	**4.** $3 - (-5)$
5. $7 - (-2)$	**6.** $-8 - (-3)$	**7.** $-7 - (-1)$	**8.** $4 - (-6)$
9. $-7 - 8$	**10.** $18 - 19$	**11.** $16 - 16$	**12.** $4 - (-4)$
13. $-8 - 8$	**14.** $-9 - (-9)$	**15.** $6 - (-12)$	**16.** $-14 - (-3)$
17. $12 - 12$	**18.** $15 - (-5)$	**19.** $-18 - 16$	**20.** $32 - 0$
21. $-14 - 0$	**22.** $-6 - 5$	**23.** $15 - (-9)$	**24.** $0 - (-6)$
25. $17 - (-23)$	**26.** $0 - 8$	**27.** $-42 - 26$	**28.** $87 - 54$
29. $-3.8 - 2.7$	**30.** $16 - 4.2$	**31.** $-2.9 - (-5.1)$	**32.** $4.8 - (-3.6)$
33. $6.8 - 4.2$	**34.** $4.2 - 6.8$	**35.** $-3.4 - (-7.2)$	**36.** $-7.2 - (-3.4)$
37. $\frac{1}{2} - \frac{1}{4}$	**38.** $\frac{1}{4} - \frac{1}{2}$	**39.** $-\frac{1}{2} - \left(-\frac{1}{8}\right)$	**40.** $\frac{1}{6} - \left(-\frac{2}{3}\right)$

Simplify.

41. $-7 + 8 - 3$	**42.** $-5 + 12 - 3$	**43.** $17 + 8 - 15$
44. $-6 - 5 - (-3)$	**45.** $-31 + 17 - 2$	**46.** $-12 + 13 - 1$
47. $-7 + 5 - 2 - 9$	**48.** $2 - 7 + 6 - (-8)$	**49.** $-13 + 5 - 2 + 7$
50. $-31 + 17 - 2 + 5$	**51.** $-6 - 3 + 20 - (-4)$	**52.** $5 + 8 - 4 - (-9)$
53. $62 - 26 + 51 + 14$	**54.** $-52 - 48 + 53 + 17$	**55.** $-71 + 82 - 46 - 5$

Evaluate for $x = -3$, $y = 9$, and $z = -7$.

56. $x - y$	**57.** $y - x$	**58.** $x + z$
59. $z + y$	**60.** $x - x$	**61.** $x + y$
62. $x - y + z$	**63.** $-x - y - z$	**64.** $-(x + y + z)$
65. $-(-x - y - z)$	**66.** $|x + y + z|$	**67.** $|x| + |y| + |z|$

Solve each problem.

68. A sea gull started 24 ft above the sea, and dove into the sea to catch a fish 8 ft beneath the surface. How far did the gull plunge from its starting point?

69. In April, Jane weighed 1.5 kg less than she weighed in May. In June she weighed 0.75 kg more than she weighed in May. What is the difference between her weight in April and her weight in June?

70. A rock cliff is 265 ft high. Jim climbed up 38 ft from the bottom. Heidi climbed down 56 ft from the top. What is the distance between Heidi and Jim?

71. The formula $C = K - 273$ can be used to convert temperatures from degrees Kelvin to degrees Celsius. Oxygen solidifies at 54°K. What is this temperature in degrees Celsius?

Simplify.

72. $|16 - 9|$ **73.** $|9 - 16|$ **74.** $|-16| - |9|$ **75.** $|9| - |-16|$

76. $|-5 + 12|$ **77.** $|12 - 5|$ **78.** $|-5| - |12|$ **79.** $|12| - |-5|$

80. $|-11 - 8|$ **81.** $|-8 - 11|$ **82.** $|-11| - |-8|$ **83.** $|-8| - |-11|$

84. Is subtraction of real numbers commutative? That is, is $a - b = b - a$ true for all real numbers a and b? Explain.

85. If a and b are real numbers, what is the relationship between $a - b$ and $b - a$?

86. Is subtraction associative? That is, is $(a - b) - c = a - (b - c)$ true for all real numbers a, b, and c? Explain.

87. Is there an identity element for subtraction? That is, is there a real number e such that $a - e = a$ and $e - a = a$ for all real numbers a? Explain.

88. Is the set of real numbers closed under subtraction? That is, is $a - b$ a real number for all numbers a and b? Explain.

89. Is the set of whole numbers closed under subtraction? That is, is $a - b$ a whole number for all whole numbers a and b? Explain.

Midchapter Review

Simplify.   *2.2–2.5*

1. $|-5|$ **2.** $4 - 8$ **3.** $-8 + 12$ **4.** $-15 + (-12)$

5. $-(-15)$ **6.** $-[6 + (-10)]$ **7.** $-6.8 - 7.5$ **8.** $\frac{1}{5} - \left(-\frac{1}{10}\right)$

Evaluate.   *2.2–2.5*

9. $a + b$, for $a = -7$ and $b = 4$ **10.** $-x$, for $x = -8$

11. $s + (-t)$, for $s = 25$ and $t = -17$ **12.** $|r + p|$, for $r = -9$ and $p = -1$

13. $h - j$, for $h = -4$ and $j = 11$ **14.** $l - m$, for $l = 9$ and $m = -5$

Give the integer that describes each situation.   *2.1*

15. five wins   **16.** eight degrees below zero   **17.** a bank withdrawal of $15

18. On the first sale of the day, Groggin Small Appliances lost $3.52. On the next sale there was a profit of $2.75. Then there were profits of $2.99 and $1.08 followed by losses of $3.01 and $2.76. Is the total result a profit or loss?   *2.4*

19. The summit of Mt. Everest is 29,002 ft above sea level. The lowest point of the Marianas Trench is 36,198 ft below sea level. Find the difference between their altitudes.   *2.5*

Application: Windchill

How cold you feel depends on more than just the actual temperature. It also depends on the speed of the wind. Scientists in Antarctica developed the idea of a second temperature, called the *equivalent temperature*, that includes this windchill factor. For example, at 20°F with a wind speed of 15 mi/h, the equivalent temperature is −5°F. This means that under these conditions your body would lose heat as quickly as on a calm day when the temperature is −5°F.

Windchill

Wind speed in mi/h	Actual temperature (°F)								
	50	40	30	20	10	0	−10	−20	−30
	Equivalent temperature (°F)								
0	50	40	30	20	10	0	−10	−20	−30
5	48	37	27	16	6	5	−15	−26	−36
10	40	28	16	4	−9	−21	−33	−46	−58
15	36	22	9	−5	−18	−31	−45	−58	−72
20	32	18	4	−10	−25	−39	−53	−67	−82
25	30	16	0	−15	−29	−44	−59	−74	−88
30	28	13	−2	−18	−33	−48	−63	−79	−94

Use the windchill table to solve each of the following exercises.

1. If the actual temperature is 30°F and the wind speed is 5 mi/h, what is the equivalent temperature?

2. If the actual temperature is 20°F but it feels more like −10°F, what is the wind speed?

3. If the equivalent temperature is −21°F and the wind speed is 10 mi/h, what is the actual temperature?

4. Give two cases where the equivalent temperature is 16°F.

5. Give two cases where the equivalent temperature is −18°F.

6. The actual temperature dropped from 20°F to 10°F in a day.
   a. If the wind speed was constant at 20 mi/h, how did the equivalent temperature change?
   b. Compare the drop in the actual temperature to the drop in the equivalent temperature.

2.6 Multiplication of Real Numbers

To multiply real numbers
To evaluate expressions involving multiplication and exponents

The formula $F = \frac{9}{5}C + 32$ can be used to convert temperatures given in degrees Celsius to degrees Fahrenheit. If the temperature is $-5°C$, you need to multiply $\frac{9}{5}$ and -5, and then add 32, to find the temperature in degrees Fahrenheit.

From arithmetic you know that the product of two positive numbers is positive. Also, the product of any real number and zero is zero. For example, $-8 \cdot 0 = 0$ and $0 \cdot (-8) = 0$.

Property of Zero for Multiplication
For all real numbers a, $a \cdot 0 = 0$ and $0 \cdot a = 0$

Now consider the product of a positive number and a negative number. Examine this pattern.

$$\left.\begin{array}{l} 3 \cdot 3 = 9 \\ 3 \cdot 2 = 6 \\ 3 \cdot 1 = 3 \\ 3 \cdot 0 = 0 \end{array}\right\} \begin{array}{l}\text{The product} \\ \text{decreases by 3} \\ \text{each time.}\end{array}$$

Continue the pattern.
$$3 \cdot (-1) = -3$$
$$3 \cdot (-2) = -6$$
$$3 \cdot (-3) = -9$$

The pattern suggests that the product of a positive number and a negative number is negative. Because of the Commutative Property for Multiplication, "the product of a positive number and a negative number" refers, for example, to both $3 \cdot (-1)$ and $-1 \cdot 3$.

To multiply two real numbers with opposite signs:
1. Multiply their absolute values.
2. The sign of the product is negative.

negative · positive = negative   positive · negative = negative
$(-)$ · $(+)$ = $(-)$ $(+)$ · $(-)$ = $(-)$

EXAMPLE 1   Multiply: **a.** $9(-8)$ **b.** $(-6.2)5$

Solutions   **a.** $9(-8) = -72$ ⟵ pos · neg = neg

                  b. $(-6.2)5 = -31$ ⟵ neg · pos = neg

TRY THIS   Multiply: **1.** $(-51)4$ **2.** $7(-3)$

We already know the product of two positive numbers is positive. To find the product of two negative numbers, examine the following pattern.

$$-3 \cdot 3 = -9$$
$$-3 \cdot 2 = -6$$
$$-3 \cdot 1 = -3$$
$$-3 \cdot 0 = 0$$

The product increases by 3 each time.

Continue the pattern.

$$-3 \cdot (-1) = 3$$
$$-3 \cdot (-2) = 6$$
$$-3 \cdot (-3) = 9$$

The pattern suggests that the product of two negative numbers is positive.

To multiply two real numbers with the same sign:
3. Multiply their absolute values.
4. The sign of the product is positive.

negative · negative = positive   positive · positive = positive
$(-)$ · $(-)$ = $(+)$ $(+)$ · $(+)$ = $(+)$

EXAMPLE 2   Multiply: **a.** $\frac{3}{4} \cdot 20$ **b.** $-6.8(-5)$

Solutions   **a.** $\frac{3}{4} \cdot 20 = 15$ ⟵ pos · pos = pos

                  b. $-6.8(-5) = 34$ ⟵ neg · neg = pos

TRY THIS   Multiply: **3.** $-8(-5)$ **4.** $\frac{2}{3} \cdot 12$

If any two real numbers are multiplied, their product is a real number. That is, the set of real numbers is *closed* under multiplication.

The commutative and associative properties allow you to multiply numbers in any order, as shown in Example 3 on the next page.

EXAMPLE 3   Multiply $-2(29)(-5)(-3)$.

Solution   Regroup to simplify computations. $\underbrace{-2(-5)}\underbrace{(-3)(29)}$

$$10(-87)$$
$$-870$$

EXAMPLE 4   Evaluate $-5a^3b$, for $a = -2$ and $b = -4$.

Solution $-5a^3b$

$-5(-2)^3(-4)$ $\longleftarrow$ Only the -2 is raised to the third power, not -5.

$-5\underbrace{(-2)(-2)(-2)}(-4)$

$\underbrace{-5(-8)}(-4)$

$40(-4) = -160$

TRY THIS   5. Evaluate $3x^2y$ for $x = -5$ and $y = -2$.

Focus on Reading

To complete each statement, choose a, b, c, or d at the right.

1. The product $0 \cdot (-1)$ is ___.

2. The product $(-4.2)(-7.5)$ is ___.

3. The product $7(-81)$ is ___.

4. The product $(3.1)(5.4)$ is ___.

5. The product of a negative number and zero is ___.

6. The product of two numbers with the same sign is ___.

a. positive

b. negative

c. zero

d. either positive, negative, or zero

Classroom Exercises

Multiply.

1. $5 \cdot 6$ **2.** $-7 \cdot 9$ **3.** $6(-3)$ **4.** $(-8)(-8)$

5. $16 \cdot 0$ **6.** $7 \cdot 7$ **7.** $-8 \cdot 0$ **8.** $4(-9)$

9. $(-6)(-9)$ **10.** $-4 \cdot 6$ **11.** $-9 \cdot 7$ **12.** $-5 \cdot 1$

13. $-3(9)(-2)$ **14.** $1(15)(-3)$ **15.** $0(15)(-5)$ **16.** $-8(-1)4$

Evaluate for $x = -4$ and $y = -5$.

17. xy **18.** x^2y **19.** $x^2 + y^2$ **20.** $x^2 - y^2$

Written Exercises

Multiply.

1. $-1 \cdot 0$ **2.** $10(-1)$ **3.** $-6(-5)$ **4.** $7 \cdot 8$

5. $0(-12)$ **6.** $6(-2)$ **7.** $-9 \cdot 9$ **8.** $-5(-5)$

9. $6 \cdot 4$ **10.** $5^2(-6)$ **11.** $-4(-12)$ **12.** $-9 \cdot 4$

13. $-\frac{3}{5}(5)$ **14.** $\frac{3}{4}\left(-\frac{4}{3}\right)$ **15.** $-\frac{1}{8}(-16)$ **16.** $-\frac{3}{8}\left(-\frac{8}{3}\right)$

17. $1(3.2)$ **18.** $-1(8.6)$ **19.** $(9.3)(0)$ **20.** $-1(-9.7)$

21. $-1(4)(-2)$ **22.** $3(6)(-1)$ **23.** $5(-9)(-1)^2$ **24.** $(-2)^2(1)(4)$

25. $-6(3)(-5)$ **26.** $8(-2)^2(-3)$ **27.** $-6(8)(-3)$ **28.** $(-5)^2(-2)$

Evaluate for $x = 2$, $y = -5$, and $z = 0$.

29. $3x$ **30.** $-3x$ **31.** $4y$ **32.** $-7z$

33. y^2 **34.** $3x^2$ **35.** $(3x)^2$ **36.** xyz

37. $6x^2y$ **38.** $(-x)^3$ **39.** $-2xy^2$ **40.** $-2(xy)^2$

41. $6x - 7$ **42.** $6y + x$ **43.** $x - y$ **44.** $y - x$

45. $(-2xy)^2$ **46.** $5x^2y$ **47.** $(5x)^2y$ **48.** $(y - x)^2$

49. $(x + y)^2$ **50.** $x^2 + y^2$ **51.** $(x - y)^2$ **52.** $x^2 - y^2$

Multiply.

53. $9(-7)(-3)(5)$ **54.** $6(0)(-8)(9)$ **55.** $5(-2)(-3)(4)$

56. $(-4)^3 \cdot 2^2$ **57.** $(-2)^3(-5)$ **58.** $-2(-4)^3$

59. $(-3)^3(-1)^3$ **60.** $6^2(-1)^5$ **61.** $(-2)^5 \cdot 3^3$

62. $(-1)^8(-3)^3(-2)$ **63.** $(-6)^2(-1)(-2)^3$ **64.** $-5^2(-3)^2(-4)$

65. The formula $F = \frac{9}{5}C + 32$ is used to convert temperatures from degrees Celsius (°C) to degrees Fahrenheit (°F). When the temperature is -10°C, what is the corresponding temperature in degrees Fahrenheit?

66. The formula $C = \frac{5}{9}(F - 32)$ is used to convert temperatures from degrees Fahrenheit (°F) to degrees Celsius (°C). When the temperature is -4°F, what is the corresponding Celsius temperature?

Simplify.

67. $(-1)^{12}8^2(-2)^3$ **68.** $-1^{15}(-2 \cdot 3)^2(-4)$

69. $(-5 + 3 - 8)(-7 + 3 - 4)$ **70.** $(-7 + 3)(7 - 8)(-5 + 2)(-7 + 7)$

71. $(-3 \cdot 4)[-2 + (-5)(-4)]$ **72.** $(-5 + 8)[-7 + (-4 \cdot 3) + (-6)]$

73. $(-8 + 6)^2[-9 + (-4)2]$ **74.** $(-2 - 1)^3(7 - 8 - 1)^5$

True or false?

75. When a negative number is squared, the result is negative.
76. When a negative number is cubed, the result is negative.
77. When a negative number is raised to an even power, the result is positive.
78. When a negative number is raised to an odd power, the result is negative.
79. When a number of factors are multiplied and one factor is zero, the result is negative.

Mixed Review

Simplify.   *1.2, 1.7, 2.4*

1. $15 + 7 \cdot 2$
2. $8 \cdot 3 - 14 \div 7$
3. $a + 5 + 7a + 2$
4. $4(7x + 12) + 2$
5. $x + 4(x + 5)$
6. $-17 + 18 + (-3)$

Find the solution set. The replacement set is $\{-4, -2, 0, 2, 4\}$.   *1.8*

7. $x + 2 = 0$
8. $x + x < x + (-1)$
9. $\dfrac{x + 6}{2} = 3$

10. The temperature was $-8°F$ in the morning and then rose $10°$ by afternoon. Find the afternoon temperature.   *2.4*

Application: *Automobile Rental Rates*

The Jacksons plan a 3-week trip with a budget of $600 for renting a car. Car rental rates are $85/wk plus $0.17/km. The following formula shows the number of kilometers the Jacksons can travel.

$$\text{number of km} = \frac{(\text{total cost}) - (\text{flat rate})}{\text{cost per km}}$$

Substituting the values for the Jacksons' trip gives the following.

$$\text{number of km} = \frac{600 - 3(85)}{0.17} = 2{,}029 \text{ km (nearest kilometer)}$$

Solve. Round answers to the nearest kilometer.

1. Earl budgeted $315 for car rental. How far can he travel if the rate is $75 plus $0.12/km?

2. Julie budgeted $200 for car rental. How far can she travel if the rate is $65 plus $0.15/km?

3. Moira rents a car for $65 plus $0.12/km. How far can she travel, to the nearest kilometer, on a budget of $260?

4. The Brodskys rent a camper for a week for $275 plus $15 insurance plus $0.13/km. How far can they go on a budget of $500?

2.7 Division of Real Numbers

Objectives	To divide real numbers
	To find the arithmetic mean of a set of real numbers

Multiplication and division are related operations. Thus, the rules for division depend upon the rules for multiplication.

Example	Conclusion
$12 \div 4 = 3$ since $3 \cdot 4 = 12$	pos ÷ pos = pos
$-30 \div (-6) = 5$ since $5 \cdot (-6) = -30$	neg ÷ neg = pos
$-56 \div 8 = -7$ since $-7 \cdot 8 = -56$	neg ÷ pos = neg
$36 \div (-9) = -4$ since $-4 \cdot (-9) = 36$	pos ÷ neg = neg

Dividing Nonzero Real Numbers
1. The quotient of two real numbers with the same sign is positive.
2. The quotient of two real numbers with unlike signs is negative.

EXAMPLE 1   Divide.

    a. $-15 \div (-5)$ **b.** $\dfrac{-27}{3}$ **c.** $4.8 \div (-0.6)$

Solutions

    a. $-15 \div (-5) = 3$ neg ÷ neg = pos

    b. $\dfrac{-27}{3} = -9$ $\dfrac{\text{neg}}{\text{pos}} = \text{neg}$

    c. $4.8 \div (-0.6) = -8$ pos ÷ neg = neg

EXAMPLE 2   Simplify $-54 \div [15 \div (-5)]$.

Solution   Divide within the brackets first. $-54 \div [15 \div (-5)]$
                                                    $-54 \div (-3)$
                                                       18

TRY THIS   Divide: **1.** $-18 \div 6$ **2.** $-12 \div (-3)$

    3. Simplify $24 \div (-12 \div 2)$.

The rules for 0 in division are related to the Property of Zero in Multiplication. Consider the following three cases.

$\frac{0}{8} = 0$ If 0 is divided by any nonzero real number such as 8, the quotient is 0, since $0 \cdot 8 = 0$.

$\frac{5}{0}$ is undefined.   There is *no* number n such that $n \cdot 0 = 5$, or any other nonzero number.

$\frac{0}{0}$ is undefined.   Since $n \cdot 0 = 0$ is true for *every* number n, mathematicians agree to leave $0 \div 0$ undefined.

Thus, if 0 is divided by a nonzero number, the quotient is 0, but division by 0 is undefined. Verify this on your calculator.

$$0 \; \boxed{\div} \; 6 \; \boxed{=} \qquad\qquad 6 \; \boxed{\div} \; 0 \; \boxed{=}$$

The *reciprocal* of a number is often used in division. Two numbers are called reciprocals, or *multiplicative inverses*, of each other if their product is 1. Notice that each product below is 1.

$4 \cdot \frac{1}{4} = \frac{4}{1} \cdot \frac{1}{4}$ Thus, $\frac{1}{4}$ is the reciprocal of 4, and

$\qquad = \frac{4}{4}$, or 1   4 is the reciprocal of $\frac{1}{4}$.

$-\frac{5}{6} \cdot \left(-\frac{6}{5}\right) = \frac{30}{30}$ Thus, $-\frac{6}{5}$ is the reciprocal of $-\frac{5}{6}$, and

$\qquad\qquad\quad = 1$ $-\frac{5}{6}$ is the reciprocal of $-\frac{6}{5}$.

Note that 0 has no reciprocal since $\frac{1}{0}$ is undefined.

Multiplicative Inverse Property

For each nonzero number a, there is exactly one number $\frac{1}{a}$ such that $a \cdot \frac{1}{a} = 1$ and $\frac{1}{a} \cdot a = 1$.

The number $\frac{1}{a}$ is called the **reciprocal** or **multiplicative inverse** of a.

Division by a nonzero real number can be defined as multiplication by the reciprocal of that number, as illustrated below.

$$\text{Division: } 12 \div 4 = 3 \qquad \text{Multiplication: } 12 \cdot \frac{1}{4} = 3$$

If a and b are real numbers and $b \neq 0$, $a \div b = a \cdot \frac{1}{b}$.

That is, to divide by a nonzero number, multiply by its reciprocal.

EXAMPLE 3 Divide.

a. $\frac{8}{9} \div \left(-\frac{2}{3}\right)$　　　　　　　　b. $-2\frac{4}{5} \div (-7)$

reciprocals　　　　　　　　　　　　reciprocals

Solutions a. $\frac{8}{9} \div \left(-\frac{2}{3}\right) = \frac{8}{9} \cdot \left(-\frac{3}{2}\right)$　　　b. $-2\frac{4}{5} \div (-7) = -\frac{14}{5} \cdot \left(-\frac{1}{7}\right)$

$= -\frac{24}{18}$, or $-\frac{4}{3}$　　　　　　　$= \frac{14}{35}$, or $\frac{2}{5}$

TRY THIS Divide: **4.** $-8 \div \frac{4}{5}$　　　　　**5.** $-\frac{3}{7} \div \left(-2\frac{1}{3}\right)$

The **arithmetic mean**, or *average*, of a set of numbers is the sum of the members of the set divided by the number of members.

EXAMPLE 4 The table below shows the gains and losses made by a football team in eight successive plays. Find the average gain or loss per play.

Play	1	2	3	4	5	6	7	8
Gain or loss	5	-8	-2	22	3	-15	0	-13

Plan Add the eight numbers and divide by 8.

Solution
$$5 - 8 - 2 + 22 + 3 - 15 + 0 - 13$$
$$\underbrace{-8 - 2 - 15 - 13}_{-38} + \underbrace{5 + 22 + 3}_{+\quad 30} \quad \leftarrow \text{Group like signs together before adding.}$$
$$-8$$

Divide the sum by 8.　　$\frac{-8}{8} = -1$

Therefore, the average *loss* was 1 yd per play.

TRY THIS **6.** Find the average gain or loss for the first 5 plays.

Classroom Exercises

Divide, if possible.

1. $\frac{-9}{-3}$　　**2.** $\frac{8}{4}$　　**3.** $\frac{-16}{2}$　　**4.** $\frac{18}{-9}$　　**5.** $-\frac{-6}{0}$　　**6.** $\frac{0}{10}$

7. $-42 \div 7$　　　　**8.** $6.2 \div (-0.2)$　　　**9.** $-1\frac{2}{3} \div \left(-\frac{5}{6}\right)$

Give the reciprocal of the number, if it exists.

10. $\frac{3}{4}$　　**11.** 7　　**12.** 0　　**13.** $-\frac{1}{3}$　　**14.** 1　　**15.** $-2\frac{3}{4}$

Written Exercises

Divide, if possible.

1. $\frac{8}{2}$ 2. $\frac{-12}{3}$ 3. $\frac{32}{-8}$ 4. $\frac{-72}{-8}$ 5. $\frac{-40}{10}$ 6. $\frac{28}{7}$

7. $\frac{-45}{9}$ 8. $\frac{9}{-9}$ 9. $\frac{-100}{4}$ 10. $\frac{80}{-8}$ 11. $\frac{0}{5}$ 12. $\frac{21}{0}$

13. $-60 \div 10$ 14. $32 \div (-8)$ 15. $1.4 \div 0.07$

16. $12 \div 0$ 17. $3.4 \div (-1.7)$ 18. $-22 \div 0.002$

19. $-32 \div 0$ 20. $-0.4 \div (-0.2)$ 21. $\frac{4}{5} \div \left(-\frac{8}{15}\right)$

22. $\frac{7}{8} \div (-14)$ 23. $-\frac{5}{9} \div 3\frac{1}{3}$ 24. $-1\frac{1}{2} \div \left(-1\frac{1}{8}\right)$

25. $-15 \div \frac{5}{7}$ 26. $3\frac{1}{3} \div \frac{5}{9}$ 27. $-1\frac{1}{3} \div \left(-2\frac{2}{3}\right)$

Simplify.

28. $-48 \div [60 \div (-30)]$ 29. $(-36 \div 18) \div (-2)$ 30. $72 \div [-24 \div (-8)]$

31. $-45 \div (-15 \div 3)$ 32. $14 \div [28 \div (-2)]$ 33. $-27 \div [-18 \div (-6)]$

34. A town's daily low temperatures for the week are shown below. Find the average low temperature for the week.

Sun.	Mon.	Tues.	Wed.	Thurs.	Fri.	Sat.
$-9°$	$-2°$	$6°$	$-3°$	$-3°$	$-7°$	$11°$

35. The table below shows the profits and losses of a small business for the four quarters of a year. What was the average profit or loss per quarter?

1st quarter	2nd quarter	3rd quarter	4th quarter
$5,200	$-$1,400	$-$2,700	$1,600

36. The table below shows Maria's weight gain or weight loss in pounds at the end of the month for six months. What was the average gain or loss per month?

Jan.	Feb.	Mar.	Apr.	May	June
5	-3	-3	4	-1	2

37. The table below shows the gain or loss in the price of a stock for a five-day period. What was the average change per day?

Mon.	Tues.	Wed.	Thurs.	Fri.
$-\frac{1}{4}$	$+\frac{3}{8}$	No change	$+\frac{1}{8}$	$-\frac{5}{8}$

Simplify.

38. $(-8 + 3 - 7 + 4) \div (-7 - 8 + 13)$

39. $(-9 - 5 + 4 - 4) \div (6 - 8 - 4 + 3)$

40. $(-7 - 4 + 2)(-5 + 3)(-8 - 4 + 12)$

41. $(-8 + 6 - 4 - 2 + 20) \div (2 \cdot 4 - 3 \cdot 6)$

42. $(8 - 6 + 14 + 6) \div [(-7 + 15) - (2 - 6)]$

43. $[(24 - 32) \div (8 - 12)] \div (1 - 5 + 6 - 8 + 4)$

Give an example to show that each statement is false.

44. Division of real numbers is commutative.

45. Division of real numbers is associative.

46. The identity element for division is 0.

47. The set of real numbers is closed under division.

Mixed Review

Simplify. *1.2, 1.3, 1.7, 2.4–2.6*

1. $7 + 5 \cdot 2$

2. $39 - 3 \cdot 6 - 6 \cdot 2$

3. $5 + 2 \cdot 4^2$

4. $7b + 5 + b$

5. $2c + 3(4c + 1)$

6. $-7 + 5$

7. $2 - (-3)$

8. $-4 \cdot 5$

9. $-6(-2)$

10. At Spearfish, South Dakota, one day in January 1943, the temperature rose from $-4°F$ to $45°F$ in two minutes! What was the change in temperature? *2.5*

Using the Calculator

A calculator can be used to find a decimal value for the reciprocal of a positive number (or at least an approximation of the reciprocal). Some calculators have a reciprocal key marked $\boxed{\frac{1}{x}}$ If yours does, you can enter a number x and press the $\boxed{\frac{1}{x}}$ key to find the reciprocal of x. If a calculator has no $\boxed{\frac{1}{x}}$ key, you can find the reciprocal as follows.

Find a decimal for the reciprocal of each number.

1. 5

2. 0.2

3. 8

4. 0.125

5. 0.4

6. 2.5

7. 0.16

8. 6.25

Find the reciprocal of the reciprocal of each number.

9. 0.8

10. 31.25

11. 64

12. 781.25

2.8 Mixed Operations

Objectives	To simplify numerical expressions To evaluate algebraic expressions

To simplify the expressions in this lesson, you will be using all of the rules for operating with real numbers. Be careful not to confuse the rules. For example,

The *sum* of two negative numbers is *negative*.
The *product* of two negative numbers is *positive*.

You also need to recall the rules for the order of operations (see Lesson 1.3). For example, an expression such as $-6 - 2 \cdot 5$ involves two operations and the multiplication $2 \cdot 5$ is performed first.

EXAMPLE 1 Simplify.

a. $-6 - 2 \cdot 5$ b. $8 - (-7)^2$

Solutions

a. $-6 - 2 \cdot 5 = -6 - 10$ b. $8 - (-7)^2 = 8 - 49$
$= -6 + (-10)$ $= 8 + (-49)$
$= -16$ $= -41$

TRY THIS Simplify: **1.** $-8 + 4(-5)$ **2.** $6 + (-2)^3$

The order of operations must be followed when you evaluate expressions involving two or more operations.

EXAMPLE 2 Evaluate $-8 - 4x$ for $x = -3$.

Solution

Multiply first.
$$-8 - 4x = -8 - 4(-3)$$
$$= -8 - (-12)$$
$$= -8 + 12 = 4$$

EXAMPLE 3 Evaluate $-8e^2 + 7f - 5g$, for $e = -3$, $f = 4$, and $g = -2.1$.

Solution

$$-8e^2 + 7f - 5g = -8(-3)^2 + 7 \cdot 4 - 5(-2.1)$$
$$= -8 \cdot 9 + 7 \cdot 4 - (-10.5)$$
$$= -72 + 28 + 10.5$$
$$= -44 + 10.5 = -33.5$$

TRY THIS **3.** Evaluate $5c^2 - 3d - 2$ for $c = -2$ and $d = -4$.

EXAMPLE 4   Evaluate $\dfrac{a - b}{-4}$ for $a = 3.6$ and $b = -1.2$.

Solution $\dfrac{a - b}{-4} = \dfrac{3.6 - (-1.2)}{-4}$

$= \dfrac{3.6 + 1.2}{-4}$

$= \dfrac{4.8}{-4} = -1.2$

TRY THIS   4. Evaluate $3a - 5b$ for $a = 0.5$ and $b = -0.7$.

Focus on Reading

True or false?

1. If two nonzero numbers are opposites, then their quotient is -1.
2. The quotient of two nonzero numbers with the same sign always has that same sign.
3. If $a \cdot b$ is negative, and a is negative, then b is negative.
4. Every real number has an additive inverse.
5. Every real number has a multiplicative inverse.
6. If a is negative, then a^3 is negative.
7. For every real number a, $a \div 0$ is undefined.
8. The sum of two negative numbers is positive.
9. The multiplicative inverse of a negative number is positive.
10. If $a + b = 0$, then a is the additive inverse of b.
11. If $a + b$ is positive, and a is positive, then b must be positive.
12. The product of a number and its multiplicative inverse is 1.

Classroom Exercises

Simplify.

1. $-7 \cdot 4 + 9$ 2. $-6 - 3 \cdot 4$ 3. $8 - 2 \cdot 3$ 4. $6 + (-8)^2$

Evaluate for the given values of the variables.

5. $-7 - 5x$, for $x = -3$ 6. $6 - 3y$, for $y = -6$

7. $\dfrac{5x - y}{5}$, for $x = -2$ and $y = 5$ 8. $2x - 4y^2$, for $x = 3$ and $y = -2$

Written Exercises

Simplify.

1. $-2 + 3 \cdot 9$
2. $-5 \cdot 8 - 7$
3. $8 - 6 \cdot 5$
4. $4 + 3(-9)$
5. $6 - 7^2$
6. $-3 + (-8)^2$
7. $5^2 - (-1)^2$
8. $13 - (-2^3)$
9. $-3 \cdot 6 + 4(-7) - 8(-5)$
10. $6(-2) + (-4)^2 - 9 \cdot 3$

Evaluate for the given values of the variables.

11. $a - 5$, for $a = -4$
12. $7 - 5y$, for $y = -2$
13. $-2x - 11$, for $x = -2$
14. $-5x - 8$, for $x = -2$
15. $-2x + 6$, for $x = -3$
16. $-8 - 6x$, for $x = -6$
17. $6 - 3x$, for $x = 2$
18. $-3m - 10$, for $m = -3$
19. $6 - 9k$, for $k = 0$
20. $5b - 3$, for $b = -7$
21. $-6 - 5t$, for $t = -6$
22. $6 - 7b$, for $b = -5$
23. $3x + 2y$, for $x = 5$ and $y = -3$
24. $7a + 5b$, for $a = -3$ and $b = 2$
25. $-6c + 3d$, for $c = -1$ and $d = 4$
26. $4p - 9q$, for $p = -8$ and $q = -7$
27. $\dfrac{a + 2b}{6}$, for $a = 4$ and $b = -5$
28. $\dfrac{4x - y}{x - 3}$, for $x = 7$ and $y = -8$
29. $2x - 4y$, for $x = -3$ and $y = -1.5$
30. $4r - 7s$, for $r = 3$ and $s = 0.2$
31. $\dfrac{5x - 8y}{-x}$, for $x = -3$ and $y = -\dfrac{3}{4}$
32. $\dfrac{15x + 2y}{3x}$, for $x = -\dfrac{2}{3}$ and $y = -3$
33. $|3a - b^2|$, for $a = -2$ and $b = 4$
34. $|-4c + d^2|$, for $c = 2$ and $d = -5$
35. $|2x^2 - (5y)^2|$, for $x = -3$ and $y = 2$
36. $|4p^2 - 3q^3|$, for $p = -3$ and $q = -1$
37. $-4p^2 - 9q + 6r$, for $p = -3$, $q = -9$, and $r = -5$
38. $|-6b - 5c^2 + 15d|$, for $b = -2$, $c = -6$, and $d = -\dfrac{3}{5}$

Simplify. Then evaluate for $x = -3$, $y = -3$, and $z = -4$.

39. $4[3x + 5(7y - 8)]$
40. $-4x + 6[2z + 3(5 + 2y)]$
41. $8x \div [2(5 + 3y)] - 2$
42. $(10z - 4y^3) \div [2(4 + 7x)]$

Mixed Review

Simplify.   *1.7, 2.2, 2.5, 2.6*

1. $5a + 3 + a + 2a$
2. $2x + 4(3x + 7)$
3. $|-5|$
4. $8 - (-3)$
5. $-7 - 2 + 4$
6. $3(-3)^3$

True or false?   *2.1*

7. $-7 > -5$
8. $-3 < 2$
9. $2.3 < 2.19$
10. $-\dfrac{1}{4} < -\dfrac{1}{5}$

2.9 Like Terms: Real Number Coefficients

Objectives
To simplify expressions by combining like terms
To evaluate expressions after combining like terms

In Lesson 1.7 you learned to simplify an expression such as $5x - 2x$ using the Distributive Property.

$$5x - 2x = (5 - 2)x = 3x$$

In this lesson you will learn to simplify expressions such as $-5x + 2x$. Now that you have learned to add positive and negative numbers, you can combine like terms as shown below.

$$-5x + 2x = (-5 + 2)x \qquad 6xy - 4xy = -6xy + (-4xy)$$
$$= -3x \qquad\qquad\qquad = [-6 + (-4)]xy$$
$$= -10xy$$

EXAMPLE 1 Simplify.
a. $-9y + 2y$ **b.** $6cd - 9cd$

Solutions
a. THINK: $-9 + 2 = -7$ **b.** THINK: $6 - 9 = -3$
       $-9y + 2y = -7y$ $6cd - 9cd = -3cd$

TRY THIS Simplify: **1.** $-4t + 7t$ **2.** $-5ab - 6ab$

EXAMPLE 2 Write a formula for the perimeter of the rectangle at the right. Simplify the formula.

$2x + y - 3$

$x - 3y - 1$

Plan Use the formula $p = 2l + 2w$, for $l = 2x + y - 3$ and $w = x - 3y - 1$.

Solution
$$p = 2(2x + y - 3) + 2(x - 3y - 1)$$
$$p = 4x + 2y - 6 + 2x - 6y - 2$$
Group like terms. $p = 4x + 2x + 2y - 6y - 6 - 2$
Combine like terms. $p = 6x - 4y - 8$

TRY THIS 3. Write the formula for the perimeter of a rectangle with $l = a - b$ and $w = 2a + b$. Simplify.

You know that $1a = a$, or $a = 1a$, from the Identity Property for Multiplication. A similar property states that the product of -1 and any real number is the opposite of that number. For example,

$$-1 \cdot 3 = -3 \qquad \text{and} \qquad -1(-4) = 4.$$

> **Property of −1 for Multiplication**
> For any real number a, $-1a = -a$ and $a(-1) = -a$

EXAMPLE 3   Simplify.

a. $-x - 7 + 6x + 4$ b. $4a - 3b - 5a + 5b$

Solutions

a. $-x - 7 + 6x + 4 = -1x - 7 + 6x + 4$ $\longleftarrow -x = -1x$
$= -1x + 6x - 7 + 4$
$= 5x - 3$

b. $4a - 3b - 5a + 5b = 4a - 5a - 3b + 5b$
$= -1a + 2b$
$= -a + 2b$ $\longleftarrow -1a = -a$

EXAMPLE 4   Simplify $6y - 5z - 7y - 4 + 6z$. Evaluate for $y = -8$ and $z = 5$.

Solution

$6y - 5z - 7y - 4 + 6z = \underbrace{6y - 7y}\ - \underbrace{5z + 6z}\ - 4$

$= \quad -1y \quad + \quad 1z \quad - 4$
$= -y + z - 4$ $\longleftarrow -1y = -y$ and $1z = z$

Now substitute -8 for y and 5 for z.
$-y + z - 4 = -(-8) + 5 - 4$
$= 8 + 5 - 4$
$= 9$

Thus, $6y - 5z - 7y - 4 + 6z = 9$, for $y = -8$ and $z = 5$.

TRY THIS   4. Simplify $3x - 2y - x$ for $x = -1$ and $y = -2$.

Classroom Exercises

Simplify.

1. $5a + a$
2. $-7m + 8m$
3. $-3m - m$
4. $9t - 8t$
5. $-a + 3a$
6. $-3x + 4x$
7. $4t - t$
8. $-k - 2k$
9. $-7j - j$
10. $-a + a$
11. $k + 7k$
12. $g + 5g$
13. $5y - 6y$
14. $-x + 6x$
15. $10b - 11b$
16. $3xy - 8 - 9xy$
17. $-4xy + 3xy - 7$
18. $2ac - 3ac - 5ac$

Simplify. Then evaluate for $x = 3$, $y = -2$, and $z = -1$.

19. $2x + y + 3x - 2y$
20. $3xy + 2xz - 3xy$
21. $8xyz - 2xyz$

Written Exercises

Simplify.

1. $8y - 3y$
2. $-7x + 9x$
3. $2a - 8a$
4. $-6b + 8b$
5. $4a - 7a$
6. $-5y + 9y$
7. $-9x + 2x$
8. $2c - 2c$
9. $-8r + 3r$
10. $-5y - 5y$
11. $-4c - 7c$
12. $-7x - 3x$
13. $-7b + 9b$
14. $-4k - k$
15. $15c - 4c$
16. $7x + x$
17. $-x - 5x$
18. $4y - y$
19. $5c - 3.4c$
20. $6x - 7 - 3x$
21. $4z - 10 - 9z$
22. $-5r - 2 + 2r - 8$
23. $9y - 3 - 7y + 4$
24. $9z - 8z + 3z$
25. $-7 + 4b + 3 - b$
26. $-2a - 7 + a$
27. $9 - b - 7 - 3b$
28. $-3x - 7 - x - 8$
29. $-2b - 3 + b - 4$
30. $8y - 4 - y + 2$
31. $5x - x + 4x$
32. $7b - b - b$
33. $3a - 7a - a$
34. $5b - 6b - b$
35. $3b - 4 - b + 8$
36. $-a - 13 - a + 4$
37. $b - 4 - 2b + 8$
38. $6 - z - 4z + 5$
39. $8c + 9 - 9c - 4$
40. $-4y - b + 4y + b$
41. $-3k - 2m + 2k + m$
42. $10c - 7 - 11c - 3$
43. $8x - 10 - 7x + 4$
44. $-4a + 5b - a - 4b$
45. $-7r + 8s + 2s - 9s$
46. $-6r - 10s + 8r + 4s - 6$
47. $-y + 6 - 5y - 4 + 3y - 2$
48. $-a + 5.2b + 3a + 3.8b - 10b$
49. $7g - 4t - 6.9g + 3t - g$

Simplify. Then evaluate for the given values of the variable.

50. $9x + 7y - 2y$ for $x = 2$ and $y = -3$
51. $-2a + 5c - 3c$ for $a = -1$ and $c = 2$
52. $-4x - 8 + 5y - 4x - 2$ for $x = 2$ and $y = -1$
53. $6c - 4b - 8 + 5b - 3c$ for $b = -3$ and $c = 2$
54. $8a - 2.1y + 11a + 1.4y$ for $a = -2$ and $y = 5$
55. $-2 - 5x + 2y + 4x - y - 8 + 7x$ for $x = 3$ and $y = -2$
56. $-t + 3 - t - 4n + 8 + 3t - 5 + 6n$ for $n = -\frac{1}{2}$ and $t = 3$

Write a formula for the perimeter of each rectangle below. Simplify.

57.

$2x$

$x - y$

58.

$3y + 2x$

$2y - x$

59.

$5a - b + 1$

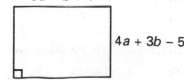

$4a + 3b - 5$

The total surface area of a geometric solid is the sum of the areas of the faces. Write a formula for the total surface area of each figure below. Combine like terms.

60. rectangular solid

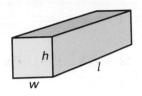

61. square pyramid

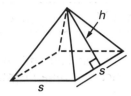

Simplify. Then evaluate for the given values of the variables.

62. $a - 4b - 2a + 5b$; $a = 7.2$, $b = -8$

63. $-x + 8y + 2x - 6y$; $x = -1.4$, $y = 5$

64. $5a - 9b - 6a + 10b$; $a = -\frac{3}{4}$; $b = \frac{7}{8}$

65. $7x + 9 - 8x$; $x = 2\frac{3}{5}$

66. $-x - y - x + 2y$; $x = 1\frac{3}{5}$, $y = 4$

67. $6a - b - 7a$; $a = -\frac{1}{2}$, $b = 4$

Simplify. Then evaluate for $x = 0$, $y = 2.5$, and $z = 0.004$.

68. $1.4x - 6 + 0.008y - 2.3y - 0.2x$

69. $4.2 - 0.06x - 8.1z + 0.1 + 4z$

70. $3.8z - 2.4x + 0.4y - 0.1z + 7y$

71. $2.4 - 0.08x + 0.3y - 0.1 + 3z$

Mixed Review

Simplify.   *1.7, 2.4–2.7*

1. $3x + 2(4x + 3)$

2. $3a + 2(5a + b) + 11a$

3. $-8 + 6$

4. $-3(-4)^2$

5. $-4 \div 2$

6. $6 \div (7 - 9)$

Evaluate for $x = -5$.   *2.8*

7. $4 + 2x$

8. $17(x + 6)$

9. $17 - 4x$

10. $12(4x - 7)$

11. $(4x)^3$

12. $4x^3$

13. $\dfrac{2x + 6}{x + 3}$

14. $\dfrac{x + 3}{x + 5}$

▰▰/Brainteaser

A 120-min cassette tape plays for 60 min on each side. As it plays, the tape moves at $1\frac{7}{8}$ in/s. Is the tape longer or shorter than a 100-yd football field?

2.10 Removing Parentheses: Negative Factors

Objective	To simplify and evaluate expressions containing negative factors

In this lesson you will simplify expressions such as $-2(3a + 4)$, where multiplication by a negative number is indicated.

EXAMPLE 1   Simplify $-4(5x + 7)$.

Solution

$$-4(5x + 7) = -4 \cdot 5x + (-4)7 \quad \longleftarrow \text{Distributive Property}$$
$$= -20x - 28 \quad \longleftarrow \text{THINK: } -20x + (-28) = -20x - 28$$

EXAMPLE 2   Simplify $-(7x - 2y + 8)$.

Solution

$$-(7x - 2y + 8) = -1(7x - 2y + 8) \quad \longleftarrow -a = -1 \cdot a$$
$$= -1 \cdot 7x + (-1)(-2y) + (-1)8 \quad \longleftarrow \text{Distributive}$$
$$= -7x + 2y - 8 \qquad\qquad \text{Property}$$

TRY THIS   Simplify.   **1.** $-3(4x - 5)$ **2.** $-(6x + 3y - 4)$

To simplify an expression such as $4x - (7 + 5x)$, you need to remove the parentheses first and then combine like terms.

EXAMPLE 3   Simplify $4x - (7 + 5x)$.

Solution

$$4x - (7 + 5x) = 4x - 1(7 + 5x)$$

$$= 4x + (-1)(7 + 5x) \quad \longleftarrow \text{Definition of subtraction}$$
$$= 4x + (-7 - 5x) \quad \longleftarrow \text{Distributive Property}$$
$$= 4x - 7 - 5x$$
$$= 4x - 5x \quad 7$$
$$= -1x - 7$$
$$= -x - 7$$

TRY THIS   **3.** Simplify $-6x - (8 - 9x)$.

The solution shown in Example 3 can be shortened by writing
$$4x - 1(7 + 5x) \text{ as } 4x - 7 - 5x.$$

Such a shortcut is used in Example 4 on page 80.

EXAMPLE 4 Simplify $-7(2 + 3x) - (9 - 3x)$. Then evaluate for $x = -1$.

Solution
$$
\begin{aligned}
-7(2 + 3x) - (9 - 3x) &= -7(2 + 3x) - 1(9 - 3x) \\
&= -14 - 21x - 9 + 3x \\
&= -21x + 3x - 14 - 9 \\
&= -18x - 23
\end{aligned}
$$

Now substitute -1 for x in $-18x - 23$ and simplify.
$$
\begin{aligned}
-18x - 23 &= -18(-1) - 23 \\
&= 18 - 23 = -5
\end{aligned}
$$

Thus, $-7(2 + 3x) - (9 - 3x) = -5$ for $x = -1$.

TRY THIS 4. Simplify $-(5 - 3x) - 2x$. Then evaluate for $x = -2$.

Classroom Exercises

Simplify.

1. $6(5x - 1)$
2. $-2(4y + 6)$
3. $-(7a + 3)$
4. $-(-2 + 8b)$
5. $-(-6 + 8p - q)$
6. $-(3z + 4y - 1)$
7. $x - (5 - x)$
8. $-3(a + b) + \frac{1}{2}(4a - 8b)$
9. $6a - 5(8 - 3a)$
10. $4x - 6(2x + 8)$

Written Exercises

Simplify.

1. $-7(3 + 4x)$
2. $-3(-9 + 2y)$
3. $-(-a + 2b + 8)$
4. $-(15x + y - 7)$
5. $5(2x - 4) - 3x$
6. $6(4 - 2y) + 9$
7. $3p - 2(4p + 7) - 5$
8. $8r - 2(2r - 5) + 6$
9. $10 + 8(4 - 3d) + 5d$
10. $-4(7 - 4y) + 7y$
11. $6x - (x + 5)$
12. $8 - (4a - 10)$
13. $-7 - (a - 5)$
14. $(7y - 4) + 2y$
15. $z - (8 - 6z) - 4$
16. $-(b + 8) - 6b + 5$
17. $5 - (7 - a) - 4a$
18. $-6x - (9 - x) - 9$
19. $-4(3x - 5) - 3(2 + 7x)$
20. $-5(3y - 7) - 2(6 + 4y)$
21. $-5(6 + 3y) - 7(2y - 9)$
22. $-3(5x - 4) + 8(-3x + 2)$
23. $-3(5x + 2) - 6(7 + 2x)$
24. $-3(8 - 7z) - 9(4 - 3z)$

Simplify. Then evaluate for the given value of the variable.
(Exercises 25–38)

25. $-(-7x + 2) - 8x + 1$, for $x = 5$
26. $-8y - (5y + 6) + 12y$, for $y = -1$
27. $5z - 9 - (7z - 6)$, for $z = 0.2$
28. $7a - (8 - a) + 12$, for $a = -0.8$
29. $-(7 + 3y) - 5(4y - 8)$, for $y = -1$
30. $-6(7x - 5) - (4 - x)$, for $x = 4$
31. $-(5z - 7) - (9 - z)$, for $z = -0.2$
32. $-(2a - 4) - (8 - a)$, for $a = 3.4$
33. $6(3z - 7) - \frac{1}{2}(-8z - 6)$, for $z = -2$
34. $-\frac{1}{4}(12 - 8d) - 2(-6d + 5)$, for $d = 3$
35. $-(-6r + 8) - (-7 - r)$, for $r = -2.1$
36. $6b - 3(b + 7) - (5 - 4b)$, for $b = 0.04$
37. $-2(3 - n) - (5n + 4) - 7n$, for $n = -\frac{4}{5}$
38. $-(-c + 5) - (-6 - c)$, for $c = -3\frac{1}{2}$

39. On Monday, Jerry jogged for m minutes. On four other days that week he jogged 9 more minutes than he jogged on Monday. On two other days he jogged 7 fewer minutes than he jogged on Monday. Write an algebraic expression in simplest form for the total number of minutes he jogged that week.

40. Amy bought x headbands and decorated them. It cost her $3 to make each headband. She sold 8 of them at a profit of $4 and the rest at a loss of $1. Write an algebraic expression in simplest form for her total profit or loss.

Simplify.

41. $x - [3(x - 2) - (4 - 5x)]$
42. $-2y - [-2(1 - 7y) - (5 - 3y)]$
43. $-5 - [5 - (3 - x)] + 3x$
44. $-x - [-(4 - x) - 2(3 - x)]$
45. $-[6 - 3(2x + 4) - x] + 8$
46. $7y - [-(2 + 3y) - 4(6 - y)] - 26$
47. $-3[-(2 - y) + 4] - 5(-y + 8)$
48. $-[-x + 6(3 - x)] - [-2(x - 3)]$
49. $a(x - y) + 2ax$
50. $ax - (ax - ay)$
51. $ay - a(x + y)$
52. $-ax - ay - (ax + ay)$
53. $ce + (c - d)e$
54. $2ce - 3de - (de + 2ce)$

Mixed Review

Which property is illustrated?   *1.5, 1.6, 2.3, 2.9*

1. $-7x + 7x = 0$
2. $-t + 8t = -1t + 8t$
3. $4a + 0 = 4a$
4. $-3 \cdot 4 = 4(-3)$
5. $-4(m + n) = -4m + (-4n)$
6. $[3 + (-6)] + (-4) = 3 + [(-6) + (-4)]$
7. $5m^2 + 3m^4 = 3m^4 + 5m^2$
8. $-4(6c) = (-4 \cdot 6)c$

Chapter 2 Review

Key Terms

absolute value (p. 46)
additive inverse (p. 51)
Additive Inverse Property (p. 51)
arithmetic mean (p. 69)
average (p. 69)
coordinate (p. 41)
counting number (p. 41)
graph (p. 41)
identity element for addition (p. 50)
Identity Property for Addition (p. 51)
integer (p. 41)

multiplicative inverse (p. 68)
Multiplicative Inverse Property (p. 68)
opposite (p. 45)
natural number (p. 41)
Property of -1 for Multiplication (p. 76)
Property of Zero for Multiplication
  (p. 62)
real number (p. 42)
reciprocal (p. 68)
whole number (p. 41)

Key Ideas and Review Exercises

2.1   On a horizontal number line, the numbers increase from left to right.

Use $<$ or $>$ to make each sentence true.

1. -5 ___ 6

2. 0 ___ -2

3. 8 ___ -8

4. -6 ___ -4

5. 0.5 ___ 0.4

6. $-3\frac{1}{2}$ ___ -3

7. -2.1 ___ 2

8. $-\frac{1}{2}$ ___ $-\frac{1}{4}$

2.2   Two numbers are opposites if they are the same distance from 0 on a number line and they are on opposite sides of 0. The opposite of 0 is 0. The symbol $-a$ means *the opposite of a.*

The absolute value of a real number x is the distance between x and 0 on a number line. The symbol $|x|$ means *the absolute value of x.*

Simplify.

9. $-(12 - 7)$

10. $-(-4)$

11. $|5|$

12. $|-4|$

Compare. Use $>$, $<$, or $=$.

13. 0 ___ $|6|$

14. $|3|$ ___ $|-3|$

15. $-(-4)$ ___ -4

16. $-|\frac{1}{2}|$ ___ $|\frac{1}{3}|$

2.3,   To add two real numbers, follow the rules in Lesson 2.4.
2.4

Add.

17. $-8 + 0$

18. $7 + (-7)$

19. $15 + (-8)$

20. $-9 + 7$

21. $-4 + (-11)$

22. $8 + 9$

23. $6.2 + (-9.1)$

24. $-2\frac{3}{4} + \left(-1\frac{1}{2}\right)$

2.5   To subtract a number, add its opposite.

Subtract.

25. $6 - 9$ **26.** $-5 - 8$ **27.** $4 - (-7)$ **28.** $-6.3 - (-9.8)$

Simplify.

29. $-28 + 18 - (-4)$ **30.** $-6 + 7 - 9 - (-5)$

31. Give two numerical examples to show that subtraction is not a commutative operation. Use at least one negative number in each example.

2.6,   The product (quotient) of two numbers with like signs is positive.
2.7   The product (quotient) of two numbers with unlike signs is negative.

Multiply.

32. $7 \cdot 9$ **33.** $-8 \cdot 5$ **34.** $-6 \cdot 0$ **35.** $(-4)(-7)$

36. $4(-8)$ **37.** $-1(-5.2)$ **38.** $16 \cdot 5^3$ **39.** $4(-8)(-1)$

Divide.

40. $\dfrac{63}{-7}$ **41.** $\dfrac{0}{-4}$ **42.** $\dfrac{9}{0}$ **43.** $\dfrac{-49}{-7}$

44. $-16 \div 2$ **45.** $5.2 \div (-1.3)$ **46.** $-\dfrac{3}{8} \div (-6)$ **47.** $-\dfrac{5}{6} \div \dfrac{2}{3}$

2.8   To simplify expressions involving more than one operation, follow the rules for the order of operations.

Simplify.

48. $6 - 4 \cdot 8$ **49.** $12 - (-6)^2$

Evaluate.

50. $7 - 5x$, for $x = 2$ **51.** $-8 - 9y$, for $y = -3$

52. $2x - 3y$, for $x = -6$ and $y = -3$ **53.** $-5c + d^2$, for $c = 3$ and $d = -5$

2.9,   To simplify the algebraic expression $4x - 3(x - 4)$, apply the Distributive
2.10   Property. Then combine like terms.

Simplify.

54. $-2a + 9a$ **55.** $-7y - y$ **56.** $x - (5 + x)$ **57.** $-(x - 2)$

58. $7a - 2(3 - a) + 6$ **59.** $-4(7 + 2y) - (y + 9)$

Chapter 2 Test

Simplify.

1. $-(-6)$

2. $-(7 - 5)$

3. $|-8|$

4. $-|-9|$

Compare. Use > , < , or =.

5. $-7 \_\_\_ -6$

6. $0.1 \_\_\_ -0.2$

7. $|-8| \_\_\_ |8|$

8. $\left|\frac{1}{4}\right| \_\_\_ -\left|-\frac{1}{2}\right|$

Add.

9. $-9 + 5$

10. $16 + (-16)$

11. $-8 + (-9)$

12. $8.2 + (-6.5)$

Subtract.

13. $8 - (-5)$

14. $-4 - 7$

15. $|-15| - |-1|$

16. $5.6 - 9.2$

Evaluate for $x = 7$, $y = -7$, and $z = -12$.

17. $x - y + z$

18. $|x| + |z|$

19. $2z$

20. $-x - 2y$

Multiply.

21. $-8(-9)$

22. $\frac{1}{6}(-30)$

23. $-8(12)$

24. $4^2(-3)^2$

Divide, if possible.

25. $\frac{-48}{-8}$

26. $\frac{0}{-2}$

27. $18 \div 0$

28. $-\frac{3}{5} \div \frac{4}{5}$

29. Evaluate $2a^2 + b^3$, for $a = -4$ and $b = -3$.

30. Evaluate $\dfrac{x - 25y}{-5y}$, for $x = -6$ and $y = \frac{3}{5}$.

Simplify.

31. $-8 + 5 - 9 - (-2)$

32. $-8 + 6(-5)$

33. $-8y + 8y$

34. $-6c + 5c + d$

35. $-4a + 3b - 6a - 2b$

36. $3c - 2(4 - 5c)$

37. $-9y - (5 - y) + 8$

38. $4.2x - 3.7y + 8.2 - 9.5x + 2.9y$

39. $(-9 + 4)(8 - 10 \cdot 2 - 3)$

40. $5y - [-(3 + 4y) - 2(7 - y)] - 4$

College Prep Test

Test-Taking Strategy

When a test is given, there is often a time limit for completing it. It is important not to spend too much time on any one problem. If you find this happening, leave the problem and continue with the rest of the test. If there is time remaining, go back to the problem later on.

Choose the best answer to each question or problem.

1. $|6 - 10| = $ ___.
   (A) 16   (B) -16 (C) 4
   (D) -4 (E) None of these

2. Find the missing number in the sequence: $-10, -7, -4, -1, $ ___.
   (A) -3 (B) 1   (C) 0   (D) 2
   (E) 3

3. A relationship exists between Figure I and Figure II.

   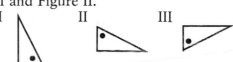

   A similar relationship exists between Figure III and which of the following figures?

   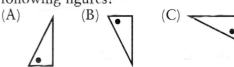

   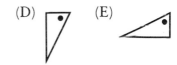

4. At 9:00 P.M. the temperature reached a low of $-15°F$. Then it rose $4°$ each hour. It reached $13°F$ at ___.
   (A) 2:00 A.M.   (B) 3:00 A.M.
   (C) 4:00 A.M.   (D) 5:00 A.M.
   (E) 6:00 A.M.

5. Which of the following is greater than $\frac{1}{2}$?
   (A) $-\frac{1}{2}$ (B) $\left(\frac{1}{2}\right)^2$ (C) $\left(\frac{1}{2}\right)^3$
   (D) 0.5   (E) None of these

6. If a water tank is leaking at a rate of 6 liters per 24 h, how much will it leak in 2 h?
   (A) 1 liter   (B) 2 liters
   (C) 0.25 liter   (D) 0.5 liter
   (E) 0.75 liter

7. For which value of x does y have the greatest value for $y = \frac{-16}{x}$?
   (A) $x = 2$ (B) $x = -2$
   (C) $x = \frac{1}{2}$ (D) $x = -\frac{1}{2}$
   (E) $x = \frac{1}{20}$

8. How much more than $-5\frac{1}{2}$ is $3\frac{3}{4}$?
   (A) $9\frac{1}{4}$ (B) $-9\frac{1}{4}$ (C) $1\frac{1}{4}$
   (D) $-1\frac{1}{4}$ (E) $3\frac{3}{4}$

9. What is the maximum total weight of a dozen apples if four of them weigh 90 to 110 g each and the rest weigh 115 to 120 g each?
   (A) 1,500 g   (B) 1,400 g
   (C) 230 g   (D) 120 g
   (E) 3

10. Find the value of $0^5 \cdot 1^4 + 1^3$.
    (A) -1 (B) 0   (C) 1   (D) 2
    (E) None of these

Cumulative Review (Chapters 1–2)

Evaluate.

1. $6x$, for $x = 9$ *1.1*
2. $7 - y$, for $y = 3$
3. $\frac{a}{b}$, for $a = 72$ and $b = 8$
4. mn, for $m = 2.1$ and $n = 3$
5. $r + s$, for $r = 5.6$ and $s = 9.8$
6. $x(y + 1) - (x - 2)$, for $x =$ *1.2*
   4 and $y = 7$
7. $4x^2 - 3x$, for $x = 2$ *1.3*
8. $(2y)^2 + y$, for $y = 12$
9. $(a^2 - 2b)^2$, for $a = 4$ and $b = 3$

Use $<$ or $>$ to make each statement true.

10. -5 ___ -4 *2.1*
11. 3 ___ -2

Simplify, if possible.

12. $|6|$ *2.2*
13. $|-9|$
14. $-|-12|$
15. $|-(-7)|$
16. $-9 + (-8)$ *2.4*
17. $-16 + 7$
18. $19 + (-19)$
19. $-4.2 + 0$
20. $1.3 + (-0.6)$
21. $16 - 9$
22. $-5 - 9$
23. $8 - (-4)$
24. $-9 - (-7)$
25. $\frac{1}{6} - \frac{2}{3}$
26. $-14 + 2 + 7 - (-8)$
27. $-1(-15)$ *2.6*
28. $2 \cdot (-9)$
29. $-9 \cdot 7$

30. $0(-10)$
31. $(2)(-9)(-3)$
32. $(3^2)(-2)^3(-1)$
33. $\frac{-16}{8}$ *2.7*
34. $\frac{0}{-19}$
35. $42 \div 0$
36. $-18 \div (-3)$
37. $-54 \div [24 \div (-4)]$

Evaluate for $x = -2$, $y = 4$, and $z = -1$.

38. $x + (-y)$ *2.4*
39. $|x - 3z|$ *2.8*
40. $|4z - 7y|$

Simplify.

41. $6x - 11x$ *2.9*
42. $3x - 4y - 7x$
43. $-a + 3 - 7a - 5 + 4a - 2$
44. $-(4x - 7y) + 2x$ *2.10*
45. $-3a - 2(7b + a) - 4b$
46. $3(2x - y) - 4(y - x)$

Solve each problem.

47. Use the formula $d = 5t^2$. Find *1.3*
    the distance d in meters that an
    object falls in a time t of 5 sec.
48. Use the formula $d = 0.04s^2$ to
    find d for $s = 60$.
49. Use the formula $p = 2l + 2w$ *1.4*
    to find p for $l = 7$ ft, $w = 5$ ft.
50. Use the formula $A = \frac{1}{2}bh$ to
    find A for $b = 7$ yd, $h = 8$ yd.
51. Use the formula $p = 4s$ to find
    p for $s = 3.2$ cm.
52. Use the formula $A = s^2$ to find
    A for $s = 4.1$ m.

53. Use the formula $A = lw$ to find A for $l = 9$ in. and $w = 6$ in.

54. Use the formula $V = lwh$ to find V for $l = 10$ cm, $w = 6$ cm, and $h = 4$ cm.

55. Use $A = \frac{1}{2}(b + c)h$ to find A for $b = 5$ in., $c = 8$ in., and $h = 12$ in.

For Exercises 56 and 57, round your answers to the nearest whole number.

56. Use the formula $C = 2\pi r$ to find C for $r = 3.6$ in. Use 3.14 for π.

57. Use the formula $A = \pi r^2$ to find A for $r = 6$ cm. Use 3.14 for π.

Choose the one best answer to each question or problem.

58. $7x^2y$ and $6xy^2$ are __?__.   *1.7*
 (A) constants
 (B) like terms
 (C) unlike terms
 (D) numerical coefficients
 (E) none of these

59. The sum of a positive number and a negative number can be __?__.   *2.4*
 (A) positive   (B) negative
 (C) zero   (D) all of these
 (E) none of these

60. Subtracting a number is the same as adding its __?__.   *2.5*
 (A) opposite
 (B) absolute values
 (C) difference
 (D) multiplicative inverse
 (E) none of these

61. The sum of two opposites is __?__.   *2.4*
 (A) positive   (B) negative
 (C) zero   (D) the additive inverse
 (E) none of these

62. Dividing by a nonzero number is the same as multiplying by its __?__.   *2.7*
 (A) reciprocal
 (B) opposite
 (C) absolute value
 (D) additive inverse
 (E) none of these

63. During one year, the highest temperature recorded in Utah was 102°F. The lowest temperature was -15°F. What was the difference between the two temperatures?   *2.5*

64. One day Len withdrew $512.32 from his checking account. The next day he deposited $326.45. What real number describes the net change in his account?   *2.4*

65. A submarine was at a depth of 245 m below sea level. It rose 75 m. Use a real number to give its new position with respect to sea level.

66. If an elephant lost $1\frac{1}{2}$ lb per week for 8 weeks and then gained $\frac{3}{4}$ lb per week for 5 weeks, what is its net gain or loss at the end of the 13 weeks?   *2.6*

67. Alvin set up a monthly budget to help him manage his finances. For six months he determined whether he spent more or less than his budget.   *2.4*
 June: $18.20 over
 July: $1.50 under
 Aug.: $2.45 over
 Sept.: $15.30 over
 Oct.: $20.65 under
 Nov.: $0.50 over
By how much was he over or under his budget at the end of the six months?

For almost 20 years, Dian Fossey and her students collected data on the daily lives of mountain gorillas inhabiting forest regions in Africa. The book she wrote reporting her findings, *Gorillas in the Mist,* was made into a movie.

3.1 Solving Equations by Adding or Subtracting

Objective

To solve equations by using the Addition or Subtraction Property of Equality

The scales at the right are balanced. If two objects of equal weight are placed on each side of the scale, the scale will remain balanced. This shows the following.

If $x = y$, then $x + 2 = y + 2$.

Suppose Bill and Jean are the same age. Then in 4 years they will still be the same age. Let b = Bill's age now in years and j = Jean's age now in years. This situation can be expressed as follows.

If $b = j$, then $b + 4 = j + 4$

This reasoning suggests one of the equality properties. These properties can be used to find solutions of equations.

Consider the equation $x = 6$. Its only solution is 6; its solution set is {6}. Suppose that you add the same number to each side of $x = 6$.

Add 7 to each side.
$$x = 6$$
$$x + 7 = 6 + 7$$
$$x + 7 = 13$$

The resulting equation, $x + 7 = 13$, also has {6} as its solution set. Equations with the same solution set, such as $x = 6$ and $x + 7 = 13$, are called **equivalent equations**.

Addition Property of Equality
For all real numbers a, b, and c, if $a = b$, then $a + c = b + c$.
This means that adding the same number to each side of an equation produces an equivalent equation.

Recall that the *replacement set* for a variable is the set of numbers that can replace the variable. For the rest of the equations in this book, *assume that the replacement set is the set of all real numbers*, unless it is otherwise stated.

To **solve** an equation means to find its solution.

EXAMPLE 1   Solve $x - 12 = 9$. Check the solution.

Plan   Notice that x is not alone on the left side of $x - 12 = 9$, since 12 is subtracted from x. To get x alone on the left, add 12 to each side.

Solution

$$x - 12 = 9$$

Add 12 to each side. $x - 12 + 12 = 9 + 12$

Simplify. $x + 0 = 21$ ⟵ $-12 + 12 = 0$

$$x = 21$$

All of these equations are equivalent. They all have the same solution.

Check   Check 21 in the original equation.

$$x - 12 = 9$$

Substitute 21 for x. $21 - 12 \overset{?}{=} 9$

$$9 = 9 \text{ True}$$

Thus, the solution is 21.

TRY THIS   1. Solve $x - 6 = -3.5$. Check the solution.

Since subtracting a number is the same as adding its opposite, the following property follows from the Addition Property of Equality.

Subtraction Property of Equality

For all real numbers, a, b, and c, if $a = b$, then $a - c = b - c$.

In other words, subtracting the same number from each side of an equation produces an equivalent equation.

This property is used in solving the equation in the next example.

EXAMPLE 2   Solve $-17 = y + 5$. Check.

Plan   The opposite of adding 5 is subtracting 5.
To get y alone on the right, subtract 5 from each side.

Solution

$$-17 = y + 5$$

Subtract 5 from each side. $-17 - 5 = y + 5 - 5$

Simplify. $-22 = y$

Check

Substitute -22 for y.	$-17 = y + 5$
	$-17 \overset{?}{=} -22 + 5$
	$-17 = -17$ True

Thus, the solution is -22.

TRY THIS   2. Solve $y + 2\frac{1}{2} = -6$. Check the solution.

Many word problems can be solved by using equations such as the ones illustrated in this lesson. Recall how you translate English phrases into algebraic expressions.

4 more than a number	16 less than a number	A number decreased by 16
4 more than n	16 less than n	n decreased by 16
$n + 4$	$n - 16$	$n - 16$

EXAMPLE 3   The $37-selling price of a tape recorder is $16 less than the original price. Find the original price.

Solution   You are asked to find the original price.
Let $x =$ the original price in dollars.

Thirty-seven is 16 less than the original price.
37 is 16 less than x.

$$37 = x - 16$$
$$37 + 16 = x - 16 + 16$$
$$53 = x$$

Check the answer, $53, in the original problem.

Check   Is it true that $37 is $16 less than $53? Yes, because $53 - 16 = 37$.

Thus, the original price is $53.

TRY THIS   3. A number has been decreased by 12. The result is -5. Find the original number. Check the solution.

Notice that in Example 3, the answer was checked in the *original problem*, not in the equation. This is important since you could have made an error in writing an equation. For example, you may have translated

37 is 16 less than x incorrectly as $37 - 16 = x$.

The solution to the equation $37 - 16 = x$ is 21, a solution that checks in the equation but *not* in the word problem itself.

Thirty-seven dollars is *not* $16 less than $21.

Classroom Exercises

What number would you add to or subtract from each side of the equation to solve it?

1. $x - 12 = -32$
2. $46 = y + 7$
3. $-3 = x - 8$

4. $p + 1 = 46$
5. $36 + y = 42$
6. $27 = y - 9$

7. $4.2 + x = 5.7$
8. $y - \frac{2}{3} = -4$
9. $-2 = z + 1\frac{1}{4}$

10–18. Solve and check the equations of Classroom Exercises 1–9.

For Exercises 19–21, let x represent the number you are asked to find. Write an equation to find the number. Then find the number.

19. Twenty is 5 more than a number. Find the number.
20. Seven less than a number is 23. What is the number?
21. Twenty-seven increased by a number is 33. Find the number.

Written Exercises

Solve and check.

1. $x - 23 = 30$
2. $y + 7 = 63$
3. $-18 = x - 35$

4. $a + 8 = -4$
5. $14 = x + 9$
6. $c - 9 = 3$

7. $6 = 15 + x$
8. $b - 10 = 8$
9. $7 + x = 5$

10. $t + 8 = -3$
11. $9 = 10 + x$
12. $4 + n = 4$

13. $x - 9 = -9$
14. $-12 + y = 18$
15. $5 = 8 + a$

16. $n - 6 = 13$
17. $4 = x + 8$
18. $x - 5 = 9$

19. $5 + y = 11$
20. $9 = c + 15$
21. $-4 + x = -4$

Translate each problem into an equation and solve.

22. The $44 selling price of a sweater is the cost increased by $18. Find the cost.

23. Nine more than a number is 42. Find the number.

24. Eight less than a number is 56. Find the number.

25. The price of a radio decreased by $35 is the discount price of $85. Find the original price.

Solve and check.

26. $0.6 + x = 1.4$
27. $y - 9.2 = 4.7$
28. $-5.2 = z - 0.9$

29. $x + 3.4 = -2.6$ **30.** $-4.3 + y = -6.7$ **31.** $z - 0.5 = 4.8$

32. $x + \frac{1}{2} = 5$ **33.** $y - \frac{2}{3} = 18$ **34.** $z + 5\frac{1}{3} = -10$

Solve.

35. $x - 246.8 = 656.32$ **36.** $254.78 + x = -234.5$ **37.** $115.3 + x = 889.36$

38. Explain in writing how the Subtraction Property of Equality follows from the Addition Property of Equality.

39. To solve the equation $5 = x + 7$, explain why you would subtract 7 from each side rather than subtract 5 from each side.

Find the solution set.

40. $x + |-8| = 17$ **41.** $|x| - 3 = -1$ **42.** $16 = |x| + 7$

43. $x + 8 = 8 + x$ **44.** $x + 6 = x - 9$ **45.** $x + 3 = -7 + x$

46. $|7 - [18 \div (-6)]| = x + 3$ **47.** $x + 4 = |-16|$

Mixed Review

Simplify.   *2.4–2.7, 2.9, 2.10*

1. $-\frac{2}{3} \cdot \frac{3}{5}$ **2.** $-1.6 + 5.4$ **3.** $6t - 11t$

4. $-3 - (7 + 5)$ **5.** $-(x + 8) - 9x$ **6.** $35 \div (-7)$

Application: Mathematics in Typing

A secretary applying for a job may have to take a typing test to determine typing speed in words per minute. The formula below is often used to determine typing speed. Note that a deduction is made for errors, since accuracy in typing is so important.

$$s = \frac{w - 10e}{m}$$

where s = speed in words per minute
w = number of words typed
e = number of errors
m = number of minutes of typing

1. On an 8-minute typing test, Jane typed 380 words with 4 errors. Find her speed in words per minute.

2. The formula above can be rewritten as $e = \dfrac{w - sm}{10}$. Use the formula to find the number of errors Barry made if he typed 320 words in 5 minutes and got a speed of 42 words per minute.

3.2 Solving Equations by Multiplying or Dividing

Objective	To solve equations by using the Multiplication or Division Property of Equality

When doing a number puzzle, Ralph and Sarah were each asked to pick a number and double it. If they both picked the same number, then they would both have the same result when they doubled it. Let r = Ralph's number and s = Sarah's number. Then the situation described above can be shown as follows.

$$\text{If } r = s, \text{ then } 2r = 2s.$$

This reasoning suggests the following property.

Multiplication Property of Equality
For all real numbers a, b, and c, if $a = b$, then $ac = bc$.
Multiplying each side of an equation by the same nonzero number produces an equivalent equation.

EXAMPLE 1 Solve $\frac{x}{4} = -7$. Check.

Plan The variable x is not alone on the left side, since x is divided by 4. To get x alone on the left, multiply each side by 4.

Solution
$$\frac{x}{4} = -7$$

Multiply each side by 4. $4\left(\frac{x}{4}\right) = 4(-7)$

Simplify. $1x = -28 \quad \longleftarrow 4 \cdot \frac{x}{4} = 4 \cdot \frac{1}{4}x = 1x$
$$x = -28$$

Check
$$\frac{x}{4} = -7$$

Substitute -28 for x. $\frac{-28}{4} \overset{?}{=} -7$

$-7 = -7$ True

Thus, the solution is -28.

TRY THIS   1. Solve $\frac{x}{-2} = 15$. Check.

If the numerical coefficient of the variable is a fraction, multiply each side of the equation by the reciprocal of the fraction.

EXAMPLE 2   Solve $6 = -\frac{2}{3}y$. Check.

Plan   The reciprocal of $-\frac{2}{3}$ is $-\frac{3}{2}$, since $\left(-\frac{2}{3}\right) \cdot \left(-\frac{3}{2}\right) = 1$. Therefore, multiply each side of the equation by $-\frac{3}{2}$.

Solution

$$6 = -\frac{2}{3}y$$

Multiply each side by $-\frac{3}{2}$. $-\frac{3}{2} \cdot 6 = -\frac{3}{2} \cdot \left(-\frac{2}{3}\right)y$

Simplify. $-9 = 1y$

$$-9 = y$$

Check

$$6 = -\frac{2}{3}y$$

Substitute -9 for y. $6 \stackrel{?}{=} -\frac{2}{3}(-9)$

$$6 = 6 \quad \text{True}$$

Thus, the solution is -9.

TRY THIS   2. Solve $-\frac{3}{5}x = -30$. Check.

Since dividing by a nonzero number is the same as multiplying by its reciprocal, each side of an equation can be divided by such a number.

Division Property of Equality

For all real numbers a, b, and c, if $a = b$, and $c \neq 0$, then $\frac{a}{c} = \frac{b}{c}$.

Dividing each side of an equation by the same nonzero number produces an equivalent equation.

EXAMPLE 3   Solve $-6x = -42$.

Solution

$$-6x = -42$$

Divide each side by -6. $\dfrac{-6x}{-6} = \dfrac{-42}{-6}$

Simplify. $1x = 7$ $\longleftarrow$ $\dfrac{-6x}{-6} = \dfrac{1}{-6}(-6)x = 1x$

$$x = 7$$

Thus, the solution is 7. The check is left for you.

TRY THIS   3. Solve $72 = -8x$. Check.

The word *of* is frequently associated with multiplication. Thus,

$$\tfrac{2}{3} \text{ of } 12 \quad \text{means} \quad \tfrac{2}{3} \cdot 12.$$

EXAMPLE 4   Joe jogged 3 mi. He jogged $\tfrac{2}{5}$ of the distance Mike jogged. How far did Mike jog?

Solution   Let $x =$ number of miles Mike jogged.

THINK: Three miles that Joe jogged is $\tfrac{2}{5}$ of the distance that Mike jogged.

$$3 = \tfrac{2}{5} \cdot x$$
$$\tfrac{5}{2} \cdot 3 = \tfrac{5}{2} \cdot \tfrac{2}{5}x$$
$$\tfrac{15}{2} = x, \text{ or } x = 7\tfrac{1}{2}$$

Check   Check the answer, $7\tfrac{1}{2}$ mi, in the original problem.

$$\tfrac{2}{5} \cdot 7\tfrac{1}{2} = \overset{1}{\underset{1}{\cancel{2}}} \cdot \overset{3}{\underset{1}{\cancel{15}}} = \tfrac{3}{1} = 3$$

Thus, Mike jogged $7\tfrac{1}{2}$ mi.

TRY THIS   4. Robin used $\tfrac{3}{4}$ of her savings to buy a new bicycle. If Robin spent $144, how much had Robin saved?

Classroom Exercises

By what number would you multiply or divide each side of the equation to solve it?

1. $6x = 12$ **2.** $\tfrac{1}{3}x = -2$ **3.** $18 = -2x$ **4.** $-\tfrac{1}{9}x = 5$

5. $-6 = \tfrac{3}{4}x$ **6.** $-6x = -18$ **7.** $-\tfrac{2}{3}x = 14$ **8.** $\tfrac{2}{9}x = -8$

9–16. Solve and check the equations of Classroom Exercises 1–8.

Written Exercises

Solve and check.

1. $4x = 20$ **2.** $-3y = 18$ **3.** $-24 = 2z$ **4.** $-5a = -30$

5. $\tfrac{1}{3}c = 2$ **6.** $7 = -\tfrac{1}{5}x$ **7.** $\tfrac{1}{4}y = -6$ **8.** $-\tfrac{1}{7}z = -3$

9. $\frac{2}{3}y = 14$ **10.** $-\frac{3}{4}x = 15$ **11.** $\frac{5}{8}z = -25$ **12.** $16 = -\frac{2}{5}c$

13. $3 - \frac{x}{8}$ **14.** $\frac{x}{7} = 4$ **15.** $\frac{y}{9} = -2$ **16.** $\frac{z}{5} = -6$

Translate each problem into an equation and solve.

17. Seven times a number is -84. Find the number.

18. Two-thirds of a number is -26. Find the number.

19. Bill worked 15 h building scenery for a play. He worked 5 times as long as Maria did. How long did Maria work? Explain your reasoning.

20. Jesse spent $\frac{2}{5}$ of her savings on a new coat. The coat cost $60. How much were her savings before she bought the coat? Explain your reasoning.

21. A class is collecting empty bottles to return for 5¢ each. The average rate of collection is 43 bottles a day. At this rate, how many days would it take to reach $100? Explain your reasoning.

Solve.

22. $-5x = \frac{3}{4}$ **23.** $\frac{2}{3} = 7y$ **24.** $-6z = -\frac{5}{8}$

25. $-\frac{3}{4} = -9c$ **26.** $1\frac{1}{3}x = 8$ **27.** $-2\frac{1}{4}y = 18$

28. $15 = 1\frac{2}{3}z$ **29.** $-4\frac{1}{2}c = -27$ **30.** $0.2a = 3$

31. $-0.7x = 14$ **32.** $2.4z = -24$ **33.** $-5.2 = -1.3y$

34. $-1 = -\frac{2}{3}n$ **35.** $-\frac{4}{5}x = 0$ **36.** $-\frac{1}{8} = 8t$

37. Explain in writing how the Division Property of Equality follows from the Multiplication Property of Equality.

Find the solution set.

38. $3|x| = 15$ **39.** $\frac{2}{3}|x| = 18$

40. $x \cdot 1 = x$ **41.** $0 \cdot x = 7$

42. $\frac{|x|}{7} = 2$ **43.** $3 = \frac{1}{5}|x|$

44. $|x| = x$ **45.** $|x| = -x$

Mixed Review

Evaluate. Simplify first for Exercises 2, 4, and 5. *1.2 1.7, 2.6, 2.8*

1. $3(2a + 4)$ for $a = 6$ **2.** $6x - 8 - x - 4$ for $x = -3$ **3.** $2a^3$ for $a = -4$

4. $5x - 4 - x$ for $x = -3$ **5.** $8x + 8 + 4x + 3$ for $x = 2\frac{1}{2}$ **6.** $-x^5$ for $x = -3$

7. At 11:00 P.M. the temperature was 6°F. That night it dropped 9° and then rose 4° by 6:00 A.M. What was the temperature at 6:00 A.M.? *2.4*

3.3 Using Two Properties of Equality

Objective

To solve equations by using two properties of equality

A plumber charges $42 for each hour he works plus $35 to come to the house. The Batistas were sent a bill for $119. The equation

$$42n + 35 = 119$$

can be solved for n to find the number of hours the plumber worked.

EXAMPLE 1

Solve the equation above. How long did the plumber work?

Plan

To get n alone on the left side, first subtract 35 from each side. Then divide each side by 42.

Solution

$$42n + 35 = 119$$

Subtract 35 from each side. $\quad 42n + 35 - 35 = 119 - 35$

Simplify. $\qquad\qquad\qquad\qquad\qquad 42n = 84$

Divide each side by 42. $\qquad\qquad \dfrac{42n}{42} = \dfrac{84}{42}$

Simplify. $\qquad\qquad\qquad\qquad\qquad n = 2 \quad \longleftarrow 2 \text{ hours}$

Check

Did the plumber work 2 h?
Yes, because $42 \times 2 + 35 = 84 + 35 = 119$.
Thus, the plumber worked 2 h.

EXAMPLE 2

Solve $5 = -16 - \frac{3}{4}y$. Check.

Solution

$$5 = -16 - \tfrac{3}{4}y$$

Add 16 to each side. $\qquad 5 + 16 = -16 - \tfrac{3}{4}y + 16$

$$21 = -\tfrac{3}{4}y$$

Multiply each side by $-\frac{4}{3}$. $\quad -\dfrac{4}{\cancel{3}_{1}} \cdot \cancel{21}^{7} = -\dfrac{4}{3}\left(-\tfrac{3}{4}y\right)$

$$-28 = y$$

Thus, the solution is -28. The check is left for you.

TRY THIS

1. Solve $-\frac{2}{3}x + 7 = -5$. Check.

Some equations need to be simplified before a property of equality is used. In the next example, like terms should be combined first.

EXAMPLE 3   Solve $8 - (-3) = 7 + 5z - 6z$. Check.

Solution

$$8 - (-3) = 7 + 5z - 6z$$

Rewrite $8 - (-3)$ as $8 + 3$. $8 + 3 = 7 + 5z - 6z$

Simplify. $11 = 7 - 1z$

Subtract 7 from each side. $11 - 7 = 7 - 1z - 7$

Simplify. $4 = -1z$

Divide each side by -1. $\dfrac{4}{-1} = \dfrac{-1 \cdot z}{-1}$

Simplify. $-4 = z$

Thus, the solution is -4. The check is left for you.

TRY THIS   **2.** Solve $3x + \frac{1}{8} - 7x = \frac{5}{8}$. Check.

Classroom Exercises

To solve the equation, what number would you add to or subtract from each side? Then, by what number would you multiply or divide each side?

1. $4x - 3 = -15$ **2.** $-2y + 7 = 3$

3. $9 - \frac{2}{3}z = 1$ **4.** $5 = 16 - x$

5. $-x - 9 = -4$ **6.** $-1 = 8 - 3c$

7–12. Solve and check the equations of Classroom Exercises 1–6.

Written Exercises

Solve and check.

1. $5x - 1 = -26$ **2.** $4y - 2 = 14$ **3.** $2z + 4 = 8$

4. $6 + 2a = 10$ **5.** $9z - 5 = 4$ **6.** $4y - 7 = 21$

7. $6 = -4x - 2$ **8.** $4 - 3y = 13$ **9.** $-4 = -8 - 2z$

10. $-7 = 3 + 5a$ **11.** $-6x + 25 = -11$ **12.** $18 = 2c + 10$

13. $17 - 3y = -10$ **14.** $8n - 14 = -22$ **15.** $-x + 3 = -4$

16. $5 - m = 12$ **17.** $-6 - z = -2$ **18.** $-4 = 6 - 2x$

19. $\frac{x}{5} + 9 = 13$ **20.** $-7 = 9 + \frac{x}{3}$ **21.** $5 + \frac{y}{3} = -4$

22. $\frac{1}{3}x - 7 = 2$ **23.** $6 - \frac{3}{5}y = 9$ **24.** $17 = -10 + \frac{3}{4}z$

25. $32 = 7x + 8 - 5x$ **26.** $6y + 8 - 5y = -11$ **27.** $-3 = 8z + 8 - 9z$

28. $5 = 5x - 7x + 25$ **29.** $3y + 7 - 5y = -9$ **30.** $-7 = 3p - 9 - 7p$

Translate each problem into an equation and solve.

31. Thirty-four is 6 less than 5 times a number. Find the number.

32. 4 increased by 3 times a number is 22. Find the number.

33. The $347 selling price of a stereo is $35 more than 3 times the cost. Find the cost.

34. Two less than 4 times the temperature is $-20°$. Find the temperature.

35. 5 times Mary's age decreased by 17 is 28. How old is she?

36. Seven pounds less than twice Jason's weight is 219 lb. What is Jason's weight?

37. For babysitting Mary charges $3 per hour plus an additional $2 for transportation. One evening she was paid $17. How many hours did she babysit?

38. A car rental company charges $19 a day plus $0.15 for each mile driven. Mr. Aboud's bill for a one-day rental was $38.50. How many miles did he drive?

Solve.

39. $0.6c - 1.5 = 3.9$ **40.** $2.3 - 0.7a = 7.2$ **41.** $0.3 + \frac{x}{0.6} = 2.8$

42. $\frac{3}{5} = \frac{4}{5} - 3x$ **43.** $\frac{1}{3} + 4y = \frac{1}{6}$ **44.** $\frac{1}{4} = \frac{1}{2} - \frac{3}{4}b$

45. $-5x + 1.7 = 1.8$ **46.** $1.4 - 0.4z = 0.9$ **47.** $-0.8 = 6x + 0.4$

48. $5 = 2x + x + 7$ **49.** $13 = -3y + 7y + 10$ **50.** $3z + z - 8 = -2$

51. $19 = 20 - 7a - a$ **52.** $-7z - 5 + 4z = -4$ **53.** $-12y - 5 - 2y = 8$

54. $x - 2x = |-3 + 8|$ **55.** $|-9 + 8| = -5x + 4x + 1$

56. Solve the equation $4x - 3 = 9$ by first using the Addition Property, and then the Multiplication Property. Then solve it by first using the Multiplication Property and then the Addition Property. Explain why the first method is simpler than the second.

Midchapter Review

Solve and check.   *3.1–3.3*

1. $x - 4 = 8$ **2.** $4 = 6 - x$ **3.** $x + 5 = 12$ **4.** $-4 = -8 + x$

5. $-2x = 12$ **6.** $7 = \frac{1}{5}x$ **7.** $-8 = -2x$ **8.** $-6 = \frac{2}{3}x$

9. $3x - 2 = 8$ **10.** $4 = -2 - \frac{1}{2}x$ **11.** $2x - 4 - 3x = -8$ **12.** $6 = 2\frac{1}{2}x - 9$

Solve each problem. Then check in the problem.   *3.1, 3.2*

13. Eighteen is $\frac{1}{3}$ of a number. Find the number.

14. Five less than Naomi's age is 16. How old is Naomi?

Problem Solving Strategies

Developing a Plan

In a baseball game, the home team has runners on second and third base when its best hitter comes up to bat. What plan, or strategy, will the manager of the opposing team use?

Part of solving a problem is choosing the strategy to use. Choosing a strategy that is effective and efficient for you is an important focus of the second step, *Develop a Plan,* in the problem-solving process.

To Solve a Problem

1. Understand the Problem
2. Develop a Plan
3. Carry Out the Plan
4. Look Back

Exercises

Column 1 contains six questions that suggest problem situations. Column 2 lists helpful problem-solving strategies. Beside the number of each question in Column 1, write the letter of one or more strategies that you think you could use to solve the related problem. Explain your choice(s).

Column 1	Column 2
1. What time will we arrive at the contest site?	**a.** Drawing a Diagram
	b. Making a Model
2. Which made more profit, the popcorn stand or the soft drink stand?	**c.** Using a Formula
	d. Making a Graph
3. Is shoe size related to the height of a person?	**e.** Using Logical Reasoning
	f. Working Backwards
4. How many computer desks will fit in the lab?	
5. What is the shortest route to deliver all the newspapers?	
6. Why are winter days shorter than summer days?	

3.4 Equations with the Variable on Both Sides

To solve equations with the variable on both sides

Until now, you have solved only equations with the variable on one side. The equation $6x - 5 = 2x - 21$ has a variable on both sides. Solving such an equation requires the additional step of getting the variable on one side only. This can be done in two different ways.

EXAMPLE 1   Solve $6x - 5 = 2x - 21$. Check.

Plan   Subtract either $2x$ or $6x$ from each side. Try both ways.

Solution

Method 1
To get x alone on the left, first subtract $2x$ from each side. Then add 5 to each side.

$$6x - 5 = 2x - 21$$
$$6x - 5 - 2x = 2x - 21 - 2x$$
$$4x - 5 = -21$$
$$4x - 5 + 5 = -21 + 5$$
$$4x = -16$$
$$\frac{4x}{4} = \frac{-16}{4}$$
$$x = -4 \quad \longleftarrow \text{Same result} \longrightarrow$$

Method 2
To get x alone on the right, first subtract $6x$ from each side. Then add 21 to each side.

$$6x - 5 = 2x - 21$$
$$6x - 5 - 6x = 2x - 21 - 6x$$
$$-5 = -4x - 21$$
$$-5 + 21 = -4x - 21 + 21$$
$$16 = -4x$$
$$\frac{16}{-4} = \frac{-4x}{-4}$$
$$-4 = x$$

Check

Substitute -4 for x.

$$6x - 5 = 2x - 21$$
$$6(-4) - 5 \stackrel{?}{=} 2(-4) - 21$$
$$-24 - 5 \stackrel{?}{=} -8 - 21$$
$$-29 = -29 \text{ True}$$

Thus, the solution is -4.

TRY THIS   1. Solve $8 - x = 5x - 4$. Check.

There are equations that have no solution at all. There are also equations for which *any* real number is a solution.

$x = x + 1$ $\frac{1}{2}(2x) = x$

(True for *no* value of x)   (True for *every* value of x)

EXAMPLE 2   Find the solution set of $-17 - x = 8x + 6 - 9x$.

Solution

Combine $8x$ and $-9x$.	$-17 - x = 6 - x$
Add x to each side.	$-17 - x + x = 6 - x + x$
Simplify.	$-17 = 6$ ⟵—— False statement

The equation $-17 - x = 8x + 6 - 9x$ is equivalent to the false statement $-17 = 6$. No value of x makes the equation true. Thus, the solution set is the empty set, $\varnothing$.

EXAMPLE 3   Find the solution set of $7x - 4 = -2x + 1 + 9x - 5$.

Solution

Combine $-2x$ and $9x$.	$7x - 4 = 7x - 4$
Subtract $7x$ from each side.	$7x - 7x - 4 = 7x - 7x - 4$
Simplify.	$-4 = -4$ ⟵—— true statement

The equation $7x - 4 = -2x + 1 + 9x - 5$ is equivalent to the true statement $-4 = -4$. All values of x makes the equation true.

The solution set is the set of all real numbers.

TRY THIS   2. Find the solution set of $5 - 2x = 4x + 8 - 6x - 3$.

The equation $\frac{1}{2}(2x) - x$ is an example of an *identity*.

An **identity** is an equation that is true for each value from the replacement set of the variable.

EXAMPLE 4   Jane has $30 and is saving at the rate of $7 per week. Susan has $50 and is saving at the rate of $3 per week. When will they have the same amount of money?

Solution   Let n = the number of weeks until they have the same amount.

After n weeks, Jane will have $30 + 7n$ dollars and Susan will have $50 + 3n$ dollars. These two expressions are equal.

	$30 + 7n = 50 + 3n$
Subtract $3n$ from each side.	$30 + 4n = 50$
Subtract 30 from each side.	$4n = 20$
	$n = 5$

Check   After 5 weeks, Jane will have $30 + 7 \cdot 5$ dollars, which is $65.
After 5 weeks, Susan will have $50 + 3 \cdot 5$ dollars, which is $65.

Thus, they will have the same amount after 5 weeks.

TRY THIS   3. In 18 years, John's age will be 3 times his present age. How old is John now?

1. Write, in order, the letters of a sequence of steps for solving the equation $-7x + 8 = -3x - 6$ to get the variable alone on the *left*.

2. Repeat Exercise 1 above, but get the variable alone on the *right*.

a. Add 6 to each side.
b. Add $7x$ to each side.
c. Divide each side by -4.
d. Add $3x$ to each side.
e. Subtract 8 from each side.
f. Divide each side by 4.

Classroom Exercises

What operation would you perform first to get the variable on the right side of the equation?

1. $5x - 6 = 2x$
2. $3y + 7 = -4y$
3. $-5c = -14 + c$
4. $6 - x = x + 2$
5. $3a + 8 = 5a - 14$
6. $y + 5 = 9 - 4y$

7–12. Solve and check the equations of Classroom Exercises 1–6.

Written Exercises

Solve and check.

1. $9y - 18 = 3y$
2. $7c - 9 = 8c$
3. $8n - 12 = 5n$
4. $-11m = 14 - 9m$
5. $-6x = 10 - 4x$
6. $-4z = 35 - 9z$
7. $8p = -5p + 65$
8. $-84 + 15r = 3r$
9. $11c + 36 = 8c$
10. $7z - 9 = 3z + 19$
11. $6 + 10t = 8t + 12$
12. $3x + 7 = 16 + 6x$
13. $18 + 3y = 5y - 4$
14. $11a + 8 = -2 + 9a$
15. $9x - 5 = 6x + 13$
16. $5 - x = x + 9$
17. $14 + 3n = n - 14$
18. $7 - x = 5 + 3x$
19. $4y + 2 = 2y + 4 + 3y$
20. $8c - 12 = 15c - 4c$
21. $5x - 3 = 7x + 7 + 3x$
22. $y + 11 = -2y + 6$
23. $-2y + 3 - y = 11 + y$
24. $16 - x = 4x + 8 + 3x$

Translate each problem into an equation and solve.

25. Courtney's allowance increased by $30 is the same as twice her allowance. Find her allowance.

26. Five times Mary's age is the same as 28 less than 7 times her age. Find her age.

27. Ten more than twice a number is the same as 4 times the number. Find the number.

28. The temperature, increased by 80 degrees, is the same as 6 times the temperature. Find the temperature.

29. Three less than 5 times Jerry's age is the same as 3 times his age increased by 37. Find his age.

30. The perimeter of a triangle increased by 3 cm is the same as 35 cm decreased by 7 times the perimeter. Find the perimeter of the triangle.

31. An automobile salesman is offered a choice of two compensation plans. The first consists of a weekly salary of $120 and a $150 commission on each car he sells. The second consists of no salary and a $180 commission on each car sold. How many cars would the salesman have to sell in one week to make the same money under both plans?

32. Two men are planting tulip bulbs. One man has already planted 57 bulbs and is planting 44 bulbs per hour. The other man has already planted 96 bulbs and is planting 32 bulbs per hour. In how many hours will each man have planted the same number of bulbs? What is the number of bulbs?

33. A number decreased by 30 is the same as 14 decreased by 3 times the number. Find the number.

Find the solution set.

34. $-6x = 5 - 6x$

35. $4y + 7 = 7 + 4y$

36. $5y - 4 + 6 - 7y = 3 + 6y$

37. $8p - 5 - 9p = 4 + p$ 6

38. $2a - 5a + 4 = 4 - 3a$

39. $6 - 3c = -3c + 2$

40. $7 + 0.6a + 2 = 15 - 1.4a$

41. $0.2x + 3.2 = 0.4x - 0.2x + 3.2$

42. $3(x - 2) = 7 - (4 - x)$

43. $3x + 4(3 - x) = 7 - x$

44. $3|x| - 7 = 2|x| + 5$

45. $5|x| - 9 = 5 - 2|x|$

46. $8 - 4|x| = 2|x| - 9$

47. $4|2x| - 5 = 7|2x| + 3$

48. $6y = 8 - 9 + 6y$

49. $5 = 3a - 3a + 2$

Mixed Review

Simplify, if possible. Then evaluate for the given value of the variable.   *2.6, 2.8, 2.10*

1. $-3x^3$ for $x = -4$

2. $3x - (4 - x)$ for $x = -5$

3. $\dfrac{2a - 3}{3a + 4}$ for $a = -2$

Insert $<$ or $>$ to make a true statement.   *2.1*

4. $-7 \underline{\ ?\ } -3$

5. $5 \underline{\ ?\ } -15$

6. $0 \underline{\ ?\ } -12$

7. $-2.5 \underline{\ ?\ } -1.75$

8. Harry bought 14 records from Melissa. That was $\frac{2}{3}$ of her records. How many records did Melissa have before she sold some to Harry?   *3.2*

3.5 Equations with Parentheses

Objective	To solve equations that contain parentheses

To solve an equation that contains parentheses, first use the Distributive Property. Then solve the resulting equation and check.

EXAMPLE 1 Solve $8x - 3(2 - 5x) = 40$. Check.

Solution

$$8x - 3(2 - 5x) = 40$$

Use the Distributive Property. $8x - 6 + 15x = 40$
Combine like terms. $23x - 6 = 40$
Add 6 to each side. $23x - 6 + 6 = 40 + 6$
  $23x = 46$
Divide each side by 23. $x = 2$

Check

$$8x - 3(2 - 5x) = 40$$

Substitute 2 for x. $8 \cdot 2 - 3(2 - 5 \cdot 2) \overset{?}{=} 40$
  $16 - 3(2 - 10) \overset{?}{=} 40$
  $16 - 3(-8) \overset{?}{=} 40$
  $16 + 24 \overset{?}{=} 40$
  $40 = 40$ True

Thus, the solution is 2.

TRY THIS 1. Solve $12 = 5x + 3(4 - x)$. Check.

In Example 2, two sets of parentheses must be removed before like terms are combined.

EXAMPLE 2 Solve $6y - (4 - 2y) = 3(7 + 2y)$.

Solution

$$6y - (4 - 2y) = 3(7 + 2y)$$

Use the property $-a = -1a$. $6y - 1(4 - 2y) = 3(7 + 2y)$
Remove parentheses. $6y - 4 + 2y = 21 + 6y$
Combine like terms. $8y - 4 = 21 + 6y$
Subtract 6y from each side. $8y - 4 - 6y = 21 + 6y - 6y$
Add 4 to each side. $2y - 4 = 21$
  $2y = 25$
Divide each side by 2. $y = \frac{25}{2}$, or $12\frac{1}{2}$

Thus, the solution is $12\frac{1}{2}$. The check is left for you.

TRY THIS 2. Solve. $2(5 - 2y) = -1 + 3(y - 1)$. Check.

EXAMPLE 3 The long-distance telephone rate to Iowa is 21¢ for the first minute and 15¢ for each additional minute or part thereof. Judy's call to Iowa cost $1.11. How long was Judy's call?

Plan Let x = the maximum number of minutes.
The first minute cost 21¢.
The remaining $x - 1$ minutes cost 15¢ each.
The call cost $1.11, which is 111¢.

Solution
$$21 + (x - 1)15 = 111$$
$$21 + 15x - 15 = 111$$
$$15x + 6 = 111$$
$$15x = 105$$
$$x = 7$$

Check Does 1 min at 21¢ and 6 min at 15¢ cost $1.11?
Yes, because $21 + 6 \cdot 15$ equals $21 + 90$, or 111.

Thus, the call lasted at least 6 minutes but not more than 7 minutes.

TRY THIS 3. Twice a number subtracted from 6 is the same as that number added to 3. What is the number?

Classroom Exercises

Use the Distributive Property to remove parentheses.

1. $2(3x + 4)$ **2.** $3(7y - 2)$ **3.** $4(n - 1)$ **4.** $-7(x + 2)$

5. $-5(2x + 3)$ **6.** $(6 + a)3$ **7.** $(4 - 3x)2$ **8.** $(6t + 2)4$

9. $-1(3x - 5)$ **10.** $-(-4 + 2y)$ **11.** $-(1 + 4z)$ **12.** $(4a - 2)(-3)$

Solve and check.

13. $3(x + 4) = 15$ **14.** $-3(a - 4) = 39$ **15.** $4(y + 1) = 14 - y$

Written Exercises

Solve and check.

1. $2(y + 7) = 16$ **2.** $3(x - 2) = 18$ **3.** $-5(a + 2) = 30$

4. $x + 9 = 2(x - 3)$ **5.** $2(y + 3) = 12 - y$ **6.** $25 - 5a = 3(2a + 1)$

7. $-2(3 - 2c) = 10 - 4c$ **8.** $23 = 12 - (6 + c)$

9. $5(x - 1) = 2x + 4(x - 1)$ **10.** $13 - (2x - 5) = 2(x + 2) + 3x$

11. $-(3 - 2n) + 7n = (n + 3)3$ **12.** $-(y + 8) - 5 = 4(y + 2) - 6y$

13. $(c + 4)3 - 6c = 2(4 - 2c)$
14. $8y - 3(4 - 2y) = 6(y + 1) - 2$
15. $-2(3 - 4z) + 7z = 12z - (z + 2)$
16. $-3(6 - 2x) + 4x = -(2x - 6)$
17. $7x - (9 - 4x) = 3(x - 11)$
18. $7r + 3(7 - r) = -(r + 4)$

Translate each problem into an equation and solve.

19. Five times the sum of a number and 3 is 35. Find the number.

20. If Jim's age in years is decreased by 9, and that difference is multiplied by 8, the result is 48 years. Find Jim's age.

21. Five more than a number is the same as 4 times the sum of the number and 8. Find the number.

22. Three times the sum of a number and 4 is the same as 18 increased by the number. Find the number.

23. If Amy's age in years is increased by 5 years and then multiplied by 2, the result is 38 more than Amy's age. Find her age.

24. First-class postage costs 25¢ for the first ounce and 20¢ for each additional ounce or part thereof. If you are charged $1.65 to mail a package, what is the maximum weight?

25. Rectangular tables that seat 6 people are being placed end-to-end for a banquet. Five people will be placed at each of the 2 end tables and 4 at each of the other tables. How many tables are needed to seat 50 people in one line of tables? Explain your reasoning.

26. Mr. Parsons is planning to take his 12-year-old son, Jamie, and some of his friends to a show. Adult tickets are $7; children's are $4. Jamie's two younger sisters will join them at the theatre. How many friends can Jamie invite if Mr. Parsons can spend $35 and if he is the only adult?

Solve and check. (HINT: **Remove the parentheses first. Then remove the brackets.**)

27. $5 - n = n - [4 + 7(2n - 1)]$
28. $-3[5 - (2 + c)] = 6c + 1$
29. $3[5 - 3(y - 4)] = 2y + 7$
30. $-9x - [2(1 + 3x) + 6] = 5x$
31. $6z - 2[7(z + 1) + 4] = 10z$
32. $-[-8 + 2(1 - 4r)] = 1 - 7r$

Mixed Review

Solve and check.   *3.2, 3.3, 3.4, 3.5*

1. $-2x + 4 = 7$
2. $-\frac{3}{5}y = 18$
3. $13 = 2x - 7$
4. $4y + 8 - y = -13$
5. $3(4a - 1) = 21$
6. $5x - 8 - 2x = 7 + 3x$

Simplify.   *2.8*

7. $-26 - (-2 + 6)$
8. $-(-12 - 4) - 18$
9. $16 + (3 - 6)$
10. $(10 - 3) - (2 + 4)$
11. $4 - 8 - (2 - 3)$
12. $-(3 - 2) - 4$

Application: *Thunder and Lightning*

During a thunderstorm there is a difference in time between when you see the lightning flash and when you hear the thunder. Both the flash and the sound are created at essentially the same time and place in the storm, but sound travels slower than light and, therefore, arrives after you have seen the flash. If you count the seconds between the flash of lightning and the sound of thunder, you can compute how far away the lightning is.

EXAMPLE   Twelve seconds elapse between the time you see lightning and then hear the thunder. How far away was the lightning? The speed of sound is 1,127 feet per second.

Use the formula, distance = rate · time.

$$d = rt$$
$$d = 1,127 \cdot 12$$
$$d = 13,524 \text{ feet}$$

The lightning was about 13,500 feet away.

(NOTE: Since light travels at approximately 186,000 miles per second, it takes about 0.000014 second for light to travel 13,524 feet. This time is so much less than 12 seconds that it can be ignored.

Solve.

1. How far away in feet is the lightning if the elapsed time after the time you hear the thunder is 1 second? 3 seconds? 6 seconds?

2. There are 5,280 feet in a mile. Use your answers to Exercise 1 to find out how many miles away the lightning is for each of the three cases.

3. Make a chart that organizes the data in the Example and in Exercises 1 and 2.

4. What rule could you use to approximate mentally the number of miles between you and a storm if you know the elapsed time in seconds?

3.6 Problem Solving: Using Formulas

Objective	To solve problems involving formulas

Suppose a school dance will cost $800 for a band and other expenses. If tickets cost $5 each, and only 100 are sold, will there be a profit? You can use the following relationship:

profit = number of tickets × price per ticket − expenses
profit =   100   ×   5   − 800
profit =   500   − 800
profit = −300

A negative profit is a *loss*, so the sale of 100 tickets is a loss of $300.

Profit = number of tickets × price per ticket − expenses, can be expressed as a *formula*: $p = nt - e$.

Notice that in a formula, different quantities are represented by different letters. Thus, t (not p) is used to represent "price per ticket" since "p" has already been selected to represent "profit."

EXAMPLE 1 Suppose that your school dance hires a band for $800.

a. If you expect to sell 200 tickets, what should be the price of each ticket in order to make a profit of $1,000?

b. If you plan to charge $5 per ticket and wish to break even (have a zero profit), how many tickets should you sell?

Solutions

a.
$$p = nt - e$$
$$1{,}000 = 200t - 800$$
$$1{,}000 + 800 = 200t - 800 + 800$$
$$1{,}800 = 200t$$
$$9 = t$$

b.
$$p = nt - e$$
$$0 = n \cdot 5 - 800$$
$$0 + 800 = 5n - 800 + 800$$
$$800 = 5n$$
$$160 = n$$

Check

The total receipts from the sale of 200 tickets, at $9 each, are $1,800. After $800 in expenses is deducted, the profit is $1,000.

The price should be $9 each.

The total receipts from the sale of 160 tickets, at $5 apiece, are $800, which equals the expenses.

Thus, 160 tickets must be sold to break even.

TRY THIS

1. Use the formula $p = nt - e$ to find the expenses, e, if 420 tickets sell for $6 each and the profit is $1,950.

Distance, rate, and time are related by the formula $d = rt$, where d is the distance, r is the rate (speed), and t is the time.

EXAMPLE 2 Gail plans to ride her bike 6 mi in 45 min. At what rate in miles per hour (mi/h) must she travel?

Plan Use the formula $d = rt$. You are asked to give your answer in miles per hour. Thus, d must be given in miles and t must be given in hours.

Solution Since $d = 6$ mi and $t = 45$ min, change minutes to hours.

45 min $= \frac{45}{60}$ h $= \frac{3}{4}$ h. So $t = \frac{3}{4}$ h.

$$d = rt$$

Substitute 6 for d and $\frac{3}{4}$ for t. $\qquad 6 = r \cdot \frac{3}{4}$

Multiply each side by $\frac{4}{3}$. $\qquad 6 \cdot \frac{4}{3} = r \cdot \frac{3}{4} \cdot \frac{4}{3}$

$$8 = r$$

Thus, Gail must travel at a rate of 8 mi/h. The check is left for you.

TRY THIS 2. It took Mr. Greenberg $4\frac{1}{2}$ hours to drive 270 miles. What is his average speed?

The surface area of a rectangular solid is the total area of its six sides. The formula for the surface area, A, of a rectangular solid with length l, width w, and height h, is $A = 2(lw + hw + lh)$.

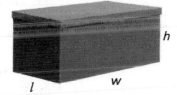

EXAMPLE 3 The surface area of a box is 94 in². Find the height of a box that is 3 in. wide and 5 in. long.

Solution $A = 94$, $w = 3$, and $l = 5$. Find h.
$A = 2(lw + hw + lh)$
$94 = 2(5 \cdot 3 + h \cdot 3 + 5 \cdot h)$
$94 = 2(15 + 8h)$
$94 = 30 + 16h$
$64 = 16h$
$4 = h$ Thus, the height of the box is 4 in.

TRY THIS 3. Find the width of a box with a surface area of 46 in.², a length of 4 in., and a height of 2 in.

Classroom Exercises

1. Using $d = rt$, find d for $r = 45$ mi/h and $t = 11$ h.
2. Using $d = rt$, find t for $d = 330$ mi and $r = 55$ mi/h.

3. Using $F = \frac{9}{5}C + 32$, find F for $C = 25$.

4. Barry jogs at a rate of 6 mi/h. How many hours must he jog in order to cover a distance of 15 mi?

A school orchestra is giving a concert. Its expenses will be $250. Use this information to answer Exercises 5–8.

5. How many tickets must be sold at $2 each to make a $1,000 profit?

6. If the orchestra expects to sell approximately 500 tickets, what should it charge for each ticket to make a $1,000 profit?

7. If the orchestra sells 550 tickets at $2 each, what will be its profit?

8. If the orchestra expects to sell only 500 tickets at $2.25 each, by how much would it have to lower expenses to make a $1,000 profit?

Written Exercises

Use the formula $p = nt - e$ for Exercises 1–4.

1. Find n for $p = \$1,878$, $t = \$8$, and $e = \$150$.

2. Find t for $p = \$2,210$, $n = 410$, and $e = \$250$.

3. A day-care center needs a profit of $600 for its variety show. Expenses are $75. How many tickets must be sold if the price of each ticket is $1.50?

4. If the day-care center expects to sell about 350 tickets, expenses are $75, and a $600 profit is the goal, what should be the price of each ticket, to the nearest quarter?

Use the formula $d = rt$ for Exercises 5–8.

5. Find r for $d = 175$ miles and $t = 3.5$ h.

6. Find t for $d = 1,716$ mi and $r = 264$ mi/h.

7. Kate lives 2 mi from school. She runs at a rate of 10 mi/h. How long must she run to get from her home to school? Use $d = rt$.

8. How fast must a train travel in order to cover a distance of 130 mi in $2\frac{1}{2}$ h? Use $d = rt$.

Use the formula $A = 2(lw + hw + lh)$ for Exercises 9–12.

9. Find l for $A = 118$ in.^{2}, $w = 5$ in., and $h = 7$ in.

10. Find w for $A = 78$ in.^{2}, $l = 4$ in., and $h = 6$ in.

11. Find h for $A = 81.4$ in.^{2}, $l = 4$ in., and $w = 5$ in.

12. Nancy is painting the surface of a wooden crate that has a surface area of 108 in.^{2} If the length and width both equal 6 in., what is the height of the crate?

The formula $\frac{W}{4A} = p$ represents the tire pressure p in pounds per square inch of a tire on a car. W is the weight of the car in pounds and A is the area in square inches of each tire's contact with the ground.

13. Find p for $W = 4{,}000$ lb and $A = 50$ in.^{2}

14. Find W for $A = 31.25$ in.^{2} and $p = 8.1$ lb/in.^{2}.

The maximum size for a package accepted by the United States Postal Service is one that satisfies the condition $l + 2w + 2h = 108$ in., where the length l, the width w, and the height h are all expressed in inches.

15. If you wish to mail a package with $l = 48$ in. and $w = 22$ in., what is its maximum permitted height?

16. If you wish to mail a package with $w = h = 1.5$ ft, what is its maximum permitted length?

On a 160-mi trip, Ray averages 50 mi/h for the first $2\frac{1}{2}$ h. After a 10-min rest, he continues driving and arrives at his destination in another 45 min.

17. What is his average speed during the last 45 min?

18. What is the average speed for the entire trip?

In a certain city, the streets are parallel, 200 ft apart, and approximately 35 ft wide. There are 5,280 ft in 1 mi.

19. How many blocks can you walk in 14 min at the rate of 3.5 mi/h?

20. Write a formula that relates the number of blocks walked to the rate in mi/h and the time in minutes.

Mixed Review

Evaluate for the given values of the variables. *1.3, 2.6, 2.8*

1. $8x^2$ for $x = \frac{1}{4}$

2. $(8x)^2$ for $x = \frac{1}{4}$

3. $3a^4b$ for $a = 2$, $b = -5$

4. $-3x - 4$ for $x = -6$

Simplify. *2.2, 2.6, 2.9, 2.10*

5. $|-16|$

6. $-x + 5 - x - 9$

7. $2x - (5 - x)$

8. $4(-4)^3$

Solve.

9. Five feet less than twice the length of a board is the same as its length increased by 12 ft. Find the length of the board. *3.4*

The Shock Wave roller coaster is located at Six Flags Great America in Gurnee, Illinois, outside of Chicago. It is the tallest roller coaster in the world and has three vertical loops, two corkscrew loops, and two boomerang loops.

Solve. Recall that 5,280 feet equal 1 mile.

1. The Shock Wave is 170 ft high at its highest point. What part of a mile is this? Give the answer to the nearest hundredth of a mile.

2. The track length of the Shock Wave is 3,900 ft. Is this closer to $\frac{2}{3}$ mile or $\frac{3}{4}$ mile? Justify your answer.

3. A ride on the Shock Wave takes about 2 min 20 s. What is the average rate of speed in feet per second? Give the answer to the nearest tenth.

4. Jerry stood in line for 42 min waiting to ride on the Shock Wave. If he could have used that time to take one ride after another without stopping, how many rides could he have taken?

5. The Shock Wave has 7 cars per train with 4 passengers per car. How many train loads would it take for 1,176 passengers to ride the Shock Wave?

6. If one trainload of passengers departs every 5 min, how many hours would it take for the 1,176 passengers to ride?

3.7 Proving Statements

To give a reason for each step in the solution of an equation
To prove theorems about real numbers

Here is a summary of the properties of operations that have been introduced so far in this book. Unless otherwise stated, a property applies to all real numbers a, b, and c.

Name of Property	Statement of Property
Closure for Addition	$a + b$ is a real number.
Closure for Multiplication	ab is a real number.
Commutative of Addition	$a + b = b + a$
Commutative of Multiplication	$ab = ba$
Associative of Addition	$(a + b) + c = a + (b + c)$
Associative of Multiplication	$(ab)c = a(bc)$
Distributive for Multiplication over Addition	$a(b + c) = ab + ac$
	$(b + c)a = ba + ca$

Additive Identity There is exactly one real number, 0, such that for each real number a, $a + 0 = a$ and $0 + a = a$.

Multiplicative Identity There is exactly one real number, 1, such that for each real number a, $a \cdot 1 = a$ and $1 \cdot a = a$.

Additive Inverse For each real number a, there is exactly one real number $-a$ such that $a + (-a) = 0$ and $-a + a = 0$.

Multiplicative Inverse For each nonzero real number a, there is exactly one real number $\frac{1}{a}$ such that $a \cdot \frac{1}{a} = 1$ and $\frac{1}{a} \cdot a = 1$.

The following *properties of equality* are also true.

Properties of Equality
For all real numbers a, b, and c,

Reflexive Property	$a = a$ (A number is equal to itself.)
Symmetric Property	If $a = b$, then $b = a$.
Transitive Property	If $a = b$ and $b = c$, then $a = c$.
Substitution Property	If $a = b$, then a can be replaced by b, and b by a.

When you solve an equation, it is possible to give a reason for each step by stating one of these properties or an equation property.

EXAMPLE 1 Solve $7x + 9 = -5$. Give a reason for each step.

Proof

Statement	Reason
1. $\quad 7x + 9 = -5$	1. Given
2. $7x + 9 - 9 = -5 - 9$	2. Subt Prop of Eq
3. $\quad 7x + 0 = -14$	3. Add Inverse Prop
4. $\quad\quad 7x = -14$	4. Add Identity Prop
5. $\quad\quad \frac{7x}{7} = \frac{-14}{7}$	5. Div Prop of Eq
6. $\quad\quad 1 \cdot x = -2$	6. Mult Inverse Prop $\left[\frac{7}{7} = 7 \cdot \frac{1}{7}\right] = 1$
7. $\quad\quad\quad x = -2$	7. Mult Identity Prop

TRY THIS **1.** Solve $x - 3 = 2$. Give a reason for each step.

A **theorem** is a statement that has been proved. In statements of theorems, variables represent real numbers.

EXAMPLE 2 Prove $(a + b) + (-a) = b$.

Proof

Statement	Reason
1. $(a + b) + (-a) = (b + a) + (-a)$	1. Comm Prop of Add
2. $\quad = b + [a + (-a)]$	2. Assoc Prop of Add
3. $\quad = b + 0$	3. Add Inverse Prop
4. $\quad = b$	4. Add Identity Prop
5. $(a + b) + (-a) = b$	5. Trans Prop of Eq

TRY THIS **2.** Prove: $a + (b + c) = (b + a) + c$

Recall that the Multiplication Property of Equality states that for all real numbers a, b, and c, if $a = b$, then $ac = bc$. Note that the property contains an *if-clause* (if $a = b$) and a *then-clause* (then $ac = bc$).

A statement that is written in if-then form is called a **conditional**. The if-clause is called the **hypothesis**, and the then-clause is called the **conclusion**.

Some conditionals, such as the Multiplication Property of Equality, can be proved to be true. To prove a conditional, you first assume that the hypothesis is true. Then you show by a series of logical steps that the conclusion must follow. For each step, or *statement*, in the proof, you must give a *reason* that has been previously accepted as true. A proof of the Multiplication Property of Equality is shown in Example 3.

EXAMPLE 3 Prove: If $a = b$, then $ac = bc$.

Proof

Statement	Reason
1. $a = b$	1. Given
2. $ac = ac$	2. Reflex Prop
3. $ac = bc$	3. Sub(b is substituted for a.)

Thus, if $a = b$, then $ac = bc$.

TRY THIS   **3.** Prove: If $a = b$ then $ca = cb$.

Classroom Exercises

Give a reason for each step.

1.

Statement	Reason
1. $\quad 3y - 4 = -19$	1. Given
2. $3y - 4 + 4 = -19 + 4$	2. _____?_____
3. $\quad 3y + 0 = -15$	3. _____?_____
4. $\quad\quad 3y = -15$	4. _____?_____
5. $\quad\quad \frac{3y}{3} = \frac{-15}{3}$	5. _____?_____
6. $\quad 1 \cdot y = -5$	6. _____?_____
7. $\quad\quad y = -5$	7. _____?_____

Give a reason for each statement.

2. If $x = y$ and $y = z$, then $x = z$.   **3.** If $x = y$, then $y = x$.

4. $(x + y) + (-y) = x + [y + (-y)]$ **5.** $x \cdot y = x \cdot y$

6. $x + [y + (-y)] = x + 0$ **7.** $x + y = x + y$

8. $y \cdot \left(x \cdot \frac{1}{x}\right) = y \cdot 1$ **9.** $(x \cdot y) \cdot \frac{1}{y} = x \cdot \left(y \cdot \frac{1}{y}\right)$

Written Exercises

Give a reason for each step.

1.

Statement	Reason
1. $\quad \frac{2}{3}x + 5 = -9$	1. Given
2. $\frac{2}{3}x + 5 - 5 = -9 - 5$	2. _____?_____
3. $\quad \frac{2}{3}x + 0 = -14$	3. _____?_____
4. $\quad\quad \frac{2}{3}x = -14$	4. _____?_____
5. $\quad \frac{3}{2} \cdot \frac{2}{3}x = \frac{3}{2}(-14)$	5. _____?_____
6. $\quad 1 \cdot x = -21$	6. _____?_____
7. $\quad\quad x = -21$	7. _____?_____

Write the missing reasons in each proof. All variables represent real numbers.

2. Prove: If $a = b$, then $a + c = b + c$.   (Add Prop of Eq)

Statement	Reason
1. $a = b$	1. Given
2. $a + c = a + c$	2. _____?_____
3. $a + c = b + c$	3. _____?_____

3. Prove: If $a + c = b + c$, then $a = b$.

Statement	Reason
1. $a + c = b + c$	1. Given
2. $(a + c) + (-c) = (b + c) + (-c)$	2. _____?_____
3. $a + [c + (-c)] = b + [c + (-c)]$	3. _____?_____
4. $a + 0 = b + 0$	4. _____?_____
5. $a = b$	5. _____?_____

4. Prove: If $x \neq 0$, then $(xy)\frac{1}{x} = y$.

Statement	Reason
1. $x \neq 0$	1. _____?_____
2. $(xy)\frac{1}{x} = (yx)\frac{1}{x}$	2. _____?_____
3. $= y\left(x \cdot \frac{1}{x}\right)$	3. _____?_____
4. $= y \cdot 1$	4. _____?_____
5. $= y$	5. _____?_____
6. $(xy)\frac{1}{x} = y$	6. _____?_____

Solve each equation. Give a reason for each step.

5. $5x - 3 = 18$ **6.** $\frac{3}{4}y + 8 = -1$ **7.** $7 - 5a = 4$ **8.** $3(x + 2) = -15$

Write a proof for each statement. All variables represent real numbers.

9. If $a = b$, then $a - c = b - c$.   **10.** If $a - c = b - c$, then $a = b$.

11. $(ax + b) + ay = a(x + y) + b$ **12.** $x + (3 + y) = 3 + (y + x)$

13. $mx + (a + x) = a + (m + 1)x$ **14.** $a(b - c) = ab - ac$

Mixed Review

Evaluate.   *2.8, 2.10*

1. $5x + 8$ for $x = 3.2$ **2.** $-9 - 2z$ for $z = 5.4$

3. $-6y - 4.8$ for $y = -8.1$ **4.** $-6.8 + 4a$ for $a = 6.8$

5. $-5 - 4(2x + 5)$ for $x = 3.5$ **6.** $3(8 - 4y) + 2.6$ for $y = 3.1$

Mixed Problem Solving

Recall that the first step in problem solving is to understand the problem. Read each problem carefully to identify the information you need. Think about what you are asked to find and the units you will use in writing the final answer. After solving the problem, ask: "Is there another way to solve this problem?"

1. Jean received time-and-a-half pay for working on her day off. This means that she received $1\frac{1}{2}$ times her normal pay. If she received $9.60/h working on her day off, what is her normal hourly pay?

2. The long-distance telephone rate for calling California is 32¢ for the first minute and 20¢ for each additional minute. Judy's call to California cost $2.32. How long did she talk?

3. Jane and Kai are both selling their bicycles. Jane is charging $72. Her price is $18 less than Kai's price. How much is Kai charging for his bicycle?

4. For babysitting, Jerry charges a $2.50 transportation fee plus $3.75 an hour. One evening he earned $28.75. How many hours did he babysit?

5. On Sunday, 12,450 people came to a concert. Sunday's crowd was $\frac{3}{4}$ as large as Saturday's crowd. How many people came on Saturday?

6. Morris bought 8 pairs of socks and a T-shirt. His bill was $18.50 without tax. The T-shirt was $6.50. What was the price of each pair of socks?

7. Martha bought 4 doz cookies. She put 3 cookies aside and divided the rest equally among 5 people. How many cookies did each of the 5 people receive?

8. On Tuesday morning, Justin's stock opened at $24\frac{3}{4}$. It had dropped $\frac{3}{8}$ of a point since the closing price on Monday. What was the stock's closing price on Monday?

9. To buy beach tokens at Paradise Beach, one must pay $25.00 for a family membership plus $3 additional for each child's token. Mrs. Breckel spent $37 for a membership and tokens. How many child's tokens did she buy?

10. Bob was paid $15 for proofreading an article plus 75¢ for each error he could find. He earned a total of $24.75 for his work. How many errors did he find?

11. After Jim withdrew $24.50 from his savings account, his balance was $276.83. How much was in his account before he made the withdrawal?

12. First-class postage costs 25¢ for the first ounce and 20¢ for each additional ounce. Joe spent $2.05 to mail a package first class. How much did it weigh?

Chapter 3 Review

Key Terms

Addition Property of Equality (p. 89)
conclusion (p. 116)
conditional (p. 116)
Division Property of Equality (p. 95)
equivalent equations (p. 89)

hypothesis (p. 116)
identity (p. 103)
if-clause (p. 116)
Multiplication Property of Equality (p. 94)
Subtraction Property of Equality (p. 90)
then-clause (p. 116)
theorem (p. 116)

Key Ideas and Review Exercises

3.1, 3.2 Adding or subtracting the same number to each side of an equation produces an equivalent equation. Also, multiplying by the same number or dividing by the same nonzero number on each side of an equation produces an equivalent equation.

Solve and check.

1. $x - 9 = -7$ **2.** $8 = 14 + y$ **3.** $-8 + z = 12$

4. $x - \frac{2}{3} = -\frac{1}{6}$ **5.** $3x = -24$ **6.** $19 = 5x$

7. $15 = -\frac{3}{5}d$ **8.** $2 = \frac{-x}{4}$ **9.** $-5 + x = -5$

10. $-7 = -\frac{2}{3}c$ **11.** $1\frac{2}{3}d = -20$ **12.** $3.2 + y = -7.4$

13. Explain in writing why you would multiply each side of $-\frac{1}{3}x = 7$ by -3 in order to solve it.

3.3, 3.4 To solve the equation $-6x + 7 = -5$, first subtract 7 from each side. Then divide each side by -6.

To solve the equation $8x - 7 = 2x + 11$, you can
(1) subtract $2x$ from each side to get $6x - 7 = 11$,
(2) add 7 to each side to get $6x = 18$, and
(3) divide each side by 6 to get $x = 3$.

Solve and check.

14. $4x - 7 = 5$ **15.** $\frac{x}{8} + 6 = 7$ **16.** $\frac{2}{3}c + 5 = 9$ **17.** $7x - 30 = 2x$

18. $-4y = 6y + 20$ **19.** $16 = -3y - 2$ **20.** $7 + y = 9 - y$ **21.** $2.5x + 0.4 = -4.6$

22. $-3x + 2 - 5x = -14$ **23.** $3x - 1 = 4x + 7 - x$

Translate each problem into an equation and solve.

24. Three times Tara's age decreased by 2 years is the same as twice her age increased by 13 years. How old is Tara?

25. The length of a rope increased by 5 ft is the same as 3 ft less than twice the length of the rope. Find the length of the rope.

3.5   To solve an equation containing parentheses, use the Distributive Property to remove the parentheses. Combine like terms on each side, if necessary. Then solve the equation.

Solve and check.

26. $3(x - 4) = 18$

27. $x + 10 = 3(2 - x)$

28. $-(-2a + 3) + 18 = 3(a - 5)$

29. $-(-6 + 2y) - 4y = -3(6 - 2y)$

30. $3r - 5(7 - r) = 5r - (2r - 10)$

31. $-7x - (8 - 12x) = 2x$

Translate into an equation and solve.

32. Six times the difference between a two-digit number and 9 is 24. Find the number.

3.6   Some formulas can be used to solve problems using the equation properties. Substitute known values into the formula and solve for the variable that does not have a given value.

33. Using $d = rt$, find d for $r = 150$ km/h and $t = 11$ h.

34. Using $p = nt - e$, find the price of a carnival ticket t if the expenses e are $800, the profit p is $2,500, and if the number of sold tickets n is 2,000.

3.7   To prove a theorem, show that it is true by a series of logical steps. Give a reason for each step.

35. Write the missing reasons in the proof. All variables represent real numbers.

	Statement		Reason
1.	$a \cdot 0 = a \cdot 0 + 0$	1.	?
2.	$= a \cdot 0 + a + (-a)$	2.	?
3.	$= a \cdot 0 + a \cdot 1 + (-a)$	3.	?
4.	$= a(0 + 1) + (-a)$	4.	?
5.	$= a \cdot 1 + (-a)$	5.	?
6.	$= a + (-a)$	6.	?
7.	$= 0$	7.	?
8.	$a \cdot 0 = 0$	8.	?

Chapter 3 Test

Solve and check.

1. $x - 14 = -5$

2. $12 = -4 + x$

3. $-\frac{2}{3}x + 5 = 3$

4. $-2x + 5 - x = 17 + x$

5. $-6 + x = -4$

6. $0.4 + x = -3.7$

7. $6x = -54$

8. $-3x = 3\frac{1}{3}$

9. $-x - 4 = 4x - 5 - 5x + 1$

10. $12 - 5y = -3$

11. $4(x + 2) = 20$

12. $2(z - 3) = z + 5$

13. $z - \frac{2}{3} = -\frac{5}{6}$

14. $6 + \frac{-x}{3} = 15$

Translate each problem into an equation and solve.

15. Eight more than a number is 42. Find the number.

16. Jim worked 12 h on a science project. He worked $\frac{3}{4}$ as long as Jessie worked. How long did Jessie work?

17. Three less than twice the temperature is -17. Find the temperature.

18. Bob's salary increased by $98 is the same as three times his salary. Find his salary.

19. Six times the difference between Margot's age and 2 is 54. Find Margot's age.

20. Use the formula $T = 3(ab - c)$ to find b for $T = 18$, $a = 3$, and $c = 15$.

21. If a number is decreased by 6 and then multiplied by -5, the result is 12 less than twice the number. Find the number.

22. Write the missing reasons in this proof. All variables represent real numbers.

    Prove: If $a = b$ and $c \neq 0$, then $\frac{a}{c} = \frac{b}{c}$.

Statement	Reason
1. $a = b$ and $c \neq 0$	1. _____?_____
2. $\frac{a}{c} = \frac{a}{c}$	2. _____?_____
3. $\frac{a}{c} = \frac{b}{c}$	3. _____?_____

    Thus, if $a = b$ and $c \neq 0$, then $\frac{a}{c} = \frac{b}{c}$.

23. Solve $-5x - [2(1 - 3x) + 4] = 7x$.

College Prep Test

Test-taking Strategy

Since time is an important factor in test-taking, it is important to look for properties that offer shortcuts in finding answers. Consider the following example.

If $5x + 10 = 30$, find the value of $x + 2$.

By the Distributive Property, $5x + 10 = 5(x + 2)$. Instead of solving $5x + 10 = 30$ for x, solve it for $x + 2$.

Use the Distributive Property. $5(x + 2) = 30$

Divide each side by 5. $\dfrac{5(x + 2)}{5} = \dfrac{30}{5}$

$$x + 2 = 6$$

Thus, the value of $x + 2$ is 6.

Choose the one best answer to each question or problem.

1. If $3x - 12 = 18$, find the value of $x - 4$.
   (A) 10   (B) 6   (C) 9
   (D) 8   (E) None of these

2. If $2x - 8 = 7$, find the value of $10x - 40$.
   (A) $\frac{7}{2}$ (B) 14   (C) 35
   (D) 56   (E) None of these

3. If $x + y = 3.9 + x$, find the value of y.
   (A) 0   (B) -3.9 (C) 3.9
   (D) x (E) None of these

4. If $5x - 9 = 23$, find the value of $5x - 7$.
   (A) 25   (B) -2 (C) 21
   (D) -23 (E) None of these

5. If $9y + 8 = -16$, find the value of $9y - 2$.
   (A) 0   (B) 10   (C) -6
   (D) -24 (E) None of these

6. If $\frac{c}{9} = 2$, find the value of $\frac{c}{2}$.
   (A) $\frac{1}{9}$ (B) $\frac{1}{2}$ (C) 2
   (D) 9   (E) None of these

7. If $3(2 - 4x) = 17$, find the value of $6 - 12x$.
   (A) 6   (B) 8   (C) 17
   (D) 51   (E) None of these

8. If $\frac{3}{4}x = -9$, find the value of $\frac{1}{4}x$.
   (A) -3 (B) 3   (C) $\frac{1}{2}$
   (D) $-\frac{1}{2}$ (E) None of these

9. If a number is decreased by 5 and then multiplied by 3, the result is 26. Find the result if the same number is decreased by 5 and then multiplied by 6.
   (A) 12   (B) 13   (C) 21
   (D) 52   (E) None of these

10. The formula for the area of a circle with radius r is $A = \pi r^2$. Find the area of the ring shaded below.

   (A) 4π (B) 25π (C) 8π
   (D) 24π (E) None of these

Jim Abbott is a pitcher with the California Angels baseball team. Born with only one hand, Jim taught himself to handle a baseball and glove. After pitching for the USA Olympic team in 1988, he went directly to the major leagues.

4.1 Translating English to Algebra

Objective
To represent two or more numbers in terms of one variable, given the relationship between the numbers

Frequently, a word problem will contain an English sentence that describes a relationship between two or more numbers. To write an equation used to solve the problem, you will have to determine:

(1) what numbers you are asked to find,
(2) which *one* of the numbers will be represented by a variable, such as x, and
(3) how to represent other numbers in terms of that variable.

EXAMPLE 1
The larger of two numbers is twice the smaller. Write representations of the two numbers.

Plan
There is a larger number and a smaller number. Use the *smaller* as the basis of comparison (larger . . . is twice smaller).

Solution
Let s = the *smaller* number.
Then $2s$ = the larger number.   ← twice the smaller number

EXAMPLE 2
The price of a book is $3 less than twice the price of a tape.
Answer each of the following questions.

Solutions

a. What are the two unknown numbers being compared? The unknown numbers are the book price and the tape price.

b. Which unknown number is the basis of comparison? (THINK: The book price is 3 *less than* twice the *tape* price.) The tape price is the basis of comparison.

c. Represent the two unknowns in terms of one variable.

Choose a variable to represent the number that is the basis of comparison. Represent the other number in terms of that variable.

Let x = the tape price in dollars.   ← basis of comparison

Then $2x - 3$ = the book price in dollars.   ← 3 less than twice the
tape price.

TRY THIS

1. Juan's age is 5 years more than three times Manuel's age. Let a represent Manuel's age. Represent Juan's age in terms of a.

2. The width of a rectangle is 8 cm less than twice its length. Let l represent the length. Represent the width of the rectangle in terms of l.

Recall that the word "of" often indicates *multiplication*.

EXAMPLE 3 This year, the price of a movie ticket increased by one-fifth of the price last year. Let l represent the price last year. Represent the price this year in terms of l.

Solution Let l = the price of a ticket last year, in dollars.

THINK: $\underbrace{\text{price last year}}_{l}$ $\underbrace{\text{increased by}}_{+}$ $\underbrace{\frac{1}{5}\text{ of}}_{\frac{1}{5}\times}$ $\underbrace{\text{price last year}}_{l}$

Thus, $l + \frac{1}{5}l$ = the price of a ticket this year, in dollars.

EXAMPLE 4 The first side of a triangle is 3 times as long as a second side.
The third side is 5 cm shorter than the first side.
Represent the lengths of the three sides in terms of one variable.

Plan In the first sentence, a first side is compared with a *second* side. The *second* side is the basis of comparison.

Solution Let s = the length of the *second* side in cm.
Then $3s$ = the length of the first side in cm. ← 3 times length of *second*
So $3s - 5$ = the length of the third side in cm. ← 5 less than the *first*

TRY THIS 3. Ling has twice as many nickels as dimes. She has 5 more quarters than nickels. If d represents the number of dimes, represent the number of nickels and quarters in terms of d.

Classroom Exercises

Complete each statement.

1. Marcie's age is 2 years more than 3 times Lou's age. Let l = Lou's age. Then ___?___ is Marcie's age.
2. The base of a triangle is 5 cm less than twice the height. Let h = the height in centimeters. Then ___?___ is the base in centimeters.
3. Bill has twice as many basketball points as George. Let g = the number of George's basketball points. Then ___?___ is the number of Bill's points.

In Classroom Exercises 4 and 5, James worked 5 h longer than Henry.

4. How much longer did James work?
5. Let h = the number of hours worked by Henry. Represent, in terms of h, the number of hours that James worked.

In Classroom Exercises 6–7, the selling price of a skirt is $4 less than 3 times the cost.

6. What are the two unknown numbers in the sentence? Which is less, the selling price or the cost?

7. Let c = the cost. Represent, in terms of c, the selling price of the skirt.

8. Bob is 4 years older than Mary. Write representations for each age in terms of one variable, m.

9. The larger of two numbers is 3 less than 5 times the smaller. Write representations for each number in terms of one variable, s.

Written Exercises

In Exercises 1–4, first choose a variable to represent the smaller of the two unknowns. Then represent the other unknown in terms of the same variable.

1. Jeanie and Bill were working together on an art project. Bill worked 2 h less than Jeanie worked.

2. This week Jack worked $6\frac{1}{2}$ more hours at the supermarket than he worked last week.

3. Kate has half as many fish as Bob has.

4. The larger of two numbers is 3 times the smaller.

Complete each statement.

5. Robert's age is 2 years less than 3 times Matt's age. Let m = Matt's age in years. Then __?__ is Robert's age in years.

6. This year Kyle's salary increased by one-fifth of his salary last year. Let l = his salary last year. Then __?__ is his salary this year.

7. A piece of wire is to be cut into two pieces so that one piece is 1 cm longer than 3 times the second piece. Let s = the shorter length in centimeters. Then __?__ is the greater length in centimeters.

8. This year a company's earnings decreased by $\frac{1}{3}$ of its earnings last year. Let l = the company's earnings last year. Then __?__ is the company's earnings this year.

Choose a variable to represent one unknown. Then represent the other unknown in terms of that variable.

9. Jason scored one-third as many points in a game as Ron scored.

10. Bobbie has 2 less than 8 times as many stamps as Selise has.

11. Kyle earned $5 more than twice what Josie earned.

12. The length of a rectangle is 2 cm less than 5 times its width.

13. This year the price of a ticket to a baseball game has increased by one-fifth of the price last year.

14. The length of one piece of wire is 1 cm greater than half the length of a second piece of wire.

Sarah has a collection of coins, consisting of pennies, nickels, and dimes. She has 6 more pennies than nickels. She has the same number of nickels as dimes.

15. What coin does she have the most of?

16. Let n = the number of nickels she has. Represent the number of pennies in terms of n.

17. Represent the number of dimes in terms of n.

A sausage pizza costs $3.25 more than a cheese pizza and $4.50 less than a combination pizza.

18. Which pizza costs the most?   **19.** Which pizza costs the least?

20. Let s = the price of the sausage pizza. Represent the price of the cheese pizza in terms of s.

21. Represent the price of the combination pizza in terms of s.

Choose a variable to represent one unknown. Then represent the other unknown(s) in terms of that variable. (Exercises 22–23)

22. On a test, a true-false problem is worth 2 points less than a short-answer problem. An essay problem is worth 1 point more than three times as much as a short-answer problem.

23. One side of a triangle is 3.2 cm longer than the second side. The third side is 1.2 cm shorter than the first side.

24. Acme Car Rental Agency charges $21 a day plus $0.19 a mile for a mid-sized car. Represent the number of miles driven in a day and the cost for that day in terms of one variable.

25. To buy a car, Bill plans to save $80 a month for 15 months and after that to save $60 a month for the next n months. Represent the total amount saved at the end of n months.

26. Shira's grandmother is 7 years older than Shira's grandfather, and 6 years older than 10 times Shira's age. Represent Shira's grandfather's age in terms of Shira's age.

27. A town is planning emergency action for a hurricane that is now 330 mi away, but moving towards the town at 15 mi/h. Represent the distance of the hurricane from the town t hours from now.

Mixed Review

Solve and check.   *3.1–3.3*

1. $x + 4 = 1$ **2.** $2t = -8$ **3.** $\frac{a}{4} = 7$ **4.** $y - 7 = 3$

5. $2n + 3 = 11$ **6.** $3n - 4 = 6$ **7.** $4x + 5 = 1$ **8.** $2x + 3 = -5$

9. Bill's 24 hits this baseball season were 3 times his number of hits last season. How many hits did he make last season?   *3.2*

4.2 Problem Solving: Two or More Numbers

Objective   To solve problems involving two or more numbers

In Example 1 of the previous lesson, you used the sentence "The price of a book is $3 less than twice the price of a tape" to represent the price of a book as x and the price of a tape as $2x - 3$. If you have more information, you may be able to write an equation that can be solved to find the actual prices, as shown below.

New information: Al spent a total of $63 for a book and a tape.

$$\text{Equation:} \quad \underbrace{63}_{} = \overset{\downarrow}{x} + \overset{\downarrow}{(2x - 3)}$$

$$63 = x + (2x - 3)$$
$$63 = 3x - 3$$
$$66 = 3x$$
$$22 = x$$
$$x = 22 \text{ and } 2x - 3 = 2 \cdot 22 - 3 = 41$$

The book cost $22 and the tape cost $41.

The step-by-step method outlined below can guide you through the entire problem-solving process.

The larger of two numbers is 17 more than the smaller. The sum of the numbers is 59. Find the two numbers.

What are you to find?	Two numbers, a larger and a smaller
What is given?	The larger number is 17 more than the smaller. The sum of the numbers is 59.
Choose a variable.	Let n = one number. Then $n + 17$ = the larger number.
Write an equation.	The sum of the two numbers is 59. $n + (n + 17) = 59$
Solve the equation.	$2n + 17 = 59$ $2n = 42$ $n = 21$ ⟵ smaller $n + 17 = 21 + 17 = 38$ ⟵ larger

Check in the original problem.	Is the larger number 17 more than the smaller? Yes, because 21 + 17 equals 38.
	Is the sum of the two numbers 59? Yes, because 21 + 38 equals 59.
State the answer.	The numbers are 21 and 38.

Think about the step-by-step method as you work the examples below.

EXAMPLE 1 A board that is 81 cm long is cut into two pieces. The first piece is 7 cm less than 3 times the second. Find the length of each piece.

Solution Let s = length of second piece, in cm. ⟵ smaller length
Then $3s - 7$ = length of first piece, in cm.
THINK: Can the answers be negative? Can they be more than 81 cm?

The combined lengths must total 81 cm.

$$s + (3s - 7) = 81$$
$$4s - 7 = 81$$
$$4s = 88$$
$$s = 22 \quad \longleftarrow \text{second length: 22 cm}$$
$$3s - 7 = 3 \cdot 22 - 7 = 59 \quad \longleftarrow \text{first length: 59 cm}$$

Check Is the length of the first piece 7 cm less than 3 times the length of the second? Yes, because $3 \cdot 22 - 7$ equals $66 - 7$, or 59.

Is the sum of the lengths 81 cm? Yes, because $22 + 59$ equals 81. Thus, the lengths are 59 cm and 22 cm.

EXAMPLE 2 Bob has 3 times as many records as Jim. Kacey has 5 fewer records than Bob. Together the boys have 16 records. How many records does each boy have?

Plan Bob's number is expressed in terms of Jim's. Kacey's is expressed in terms of Bob's. You can express Bob's and Kacey's in terms of Jim's.

Solution Let j = the number that Jim has.
Then $3j$ = the number that Bob has,
and $3j - 5$ = the number that Kacey has.

$$j + 3j + (3j - 5) = 16 \quad \longleftarrow \text{Together they have 16 records.}$$
$$7j - 5 = 16$$
$$7j = 21$$
$$j = 3 \quad \longleftarrow \text{Jim: 3 records}$$
$$3j = 3 \cdot 3 = 9 \quad \longleftarrow \text{Bob: 9 records}$$
$$3j - 5 = 3 \cdot 3 - 5, \text{ or } 4 \quad \longleftarrow \text{Kacey: 4 records}$$

Check	Bob has 3 times as many records as Jim: $9 = 3 \cdot 3$
	Kacey has 5 fewer records than Bob: $9 - 5 = 4$
	Together they have 16 records: $3 + 9 + 4 = 16$
	Thus, Jim has 3 records, Bob has 9, and Kacey has 4.

TRY THIS

1. Solve.

Tim's age is 4 times Gina's age. John is 6 years younger than Tim. The sum of their ages is 57. Find their ages.

Example 3 is based on Example 3 on page 126.

EXAMPLE 3 This year, the price of a movie ticket increased by one-fifth of the price last year. The price this year is $3.00. Find the price of a movie ticket for last year.

Solution Let l = the price of a movie ticket last year, in dollars.

Then $\frac{1}{5}l$ = the price increase in dollars ← $\frac{1}{5}$ of the price last year

$l + \frac{1}{5}l = 3$ ← last year's price + increase = this year's price

$1l + \frac{1}{5}l = 3$

$1\frac{1}{5}l = 3$

$\frac{6}{5}l = 3$

$\frac{5}{6} \cdot \frac{6}{5}l = \frac{5}{6} \cdot 3$

$l = \frac{5}{2}$, or 2.5 ← last year's price: $2.50

Check Is the amount of increase equal to $\frac{1}{5}$ of last year's price?

Yes, because $\frac{1}{5}(2.50)$ is 0.50 and $2.50 + 0.50 = 3.00$.

Thus, the price of a movie ticket last year was $2.50.

TRY THIS

2. Solve.

This year, the price of a stamp increased by one-fifth of the price last year. The price this year is 30¢. Find the price of the stamp last year.

Classroom Exercises

Using one variable, represent the numbers described in each exercise.

1. Jim's age is twice Mary's age.
2. One number is 6 less than another.
3. One ribbon is 9 inches longer than another ribbon.
4. The larger of two numbers is 5 less than 3 times the smaller.
5. The width of a rectangle is 3 cm less than twice the length.
6. Caroline's weekly salary is $5 more than twice Sarah's salary.

For Classroom Exercises 1–6, the following additional relationship between the two quantities is known. Write an equation, solve it, and find the quantities.

7. For Exercise 1, the sum of the ages is 39.
8. For Exercise 2, the sum of the numbers is 47.
9. For Exercise 3, there are 215 in. of ribbon in all.
10. For Exercise 4, the sum of the numbers is 19.
11. For Exercise 5, the *semiperimeter* (half the perimeter) is $4\frac{1}{2}$ cm.
12. For Exercise 6, Caroline and Sarah together earn $365 each week.

Solve.

13. The larger of two numbers is 3 times the smaller. The sum of the numbers is 28. Find the numbers.
14. Joe's age is 3 less than twice Bill's age. The sum of their ages is 21. Find the age of each.

Written Exercises

Solve.

1. One number is 4 times another. The sum of the numbers is 65. Find the numbers.
2. Seventy-two students are separated into two groups. The first group is 5 times as large as the second. How many students are in each group?
3. Gus has 7 more tapes than Brian. Together they have 39 tapes. How many tapes does each boy have?
4. One number is 7 less than another. The sum of the numbers is 35. Find the numbers.
5. Clyde worked 8 hours longer than Barry worked. Together they worked 40 hours. How long did each boy work?
6. A board that is 45 m long is separated into two pieces. The longer piece is 8 m longer than the shorter. Find the length of each piece.
7. Aaron's bowling score is 12 less than twice Dan's score. The sum of their scores is 258. Find each score.
8. Juan's age is 5 years more than twice Margo's age. The sum of their ages is 29 years. Find their ages.

9. A fish tank contained 23 fish which were either guppies or swordtails. The number of guppies was 1 less than 3 times the number of swordtails. How many of each kind of fish were there?

10. The larger of two numbers is 2 more than 4 times the other. Their sum is 33. Find the two numbers.

11. James has saved $560 in two years. He saved 3 times as much during the first year as during the second year. How much did he save each year?

12. In a game, Bob's score was 3 times Otto's score. Together they scored 72 points. Find their scores.

13. A salesperson's profit on a portable TV set is $10 more than the cost. The set sells for $130. Find the cost and the profit. (HINT: selling price = cost + profit)

14. Last month, a salesman earned $560 more than he did this month. Total earnings for the two months were $8,720. Find each month's earnings.

15. Bessie's age is $\frac{1}{2}$ of Jean's age. The sum of their ages is 27 years. How old is each girl?

16. A house costs $3\frac{1}{2}$ times as much as the lot. Together they sold for $135,000. Find the cost of each.

17. If the cost of a shirt is increased by one-fourth of the cost, the result is the selling price of $35. Find the cost.

18. Separate 53 people into two groups so that the first group has 7 fewer than 4 times the number of people in the second group.

19. An air pump and a gang valve for an aquarium cost $31. The air pump costs 1 dollar less than 3 times the cost of the gang valve. Find the cost of each.

20. This year, Gregg bought 3 more than twice the number of tapes he bought last year. He bought 11 tapes last year. How many did he buy this year?

21. This year, Christy has 15 fish in her tank. She has one fish fewer than twice the number she had last year. How many fish did she have last year?

22. Hisako has 2 records fewer than 3 times the number Gretchen has. Together they have 42 records. How many records does Gretchen have?

23. Last month's phone bill was $2.51 more than this month's bill. The bill for the two months totaled $44.45. Find the bill for each month.

24. It costs $88.35 to buy a pair of slacks and a jacket. The cost of the jacket is $1.80 more than twice the cost of the slacks. Find the cost of each.

25. The price of an antique book is $91, which is two-fifths more than the cost to the book dealer. Find the cost.

26. The larger of two numbers is 5 times the smaller. The difference between them is 36. Find the numbers.

27. Amy's part-time salary is 4 times Katie's part-time salary. The difference between their salaries is $126. Find each girl's salary.

28. A number is decreased by $\frac{1}{3}$ of the number. The result is 62. Find the number.

29. After Sten gave away $\frac{1}{8}$ of his record collection, he had 14 records left. How many records did he have before he gave some away?

30. This year, a theater ticket costs $5 less than twice what it cost last year. This year 4 tickets cost $36. What did 4 tickets cost last year?

31. Horace's mother is three times as old as her only child. Horace's grandmother is 35 years older than Horace's mother. If Horace's grandmother were 7 years younger, she would be 5 times as old as Horace. How old is Horace's grandmother?

32. The second of three numbers is 4 times the first. The third is 2 more than the second. If the second number is decreased by twice the third, the result is 28. Find the three numbers.

33. The first of three numbers is 4 times the second. The third is 15 more than the first. The average of the 3 numbers is -1. Find the three numbers.

34. The second of three numbers is 8 less than 3 times the first. The third number is 18 less than 6 times the first. If twice the first number is decreased by the third number, the result is -2. Find the three numbers.

35. Jack bought a shirt, a tie, and a sport jacket. The cost of the shirt is 3 dollars more than twice the cost of the tie. The cost of the sport jacket is 8 dollars less than 4 times the cost of the shirt. The combined cost of the three items is $84. Find the cost of each.

36. Jessie went jogging on Monday. On Tuesday she jogged 1 mi farther than twice the number of miles she jogged on Monday. On Wednesday she jogged 1 mi less than 3 times the number of miles she jogged on Monday. She jogged a total of 18 mi in the three days. How many miles did she jog on each of the three days?

37. A double bed costs $80 more than a twin bed. Three twin beds cost as much as two double beds. Find the cost of each bed.

38. On a social studies test, Charlayne scored 85 points. On a science test, she scored 6 points more than on a mathematics test. Her average score for the three tests was 89 points. What did she score on the mathematics test?

Mixed Review

Simplify.   2.2, 2.6, 2.9, 2.10

1. $-2(-3)^3$ 2. $3x - (4 - x)$ 3. $7 - a - 5 - 2a$ 4. $|-7|$

Solve.   3.2, 3.5

5. $9 = \frac{3}{4}x$ 6. $3x - (4 - x) = 2x + 8$ 7. $3(x + 2) = 3x + 5$ 8. $-2y = 3$

▰▰/Brainteaser

A cyclist completed an 84-km course in three hours. In the first hour she covered $\frac{4}{7}$ of the distance; in the second hour she covered $\frac{1}{2}$ the distance covered in the first hour; in the third hour she covered the remaining distance. How far did she travel in the third hour?

4.3 Problem Solving: Consecutive Integer Problems

Objective To solve problems involving consecutive integers

The years 1991, 1992, and 1993 are examples of three consecutive integers. Here are four other examples of consecutive integers.

$$1, 2, 3, 4, \qquad -5, -4, -3 \qquad 29, 30 \qquad -1, 0, 1, 2, 3$$

If n is the first of two or more consecutive integers, then those integers can be represented by n, $n + 1$, $n + 2$, and so on.

EXAMPLE 1 Find two consecutive integers with a sum of 63.

Solution Let n = the first integer. Then $n + 1$ = the next consecutive integer. The sum is 63. Use this fact to write an equation.

$$n + (n + 1) = 63$$
$$2n + 1 = 63$$
$$2n = 62$$
$$n = 31 \quad \longleftarrow \text{first integer: 31}$$
$$n + 1 = 31 + 1, \text{ or } 32 \quad \longleftarrow \text{second integer: 32}$$

Check Are 31 and 32 consecutive integers? Yes.
Is their sum 63? Yes, because $31 + 32 = 63$.

Thus, the integers are 31 and 32.

EXAMPLE 2 Find two consecutive integers with a sum of 32.

Solution Let n = the first integer. Then $n + 1$ = the second integer.

$$n + (n + 1) = 32 \quad \longleftarrow \text{The sum is 32.}$$
$$2n + 1 = 32$$
$$2n = 31$$
$$n = 15\tfrac{1}{2}$$

But $15\tfrac{1}{2}$ is not an integer.

Thus, no two consecutive integers have a sum of 32.

TRY THIS 1. Find two consecutive integers with a sum of 55.

An **even integer** is an integer that is divisible by 2. Examples of even integers are -10, -4, 0, 20, and 100.

An **odd integer** is an integer that is not divisible by 2. Examples of odd integers are -7, -1, 13, and 121.

Three consecutive odd integers can be represented algebraically by n, $n + 2$, and $n + 4$ where n is an odd integer. Similarly, three consecutive even integers can also be represented by n, $n + 2$, and $n + 4$, where n is an even integer.

EXAMPLE 3   Find three consecutive even integers such that the third is 8 less than twice the second.

Solution

Let $n =$ the first even integer.
Then $n + 2 =$ the second even integer,
and $n + 4 =$ the third even integer.
The third is 8 less than twice the second.

$$n + 4 = 2(n + 2) - 8$$
$$n + 4 = 2n + 4 - 8$$
$$n + 4 = 2n - 4$$
$$8 = n, \text{ or } n = 8 \quad \longleftarrow \text{ first even integer: 8}$$
$$n + 2 = 10 \quad \longleftarrow \text{ second even integer: 10}$$
$$n + 4 = 12 \quad \longleftarrow \text{ third even integer: 12}$$

Thus, the three consecutive even integers are 8, 10, and 12.

EXAMPLE 4   Is the sum of two consecutive odd integers *never* an even integer, *sometimes* even, or *always* even? Use the following two facts to justify your answer.

Fact 1: An integer is divisible by 2 if and only if it is even.
Fact 2: The sum of two integers is an integer.

Solution

Look at specific numbers. Then use algebra to find a general answer.

$$9 + 11 = 20 \qquad 15 + 17 = 32 \qquad 41 + 45 = 86$$

These sums are even integers. So the answer is either *sometimes* even or *always* even.

Next, let $n = $ *any* odd integer.
Then, $n + 2 = $ the next consecutive odd integer.
The sum of these two integers is an integer, namely
$$n + (n + 2) = 2n + 2 = 2(n + 1).$$

Since $2(n + 1)$ is divisible by 2, it is even. Thus, the sum of two consecutive odd integers is *always* even.

TRY THIS   **2.** Find three consecutive odd integers such that the second is 20 less than 3 times the third integer.

Match each item at the left with one expression or phrase at the right.

1. $-4, -3, -2$
2. $5, 7, 9$
3. $24, 26, 28$
4. consecutive integers if x is an integer
5. consecutive odd integers if x is odd
6. consecutive even integers if x is even

a. three consecutive even integers
b. $x, x + 2, x + 4$
c. three consecutive integers
d. $x, x + 1, x + 2$
e. three consecutive odd integers
f. $x, x + 1, x + 3$

Classroom Exercises

Give the next three consecutive integers.

1. 7   2. -21 3. 78   4. -2 5. n 6. $n + 5$

Give the next three consecutive odd integers.

7. 1   8. -3 9. -33 10. 5   11. k 12. $k + 6$

Give the next three consecutive even integers.

13. 10   14. -4 15. 56   16. -42 17. t 18. $t + 8$

Suppose n is the first of three consecutive odd integers. Represent each of the following with an algebraic expression. (Exercises 19 and 20)

19. the sum of the three integers
20. the sum of the second and the third integers

21. Find three consecutive integers with a sum of 42.
22. Find two consecutive even integers with a sum of 82.
23. Find three consecutive odd integers with a sum of 171.

Written Exercises

Solve each problem. If there is no solution, so indicate. (Exercises 1–14)

1. The sum of two consecutive integers is 75. Find the integers.
2. The sum of two consecutive integers is -63. Find the integers.
3. Find two consecutive even integers with a sum of 78.
4. Find two consecutive odd integers with a sum of -56.
5. Find two consecutive integers with a sum of 52.
6. Find two consecutive even integers with a sum of 41.
7. Find two consecutive odd integers with a sum of 65.
8. The sum of three consecutive integers is -51. Find the integers.

9. Find three consecutive odd integers with a sum of 273.

10. Find three consecutive even integers with a sum of -126.

11. Find four consecutive integers with a sum of 113.

12. Find five consecutive integers with a sum of -45.

13. The sum of four consecutive even integers is 4. Find the integers.

14. The sum of four consecutive odd integers is -8. Find the integers.

In Exercises 15–20, complete the statement by writing *never*, *sometimes*, or *always*.

15. The sum of any two consecutive integers is ___?___ even.

16. The sum of any two consecutive even integers is ___?___ even.

17. The sum of any two consecutive odd integers is ___?___ odd.

18. The sum of any three consecutive even integers is ___?___ even.

19. The sum of any three consecutive odd integers is ___?___ odd.

20. The sum of any four consecutive integers is ___?___ odd.

21. Find three consecutive odd integers such that their sum decreased by 18 is equal to the first integer.

22. Show that for all integers n, if $n + (n + 1) = S$, then $n = \dfrac{S - 1}{2}$.

    Is it true that if you know the sum of any two consecutive integers, you can find the first integer by subtracting 1 from the sum and dividing the result by 2?

23. Show that for all integers n, if $n + (n + 2) + (n + 4) = S$, then $n = \dfrac{S - 6}{3}$. Is it true that if you know the sum of any three consecutive odd integers, you can find the first integer by subtracting 6 from the sum and dividing the result by 3?

24. Give a rule for finding the first of four consecutive odd integers if you know the sum of the four integers.

25. Give a rule for finding the first of four consecutive integers if you know the sum of the four integers.

Mixed Review

Evaluate for the given values of the variable.   *1.3*

1. $(8x)^2$, for $x = \dfrac{1}{4}$

2. $x^3 y^2$, for $x = 1$ and $y = 7$

3. $\dfrac{x^2 - y^2}{x - y}$, for $x = 5$ and $y = 2$

4. $3a^4 b$, for $a = 2$ and $b = 5$

Simplify.   *2.2*

5. $|-16|$

6. $|-2| + |8|$

7. $|5 - 7|$

8. $-|6| \cdot |-6|$

4.4 Problem Solving: Perimeter and Angle Measure

Objectives
To solve problems about perimeter
To solve problems about angle measure

In this lesson, you will find it helpful to draw figures and label them.

In designing a quilt, Jackie needs to cut rectangular pieces of cloth. The length of each rectangular piece must be 2 cm less than 3 times the width. The perimeter must be 44 cm. How can you find the length and width of each rectangular piece?

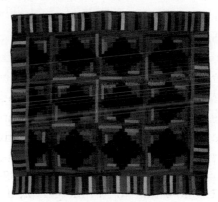

What are you to find?   The length and width of a rectangle

Draw and label a figure.

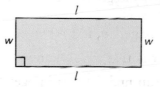

What is given?   The length is 2 less than 3 times the width.
The perimeter is 44 cm.

Choose a variable.   Let w = the width, in cm.
Then $3w - 2$ = the length, in cm. ← 2 less than 3 times the width

Write an equation. $p = 2l + 2w$ ← the perimeter of a rectangle
$44 = 2(3w - 2) + 2w$ ← Substitute 44 for p and $3w - 2$ for l.

Solve the equation.
$44 = 6w - 4 + 2w$
$44 = 8w - 4$
$48 = 8w$
$6 = w$ ← width: 6 cm
$l = 3w - 2 = 3 \cdot 6 - 2 = 16$ ← length: 16 cm

Check in the original problem.   The check is left for you.

State the answer.   Thus, the length is 16 cm; the width is 6 cm.

The *perimeter* of a triangle is the sum of the lengths of its sides. Therefore, the formula for the perimeter of a triangle with sides a, b, and c is

$$p = a + b + c.$$

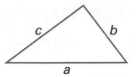

EXAMPLE 1 The first side of a triangle is 3 cm longer than the second side. The third side is 4 cm shorter than twice the length of the second side. The perimeter is 31 cm. How long is each side?

Plan Draw and label a figure (see below). Represent the first and third sides in terms of the *second* side.

Solution Let s = the length of the second side, in cm.
Then $s + 3$ = the length of the first side, in cm,   ← 3 cm longer than s
and $2s - 4$ = the length of the third side, in cm.   ← 4 cm shorter than twice s

Use $p = a + b + c$.

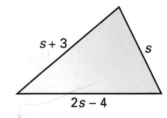

$31 = (s + 3) + s + (2s - 4)$
$31 = 4s - 1$
$32 = 4s$
$8 = s$, or
$s = 8$ ←—— second side: 8 cm
$s + 3 = 11$ ←—— first side: 11 cm
$2s - 4 = 2 \cdot 8 - 4 = 16 - 4 = 12$ ←—— third side: 12 cm

Check The check is left for you.

Thus, the lengths of the sides are 8 cm, 11 cm, and 12 cm.

TRY THIS 1. The length of a rectangle is 7 cm longer than 3 times the width. The perimeter is 78 cm. Find the length and the width.

For any triangle, the sum of the degree measures of the angles is 180.

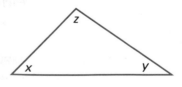

$$x + y + z = 180$$

In an **isosceles triangle**, two sides have the same length. These two sides are called the **legs** and the third side is called the **base**. An isosceles triangle also has two angles with the same measure. These two angles are called the **base angles** and the third angle is called the **vertex angle**.

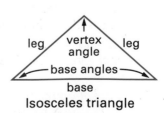

EXAMPLE 2   The degree measure of the vertex angle of an isosceles triangle is 30 more than that of a base angle. Find the degree measure of each angle of the triangle.

Solution   Let b = the measure of each base angle, in degrees.

Then $b + 30$ = the measure of the vertex angle, in degrees.

The sum of the degree measures of the angles is 180.

$$b + b + (b + 30) = 180$$
$$3b + 30 = 180$$
$$3b = 150$$
$$b = 50 \longleftarrow \text{degree measure of each base angle: 50}$$
$$b + 30 = 50 + 30 = 80 \longleftarrow \text{degree measure of vertex angle: 80}$$

Check   Does the vertex angle have a degree measure that is 30 more than that of a base angle? Yes, because 50 + 30 equals 80. Is the sum of the measures of the three angles 180? Yes, because 50 + 50 + 80 equals 180. Thus, the degree measure of each base angle is 50 and the degree measure of the vertex angle is 80.

TRY THIS   2. The degree measure of the vertex angle of an isosceles triangle is 4 times that of a base angle. Find the degree measure of each angle of the triangle.

Classroom Exercises

Find the indicated measure for each geometric figure. (Exercises 1–3)

1. Rectangle: length, $2x$; width, x; perimeter, 24 in.
   Find the length and the width.
2. Rectangle: length, $2x - 4$; width, x; perimeter, 28 m
   Find the length and the width.
3. Square: each side of length x; perimeter, 40 ft
   Find the length of each side.

Solve each problem.

4. The length of a rectangle is 3 times the width. The perimeter is 42 cm. Find the length and width.
5. The perimeter of an isosceles triangle is 40 ft. The length of the base is 10 ft. Find the length of each leg.
6. The base of an isosceles triangle is 5 ft longer than either of the other two sides. The perimeter is 41 ft. Find the lengths of all three sides.
7. The degree measure of the vertex angle of an isosceles triangle is 42. Find the measure of each base angle.

Written Exercises

Solve each problem.

1. The length of a rectangle is 3 times the width. The perimeter is 52 cm. Find the length and the width.

2. The width of a rectangle is one-fourth of the length. The perimeter is 130 cm. Find the length and the width.

3. The width of a rectangle is 7 ft less than the length. The perimeter is 34 ft. Find the length and the width.

4. The length of a rectangle is 3 m more than 5 times the width. The perimeter is 126 m. Find the length and width.

5. The width of a rectangle is 2 ft more than twice the length. The perimeter is 28 ft. Find the length and width.

6. The degree measure of the vertex angle of an isosceles triangle is 46. Find the measure of each base angle.

7. For an *equiangular* triangle, all three angles have the same degree measure. Find the degree measure of each angle of an equiangular triangle.

8. The degree measure of the vertex angle of an isosceles triangle is 20 more than twice the measure of a base angle. Find the degree measure of each angle.

9. The length of each leg of an isosceles triangle is 4 km longer than the base. The perimeter is 35 km. Find the length of each side.

10. The length of each leg of an isosceles triangle is 3 times the length of the base. The perimeter is 77 m. Find the length of each side.

11. The perimeter of a triangle is 45 in. The first side is 5 in. shorter than twice the second side. The third side is 2 in. longer than the second side. Find the length of each side.

12. The first side of a triangle is 2 cm longer than the second side. The third side is 5 cm shorter than twice the second side. The perimeter is 49 cm. Find the length of each side.

13. One side of a triangle is 5 yd shorter than a second side. The remaining side is 3 yd longer than the second side. The perimeter is 52 yd. Find the length of each side.

14. One side of a triangle is twice as long as a second side. The remaining side is 5 m longer than the second side. The perimeter is 75 m. Find the length of each side.

15. In triangle ABC, the measure of angle A is 1 less than twice the measure of angle B. The measure of angle C is 22 more than the measure of angle A. Find the measure of each angle.

16. For triangle XYZ, the measure of angle Z is 3 more than half the measure of angle Y. The degree measure of angle X is 17 less than 4 times the measure of angle Z. Find the degree measure of each angle.

17. A rectangle's length is 1 cm less than twice its width. If the length is decreased by 3 cm and the width is decreased by 2 cm, the perimeter will be 36 cm. Find the length and width of the original rectangle.

18. A rectangular field is 3 times as long as it is wide. If the length is decreased by 3 m and the width is increased by 2 m, the perimeter will be 54 m. Find the length and width of the original field.

In Exercises 19 and 20, a rectangular house lies on a rectangular lot. The owner plans to enclose the lot with a fence from a corner of the house (Point A) around the lot and finishing at another corner of the house (Point B). Find the length of the fence. All dimensions are in feet.

19.

```
        121
┌──────────────────────┐
│          3x          │ A
x+20 │   ┌──────────┐    │
│   x│  house   │    │
│    └──────────┘    │
└──────────────────────┘
        B
```
perimeter of house: 200

20.

```
        2y+20
┌──────────────────────┐
│    ┌──────────┐      │ y
│ 25 │  house   │      │
│    └──────────┘      │
│  30    B      A      │
└──────────────────────┘
```
perimeter of property: 280
perimeter of house: 170

Midchapter Review

1. Find three consecutive odd integers whose sum is 117. **4.4**

2. The length of a rectangle is twice the width. The perimeter is 72 cm. Find the length and the width. **4.2**

3. The degree measure of the vertex angle of an isosceles triangle is 10 less than twice the measure of each base angle. Find the degree measure of each angle of the triangle. **4.2**

4. Lola's age is 14 more than 6 times Juan's age. The sum of their ages is 35. How old is each? **4.3**

Application: Gear Depths

The depth of a gear tooth is found by multiplying the difference of the larger and smaller diameters of the gear by $\frac{1}{2}$. Use the formula $D = \frac{1}{2}(d_1 - d_2)$, where D is the depth of the tooth, d_1 is the larger diameter, and d_2 is the smaller diameter. The formula can be solved for d_1 as follows.

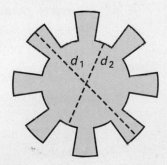

$$D = \tfrac{1}{2}(d_1 - d_2)$$

Multiply each side by 2. $$2 \cdot D = 2\left[\tfrac{1}{2}(d_1 - d_2)\right]$$

Simplify. $$2D = d_1 - d_2$$

Add d_2 to each side. $$2D + d_2 = d_1, \text{ or } d_1 = d_2 + 2D$$

Exercises

1. Find D if $d_1 = 8.2$ cm and $d_2 = 7.6$ cm.
2. Find d_1 if $D = 5.1$ mm and $d_2 = 23.5$ mm.
3. Solve the formula for d_2.
4. Find d_2 if $D = 12.8$ mm and $d_1 = 61.3$ mm.

4.5 Equations with Fractions

Objective To solve equations that contain fractions

You know that an equation containing fractions, such as $\frac{4}{5}x + \frac{3}{10} = \frac{1}{2}$, can be solved by applying the properties of equality. However, there is a much more efficient method for solving this equation. First, multiply each side by the *least* number that is divisible by all three denominators, 5, 10, and 2. That number is 10, the **least common multiple** (LCM) of 5, 10, and 2. The number 10 is also referred to as the **least common denominator** (LCD) of the three fractions $\frac{4}{5}$, $\frac{3}{10}$, and $\frac{1}{2}$. If you multiply each side of $\frac{4}{5}x + \frac{3}{10} = \frac{1}{2}$ by 10, the resulting equation will not contain fractions.

EXAMPLE 1 Solve $\frac{4}{5}x + \frac{3}{10} = \frac{1}{2}$. Check the solution.

Solution Multiply each side by 10.
$$10\left(\frac{4}{5}x + \frac{3}{10}\right) = 10 \cdot \frac{1}{2}$$

Use the Distributive Property.
$$10 \cdot \frac{4}{5}x + 10 \cdot \frac{3}{10} = 10 \cdot \frac{1}{2}$$

$$8x + 3 = 5 \quad \longleftarrow \quad \overset{2}{\cancel{10}} \cdot \frac{4}{\cancel{5}}x = 8x$$

$$8x = 2$$

$$x = \frac{2}{8}, \text{ or } \frac{1}{4}$$

Check
$$\frac{4}{5}x + \frac{3}{10} = \frac{1}{2}$$

Substitute $\frac{1}{4}$ for x.
$$\frac{4}{5} \cdot \frac{1}{4} + \frac{3}{10} \overset{?}{=} \frac{1}{2}$$

$$\frac{1}{5} + \frac{3}{10} \overset{?}{=} \frac{1}{2}$$

$$\frac{2}{10} + \frac{3}{10} \overset{?}{=} \frac{1}{2}$$

$$\frac{1}{2} = \frac{1}{2} \text{ True}$$

Thus, the solution is $\frac{1}{4}$.

EXAMPLE 2 Solve $\frac{a + 3}{3} - \frac{a - 2}{5} = \frac{a}{4}$.

Plan Multiply each side by 60, the LCD of the three fractions.

Solution

$$60\left(\frac{a+3}{3} - \frac{a-2}{5}\right) = 60 \cdot \frac{a}{4}$$

$$60 \cdot \frac{a+3}{3} - 60 \cdot \frac{a-2}{5} = 60 \cdot \frac{a}{4}$$

$$20(a+3) - 12(a-2) = 15a$$

$$20a + 60 - 12a + 24 = 15a$$

$$8a + 84 = 15a$$

$$84 = 7a$$

$$12 = a$$

Thus, the solution is 12.

TRY THIS

1. Solve $\dfrac{x+8}{4} - \dfrac{x-5}{8} = \dfrac{x}{5}$

Recall that the *average* or *arithmetic mean* of a set of numbers is the *sum* of the numbers divided by the number of numbers.

EXAMPLE 3 Mary received the following test scores: 70, 80, and 90. What grade must she earn on a fourth test to have a passing average of 70?

Solution Let s = the score on the fourth test.
The sum of four scores divided by 4 is 70.

$$\frac{70 + 80 + 90 + s}{4} = 70$$

$$4 \cdot \frac{70 + 80 + 90 + s}{4} = 4 \cdot 70$$

$$240 + s = 280$$

$$s = 40$$

Thus, Mary must score at least 40 on the fourth test to pass the course.

TRY THIS

2. Joe received the following test scores: 86, 92, 78, and 95. What grade must he earn on a fifth test to have an average of 90?

Classroom Exercises

For each equation, by what number would you multiply each side to eliminate the fractions?

1. $\frac{1}{5}x - \frac{1}{3} = -\frac{8}{15}$ 2. $\frac{5}{6}y + \frac{1}{2} = \frac{7}{3}$ 3. $\frac{5}{12} = \frac{2}{3}c + \frac{1}{4}$ 4. $\frac{5}{6}y - 8 = \frac{1}{3}y + \frac{1}{8}$

5–8. Solve the equations of Exercises 1–4 above.

Written Exercises

Solve each equation.

1. $\frac{3}{4}c = 15$ **2.** $\frac{3}{5}y = \frac{2}{15}$ **3.** $\frac{5}{9} = \frac{2}{3}c$ **4.** $\frac{1}{4}c + \frac{2}{3} = \frac{1}{3}$

5. $\frac{3}{4}y - \frac{1}{2} = \frac{5}{3}$ **6.** $\frac{5}{8} = \frac{3}{2}a + \frac{1}{4}$ **7.** $\frac{2}{3}x + 7 = 9$ **8.** $9 = \frac{1}{2}x + 6$

9. $\frac{1}{2}x + 6 = \frac{3}{4}x - 3$ **10.** $\frac{1}{2}y - 4 = \frac{1}{5}y + 7$

11. $\frac{3}{2}x - 3 = \frac{2}{3}x + 2$ **12.** $\frac{1}{3}r - 1 = \frac{2}{5}r + 2$

Solve each problem.

13. Seven years more than $\frac{3}{5}$ of Juan's age is 25 years. How old is Juan?

14. Six less than $\frac{2}{3}$ of a number equals the number. Find the number.

15. The income for 7 weeks of football-game refreshments were: $200, $350, $500, $375, $400, $625, and $250. What income from the 8th and last game will give an average income of $400?

16. Megan's batting averages for her first 3 years of high school are .225, .325, and .300. What batting average for the senior year will she need in order to have a yearly batting average of .300 for the four years?

Solve.

17. $\frac{3a + 4}{12} - \frac{5}{3} = \frac{2a - 1}{2}$ **18.** $\frac{2x - 3}{7} - \frac{x}{2} = \frac{x + 3}{14}$

19. $\frac{3y}{4} - \frac{2y - 9}{3} = \frac{y + 1}{5}$ **20.** $\frac{3b}{4} - \frac{2b - 1}{2} = \frac{b - 7}{6}$

21. When the second of two consecutive even integers is divided by 2 and added to the first even integer, the sum is 25. What are the two integers?

22. The price of a football is decreased by one-third to give the discount price of $38. Find the original price.

23. Solve for x: $\frac{2}{3}(x - 5) - \frac{3x - 2}{4} = \frac{2}{3}[1 - (4 - x)] - 5\frac{1}{3}$.

Mixed Review

Simplify.   *1.3, 2.2, 2.6, 2.9, 2.10*

1. $\left| -8 + 3 \right|$ **2.** $\left(-\frac{3}{4} \right)^3$ **3.** $-y - 4 - y + \frac{3}{4}$ **4.** $7 - (6 - b) - 3b$ **5.** $(-1)^3$

6. Find the number of meters a bowling ball drops in 6.3 seconds. Use $d = 5t^2$.   *1.3*

4.6 Equations with Decimals

Objective	To solve equations that contain decimals

The equation $1.2x - 0.04 = 0.8$ contains *decimals*. It can be solved by adding 0.04 to each side and then dividing each side by 1.2. However, it is often easier to solve an equation such as this by first finding an equivalent equation that does not contain decimals.

Recall that multiplying a decimal by a power of ten, such as 10, 100, or 1,000, may result in an integer.

$10 \times 1.2 = 12$	(Move the decimal point one place to the right.)
$100 \times 0.04 = 4$	(Move the decimal point two places to the right.)
$1,000 \times 0.800 = 800$	(Move the decimal point three places to the right.)

EXAMPLE 1   Solve $1.2x - 0.04 = 0.8$.

Plan   First, find the number of digits at the right of each decimal point.

$$1.2x - 0.04 = 0.8$$
$$\text{one} \quad\quad \text{two} \quad\quad \text{one}$$

The greatest number of digits at the right of any decimal point is two. Thus, you should multiply each side of the equation by 10^2, or 100.

Solution

$$1.2x - 0.04 = 0.8$$

Multiply each side by 100. $100(1.2x - 0.04) = 100(0.8)$
Use the Distributive Property. $100(1.2x) - 100(0.04) = 100(0.8)$
Simplify. $120x - 4 = 80$
$$120x = 84$$
$$x = \frac{84}{120}, \text{ or } 0.7$$

Check   Substitute 0.7 for x.

$$1.2x - 0.04 = 0.8$$
$$1.2(0.7) - 0.04 \stackrel{?}{=} 0.8$$
$$0.84 - 0.04 \stackrel{?}{=} 0.8$$
$$0.80 = 0.8 \text{ True}$$

Thus, the solution is 0.7.

TRY THIS   1. Solve $0.05x + 4.27 = 4.3$.

EXAMPLE 2   This year, Jim's wages increased by 0.125 of last year's wages. If his hourly wage is now $9.45, what was his wage last year?

Solution   Let w = Jim's wage last year, in dollars.

wage last year increased by 0.125 of wage last year = wage this year
$$\underbrace{w} \quad \underbrace{+} \quad \underbrace{0.125w} \quad = 9.45$$

$$w + 0.125w = 9.45$$
$$1{,}000(w + 0.125w) = 1{,}000(9.45) \quad \longleftarrow \text{Greatest number of digits to the}$$
$$\text{right of a decimal point: 3;}$$
$$10^3 = 1{,}000$$

$$1{,}000w + 125w = 9{,}450$$
$$1{,}125w = 9{,}450$$
$$w = 8.40 \quad \longleftarrow \text{Jim's wage last year: \$8.40}$$

Check   Is last year's wage increased by 0.125 of last year's wage equal to this year's wage? Yes, because $8.40 + 0.125(8.40)$ is $8.40 + 1.05$, or 9.45.

Thus, Jim's wage last year was $8.40.

TRY THIS   2. A number decreased by 0.79 of the number is 6.3. What is the number?

Classroom Exercises

For each equation, by what number would you multiply each side to eliminate the decimals?

1. $4.1x + 2 = 14.3$ **2.** $1.2y + 0.05 = 8.45$ **3.** $0.005z + 0.02 = 0.1z - 1.5$
4. $0.3y - 7.5 = 0.6$ **5.** $9.8 = 0.02 - 0.1x$ **6.** $0.004 + 5x = 7.1$
7–12. Solve the equations of Classroom Exercises 1–6 above.

Written Exercises

Solve each equation.

1. $0.2x = 1.8$ **2.** $2.6x = -7.8$ **3.** $1.3y - 1.7 = 7.4$
4. $0.05m = 7.45$ **5.** $8.2 - 3.2c = -17.4$ **6.** $0.25q = 8.75$
7. $0.10d = 3.40$ **8.** $0.036x = -1.08$ **9.** $0.03r = 0.018$
10. $1.3 = 0.15x - 3.2$ **11.** $0.02d - 2.6 = 0.84$ **12.** $0.05n + 1.45 = 10.20$
13. $0.25q - 1.50 = 13.75$ **14.** $1.75 + 0.25q = 15.50$
15. $0.006x - 7.3 = 0.14$ **16.** $0.08 - 0.2y = -4.4$
17. $0.7z - 0.1071 = 0.07z$ **18.** $-0.009 = 5.2 - 0.1x$
19. $0.112y + 2 = 0.012y - 4$ **20.** $0.7x - 0.11 = 5 - 0.03x$

21. $0.5n + 0.02 = -0.2 - 0.6n$

22. $0.23z + 119.7 = 0.8z$

23. $1.2x + 0.004 = 1.4x - 2$

24. $0.09 - 5.1 = 1.5 - 0.24c$

Solve each problem.

25. A number increased by 0.8 of the number is 16.2. Find the number.

26. A number decreased by 0.37 times the number is 12.6. Find the number.

27. This year a company's earnings increased by 0.28 of last year's earnings. If the company's earnings are $135,680 this year, what were the earnings last year?

28. The greater of two numbers is 3.2 more than twice the smaller. If 0.3 times the smaller is added to the larger, the result is 11.48. Find the numbers.

29. One number is 0.9 of another. Find the numbers if their sum is 0.038.

30. A taxicab driver charges $1.75 for the first mile and $12\frac{1}{2}$¢ ($0.125) for each additional tenth of a mile. How far can you go for $5.00?

31. An adult's ticket to a movie theater costs 2.5 times as much as a child's ticket. If John, an adult, pays $18.75 for tickets for himself and 5 children, how much did he pay in all for the children's tickets?

32. Jan has 3.5 times as much money as Lucia who has $75.60 less than Ken. Jan has $113.10 more than Lucia and Ken together. How much money does Jan have?

On the Kelvin temperature scale, a temperature of 0 ("absolute zero") is the lowest temperature that can be reached anywhere in the universe. To convert from the Kelvin scale to the Fahrenheit scale (or vice versa), use the formula $1.8K = F + 459.67$.

33. Convert the temperature of outer space, $-454.27°F$, to degrees Kelvin.

34. Is a temperature of 300°K comfortable? Explain your answer.

Mixed Review

Solve each equation. *3.3, 3.5, 4.5*

1. $6 - 2x = 8$

2. $4 - 3x = 7 - x$

3. $\frac{2}{3}x - \frac{1}{2} = \frac{5}{6}$

4. $7 - (3 - x) = 1$

Simplify. *2.2, 2.6, 2.9, 2.10*

5. $|8 - 9|$

6. $-5(-2)^3$

7. $7 - (4 - x) - 3x + 1$

8. Bill is one-third as old as his dad. Bill is 12 years old. How old is his dad? *3.2*

4.7 Percent Problems

Objective   To solve problems involving percent

Algebra can be used to deal with many situations involving percent. **Percent**, written %, means *per hundred*, or *hundredths*. A percent can be expressed as a fraction or as a decimal, as illustrated below.

$$38\% = \frac{38}{100} = 0.38 \qquad 2\% = \frac{2}{100} = 0.02$$

$$150\% = \frac{150}{100} = 1.5 \qquad 6\tfrac{1}{2}\% = 6.5\% = \frac{6.5}{100} = 0.065$$

There are three basic types of percent problems. Each involves an equation with two known numbers and one unknown number.

EXAMPLE 1   *Finding a percent of a number*
What number is 65% of 132?

Plan   Translate the statement of the problem into an equation. Use the fact that "of" means "multiplied by."

Solution   Let n = the number.

What number is 65% of 132?

$$n \quad = 0.65 \cdot 132$$
$$n = 85.8 \quad \longleftarrow \text{Calculator steps: } 0.65 \; \boxed{\times} \; 132 \; \boxed{=} \; 85.8$$

Thus, the number is 85.8.

EXAMPLE 2   *Finding what percent one number is of another*
3 is what percent of 8?

Solution   Let p = the percent.

3 is what percent of 8?

$$3 = \quad p \quad \cdot 8$$
$$\frac{3}{8} = p, \text{ or } \quad p = \frac{3}{8} = 0.375$$

Write as a percent. $0.375 = 37.5\%$.

Thus, 3 is 37.5% of 8.

TRY THIS   1. What number is 76% of 112?   2. 4 is what percent of 5?

EXAMPLE 3 *Finding the number when a percent of it is known*
72 is 150% of what number?

Solution

Let n = the number.
72 is 150% of what number?

Write 150% of n as   72 = 1.5 · n
1.50n.

Multiply each side by 10. $10(72) = 10(1.5n)$
                                                       $720 = 15n$
                                                        $48 = n$

Thus, 72 is 150% of 48.

TRY THIS   3. 44 is 110% of what number?

When the price of a T-shirt increases from $5 to $6, you subtract to
find the amount of increase: $6 - 5 = 1$. To find the percent increase,
you compare the amount of increase, $1, to the original price, $5.

$$\text{percent increase} = \frac{\text{amount of increase}}{\text{original amount}} = \frac{1}{5} = 0.2 = 20\%$$

So, the percent increase is 20%.

If the price of a T-shirt decreases from $6 to $5, you subtract to find
the amount of decrease: $6 - 5 = 1$.

$$\text{percent decrease} = \frac{\text{amount of decrease}}{\text{original amount}} = \frac{1}{6} = 0.16\frac{2}{3} = 16\frac{2}{3}\%$$

So, the percent decrease is $16\frac{2}{3}\%$.

EXAMPLE 4 Susan's salary was raised from $7 to $9 per hour. Find the percent
increase, to the nearest whole percent.

Solution   Amount of increase: $9 - $7 = $2

$2 is what percent of $7? Let p = the percent.

$$2 = \frac{p}{100} \cdot 7$$

$$\frac{2}{7} = \frac{p}{100} \qquad \longleftarrow \text{Calculator steps: } 2 \boxed{\div} 7 \boxed{=} \; 0.2857142$$

$$p = \frac{200}{7} \approx 29 \qquad \longleftarrow \approx \text{ means } \textit{is approximately equal to.}$$

Thus, the percent increase is 29%, to the nearest whole percent.

TRY THIS   4. David's salary was decreased from $8 to $6 per hour. Find the
percent decrease, to the nearest whole percent.

Sometimes interest can be computed using the formula for *simple interest,*

$$i = prt$$

where i is the interest earned, p is the principal (the amount invested), r is the annual rate of interest, and t is the time in years. This formula is used when interest is not paid on interest previously earned.

EXAMPLE 5   Mrs. King invested $1,000 in municipal bonds at a simple-interest rate of 5% per year for 3 years. Find the interest earned.

Solution $p = 1,000$, $r = 5\% = 0.05$, and $t = 3$
interest = principal · rate · time, or $i = prt$
$= 1,000(0.05)(3) = 150$

Thus, the interest earned was $150.

TRY THIS   5. If $850 is invested at a simple-interest rate of 6% per year for 5 years, how much interest is earned?

Classroom Exercises

Give a decimal for each percent.

1. 20%   **2.** 45%   **3.** 3%   **4.** 12.5%   **5.** 0.5%   **6.** $7\frac{1}{2}\%$ **7.** $8\frac{3}{4}\%$

Give a percent for each decimal or fraction.

8. 0.26   **9.** 0.05   **10.** 0.125   **11.** $\frac{2}{5}$ **12.** 1.4   **13.** $\frac{3}{8}$ **14.** 0.003

15. 24 percent of 6 is what number?   **16.** What is $33\frac{1}{3}\%$ of 81?

17. 12% of what number is 24?   **18.** 3 is what percent of 9?

19. A price is lowered from $5 to $3. What is the percent decrease?

Written Exercises

1. What number is 15% of 60?   **2.** What number is 8% of 50?

3. 16 is what percent of 80?   **4.** 13 is what percent of 52?

5. 20 is 40% of what number?   **6.** 8 is 5% of what number?

7. What number is 32% of 80?   **8.** What number is 5% of 142?

9. 24 is what percent of 42?   **10.** 32 is what percent of 48?

11. 84 is 12% of what number?   **12.** 48 is $37\frac{1}{2}\%$ of what number?

13. What number is 43% of 78?   **14.** 38 is 25% of what number?

15. 15 is what percent of 40?   **16.** 18 is 150% of what number?

17. What number is $3\frac{1}{2}\%$ of 150?   **18.** 30 is what percent of 25?

19. A football team won 15 out of 20 games. What percent of their games did they win?

20. If $600 is invested at a simple-interest rate of 5% per year for 3 years, how much interest is earned?

21. If there are 30 points possible on a quiz and a student scored 24 points, what percent did she get right?

22. Roberto got 6 hits in 24 times at bat. The number of hits is what percent of the number of times at bat?

23. A band gets 6% of the total sales of a record that it made. If it got $67,500, what were the total sales?

24. The price of a stock dropped from $72 a share to $63 a share. What was the percent decrease in price?

25. If $8,000 is invested at a simple-interest rate of 6.2% per year for 4 years, how much interest is earned?

26. If $4,000 is invested at a simple-interest rate of 6% for 5 years, how much interest is earned?

27. A price is decreased from $10 to $8. What is the percent decrease?

28. A price is increased from $8 to $10. What is the percent increase?

29. The price of an airline ticket was $320. Then the price was increased 15%. What was the new price?

30. A man flipped a coin 6,000 times. He got heads 3,069 times. What percent of the time did he get heads?

31. How much money must be invested at a simple-interest rate of 7.2% to earn $1,440 in interest in 5 years?

32. At what simple-interest rate should $25,000 be invested to earn interest of $13,000 in 8 years?

33. A price is raised from $6 to $7. What is the increase, to the nearest whole percent?

34. A price is lowered from $7 to $6. What is the decrease, to the nearest whole percent?

35. There are 2,374 students in a school. If 6% are absent, how many students are present, to the nearest whole number?

36. Seven percent of a country is ambidextrous. If that represents 1,200,000 people, what is the total population of the country, to the nearest 100,000?

37. In 1987, Bob earned $280. In 1988, his earnings increased 15%. In 1989, his earnings decreased 15% from his earnings in 1988. Was $280 his earnings for 1989? Show why or why not.

38. In 1987, Jane earned d dollars. In 1988, her earnings decreased p percent. In 1989, her earnings increased p percent from her 1988 earnings. Express her 1989 earnings in terms of d and p.

Mixed Review

Solve. *3.4–3.6*

1. $5x - 8 = 3x + 12$

2. $2(3x - 2) - 4 = 6x + 12$

3. $0.6a - 1 = 0.5a + 0.03$

Evaluate for the given values of the variables. *2.6, 2.8*

4. $-8x^3$, for $x = -5$

5. $3x - 4y$, for $x = -3$ and $y = -6$

6. $\dfrac{a - b}{-6}$, for $a = -2, b = 4$

4.8 Problem Solving: Using Percent

Objective To solve problems about sales tax, profit, discount, and commission

When you buy a sweater with a marked price and a known sales tax, you can find the total price by using the following relationship.

marked price + sales tax = total price

EXAMPLE 1 Ahmed bought a sweater with a marked price of $32.99. If the sales tax was 8%, what was the total price of the sweater?

Solution
sales tax = 8% of marked price
$= 0.08 \times \$32.99 = \$2.6392$
sales tax = $2.64 ←—— to the nearest cent
marked price + sales tax = total price
$32.99 + $2.64 = total price
$35.63 = total price

Thus, the total price was $35.63.

TRY THIS
1. Jack bought a jacket with a marked price of $89.99. If the sales tax was 6%, what was the total price of the sweater?

If a book dealer buys a book at a *cost* of $10 and wants to make a *profit* of $6, then he must add the profit to the cost to determine his *selling price*. So, his selling price must be 10 + 6, or $16.

cost + profit = selling price

The profit is often determined as a percent of the cost.

EXAMPLE 2 A store manager lists the selling price of a bicycle at $78. This includes a 20% profit on her cost. Find the cost of the bicycle.

Solution
Let c = the cost, in dollars.
Then the profit = 20% of cost = $0.20c$, or $0.2c$, in dollars.

cost + profit = selling price
$c + 0.2c = 78$
Multiply each side by 10. $10(c + 0.2c) = 10 \cdot 78$
$10c + 2c = 780$
$12c = 780$
$c = 65$ ←—— Cost: $65

Thus, the cost of the bicycle is $65.

TRY THIS
2. The selling price of a stereo is $124. This includes a 25% profit on the cost. Find the cost of the stereo.

Stores often sell items at a *discount*, stated as a percent of the *regular price*. The *sale price* is the regular price minus the *amount of discount*.

regular price − amount of discount = sale price

EXAMPLE 3   A radio is on sale for $57.85. The discount is 35%. Find the regular price of the radio and the amount of discount.

Solution   Let r = the regular price, in dollars.
Then the amount of discount = 35% of regular price = $0.35r$, in dollars.
    regular price − amount of discount = sale price
$$r - 0.35r = 57.85$$
Multiply each side by 100. $100r - 35r = 5785$
$$65r = 5785$$
$$r = 89 \longleftarrow \text{regular price } \$89.00$$
Amount of discount = $0.35r$ = $0.35(89)$ = 31.15

Thus, the regular price is $89.00 and the amount of discount is $31.15.

TRY THIS   3. A shirt is on sale for $24.48. The discount is 20%. What is the regular price of the shirt and the amount of discount?

Salespeople often receive a percent of the amount they sell. The payment is called a *commission*. A regular salary may also be paid.

salary + commission = total earnings

EXAMPLE 4   Hector earned $350 last week plus a 2% commission on each car he sold. If his total earnings were $710, what were his sales?

Solution   Let s = the amount of sales needed, in dollars.
Then the commission = 2% of sales = $.02s$, in dollars.
salary + commission = total earned
$$350 + 0.02s = 710$$
$$0.02s = 360$$
$$2s = 36,000$$
$$s = 18,000 \quad \text{Thus, Hector's sales were } \$18,000.$$

TRY THIS   4. Tamara earned $300 last week plus a 4% commission on sales. If her total earnings were $500, what were her sales?

Classroom Exercises

State the formula that relates the three items.

1. cost, selling price, profit

2. sales tax, total price, marked price

3. commission, total earned, salary

4. amount of discount, regular price, sale price

Find the missing item.

5. salary: $175 plus 2% of sales
total earnings: $355
total sales: ___?___

6. marked price: $12.95
sales tax: 7%
total price: ___?___

Written Exercises

1. A jacket is marked $159. If the tax is $6\frac{1}{2}\%$, what is the total price?

2. If a record is marked $8.99 and the tax is 7%, what is the total price?

3. The marked price of a T-shirt is $9.00. If it is on sale for 15% off, what is the sale price?

4. The regular price of a tape is $8. If the discount is 20%, what is the sale price?

5. The selling price of a TV set is $360. The profit is 20% of the cost. Find the cost of the set.

6. Matt was paid $125 last week plus a 5% commission on his sales of $6,720. What were his total earnings?

7. The selling price of a turntable is $156. The profit is 30% of the cost. Find the cost.

8. Mr. King bought 150 shares of stock at $39 per share plus $3\frac{1}{2}\%$ commission. How much did he pay in all?

9. A book is on sale for $10.20. The rate of discount is 25%. Find the regular price and the amount of discount.

10. A camera's selling price is $260. Find the dealer's cost if the profit is 30% of the cost.

11. Marcus is paid an 8% commission on all sales plus $3.50 an hour for 40 hours a week. What must be his total sales to earn a total of $220?

12. Sofia is paid $125 plus a commission of 15% on all sales over $300. What must her total sales be if she is to earn a total of $185?

13. Gary is paid a 15% commission on his sales plus $6.50 an hour. One week his sales were $1,240. How many hours did he work to earn $459?

14. The regular price of a video-cassette recorder is $480. It is on sale for $390. Find the discount.

15. The original price of a TV set allowed for a profit of 30% of the cost. The new price is $195, an increase of 25%. Find the dealer's cost.

16. The sale price s of an item with a regular price r, sold at a 15% discount, is given by the formula $s = kr$. Find the value of k. Justify your answer.

Mixed Review

Simplify. *2.10*

1. $9^2 \div (5^2 - 4^2)$ **2.** $2^2(125 - 8^2)$ **3.** $(12 - 7)^2$ **4.** $12^2 - 7^2$

Simplify. *1.3*

5. $-4n(n - 10)$ **6.** $3 - (a + b)$ **7.** $-(c - 8) + 9$ **8.** $a - (-a + 1)$

Problem Solving Strategies

Carrying Out the Plan

Carrying Out the Plan in problem solving involves these things.

a. Estimating the answer and thinking about the appropriate units for the answer.

b. Applying the strategy or strategies you have chosen. A good strategy helps you to find a correct solution in an efficient way.

Example Jean wants to buy some cassettes that are on sale for $2.59 each. How many can she buy with a $20 bill?

Plan Use the guess-and-check strategy.

Solution THINK: The number of cassettes will be a small whole number. So try 10 as a first guess. Use a calculator to check.

Guess	Check	Does it check?
10	10 × $2.59 = $25.90	No. Too many
8	8 × $2.59 = $20.72	No. Too many
7	7 × $2.59 = $18.14	Reasonable answer

So Jean can buy 7 cassettes with the $20 bill.

Exercises

Solve. Use the guess-and-check strategy.

1. A tree trimmer charges $35 plus $18 per hour for trimming trees. Mrs. Danoff pays $143 for his work. How long did the tree trimmer work for Mrs. Danoff?

2. Travis has $1.00 in 7 coins of two different kinds. What are the coins and how many of each does he have?

3. Find two consecutive odd integers whose product is 323.

4. A veterinarian has a rectangular pen with an area of 96 ft². It is surrounded by a fence 44 feet long. What are the dimensions of the pen?

5. Chris, Mike, and John play on the Wheelchair Whiz basketball team. The numbers on their jerseys are consecutive even integers. The sum of the integers is 42. Find the numbers.

Chapter 4 Review

Key Terms

even integer   (p. 135)
isosceles triangle   (p. 140)
  base angles of,   (p. 140)
  base of,   (p. 140)
  legs of,   (p. 140)
  vertex angles of,   (p. 140)

least common denominator (LCD)   (p. 144)
least common multiple (LCM)   (p. 144)
odd integer   (p. 136)
percent   (p. 150)
perimeter of a triangle   (p. 140)

Key Ideas and Review Exercises

4.1,
4.2
If a word problem describes a relationship between two or more numbers, choose a variable and let it represent the number that is the *basis of comparison*. Then represent the other numbers in terms of that variable. Write an equation and solve it. Find the numbers, and check them in the original problem.

Bonita picked 6 more red apples than green apples and 8 more green apples than yellow apples. Let y be the number of yellow apples Bonita picked. (Exercises 1–4)

1. Represent the number of green apples in terms of y.
2. Represent the number of red apples in terms of y.
3. The total number of apples picked was 115. Write an equation and solve it.
4. How many apples of each color were picked?

Solve each problem.

5. One number is 6 times another. Their sum is 48. Find the numbers.
6. Separate $71 into 2 parts such that the second part is $5 less than 3 times the first part.

4.3
To solve problems involving consecutive integers, remember that consecutive integers can be represented by n, $n + 1$, $n + 2$, and so on, and that consecutive odd integers and consecutive even integers can be represented by n, $n + 2$, $n + 4$, and so on.

Solve each problem.

7. Find two consecutive integers with a sum of -25.
8. Find three consecutive even integers such that their sum decreased by 34 is equal to the first integer.

4.4   To solve problems involving perimeter and angle measure, first draw and label a figure. Then follow the usual problem-solving process.

9. The length of a rectangle is 10 ft less than 4 times the width. The perimeter is 50 ft. Find the length and the width.

10. Each base angle of an isosceles triangle has a degree measure that is 5 more than twice that of the vertex angle. Find the measure of each angle of the triangle.

4.5   To solve an equation that contains fractions, multiply each side by the LCD of all the fractions. Then solve in the usual way.

Solve each equation.

11. $\frac{2}{3}y - \frac{1}{2} = \frac{5}{6}$ 12. $\frac{3}{8} + \frac{1}{4}c = \frac{1}{2}c$ 13. $\frac{4x - 1}{3} - \frac{x}{4} = \frac{11x + 4}{12}$

4.6   To solve an equation with decimals, multiply each side by a power of ten that will give you an equivalent equation with integers in place of the decimals. Then solve in the usual way.

Solve each equation.

14. $0.03y = 0.6$ 15. $10.4 - 0.2c = -0.018$ 16. $0.6y + 0.002 = 0.7y - 1$

4.7   To solve any of the three basic types of percent problems, write an equation and solve as in Examples 1, 2, and 3 of Lesson 4.7.

To find the percent increase or decrease from one number to another:
a. Subtract to find the amount of increase or decrease.
b. Find what percent this is of the original number.

17. What number is 62% of 150?

18. Forty-one is 25% of what number?

19. Pierre got 12 hits in 40 times at bat. The number of hits is what percent of the number of times at bat?

20. Last year Jake was paid $7.50 an hour. This year he is paid $8.00 an hour. What is the percent increase in his wages?

4.8   For business problems involving percents, use these relationships.

cost + profit = selling price
regular price − amount of discount = sale price
salary + commission = total earned

21. The selling price of a radio is $70. The profit is 40% of the cost. Find the cost.

22. Jane is paid $140 a week plus 5% commission on all sales. Find the total sales needed to make her total earnings $350.

Solve each problem.

1. A 49-cm piece of ribbon is cut into two parts. The first part is 5 cm shorter than twice the second part. Find the length of each part.

2. The larger of 2 numbers is 3 times the smaller. The difference between the numbers is 14. Find the numbers.

3. The length of a rectangle is 3 ft greater than 4 times the width. The perimeter is 86 ft. Find the length and the width.

4. Each base angle of an isosceles triangle measures 12 degrees less than the vertex angle. Find the measure of each angle of the triangle.

5. The sum of two consecutive odd integers is -72. Find the integers.

6. Find 3 consecutive integers such that 4 times the middle integer plus the largest integer is 9 less than 6 times the smallest.

Solve each equation.

7. $\frac{1}{2}y = \frac{1}{3}y + 8$

8. $\frac{6a}{7} - \frac{a}{2} = 5$

9. $3.78 = 0.06x - 4.2$

10. $1.4x - 0.2142 = 0.14x$

Solve each problem.

11. 15 is 20% of what number?

12. 54 is what percent of 60?

13. The price of a jacket rose from $60 to $70. What was the percent increase in the price?

14. Olga is paid $160 a week plus a commission of 4% of her sales. How much must she sell to earn $250 in a week?

15. The regular price of a radio is $64. It is on sale for $56. Find the rate of discount.

16. Mr. Golden bought a shipment of paperweights for a total of $576. He will make a profit of 60% of that amount when he sells them. He priced each paperweight at $4.80. How many paperweights were there?

17. The selling price s of an item when there is a cost c and a profit of 40% of the cost is given by a formula of the form $s = kc$. Find the value of k.

College Prep Test

Choose the one best answer to each question or problem.

1. At Harper School, which grade had the largest percent increase in the number of students?

Grade	8	9	10	11	12
1989	60	55	65	62	60
1990	80	62	72	72	70

   (A) 8   (B) 9   (C) 10
   (D) 11   (E) 12

2. If n is an odd integer, which of the following represents the sum of n and the next two consecutive odd integers?
   (A) $3n$ (B) $3n + 3$
   (C) $3n + 4$ (D) $3n + 6$
   (E) None of these

3. If m and n are integers and m is divisible by 5, which of the following is always true?
   (A) $m + n$ is odd.
   (B) $m + n$ is even.
   (C) $m + n$ is divisible by 5.
   (D) mn is odd.
   (E) mn is divisible by five.

4. If 12% of a class of 25 students failed an exam, how many students passed the exam?
   (A) 22   (B) 20   (C) 13
   (D) 12   (E) 3

5. Evaluate $\dfrac{x^2 + x^3}{x - 1}$ if $x^3 = 8$.
   (A) $\dfrac{16}{7}$ (B) 4   (C) 12
   (D) 16   (E) 24

6. A truck was originally priced at $7,000. The price was reduced 20% and then raised 5%. What was the net reduction in price?
   (A) $5,950   (B) $5,880
   (C) $1,400   (D) $1,120
   (E) $1,050

7. A rectangle is 3 units longer than it is wide. Find its length if the perimeter is 38 units.
   (A) 4   (B) 6   (C) 8   (D) 11
   (E) 19

8. How many 25-cent stamps may be purchased for d dollars?
   (A) $\dfrac{d}{25}$ (B) $\dfrac{25}{d}$ (C) $25d$
   (D) $\dfrac{25}{100d}$ (E) $\dfrac{100d}{25}$

9. Mary receives D dollars for a 5-day work week. What is her daily salary after receiving a $10.00 per week raise?
   (A) $D + 10$ (B) $\dfrac{D}{5} + 2$
   (C) $\dfrac{D}{5} + 10$ (D) $5D + 2$
   (E) $5D + 10$

10. The sum of 4 consecutive odd integers exceeds twice the largest by 22. Find the sum of the 4 numbers.
    (A) 11   (B) 48   (C) 56
    (D) 60   (E) 88

11. Find the perimeter of the figure.

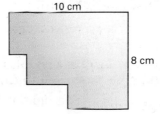

    (A) 18 cm   (B) 28 cm   (C) 30 cm
    (D) 36 cm   (E) 80 cm

12. Bob is 5 times as old as Jean, who is 2 years younger than Mike. If Mike is 5 years old, how old is Bob?
    (A) 27   (B) 25   (C) 15
    (D) 10   (E) 3

Cumulative Review (Chapters 1–4)

Each of Exercises 1–8 has five choices for answers. Choose the best answer.

1. Evaluate $6.1x$ for $x = 4$. **1.1**
   (A) 244   (B) 2.44
   (C) 24.4   (D) 6.5
   (E) None of these

2. Simplify $\dfrac{3 + 8 \cdot 6}{17}$. **1.2**
   (A) 1   (B) 3   (C) $\dfrac{1}{17}$
   (D) $3\dfrac{15}{17}$ (E) None of these

3. In the formula $p = 2l + 2w$, find p for $l = 3.4$, $w = 4.1$. **1.4**
   (A) 15   (B) 7.5   (C) 0.7
   (D) 30   (E) None of these

4. Solve $3x - 9 = 2(4 + x)$. **3.5**
   (A) $\dfrac{17}{4}$ (B) -1 (C) 1
   (D) -17 (E) None of these

5. Simplify $5(2x - 6) - (3 - 6x)$. **2.10**
   (A) $4x - 9$ (B) $4x - 33$
   (C) $16x - 9$ (D) $16x - 33$ (E) None of these

6. Simplify $-6 - (-5)$. **2.5**
   (A) 11   (B) -1
   (C) -11 (D) -30
   (E) None of these

7. Simplify $-15 + 2 - (-8) - 3$. **2.5**
   (A) -8 (B) -24
   (C) -28 (D) 8
   (E) None of these

8. Rewrite $(5x - 9)4$ without parentheses. **2.10**
   (A) $5x - 36$ (B) $5x + 36$
   (C) $20x + 36$ (D) $20x - 36$
   (E) None of these

Solve each equation.

9. $x - (-4) = 7$ **3.1**

10. $46 = -2y$ **3.2**

11. $\dfrac{2}{3}x = -22$

12. $-5y + 2 = -18$ **3.3**

13. $2(5y + 7) = -y - 8$ **3.5**

14. $3x - 7 = 4 - (x + 1)$

15. $5.6 - 2.4y = 7.2$ **4.6**

16. $3(2 - a) = 4(a + 5)$ **3.5**

Simplify.

17. $6a - 9(2a + 3) - 7$ **2.10**

18. $-5x + 3(2 + x) - (x - 1)$

19. $3c + 2d - 5(c - 4d)$

Evaluate. (Exercises 20–24)

20. x^3, for $x = -3$ **2.6**

21. $4b^4$, for $b = -1$

22. $-7 - 3x$, for $x = 2$ **2.8**

23. $6a^2 - b$, for $a = -2$, $b = -9$

24. $6(x - 9)$, for $x = 4$ **1.2**

25. If Jim's age is increased by 3 years more than twice his age, the result is 51 years. Find Jim's age. **4.2**

26. This year, a ring selling for \$53 costs 7 dollars less than twice what it cost last year. What did the ring cost last year?

27. Phyllis has 28 records in her collection. She has $\dfrac{2}{3}$ as many as Josie has. How many records does Josie have? **3.2**

28. The temperature at 6:00 P.M. was 5°F. By 1:00 A.M. it had dropped 9°. By 4:00 A.M. it had risen 6°. What was the temperature at 4:00 A.M.?   *2.4*

29. The lowest point in a valley is 160 ft below sea level. A helicopter was flying 2,200 ft above this point. The helicopter dropped 500 ft. Find the altitude of the helicopter relative to sea level.   *2.4*

30. Use $C = \frac{5}{9}(F - 32)$ to find the temperature in degrees Celsius (C) when a thermometer reads 50°F.   *1.3*

31. The daily high temperatures for the first 5 days of January are shown below. What was the average high temperature for the 5 days?   *2.7*

Jan. 1	Jan. 2	Jan. 3	Jan. 4	Jan. 5
−3	10	6	−4	−9

32. On Monday, Katie ran the 100-yard dash in 12.3 seconds. On Tuesday she improved her time by 0.9 s. What was her time for the 100-yard dash on Tuesday?

33. After jogging 4 mi from home, Jordan was $\frac{2}{3}$ of the way to the shopping center. How far was the shopping center from his home?   *3.2*

34. The $56 price of a coat is $1 less than 3 times the cost. Find the cost of the coat.   *4.2*

35. After Jean gave away $\frac{2}{5}$ of her fish, she had 12 fish left. How many fish did she have before she gave some away?

36. This year a party favor costs $0.60 less than twice what one cost last year. This year a favor costs $1.10. What did it cost last year?   *4.2*

37. If a number is increased by 8 and then multiplied by −3, the result is 21. Find the number.   *4.2*

38. For the square below, write a formula for the perimeter in terms of k. Express the formula in simplest form.   *2.9*

39. Separate 31 into two parts so that the larger is 5 less than 3 times the smaller.   *4.2*

40. The sum of two consecutive integers is 75. Find the two integers.   *4.3*

41. Find three consecutive odd integers whose sum is −39.

42. In a rectangle, the length is 3 m shorter than twice the width. The perimeter is 36 m. Find the length and the width.   *4.4*

43. What number is 8% of 40?   *4.7*

44. The price of a tape deck is $156. The profit is 30% of the cost. Find the cost.   *4.8*

45. What percent of 90 is 15?   *4.7*

46. Six is 5% of what number?

47. Use the formula $i = prt$ to find the amount of simple interest received when $2,500 is invested for 3 years at an interest rate of $6\frac{1}{2}\%$.

5 INEQUALITIES AND ABSOLUTE VALUE

These surveyors study the movement of glaciers in the Juneau icefield in Alaska. Most glaciers move, or "flow" at less than one foot per day. Scientists, however, have measured a flow of more than 50 feet in one day.

5.1 The Addition and Subtraction Properties of Inequality

Objective

To solve and graph the solution set of an inequality by using the Addition or Subtraction Property of Inequality

Examine the chart below to review the two inequality symbols, $<$ and $>$.

Inequality	Read	Meaning
$a < b$	a is less than b.	a is to the *left* of b on a number line.
$c > d$	c is greater than d.	c is to the *right* of d on a number line.

The open sentence $x < -2$ is an example of an *inequality*. An **inequality** contains at least one variable and consists of two expressions with an inequality symbol such as $<$, $>$, or $\neq$ between them. To **solve an inequality** means to find its solution set. The replacement set for the variable is assumed to be the set of all real numbers. To solve the inequality $x < -2$, you must find all the real numbers that make the open sentence true. Some real numbers make $x < -2$ a true statement and some real numbers make $x < -2$ a false statement.

$$x < -2$$

$-3 < -2$	true	$2 < -2$	false
$-5.4 < -2$	true	$0 < -2$	false
$-100 < -2$	true	$-2 < -2$	false

It is not possible to list all the solutions of $x < -2$. However, a number line can be used to graph the solution set.

The graph of the solution set of $x < -2$ includes every point with a coordinate that is less than -2. To indicate that -2 itself is not a solution, an open circle appears at -2. A heavy arrow to the *left* of the open circle indicates that the coordinate of every point to the left of -2 is a solution.

graph of the solution set of $x < -2$

EXAMPLE 1   Graph the solution set of $x > 0$.

Solution   Make an open circle at 0. Then draw a heavy arrow to the right of the circle to show all the points with coordinates that are greater than 0.

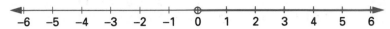

-6 -5 -4 -3 -2 -1   0   1   2   3   4   5   6

TRY THIS   1. Graph the solution set of $x < 3$.

The Addition and Subtraction Properties of Equality allow you to add or subtract the same number from each side of an equation to obtain an equivalent equation. Examine the chart below to determine whether there are similar properties for inequalities.

True Inequality	Operate on each side	New Inequality	True or False?
$2 < 6$	Add 5.	$2 + 5 < 6 + 5$ $7 < 11$	True
$3 > -7$	Subtract 2.	$3 - 2 > -7 - 2$ $1 > -9$	True
$-8 < -2$	Subtract 4.	$-8 - 4 < -2 - 4$ $-12 < -6$	True

In each case above, the new inequality is true. These cases suggest the properties below.

Definition

Open inequalities with the same solution set are called **equivalent inequalities**.

Addition Property of Inequality
For all real numbers a, b, and c,
  if $a < b$, then $a + c < b + c$, and
  if $a > b$, then $a + c > b + c$
That is, adding the same number to each side of an inequality produces an *equivalent inequality*.

Subtraction Property of Inequality
For all real numbers a, b, and c,
  if $a < b$, then $a - c < b - c$, and
  if $a > b$, then $a - c > b - c$
That is, subtracting the same number from each side of an inequality produces an equivalent inequality.

EXAMPLE 2   Solve $x - 8 < -11$. Graph the solution set.

Plan   Use the Addition Property of Inequality.

Solution
$$x - 8 < -11$$
Add 8 to each side. $$x - 8 + 8 < -11 + 8$$
$$x < -3$$

Check   You cannot check every solution. Try numbers less than -3 and greater than -3. Also try -3 itself. Check in the *original* inequality.

Let $x = -4$.   Let $x = -3$.   Let $x = -2$.

$$x - 8 \overset{?}{<} -11$$ $$x - 8 \overset{?}{<} -11$$ $$x - 8 \overset{?}{<} -11$$
$$-4 - 8 \overset{?}{<} -11$$ $$-3 - 8 \overset{?}{<} -11$$ $$-2 - 8 \overset{?}{<} -11$$
$$-12 < -11$$ $$-11 \nless -11$$ $$-10 \nless -11$$
(True)   (False)   (False)

Thus, the solution set is the set of all real numbers less than -3.

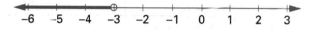

EXAMPLE 3   Solve $7 < 5 - \left(\frac{1}{2} - x\right)$. Graph the solution set.

Plan   First simplify the expression on the right side of the inequality. Then find an equivalent inequality that has x alone on the right.

Solution
$$7 < 5 - \left(\tfrac{1}{2} - x\right)$$
$$7 < 5 - \tfrac{1}{2} + x$$
$$7 < 4\tfrac{1}{2} + x$$
Subtract $4\frac{1}{2}$ from each side. $$7 - 4\tfrac{1}{2} < 4\tfrac{1}{2} + x - 4\tfrac{1}{2}$$
$$2\tfrac{1}{2} < x, \quad \text{or} \quad x > 2\tfrac{1}{2}$$

Thus the solution set is the set of all real numbers greater than $2\frac{1}{2}$.

$2\frac{1}{2}$

    -3 -2 -1 0 1 2 3 4 5 6 7 8 9

TRY THIS   2. Solve $-8 > -2 - (4 - x)$.

EXAMPLE 4 After Mary paid $8.36 for a tape, she had less than $2.50 left. How much money did she have originally?

Solution Let m = the original amount of money.
Then $m - 8.36$ = the amount of money after the purchase of a tape.
The amount of money after purchase is less than $2.50.

Inequality: $m = 8.36$ $\quad\quad\quad\quad < \quad\quad 2.50$

Solve the inequality. $\quad m - 8.36 + 8.36 < 2.50 + 8.36$
$$m < 10.86$$

Thus, the original amount of money was less than $10.86.

TRY THIS 3. After Bill paid $7.21 at the movies, he had less than $1.75 left. How much money did he have originally?

Classroom Exercises

Complete each statement. Use $<$, $>$, or $=$.

1. $7 > 6$. Therefore, $7 - 2 \underline{\ ?\ } 6 - 2$
2. $-3 < 0$. Therefore, $-3 + 3 \underline{\ ?\ } 0 + 3$
3. $-9 + 4 = -5$. Therefore, $-9 + 4 - 4 \underline{\ ?\ } -5 - 4$
4. $-8 < -3 - 4$. Therefore, $-8 + 8 \underline{\ ?\ } -3 - 4 + 8$
5. If $x + 6 < 2$, then $x + 6 - 6 \underline{\ ?\ } 2 - 6$

Match each open sentence with the correct graph.

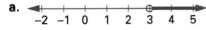

a. number line from -2 to 5 with open circle at 3, shaded left

b. number line from -2 to 5 with open circle at 3, shaded left

6. $x < 3$
8. $3 < x$
10. $x - 5 < -2$

7. $x > 3$
9. $3 > x$
11. $7 < x + 4$

Solve each inequality. Graph the solution set.

12. $y - 4 < 2$
13. $x + 7 > 0$
14. $c - 5 < -1$

Written Exercises

Solve each inequality. Graph the solution set.

1. $x + 8 > 5$
2. $y - 7 < 2$
3. $z + 3 < -7$
4. $c - 5 > -2$
5. $r + 7 < 0$
6. $x - 8 > 1$

7. $y - \frac{1}{4} < 2$

8. $z + 0.5 > -4$

9. $d - 2\frac{1}{3} > -6$

10. $5 < x - 3$

11. $2 > y + \frac{1}{2}$

12. $-6 < -2.8 + c$

13. $6.2 + y < -8.1$

14. $-5.7 + a > 3.6$

15. $-7\frac{1}{2} < 3\frac{1}{4} + z$

Write the inequality for each problem. Then solve the problem.

16. If Sarah gains 6 lb, she will weigh more than 113 lb. How much does Sarah weigh now?

17. After Jim deposited $6.25 in his savings account, he had less than $50 in the account. How much was in the account before he made the deposit?

18. After Jason gave 8 tapes away, he had more than 35 tapes. How many tapes did he have before he gave 8 away?

19. After selling 13 copies of the Daily Gazette, a newsdealer had fewer than 90 copies left. How many copies did the newsdealer have originally?

Solve each inequality. Graph the solution set.

20. $5x - (1 + 4x) > -4$

21. $-2x - 3(4 - x) < 14$

22. $1.5x - 0.5(x + 4) < 12$

23. $6.5 - 4.2c + 5.2(c - 1) > 3.7$

24. The Symmetric Property of Equality states that for the equality symbol, $=$, if $x = y$, then $y = x$. Is there a similar property for the inequality symbol, $<$? If so, state it. If not, give a numerical example that disproves it.

25. The Reflexive Property of Equality states that for the equality symbol, $=$, $x = x$. Is there a reflexive property for the inequality symbol, $>$? If so, state it. If not, give an example to disprove it.

26. Begin with a true inequality, such as $5 > -1$. Use a number line to show that the Addition Property of Inequality holds for $>$ when you add either a positive or a negative number to each side of the inequality.

27. Use the Addition Property of Inequality to prove the Subtraction Property of Inequality. (HINT: In the Addition Property, let $c = -d$.)

Mixed Review

Solve.   *3.3, 3.4, 3.5, 4.6, 4.7*

1. $2x - 5 = 9$

2. $5y - y = 11 + 3y$

3. $5c - (4c - c) = 3 + 5c + 2$

4. $1.6x = 0.72 - 0.8x$

5. What number is 6% of 50?

6. Forty-two is 150% of __?__ .

7. Fifteen is what percent of 75?

8. Twelve is __?__ % of 3?

5.2 The Multiplication and Division Properties of Inequality

Objective

To solve and graph the solution set of an inequality by using the Multiplication or Division Property of Inequality

The Multiplication and Division Properties of Equality allow you to multiply or divide each side of an equation by the same number. There are similar properties for inequalities.

True Inequality	Operate on each side.	New Inequality	True or False?
$3 < 4$	Multiply by 5. (5 is *positive*.)	$3 \cdot 5 < 4 \cdot 5$ $15 < 20$	True
$-4 > -20$	Divide by 2. (2 is *positive*.)	$\dfrac{-4}{2} > \dfrac{-20}{2}$ $-2 > -10$	True
$-5 < -3$	Multiply by -1. (-1 is *negative*.)	$-5(-1) < -3(-1)$ $5 < 3$	False. Reverse the order of the inequality. $5 > 3$ True
$18 > -6$	Divide by -3. (-3 is *negative*.)	$\dfrac{18}{-3} > \dfrac{-6}{-3}$ $-6 > 2$	False. Reverse the order of the inequality. $-6 < 2$ True

Notice that multiplying (or dividing) each side of a true inequality by a *negative* number produces a *false* inequality. The order of the inequality must be *reversed* to make the new inequality true. These results suggest the following property.

Multiplication Property of Inequality
For all real numbers a, b, and c,
  if $a < b$ and $c > 0$, then $ac < bc$, and
  if $a > b$ and $c > 0$, then $ac > bc$
That is, multiplying each side of an inequality by the same *positive* number produces an equivalent inequality.
For all real numbers a, b, and c,
  if $a < b$ and $c < 0$, then $ac > bc$, and
  if $a > b$ and $c < 0$, then $ac < bc$
That is, multiplying each side of an inequality by the same *negative* number and *reversing the order of the inequality* produces an equivalent inequality.

EXAMPLE 1   Solve each open inequality. Graph the solution set.

a. $7x < -56$ b. $-\frac{2}{3}x > 16$

Plan   Multiply each side of the inequality by the *reciprocal* of the coefficient of x.

Solutions

a. $7x < -56$

$\frac{1}{7}(7x) < \frac{1}{7}(-56)$

$x < -8$

The solution set is the set of all real numbers less than -8.

b. $-\frac{2}{3}x > 16$

$\left(-\frac{3}{2}\right)\left(-\frac{2}{3}x\right) < \left(-\frac{3}{2}\right)16$ ⟵ $-\frac{3}{2}$ is negative; change $>$ to $<$.

$x < -\frac{48}{2},$ or $x < -24$

The solution set is the set of all real numbers less than -24.

TRY THIS   1. Solve $-4 < -2x$. Graph the solution set.

The second step of Example 1a could be

$$\frac{7x}{7} < \frac{-56}{7}$$ rather than $\frac{1}{7}(7x) < \frac{1}{7}(-56).$

This illustrates the *Division Property of Inequality.*

Division Property of Inequality
For all real numbers a, b, and c,

if $a < b$ and $c > 0$, then $\frac{a}{c} < \frac{b}{c}$, and

if $a > b$ and $c > 0$, then $\frac{a}{c} > \frac{b}{c}$.

That is, dividing each side of an inequality by the same *positive* number produces an equivalent inequality.

For all real numbers a, b, and c,

if $a < b$ and $c < 0$, then $\frac{a}{c} > \frac{b}{c}$, and

if $a > b$ and $c < 0$, then $\frac{a}{c} < \frac{b}{c}$.

That is, dividing each side of an inequality by the same *negative* number and *reversing the order of inequality* produces an equivalent inequality.

A calculator may be helpful in solving problems involving inequalities.

EXAMPLE 2

If Jill sells more than $100 worth of peanut brittle, she will win a radio. Each box of peanut brittle sells for $2.75. How many boxes must she sell to win the radio?

Solution

Let p = the number of boxes Jill must sell.

$$2.75p > 100$$

$$p > \frac{100}{2.75}$$

$p > 36.36\overline{36}$ (THINK: She must sell a whole number of boxes.)

Jill must sell more than 36 boxes.
Thus, she must sell 37 or more boxes.

EXAMPLE 3

Solve $-3x + 6 < -5$.

Plan

Use the Subtraction Property of Inequality first. Then use the Division Property of Inequality.

Solution

Subtract 6 from each side. $\quad -3x + 6 < -5$

Divide each side by -3 $\qquad\qquad -3x < -11$

(or multiply by $-\frac{1}{3}$). $\qquad \dfrac{-3x}{-3} > \dfrac{-11}{-3} \quad \longleftarrow$ Change < to >.

$$x > \frac{11}{3}, \text{ or } x > 3\tfrac{2}{3}$$

Thus, the solution set is the set of real numbers greater than $3\frac{2}{3}$.

EXAMPLE 4

Solve $5 - 4x < 2x - 7$.

Solution

Method 1	**Method 2**
$5 - 4x < 2x - 7$	$5 - 4x < 2x - 7$
$5 < 6x - 7$	$5 - 6x < -7$
$12 < 6x$	$-6x < -12$
$2 < x, \text{ or } x > 2$	$x > 2$

Thus, the solution set is the set of all real numbers greater than 2.

TRY THIS

2. Solve $6x - 5 < 8x + 3$.

It is possible for the solution set of an inequality to be the empty set, $\varnothing$, or to be the set of all real numbers.

EXAMPLE 5   Solve $-\frac{3}{2}x + 4 > 7 - \frac{3}{2}x$. Graph the solution set.

Solution

$$-\frac{3}{2}x + 4 > 7 - \frac{3}{2}x$$

Add $\frac{3}{2}x$ to each side. $-\frac{3}{2}x + 4 + \frac{3}{2}x > 7 - \frac{3}{2}x + \frac{3}{2}x$

$$4 > 7 \quad \longleftarrow \text{False}$$

When solving an inequality results in a false inequality (involving no variable), then *no* value of x will make the original inequality true. Thus, the solution set is the empty set $\varnothing$.

(No points are graphed.)

EXAMPLE 6   Solve $-2(2x + 1) + 5x < x + 5$. Graph the solution set.

Solution

$$-2(2x + 1) + 5x < x + 5$$
$$-4x - 2 + 5x < x + 5 \quad \longleftarrow \text{Distributive Property}$$
$$x - 2 < x + 5$$

Add $-x$ to each side. $-x + x - 2 < -x + x + 5$

$$-2 < 5 \quad \longleftarrow \text{True}$$

When solving an inequality results in a true inequality (involving no variable), then *every* real-number value of x will make the original inequality true. Thus, the solution set is the set of all real numbers.

graph of the set of all real numbers
(All points are graphed.)

TRY THIS   3. Solve $-5\left(2 - \frac{4}{5}x\right) + 3x > -4\left(\frac{1}{4} - x\right)$.

Classroom Exercises

Complete each statement. Use $<$, $>$, or $=$.

1. If $8 > 5$, then $8 \cdot 3 \underline{\ ?\ } 5 \cdot 3$
2. $-7 < 0$. So, $-7(-4) \underline{\ ?\ } 0(-4)$
3. If $4x < 12$, then $x \underline{\ ?\ } 3$
4. If $-3y > 15$, then $y \underline{\ ?\ } -5$
5. If $-20 < -5x$, then $4 \underline{\ ?\ } x$, or $x \underline{\ ?\ } 4$
6. If $0 > -7x$, then $0 \underline{\ ?\ } x$, or $x \underline{\ ?\ } 0$

Solve each open inequality. Graph the solution set.

7. $4a > 12$
8. $-2c < 18$
9. $3x - 5 > 22$

Written Exercises

Solve each inequality. Graph the solution set.

1. $3y < 18$
2. $-4x > 16$
3. $-7z < -2$
4. $-16 > 2y$
5. $-\frac{1}{3}a > 5$
6. $\frac{2}{3}k < -12$
7. $2x + 3 < 1$
8. $-3y - 4 > -7$
9. $-2 + 5z > 8$
10. $3 < -7a - 8$
11. $-6 < 2y + 3$
12. $9 - 4k > -15$
13. $\frac{1}{3}x + 7 < -2$
14. $-\frac{3}{5}y - 1 > -4$
15. $5 < \frac{1}{2} + \frac{3}{2}x$
16. $x + 8 > x - 3$
17. $4y - 4 > 7 + 4y$
18. $-6x - 6 < 3x - 27$
19. $7 - 5x > 9 - 4x$
20. $17 - 2z < 3z - 8$
21. $10c - 16 < 12c - 18$
22. $2x - 7 > -7x + 20$
23. $5x - 9 > 8 + 5x$
24. $35 - 4y > -9 + 7y$
25. $9c - 7 < 4c + 18$
26. $-6z + 8 > -3 - 6z$

Write an inequality for each problem. Then solve the problem.

27. Bert and Juan made more than $63. If they divided the money equally, how much did each boy receive?

28. Morey paid less than $5.10 for a package of three golf balls. What was the cost of each golf ball?

29. Dana has saved $62 toward the cost of a ten-speed bike. This is less than $\frac{1}{3}$ of the cost of the bike. What is the cost of the bike?

30. Helena and Grace must take in more than $150 to make a profit on some T-shirts they are selling. If each T-shirt costs $6.50, how many must be sold to make a profit?

Solve each inequality.

31. $2x + 4 < 3(x - 4)$
32. $5(x - 2) > 7 + 5x$
33. $-(3 - 2c) > 10c + 5$
34. $\frac{1}{2}y - 8 > \frac{2}{5}y - 7$
35. $\frac{1}{2}c + 1 < \frac{3}{4}c - 1$
36. $6 + \frac{1}{2}z > 5 + \frac{2}{3}z$
37. $8x - 2(5x - 2) < 7 + 3x$
38. $3(4y + 1) + 7 > 3y - 2$
39. $2 + 5(y + 1) > y - 3(2y + 1)$
40. $x + 2 < 5x - 7 - (3 + x)$

Solve for x. (HINT: Where appropriate, consider more than one case.)

41. $x + a < b$
42. $ax < b, a \neq 0$
43. $\dfrac{ax + bx}{c} < d, c \neq 0, a \neq -b$

Mixed Review

Simplify.   *1.2, 1.3, 2.2, 2.8*

1. $18 - 5 \cdot 3$
2. $6^2 - 5^2$
3. $|-4.6|$
4. $-(-1)^8$
5. $14 - 3(-5)$
6. The length of a rectangle is 10 m less than twice the width. The perimeter is 112 m. Find the length and the width of the rectangle.   *4.7*

5.3 Conjunctions and Disjunctions

Objective	To determine whether a conjunction or a disjunction is true or false

The words "and" and "or" occur frequently in everyday life. These two familiar words also occur in mathematical settings, for example, when forming combined, or *compound*, mathematical sentences.

A **conjunction** is composed of two sentences connected by the word *and*. Whether a conjunction is true (T) or false (F) depends upon the two sentences. Examine the chart below.

Conjunctions

First sentence	T or F?	Second sentence	T or F?	Conjunction	T or F?
$5 < 8$	T	$2 + 9 = 11$	T	$5 < 8$ and $2 + 9 = 11$	T
$6 - 4 = 2$	T	$-3 > 1$	F	$6 - 4 = 2$ and $-3 > 1$	F
$2 < 0$	F	$8 = 5 + 4$	F	$2 < 0$ and $8 = 5 + 4$	F

A conjunction is true only if *both* of the sentences are true.

EXAMPLE 1   Determine whether each conjunction is true or false.

a. $5 - 2 = 7$ and $6 - 4 > -1$
b. $-7 + 3 < -2$ and $6 - 3 > -1$

Plan   For each sentence of the conjunction, determine whether it is true or false.

Solutions

a. $5 - 2 = 7$ and $6 - 4 > -1$
    $\quad\quad 3 \neq 7 \quad\quad\quad\quad 2 > -1$
    $\quad\quad\quad$ F $\quad\quad\quad\quad\quad$ T

One sentence is false. Thus, the conjunction is false.

b. $-7 + 3 < -2$ and $6 - 3 > -1$
    $\quad\quad -4 < -2 \quad\quad\quad\quad 3 > -1$
    $\quad\quad\quad$ T $\quad\quad\quad\quad\quad$ T

Both sentences are true. Thus, the conjunction is true.

TRY THIS   Determine whether the conjunction is true or false.
1. $6 + 5 < 2$ and $2 - 3 > 1$
2. $5 - 8 < 0$ and $8 - 5 > 0$

A **disjunction** is composed of two sentences connected by the word *or*. Whether a disjunction is true or false depends upon the two sentences.

Disjunctions

First sentence	T or F?	Second sentence	T or F?	Disjunction	T or F?
$5 > -2$	T	$8 + 2 = 10$	T	$5 > -2$ or $8 + 2 = 10$	T
$5 \cdot 8 = 40$	T	$9 - 10 = 1$	F	$5 \cdot 8 = 40$ or $9 - 10 = 1$	T
$6 < -4$	F	$3 \cdot 5 = 10$	F	$6 < -4$ or $3 \cdot 5 < 10$	F

A disjunction is false only if *both* sentences are false.

EXAMPLE 2   Determine whether each disjunction is true or false.

a. $6 > 3 + 5$ or $9 = 12 - 3$
b. $5^3 < 100$ or $6 \cdot 8 > 50$

Plan   Determine whether *either* sentence of the disjunction is true.

Solutions
a. $6 > 3 + 5$ or $9 = 12 - 3$
    $6 \not> 8$ $9 = 9$ One sentence is true.
     F   T   Thus, the disjunction is true.

b. $5^3 < 100$ or $6 \cdot 8 > 50$
    $125 \not< 100$ $48 \not> 50$ Both sentences are false.
      F   F   Thus, the disjunction is false.

TRY THIS   3. Determine whether the disjunction is true or false.

$$9 + 6 > 5 \quad or \quad 4^2 < 24$$

The truth of a conjunction and a disjunction can be summarized in **truth tables**, as shown below. The letters p and q represent sentences.

Conjunction

p	q	p and q
T	T	T
T	F	F
F	T	F
F	F	F

A conjunction is true only if both p and q are true.

Disjunction

p	q	p or q
T	T	T
T	F	T
F	T	T
F	F	F

A disjunction is false only if both p and q are false.

EXAMPLE 3   In a laboratory stress test, a tube of material is found to fail if it is stretched to a length of more than 21.3 cm or compressed to a length of less than 19.7 cm. Use a conjunction or disjunction to describe the complete failure zone for the material.

Plan   Write two inequalities, one for each failure zone. Then combine into one open sentence using "and" or "or."

Solution   Let x = the length of the tube in a failure zone.

Then $x < 19.7$ describes the failure zone under compression, and $x > 21.3$ describes the failure zone under stretching.

The material fails if its length is less than 19.7 cm *or* greater than 21.3 cm.

This is described by the *disjunction* $x < 19.7$ or $x > 21.3$.

TRY THIS   4. Write a conjunction or a disjunction to describe the problem. Mark weighs more than 160 lb but less than 168 lb.

Classroom Exercises

Determine whether the given sentence is *true* or *false*.

1. $7 \neq 5 + 2$
2. $8 = -1 + 9$
3. $7 \neq 5 + 2$ *and* $8 = -1 + 9$
4. $7 \neq 5 + 2$ *or* $8 = -1 + 9$
5. $5 < -6^2$
6. $0 > 7 - 2^3$
7. $5 < -6^2$ *and* $0 > 7 - 2^3$
8. $5 < -6^2$ *or* $0 > 7 - 2^3$

Written Exercises

Determine whether the given conjunction or disjunction is *true* or *false*.

1. $-2 < 5$ *and* $6 = 2 + 4$
2. $5 > 1$ *or* $3 = -2$
3. $7 \neq 2$ *and* $5 = -1 + 4$
4. $8 > -2$ *and* $-5 < -2$
5. $7 < 3 + 3$ *or* $6 \neq 4 + 2$
6. $8 < 10 - 1$ *or* $4^2 = 16$
7. $10 - 5 \cdot 2 < 0$ *or* $5^3 > 100$
8. $-3 > 2$ *and* $(-6)^2 = 36$
9. $5 \cdot 6 > 30$ *or* $7 \cdot 2 < 15$
10. $8 \neq 5 + 2$ *and* $9 > -9$

For each problem, use x for the variable and write a conjunction or a disjunction to describe the problem.

11. Mary would like to weigh more than 110 lb but less than 115 lb.

12. The new addition to Fairview Stadium must have 6 or more gates.

13. Jack hopes to save at least $150.

14. When Mark makes a cake, he bakes it no more than 50 min.

Give a value of x that will make each conjunction or disjunction true. If there is no such value, state this. (For each exercise, the same value of x must be used in both sentences.)

15. $x = 3$ *and* $x > 2$ **16.** $x < 2$ *or* $x < -7$ **17.** $x > -3$ *or* $x = -3$

18. $x < 5$ *and* $x = 5$ **19.** $x > -1$ *or* $x < 2$ **20.** $x > -2$ *and* $x < 3$

21–26. Give a value of x that will make each conjunction or disjunction of Exercises $15-20$ *false*. If there is no such value, state this.

27. The *negation* of sentence p is *not p*, written $\sim p$. If p is true, then $\sim p$ is false. If p is false, then $\sim p$ is true. See the truth table at the right.

Complete the truth table below.

Negation

p	$\sim p$
T	F
F	T

p	q	$\sim p$	$\sim q$	$\sim p$ and $\sim q$
T	T			
T	F			
F	T			
F	F			

Write a truth table for each conjunction, disjunction, or negation.

28. $\sim(\sim p)$ **29.** $\sim p$ *or* $\sim q$ **30.** p *and* $\sim q$ **31.** $\sim p$ *or* q **32.** $\sim(p$ *and* $\sim q)$

Mixed Review

Simplify. *1.2, 2.8*

1. $3y - 7 - 4y - 9$

2. $11x - (7 - x) - 13x$

Solve. *3.3, 3.5*

3. $3(x + 1) = 5 - (4 - x)$

4. $13 = -\frac{1}{2}x + 2$

Evaluate. *2.8, 2.9*

5. $5 - 3z$, for $z = -7$

6. $14c + 1.7$, for $c = 0.2$

7. Mr. Rosenfeld sells dishwashers for \$360. The profit is 20% of the cost. How many dishwashers must he sell to make a total profit of \$900? *4.8*

5.4 Combining Inequalities

Objective   To graph the solution sets of conjunctions and disjunctions of inequalities

The disjunction $x < 2$ *or* $x = 2$ can be written as $x \leq 2$ (*x is less than or equal to 2*).

Recall that a disjunction is true if either or both of its sentences are true. Thus, the solution set of a disjunction contains all the solutions of the two sentences.

Sentence   **Graph**

$x < 2$

$x = 2$

$x < 2$ or $x = 2$ ($x \leq 2$)

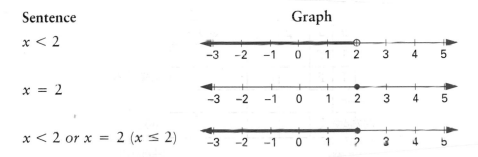

In the first graph above, an open circle at 2 indicates that 2 is not a member of the solution set of $x < 2$. In the third graph, the heavy dot at 2 indicates that 2 *is* a member of the solution set of $x \leq 2$.

When finding the solution set of a disjunction containing $\leq$ or $\geq$, you can use the inequality properties of Lessons 5.1 and 5.2.

EXAMPLE 1   Graph the solution set of $11 - 3x \leq 26$.

Solution $11 - 3x \leq 26$

Subtract 11 from each side. $-3x \leq 15$

Divide each side by -3 and $x \geq -5$
reverse the order of the inequality.

Thus, the solution set is the set of all real numbers greater than or equal to -5.

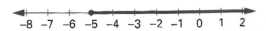 $\longleftarrow$ Note the heavy
                                    dot at -5.

TRY THIS   Graph the solution set of $2y + 1 \leq 7$.

Recall that a conjunction is true only if both sentences are true. Thus, the solution set contains only the solutions common to both sentences.

EXAMPLE 2   Graph the solution set of $x \leq -2$ *or* $x > 3$. Then graph the solution set of $x \leq -2$ *and* $x > 3$.

Plan   First, graph the solution set of $x \leq -2$ and the solution set of $x > 3$. Then use the definition of *disjunction* and of *conjunction* to draw the other two graphs.

Solutions $x \leq -2$

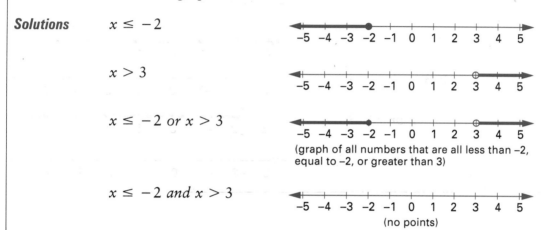

$x > 3$

$x \leq -2$ *or* $x > 3$

(graph of all numbers that are all less than –2, equal to –2, or greater than 3)

$x \leq -2$ *and* $x > 3$

(no points)

In Example 2, there are no solutions common to both $x \leq -2$ and $x > 3$. Therefore, the solution set of "$x \leq -2$ *and* $x > 3$" is the empty set.

EXAMPLE 3   Graph the solution set of $x > -1$ *or* $x < 4$. Then graph the solution set of $x > -1$ *and* $x < 4$.

Solutions $x > -1$

$x < 4$

$x > -1$ *or* $x < 4$

(entire number line since *every* number is less than –1 or greater than 4)

$x > -1$ *and* $x < 4$

(only the numbers that are both greater than –1 and less than 4)

EXAMPLE 4   Graph the solution set of $x - 1 \geq -3$ or $4 < 2x - 2$. Then graph the solution set of $x - 1 \geq -3$ and $4 < 2x - 2$.

Plan   Solve $x - 1 \geq -3$. Then solve $4 < 2x - 2$. Graph their solution sets on separate number lines. Finally, graph the solution set of the disjunction and the solution set of the conjunction.

Solutions

$$x - 1 \geq -3 \qquad\qquad 4 < 2x - 2$$
$$x \geq -2 \qquad\qquad\quad 6 < 2x$$
$$\qquad\qquad\qquad\qquad 3 < x, \text{ or } x > 3$$

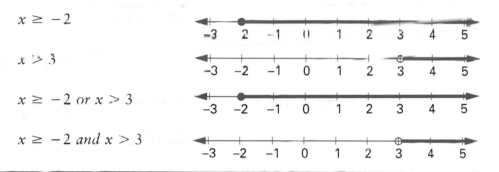

$$x \geq -2$$

$$x > 3$$

$$x \geq -2 \text{ or } x > 3$$

$$x \geq -2 \text{ and } x > 3$$

The conjunction $x > -1$ and $x < 4$ can be written as $-1 < x < 4$. This can be read in three ways.

> -1 is less than x and x is less than 4.
>
> x is greater than -1 and x is less than 4.
>
> x is between -1 and 4.

EXAMPLE 5   Graph the solution set of $-3 < 2x + 5 \leq 9$.

Plan   Write the conjunction as $-3 < 2x + 5$ and $2x + 5 \leq 9$. Solve each sentence and graph the solution set of the resulting conjunction.

Solution

$$-3 < 2x + 5 \quad and \quad 2x + 5 \leq 9$$
$$-8 < 2x \qquad\qquad\qquad 2x \leq 4$$
$$-4 < x \qquad\qquad\qquad\quad x \leq 2$$
$$-4 < x \leq 2$$

$\longleftarrow$ x is between -4 and 2, including 2.

EXAMPLE 6 This year, Jim's weight fluctuated within a 7-lb range. At times he weighed as little as 125 lb. At other times he weighed almost 132 lb. Write a conjunction that describes the range of values for Jim's weight.

Solution Let x = Jim's weight.

If Jim weighed "as little as" 125 lb, then sometimes he weighed 125 lb and sometimes he weighed more than 125 lb. This is expressed by the compound inequality

$$125 = x \; or \; 125 < x; \text{ that is, } 125 \leq x$$

If Jim weighed "almost 132 lb" then sometimes he weighed less than 132 lb, but never actually 132 lb. This is expressed by the inequality $x < 132$.

Jim's weight in the 7 lb range is expressed by this conjunction.

$$125 \leq x \; and \; x < 132, \text{ or } 125 \leq x < 132.$$

Focus on Reading

Match each conjunction or disjunction with its graph.

1. $x \geq -5 \; and \; x < 0$

2. $x \leq -5 \; or \; x > 0$

3. $x \geq -5 \; or \; x > 0$

4. $x \leq -5 \; and \; x > 0$

5. $x \geq -5 \; or \; x < 0$

a.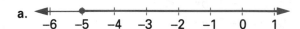

b.

c.

d.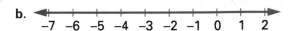

e.

Classroom Exercises

Rewrite using *and* or *or*.

1. $x \leq 5$

2. $-2 < x < 7$

3. $y \geq -6$

4. $0 < y < 12$

5. $-2 \leq 7 + x$

6. $-8 < x < 9$

7. $x - 3 \geq 15$

8. $-7 < x + 2 < 11$

Rewrite without *and* or *or*.

9. $x > -5$ and $x < 7$

10. $x = -8$ or $x > -8$

11. $x < 0$ or $x = 0$

12. $x \geq -6$ and $x < 9$

13. $x > 0$ and $x < 10$

14. $x > 5$ or $x = 5$

Graph the solution set.

15. $2x - 3 = 5$

16. $-7 \leq 5 + 4y$

17. $y \geq 5$ or $y < -1$

18. $x > -2$ and $x \leq -1$

19. $-3 < x + 1 \leq 0$

20. $-2x > 6$ or $x - 7 < -2$

Written Exercises

Graph the solution set.

1. $3x - 8 \geq 7$

2. $2x + 15 \leq 21$

3. $-17 \geq 9c - 8$

4. $-15 \leq -3a + 12$

5. $-3d + 4 \leq -11$

6. $8r - 8 \leq -24$

7. $9x - 7 \geq 18 + 4x$

8. $2y - 5 \geq 2y + 7$

9. $3z + 2 \leq 4 + 3z$

10. $7a - 9 \geq 35 - 4a$

11. $x < -2$ or $x > 1$

12. $y > -3$ and $y < -1$

13. $z > -5$ or $z < 7$

14. $-1 < x < 3$

15. $c \leq -3$ and $c > 0$

16. $x \geq -2$ or $x > 5$

17. $0 \leq x < 6$

18. $y < 3$ or $y \geq -1$

19. $c > -2$ or $c > 2$

20. $a \geq 5$ and $a < 5$

21. $x \leq 3$ or $x > 4$

22. $-5 \leq x \leq 0$

23. $t > 7$ or $t < 7$

24. $7 < t < 7$

25. $c \leq 2$ or $c < -8$

26. $x \leq 4$ and $x < -2$

27. $-2y + 5 < 13$ or $-2 < 2y + 4$

28. $5 + x > 6$ and $3x + 5 > 20$

29. $3z + 4 \leq 19$ and $z + 5 > 8$

30. $-3x > -27$ or $2x - 8 > 6$

31. $-11 \leq 3y - 2 < 18$

32. $3 \leq 2x - 5 < 1$

33. $5 < -z - 8 \leq 7$

34. $4 > -2 - x > -5$

Solve.

35. The high temperature today was 56° Fahrenheit, while the low was 42°. If t represents the temperature, then ___?___ $\leq t \leq$ ___?___ .

36. In one year the least amount Jane had in her savings account was $102.55. The greatest amount was $221.42. Let s represent the amount in her savings account, and write a conjunction.

37. Riley took his car to United Car Dealers for repairs. The mechanic estimated that repairs would cost \$200. The final bill came within \$30 of the estimate. Let d = the cost of the repairs and write a conjunction to describe the range of values for d. Explain your reasoning.

Graph the solution set.

38. $7 \leq 2x - 1 \leq 17 \ and \ 8 > 2x - 4 > 6$ **39.** $4y > 20 \ and \ 2y - 4 > 6$

40. $2z + 6 < 2z + 4 < 2z - 1$ **41.** $3x - 2 < 3x + 5 < 3x + 7$

42. $2y + 5 < 10 \ or \ 4y - 1 \geq y + 11$ **43.** $a - 5 < 2a + 4 \ or \ -3a > 27$

44. $9 < 2c + 1 < 15 \ or \ 2c - (4 - 6) \geq 11$ **45.** $2 < x \leq 4 \ and \ 6x - (4 - x) < 17$

46. Graph the solution set of $-a < x \ and \ x < a$, where a is positive.

47. Graph the solution set of $-a < x \ and \ x < a$, where a is negative.

48. Graph the solution set of $x > a \ or \ x < b$, where $a > b$.

49. Graph the solution set of $x > a \ and \ x < b$, where $a > b$.

50. Graph the solution set of $x > a \ or \ x < b$, where $a < b$.

51. Graph the solution set of $x > a \ and \ x < b$, where $a < b$.

Midchapter Review

Solve each open inequality. Graph the solution set.   *5.1, 5.2*

1. $4x < 24$ **2.** $-2y > 14$ **3.** $-3 > -x - 5$

4. $0.2x - 0.9 > 1.5$ **5.** $2y - 9 \leq 4 + 3y$ **6.** $3c - 9 < 2(-3 + c) - 6$

For each conjunction or disjunction, determine whether it is *true* or *false*.   *5.3*

7. $3 - 2 < 1 \ or \ 6^2 = 36$ **8.** $7 + (-4) = 3 \ and \ 6 < -8$

9. $14 < 9 + 4 \ or \ -9 = 9 + 0$ **10.** $3 > -4 + 1 \ and \ -7 < 0$

Graph the solution set.   *5.4*

11. $y - 9 > -2$ **12.** $5 < x \ or \ x < -3$ **13.** $-4 < x + 7 < 2$

▬▬/*Brainteaser*

A bug was trying to crawl to the top of an 18-ft drain pipe. Each day it climbed 4 ft, but each night it slipped back 3 ft. How many days did it take it to crawl out of the pipe?

Looking Back

Looking Back is the fourth step in problem solving. As you look back after solving a problem, check these points.

a. Did you use all the necessary information?
b. Are your calculations correct?
c. Does the answer fit your estimate?
d. Does your answer make sense?
e. Does your answer respond to the question asked?
f. Is your answer written in correct form and with the correct units?

Exercises

In these exercises, the person who worked the problem forgot to *Look Back* after arriving at a solution. Find what is wrong with each solution and explain what was forgotten. Then write the correct answer to the problem.

1. A circle has a radius of 2 feet. Find the area.

Solution: Since $A(circle) = \pi r^2$ and $r = 2$, $A = \pi(2)^2$.
So the area of the circle is 4π.

2. The sum of Jaime's and Cheryl's ages is 26. Cheryl is two years older than Jaime. How old is Cheryl?

Solution: Let x = Jaime's age. Then $x + 2$ = Cheryl's age.
So $x + (x + 2) = 26$
$2x + 2 = 26$
$2x = 24$
$x = 12$ Thus, Jaime is 12 years old.

3. Chad uses a calculator for this problem.
$256.2 + 312.6 + 613 = \underline{\quad ? \quad}$

Solution: 630.1

4. Jennifer buys 5 yards of ribbon at 60¢ per yard and 2 yards of ribbon at 70¢ per yard. How much change will she get from a $5-bill?

Solution: $5(0.60) + 2(0.70) = 3.00 + 1.50 = \$4.40$

5.5 Problem Solving: Using Inequalities

Objective   To solve problems by using inequalities

The chart below lists sentences that can be translated into inequalities.

English sentence	Inequality
x is greater than a.	$x > a$
x is less than a.	$x < a$
x is greater than or equal to a. x is at least a. x is not less than a. $(x \not< a)$	$x \geq a$
x is less than or equal to a. x is at most a. x is not greater than a. $(x \not> a)$	$x \leq a$
x is between a and b.	$a < x < b$ (if $a < b$)

> **Trichotomy Property**
> For all real numbers a and b, exactly one of the following three statements is true.
> $$a < b \qquad a = b \qquad a > b$$

Suppose that the number of records in Jane's collection *is at least* 30. Then the number of records is not less than 30. By the Trichotomy Property, there are two remaining possibilities. The number is equal to 30 or is greater than 30. Thus, *is at least* is translated as *is greater than or equal to*, that is, as "$\geq$." Similarly, if the number of records *is at most* 30, then Jane has 30 records or less than 30 records. Thus, *is at most* is translated as *is less than or equal to*, that is, as "$\leq$."

EXAMPLE 1   Translate each sentence into an inequality.

a. Roberto weighs no less than 125 lb.

b. Jesse has between 20 and 30 books.

Solutions   a. Let r = Roberto's weight. Then $r \geq 125$

b. Let b = the number of books. Then $20 < b < 30$.

TRY THIS   1. Translate this sentence into an inequality. John has at most 28 records.

EXAMPLE 2   Mr. Johnson rented a car for $39 a day plus $0.20 a mile. How far can he drive in one day if he wants to spend at most $100.

What are you to find?	The distance Mr. Johnson can drive in a day
What is given?	The rental charge is $39 a day plus $0.20 a mile. At most, $100/day can be spent.
Choose a variable. What does it represent?	Let m = the number of miles Mr. Johnson can drive in a day.
Write an inequality.	The one-day cost *is at most* $100.
Solve the inequality.	$39 + 0.20m \leq 100$ $0.20m \leq 61$ $m \leq 305$ ⟵ 305 mi
Check.	The check is left for you.
State your answer.	Mr. Johnson can drive at most 305 mi.

EXAMPLE 3   The sum of two consecutive positive odd integers is at most 24. Find the integers.

Solution   Let x and $x + 2$ represent the two odd integers.
Their sum *is at most* 24, they are positive, and they are odd integers.

$$x + (x + 2) \leq 24 \quad and \quad \qquad x > 0 \quad and \quad x \text{ is an}$$
$$2x \leq 22 \qquad\qquad\qquad\qquad\qquad\qquad\qquad \text{odd integer.}$$

First integer: $\qquad x \leq 11 \quad and \quad\qquad x > 0 \quad and \quad x$ is odd.
Second integer: $x + 2 \leq 13 \quad and \quad x + 2 > 2 \quad and \quad x + 2$ is odd.

All possible pairs of integers are shown in the chart below.

First integer (x)	1	3	5	7	9	11
Second integer ($x + 2$)	3	5	7	9	11	13

TRY THIS   2. The result of 5 more than 4 times a number is between 17 and 41. What real numbers are possible solutions?

Classroom Exercises

Translate each sentence into an inequality.

1. Mary has at least 8 goldfish.

2. Bob weighs between 110 and 120 lb.

3. A number is greater than 50.

4. Bill has at most 6 cats.

5. Twice a number is not greater than 15.

6. Josh has at most $5 to spend.

Use an inequality to solve each problem.

7. The Sports Club raises money by selling boxes of nuts at a profit of $2 on each box. How many boxes must they sell to make a profit of at least $350?

8. Margaret rented a car for $25 a day plus 15¢ a mile. How far can she travel in one day if she can spend at most $55?

Written Exercises

Translate each sentence into an inequality.

1. Five more than 3 times a number is at least 95.

2. Two less than 5 times a number is not less than 60.

3. The sum of a number and 4 times the number is at most 40.

4. Half of Juanita's age is not equal to 16 years.

Solve each problem by using an inequality.

5. A store makes a profit of $6 on each book sold. How many books must be sold to make a profit of at least $450?

6. A freight elevator can carry 2,000 lb safely. Shipping crates weigh 70 lb each. At most, how many crates can be safely carried on the elevator?

7. Michael is paid $175 a week plus a commission of $25 on each TV he sells. How many sets must he sell to earn not less than $400 a week?

8. Melinda rented a car for $60 a week plus 12¢ a kilometer. How far can she drive in a week if she can spend not more than $120?

Give all possible solutions.

9. The sum of two consecutive positive integers is less than 15. Find the numbers.

10. Barry has 6 more tropical fish than Marcel. Together they have fewer than 28. How many fish can each have?

11. The sum of two consecutive positive even integers is at most 14. Find the numbers.

12. The sum of two consecutive positive odd integers is not greater than 16. Find the numbers.

13. Lightweight boxers must weigh more than 58 kg but no more than 60 kg. Rocky weighs 53 kg. How many kilograms could he possibly gain to be in the lightweight class? Explain.

14. If a number is doubled, the result is between 2 and 17. What real numbers are possible solutions?

15. If a number is tripled, the result is between −6 and 15. What real numbers are possible solutions?

16. If a number is multiplied by −4, the result is between −1 and 8. What real numbers are possible solutions?

17. Helena earns $14,000 a year in salary plus an 8% commission on her sales. How much must her sales be if her annual income is to be between $20,000 and $25,000?

18. Five less than 3 times a number is between -7 and 16. What real numbers are possible solutions?

19. Seven more than half of a number is between -10 and 10. What real numbers are possible solutions?

20. The reciprocal of a number is between $\frac{1}{3}$ and 10. What real numbers are possible solutions?

21. Compare the English words "3 less than x" and "3 is less than x" and translate each into algebraic symbols. Are the algebraic expressions the same? Explain your reasoning.

Mixed Review

Simplify.   *1.2, 1.3, 2.2, 2.9, 2.10*

1. $(2 \cdot 5)^2$
2. $2 \cdot 5^2$
3. $25 + 6(3 - 4)$

4. $7x - 11x$
5. $3(2y - 1) + (4y - 8)\frac{3}{4}$
6. $|-3| + |3|$

7. Seven more than 5 times a number is -18. Find the number.   *3.3*

8. At 8:00 P.M. the temperature was 5°C. That night it dropped 12°. By 6:00 A.M. it had risen 8°. What was the temperature at 6:00 A.M.?   *2.4*

Application: *Triangle Inequality*

Suppose a triangle is to be constructed from three pieces of wood, with one piece being 10 in. long. In order to form a triangle, the sum of the lengths of the other two pieces must be greater than 10 in. In other words, $x + y > 10$. Similarly, $10 + x > y$ and $10 + y > x$. This relationship, called the **Triangle Inequality**, states that the sum of the lengths of two sides of a triangle is greater than the length of the third side.

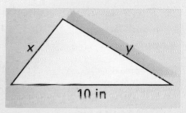

1. Can a triangle have sides with the three given lengths?
   a. 6 cm, 2 cm, 4 cm
   b. 5 ft, 5 ft, 5 ft
   c. 3 m, 8 m, 4 m

2. State three inequalities that apply to a triangle with sides having lengths a, b, and c.

3. Suppose two sides of a triangular lot measure 75 ft and 62 ft. Then the length of the third side must be between what lengths?

5.6 Equations with Absolute Value

Objective

To solve equations containing absolute value

Recall (Lesson 2.2) that the absolute value of a real number is the distance between the number and 0 on a number line. Thus, 5 and − 5 both have an absolute value of 5, since both are 5 units from 0.

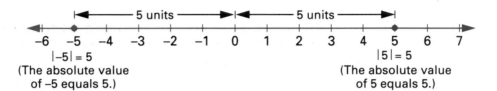

$|-5| = 5$
(The absolute value of −5 equals 5.)

$|5| = 5$
(The absolute value of 5 equals 5.)

The equation $|x| = 5$ can be written as the disjunction $x = 5$ or $x = -5$. It has two solutions, 5 and − 5. Since an absolute value cannot be negative, an equation such as $|x| = -3$ has no solution.

EXAMPLE 1   Solve each equation: **a.** $|x - 1| = 3$ **b.** $|9 - 2x| = 15$

Plan   Write the equation as a disjunction and solve.

Solutions

a. $x - 1 = 3$ or $x - 1 = -3$
   $\quad\quad x = 4$ $\quad\quad\quad\quad x = -2$

b. $9 - 2x = 15$ or $9 - 2x = -15$
   $\quad\quad -2x = 6$ $\quad\quad\quad -2x = -24$
   $\quad\quad\quad x = -3$ $\quad\quad\quad\quad x = 12$

Checks

a. $|x - 1| = 3$

$|x - 1| = 3$ $\quad$ $|x - 1| = 3$
$|4 - 1| \overset{?}{=} 3$ $|-2 - 1| \overset{?}{=} 3$
$\quad\ |3| \overset{?}{=} 3$ $\quad\ |-3| \overset{?}{=} 3$
$\quad\ \ 3 = 3$ $\quad\quad\ \ 3 = 3$

b. $|9 - 2x| = 15$

$|9 - 2(-3)| \overset{?}{=} 15$ $\quad$ $|9 - 2x| = 15$
$\quad\ |9 + 6| \overset{?}{=} 15$ $|9 - 2(12)| \overset{?}{=} 15$
$\quad\quad\ |15| \overset{?}{=} 15$ $\quad |9 - 24| \overset{?}{=} 15$
$\quad\quad\ 15 = 15$ $\quad\quad\ |-15| \overset{?}{=} 15$
$\quad\quad\quad\quad\quad\quad\quad\quad\quad\quad 15 = 15$

Thus, the solutions are -2 and 4.   Thus, the solutions are -3 and 12.

TRY THIS   Solve each equation.   **1.** $|x + 5| = 8$

2. $|4x - 6| = 46$

EXAMPLE 2 Solve $-2|3y + 5| + 4 = 2$.

Solution

$$-2|3y + 5| + 4 = 2$$

Subtract 4 from each side. $-2|3y + 5| = -2$
Divide each side by -2.

$$|3y + 5| = 1$$

Write a disjunction.

$$3y + 5 = 1 \quad or \quad 3y + 5 = -1$$
$$3y = -4 \qquad\qquad 3y = -6$$
$$y = -\frac{4}{3} \qquad\qquad y = -2$$

Thus, the solutions are $-\frac{4}{3}$ and -2. The check is left for you.

TRY THIS   3. Solve $8 + 5|6 - 2y| = 68$.

Classroom Exercises

Solve each equation.

1. $|x| = 6$ **2.** $|y| = -1$ **3.** $|z| = 0$ **4.** $|d| + 1 = 4$
5. $2|b| = -8$ **6.** $|y - 6| = 10$ **7.** $|2y| = 10$ **8.** $|4x - 1| = 5$

Written Exercises

Solve each equation.

1. $|x| = 4$ **2.** $|x| = -4$ **3.** $2|x| = 6$ **4.** $-3|x| = -12$
5. $|x - 4| = 5$ **6.** $|y - 3| = 7$ **7.** $|y + 8| = -3$ **8.** $|5 - z| = 3$
9. $|-5c| = 15$ **10.** $5|-c| = 15$ **11.** $|3y + 1| = -2$ **12.** $2|d + 2| = 14$
13. $5|x - 2| - 13 = 7$ **14.** $4|y - 3| - 2 = 10$ **15.** $3|z + 5| + 5 = 8$
16. $-6 - 3|4x - 2| = 8$ **17.** $10 = 6|a - 7| - 14$ **18.** $1 = 8 - |2y - 5|$

Complete each sentence. Use $>$, $<$, or $=$.

19 The solution set of $|x| = a$ is $\{0\}$ if $a \underline{} 0$.
20. The solution set of $|x| = a$ is $\varnothing$ if $a \underline{} 0$.

Mixed Review

Solve. *3.2, 3.5, 4.6*

1. $\frac{1}{2}x = \frac{1}{3}$ **2.** $4(x + 2) = 3x - 9$ **3.** $3x + 1 = -(4 - x)$ **4.** $-0.2 = y + 4.9$
5. Last year a particular car cost \$10,000. This year the same model costs \$10,600. What is the percent increase in the cost? *4.7*

5.7 Inequalities with Absolute Value

Objective   To graph solution sets of inequalities containing absolute value

One winter night, the temperature remained within 5° of 0 degrees Fahrenheit (0°F). If x represents the temperature in °F at any time that night, then these temperature conditions can be described by the inequality $|x| < 5$.

The situation just described can be represented by a graph on a number line. First, recall from the previous lesson that the equality $|x| = 5$ has two solutions, 5 and -5.

graph of solution
set of $|x| = 5$

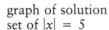

It follows that the solutions of $|x| < 5$ will be *less than* 5 units from 0.

graph of solution
set of $|x| < 5$

From the graph above, you can see that $|x| < 5$ is equivalent to the conjunction $x > -5$ *and* $x < 5$. (This can be written as $-5 < x < 5$.) Similarly, the solutions of $|x| > 5$ will be *greater than* 5 units from 0 on a number line.

graph of solution
set of $|x| > 5$

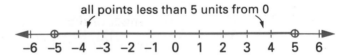

$|x| > 5$ is equivalent to the disjunction $x < -5$ *or* $x > 5$.

EXAMPLE 1   Graph the solution set of $|5 - 3x| \geq 9$.

Plan   All values of x that make $5 - 3x$ greater than or equal to 9 units from 0 on a number line are solutions of $|5 - 3x| \geq 9$. Solve the equivalent disjunction $5 - 3x \leq -9$ or $5 - 3x \geq 9$.

Solution

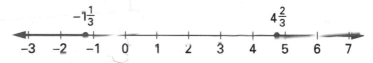

$$|5 - 3x| \geq 9$$

$$5 - 3x \leq -9 \quad or \quad 5 - 3x \geq 9$$
$$-3x \leq -14 \qquad\qquad -3x \geq 4$$
$$x \geq \frac{-14}{-3} \qquad\qquad x \leq -\frac{4}{3} \quad \longleftarrow \text{When dividing by a}$$
$$x \geq 4\frac{2}{3} \qquad\qquad x \leq -1\frac{1}{3} \qquad\quad \text{negative number, reverse}$$
$$\qquad\qquad\qquad\qquad x \leq -1\frac{1}{3} \qquad\qquad \text{the order of inequality.}$$

```
        -1⅓                          4⅔
   ◄──┼──┼──●──┼──┼──┼──┼──┼──●──┼──►
     -3  -2  -1   0   1   2   3   4   5   6   7
```

EXAMPLE 2   In an automobile assembly plant, a certain kind of connecting rod is accepted for installation in an automobile only if the length of the rod is within 0.5 cm of 27 cm. For the acceptable lengths of the rod, write an inequality with absolute value and graph the solution set of the inequality.

Solution   Let x = the length of the connecting rod.

$$|x - 27| < 0.5$$

$$x - 27 > -0.5 \quad and \quad x - 27 < 0.5$$
$$x > 26.5 \qquad\qquad x < 27.5$$
$$26.5 < x < 27.5$$

```
                                26.5  27.5
   ◄──┼──┼──┼──┼──┼──┼─ ─ ─ ─┼──○──┼──○──┼──┼──►
      0   1   2   3   4   5      25  26  27  28  29  30
```

TRY THIS   1. Graph the solution set of $|4y - 1| \geq 7$.

2. Yesterday the temperature stayed within 6° of 70°C. Graph the solution set.

Classroom Exercises

For each inequality, give an equivalent conjunction or disjunction.

1. $|x| > 6$ **2.** $|x| \le 3$ **3.** $|y| \ge 1$ **4.** $|4 - 7x| > 2$ **5.** $|3c + 1| \le 0$

6–10. Graph the solution set of each inequality of Classroom Exercises 1–5.

Written Exercises

Graph the solution set of each inequality.

1. $|x| < 4$ **2.** $|x| \ge 4$ **3.** $|x| > 0$ **4.** $|x - 5| < 3$

5. $|y + 4| < 7$ **6.** $|z - 2| \ge -4$ **7.** $|2y - 8| > 6$ **8.** $|3x + 3| \le 9$

9. $|4x - 8| \ge 20$ **10.** $|7z - 14| < 7$ **11.** $|c + 2| < 5$ **12.** $|6k - 18| \le 12$

13. $|5 + 2x| > 7$ **14.** $|-3 + 2y| \ge 9$ **15.** $|-8 + 4y| \le 28$ **16.** $|4 - 7x| \ge -2$

17. $|2y - 5| < 6$ **18.** $|3x + 4| < 2$ **19.** $|5 - 4x| \le 3$ **20.** $|3 - 2z| \le 0$

For each problem, use x for the variable and write an inequality with absolute value. Then graph the solution set of the inequality.

21. Last night, the temperature stayed within 8° of 0°C.

22. Marian's golf score stayed within 3 strokes of par (75 strokes).

23. The monthly profits or losses for the Spedini Corporation were within $2,000 of the goal of $10,000.

24. Last week the price of Enton Company's common stock changed less than $1\frac{1}{8}$ points from its opening price of $10.

Graph the solution set of each inequality.

25. $|x - (5 - x)| > 3$ **26.** $|6 - (4 - y)| \le 5$ **27.** $|5z - (3z - 6)| < 4$

28. $|2y - (y - 6)| \ge 3$ **29.** $|x - 3| - 2 < 4$ **30.** $4 + |y - 2| > 3$

31. $7 - 2|x - 4| \le 3$ **32.** $4|c - 2| + 3 < 5$ **33.** $3 - 2|2x + 7| \le -5$

Mixed Review

1. Use the formula $A = \frac{1}{2}bh$ to find A if $b = 9$ cm and $h = 12$ cm.   *1.4*

Evaluate.   *2.6, 2.8*

2. x^5, for $x = -2$ **3.** $-9 - 5x$, for $x = -3$

4. The length of a rectangle is 3 cm more than twice the width. The perimeter is 36 cm. Find the length and the width.   *4.2*

5. José is paid $130 a week plus a commission of 7% on all sales. What must be his weekly sales if José is to earn a total of $200/week?   *4.8*

Mixed Problem Solving

The algebra skills you have acquired up to this point provide you with tools for problem solving. As part of a problem-solving plan, you choose a variable and use it to represent the unknown quantity or quantities, translate the words of the problem into an equation, and solve the equation.

For some of the problems on this page, try the strategy of *Drawing a Diagram* to represent the problem situation. For example, a diagram or sketch may help you in solving Exercises 3, 5, and 9.

Solve each problem.

1. The table below shows the profits and losses of a small business for four successive months. What is the average profit or loss per month?

Jan	Feb	March	April
+ $6,700	+ $2,300	− $1,600	− $480

2. Bonnie needs $\frac{3}{4}$ yd of ribbon to make each hair bow. To be safe, she bought an extra $\frac{1}{2}$ yd of ribbon. How many hair bows can she make if she bought $7\frac{1}{4}$ yd of ribbon?

3. Between midnight and 4:00 A.M. the temperature dropped 8°. If the temperature was −3°F at 4:00 A.M., what was the temperature at midnight?

4. On Tuesday Mary swam $\frac{2}{3}$ as many laps as she swam on Monday. If she swam 48 laps on Tuesday, how many laps did she swim on Monday?

5. Yesterday Mark jogged 1.2 km farther than he jogged today. If he jogged 5.9 km yesterday, how far did he jog today?

6. The selling price of a book is $\frac{1}{3}$ more than the cost. If a book sells for $18, find the cost.

7. Martha has $100 and is saving at a rate of $5/week. Kate has $50 and is saving at a rate of $10/week. After how many weeks will they have the same amount of money?

8. Jackie showed a profit of $560 in her business in January. In February she showed a profit of $490. What was the percent decrease in her profit from January to February?

9. The vertex angle of an isosceles triangle measures 62. Find the measure of each base angle.

10. The sum of two consecutive integers is −77. Find the integers.

11. Of three consecutive odd integers, x represents the second integer. Give an algebraic expression for the first integer and for the third integer.

12. A collection of nickels and dimes is worth $2.75. There are 7 more nickels than dimes. How many of each type of coin are there?

13. An electrician earns $6.50 more per hour than his apprentice. For a 6-h job, their total earnings were $267. How much does each make per hour?

Chapter 5 Review

Key Terms

Addition Property of Inequality   (p. 166)
conjunction   (p. 175)
disjunction   (p. 176)
Division Property of Inequality   (p. 171)
equivalent inequalities   (p. 166)

Multiplication Property of Inequality
   (p. 170)
Subtraction Property of Inequality
   (p. 166)
Trichotomy Property   (p. 186)
truth table   (p. 176)

Key Ideas and Review Exercises

5.1   Adding (or subtracting) the same number to (or from) an inequality produces an equivalent inequality.

Solve each inequality. Graph the solution set.

1. $x + 6 < 2$

2. $y - 4 > -9$

3. $-2 < x + 3$

4. $0.4 + x > 1.7$

5. $-2\frac{1}{2} > y - 1\frac{3}{4}$

6. $3x - 2(x + 7) < -10$

5.2   Multiplying (or dividing) each side of an inequality by the same positive number produces an equivalent inequality. Multiplying (or dividing) each side of an inequality by the same negative number and reversing the order of the inequality produces an equivalent inequality.

Solve each inequality. Graph the solution set.

7. $4x < 20$

8. $-3z > 18$

9. $\frac{2}{5}k > -4$

10. $x + 7 < x - 1$

11. $7 - 3x > 4x - 21$

12. $4a + 5 < -(2 - 3a) - 4a - 8$

5.3   A *conjunction* (two sentences connected by *and*) is true only if both of the sentences are true. Otherwise it is false. A *disjunction* (two sentences connected by *or*) is false only if both of the sentences are false. Otherwise it is true.

Determine whether the given conjunction or disjunction is *true* or *false*.

13. $-2 < -1$ *or* $5 > 7$

14. $3 > -1$ *and* $6 < -6$

15. $5^2 = 25$ *and* $8 \neq 5 + 1$

16. $4 = 9 - 5$ *or* $7 > 5 + 3$

5.4   To graph the solution set of a *disjunction* of two sentences, graph the set that contains all the solutions of the two sentences. To graph the solution set of a *conjunction* of two sentences, graph the set that contains only the solutions common to both sentences.

Graph the solution set.

17. $4a - 5 \geq -2 + 3a$ **18.** $-3c + 6 \leq -4c - 2$

19. $x > 2$ or $x \leq 0$ **20.** $-5 < x < -1$

21. Write a short explanation of why the solution set of $x \geq a$ and $x \leq a$ is $\{a\}$.

5.5   The inequality $x \geq a$ can mean *x is greater than or equal to a, x is at least a,* or *x is not less than a.* The inequality $x \leq a$ can mean *x is less than or equal to a, x is at most a,* or *x is not greater than a.* The inequality $a < x < b$ means *x is between a and b* with $a < b$.

Solve each problem.

22. Jake rented a car for $21/day plus 18¢/mi. How far can he travel in one day if he can spend at most $62.40?

23. The sum of two positive, consecutive odd integers is at most 20. Find all possible pairs of integers.

5.6   To solve an equation involving absolute value, solve a disjunction.

        For example, to solve $|2x - 5| = 11$, solve the disjunction $2x - 5 = 11$ *or* $2x - 5 = -11$.

Solve each equation.

24. $|x - 2| = 3$ **25.** $|4 - y| = 6$

26. $|c + 3| = -1$ **27.** $|2y - 4| = 14$

28. $4 = |5a - 2|$ **29.** $-2|4x - 2| - 8 = 16$

5.7   To solve an inequality with absolute value that contains $<$ or $\leq$, solve a conjunction. For example, to solve $|3x + 6| \leq 9$, solve the conjunction $3x + 6 \geq -9$ *and* $3x + 6 \leq 9$.

        To solve an inequality with absolute value that contains $>$ or $\geq$, solve a disjunction. For example, to solve $|-2y - 1| \geq 7$, solve the disjunction $-2y - 1 \leq -7$ *or* $-2y - 1 \geq 7$.

Graph the solution set of each inequality.

30. $|x - 4| < 2$ **31.** $|y + 3| \geq 5$

32. $|5 + 2x| > 9$ **33.** $|-4 + 3y| \leq 2$

34. $|-2y + 1| < -1$ **35.** $9 - 3|x - 2| < 6$

Solve each inequality. Graph the solution set.

1. $x - 4 > -3$

2. $7 > y + 9$

3. $-5x < 35$

4. $-3c + 4 > -8$

5. $2p - 9 > 16 + 2p$

6. $-2(4x + 5) < 1 + 3x$

Determine whether the given conjunction or disjunction is *true* or *false.*

7. $7 = 3 + 5$ or $6 \neq 5 + 2$

8. $-3 > -2 + 1$ and $(-6)^2 > 30$

Graph the solution set.

9. $-2x - 11 \leq 13$

10. $-5 \leq x < -1$

11. $-3y > -24$ or $2y - 6 > 8$

12. $3x - 1 < 2$ and $x + 4 > -1$

Solve each problem.

13. Mr. Heisler makes a profit of $7 on each shirt he sells. How many shirts must he sell to make a profit of at least $224?

14. An elevator can carry up to 1,800 lb safely. At most, how many 80-lb crates can be carried in the elevator without overloading it?

15. Eight less than 4 times a number is between -5 and 12. What real numbers are possible solutions?

16. The selling price of a stereo is $270. The profit is 35% of the cost. Find the cost.

17. The first side of a triangle is 4 cm longer than twice the second. The third side is 2 cm shorter than the second side. The perimeter is 30 cm. Find the length of each side.

18. The second of three numbers is one more than twice the first. The third is 10 less than the second. The sum of the three numbers is 27. Find each.

Solve each equation.

19. $|x - 7| = 2$

20. $-|x + 1| = -3$

21. $|4x + 1| = -5$

22. $3 - 4|3y - 1| = -5$

Graph the solution set of each inequality.

23. $|2x + 3| < 7$

24. $|6 - (4 + c)| < 1$

25. $|r| < 4$ or $|r| > 4$

26. $3c + 4 < 6$ and $5c - 1 > c + 7$

27. Solve for x: $ax + b < c$, where $a < 0$.

In each item you are to compare a quantity in Column 1 with a quantity in Column 2. Write the letter of the correct answer from these choices:

A—The quantity in Column 1 is greater than the quantity in Column 2.
B—The quantity in Column 2 is greater than the quantity in Column 1.
C—The quantity in Column 1 is equal to the quantity in Column 2.
D—The relationship cannot be determined from the information given.

NOTES: Information centered over both columns refers to one or both of the quantities to be compared. A symbol that appears in both columns has the same meaning in each column, and all variables represent numbers.

Sample Question $2x + 1 > 7$		Answer
Column 1	Column 2	The solution to $2x + 1 > 7$ is $x > 3$. Therefore, the quantity in Column 2 is greater. The answer is B.
3	x	

	Column 1	Column 2		Column 1	Column 2
1.	$x + 2 < 7$		**8.**	$0 < x < 1$	
	x	5		x^2	1
2.	$5y < 0$		**9.**	$-1 < y < 0$	
	y	1		y^2	1
3.	$x < y$		**10.**	$x > 0, y < 0$	
	$x - y$	$y - x$		0	xy
4.	$0 < x < 8$ $0 < y < 10$		**11.**	$x = 0, y < 0$	
	x	y		0	xy
5.	$\lvert x - y \rvert$	$\lvert y - x \rvert$	**12.**	$x > 0, y < 0$	
				$\dfrac{1}{x}$	$\dfrac{1}{y}$
6.	a is a real number.		**13.**	$-1 < x < 1, x \neq 0$	
	a	$-a$		$\dfrac{1}{x}$	0
7.	$x > 0, y < 0$		**14.**	$x > 1$	
	$\dfrac{x}{y}$	$\dfrac{y}{x}$		$\dfrac{1}{x}$	1

6 POWERS AND POLYNOMIALS

Marine biologists study animal and plant life in the Antarctic to help monitor the air and water quality of the planet. Computer models, built from sets of equations, make possible early warnings of possible pollution problems.

6.1 Multiplying Monomials

Objective

To multiply monomials

The power 3^6 can be broken into factors in many ways. For example,

$$3^6 = (3 \cdot 3) \cdot (3 \cdot 3 \cdot 3 \cdot 3) = 3^2 \cdot 3^4$$
$$3^6 = (3 \cdot 3 \cdot 3) \cdot (3 \cdot 3 \cdot 3) = 3^3 \cdot 3^3$$
$$3^6 = (3 \cdot 3 \cdot 3 \cdot 3 \cdot 3) \cdot (3) = 3^5 \cdot 3^1$$

In each case the sum of the exponents of the factors is equal to 6. This idea is used in multiplying *monomials*.

Each of the following is an example of a monomial.

$$-7 \qquad\qquad x \qquad\qquad 4x^3 \qquad -5xy$$

a constant   a variable   a product of a constant
and one or more
variables

A **monomial** is an algebraic expression that is either a constant, a variable, or a product of a constant and one or more variables.

The monomials a^3 and a^4 have the same base a but different exponents, 3 and 4. To multiply a^3 and a^4, write a as a factor 3 times and a as a factor 4 more times, as shown below.

$$a^3 \cdot a^4 = (a \cdot a \cdot a) \cdot (a \cdot a \cdot a \cdot a) = a^{3+4} = a^7$$

The result is a as a factor 7 times. Similarly,

$$y^3 \cdot y^3 = (y \cdot y \cdot y) \cdot (y \cdot y \cdot y) = y^6$$
$$x \cdot x^4 = x^1 \cdot x^4 = x \cdot (x \cdot x \cdot x \cdot x) = x^5$$

This suggests that to multiply powers with the same base, you add the exponents and keep the same base. In general,

$$\overbrace{\phantom{m \text{ factors}}}^{m \text{ factors}} \quad \overbrace{\phantom{n \text{ factors}}}^{n \text{ factors}}$$
$$b^m \cdot b^n = (b \cdot b \ldots \cdot b) \cdot (b \cdot b \ldots \cdot b) = b^{m+n}$$

Product of Powers
For all real numbers b and all positive integers m and n,
$$b^m \cdot b^n = b^{m+n}$$

EXAMPLE 1   Simplify each product, if possible.

   a. $r^7 \cdot r$

   b. $c^2 \cdot d^2$

Solutions

a. Rewrite r as r^1. Since the bases are the same, add the exponents.

$$r^7 \cdot r = r^7 \cdot r^1 = r^{7+1} = r^8$$

b. The bases, c and d, are different. Thus, $c^2 \cdot d^2$ cannot be simplified.

TRY THIS   Simplify each product, if possible.

1. $x^4 \cdot y^6$

2. $a^2 \cdot a^3$

To simplify a product of monomials such as $(-3c^2d)(7cd^3)$, use the Commutative and Associative Properties of Multiplication to group the constant coefficients together and the like bases together. Then multiply the coefficients and apply the Product-of-Powers Property to the factors with the same base.

EXAMPLE 2   Simplify: **a.** $-3c^2d(7cd^3)$

   b. $(-5x^2y)(-xz^3)$

Solutions

a. $-3c^2d(7cd^3)$
$= (-3 \cdot 7)(c^2 \cdot c^1)(d^1 \cdot d^3)$
$= -21 \cdot c^{2+1} \cdot d^{1+3}$
$= -21c^3d^4$

b. $(-5x^2y)(-xz^3)$
$= (-5 \cdot x^2y^1)(-1 \cdot x^1z^3)$
$= [-5(-1)] \cdot (x^2 \cdot x^1) \cdot y^1 \cdot z^3$
$= 5 \cdot x^{2+1} \cdot y \cdot z^3 = 5x^3yz^3$

EXAMPLE 3   Simplify $x^2y(x^2y^2)$. Then evaluate for $x = -3$ and $y = -1$.

Solution $x^2y(x^2y^2) = x^2 \cdot x^2 \cdot y^1 \cdot y^2 = x^{2+2} \cdot y^{1+2} = x^4y^3$

If $x = -3$ and $y = -1$, then $x^4y^3 = (-3)^4(-1)^3$
$= (81)(-1)$, or -81

TRY THIS   3. Simplify $(3a^5b^4c)(-2b^3c^8)$.

4. Simplify $(xy^3)(x^2y^3)$. Then evaluate for $x = -5$ and $y = 2$.

Classroom Exercises

Simplify, if possible.

1. $(-1)^4$
2. $(-1)^{21}$
3. $x^2 \cdot x^3$
4. $y^5 \cdot z^2$
5. $(-2)^3 \cdot (-2)^2$
6. $-2^3 \cdot [-(2^2)]$
7. $-a^4 \cdot a$
8. $5y(7y)$
9. $6c(-5d)$
10. $-ab(-ab)$
11. $3a^2b(5ab^2)$
12. $-7x^4y(4xy)$

Written Exercises

Simplify, if possible.

1. $2x \cdot x^3$
2. $-3y^4 \cdot y^2$
3. $4a^4 \cdot b^2$
4. $-y \cdot 2y^2$
5. $(-z^2) \cdot (-z^2)$
6. $-z^2 \cdot (-z)^2$
7. $4a^2(3a^5)$
8. $-6x^3y^2$
9. $5y(-10z^3)$
10. $(-3c^4)(4d)$
11. $(2b)(-6b^7)$
12. $(-5x^2)(-4x^3)$
13. $(5x^2y)(-2xy^2)$
14. $(3c^2d)(7c^2d^4)$
15. $-xy(-xy)$
16. $(2a^2b)(3b^2c)$
17. $(2x^4z)(-3y^3z)$
18. $(-5x^2y^2z)(2xz^3)$
19. $3x(2x^2)(5x^3)$
20. $(5y)(4y^2)(-y)$
21. $-3z^2(-7z)(-2z^4)$
22. $\frac{1}{3}a^2(-6ab^2)$
23. $-\frac{3}{4}xy^3(4xyz)$
24. $(-0.5c^2d)(2d^3c)$
25. $(-12x)(\frac{2}{3}x^2y)(-4y)$
26. $(-a^2b)(-ab^2)(-ab^4)$
27. $(16x^3yz)(-\frac{3}{4}y^2z)$

Simplify. Then evaluate for $x = -1$ and $y = -2$.

28. $x^5 \cdot x^3$
29. $x^2y \cdot xy$
30. $-x^4y^3(x^3y)$

Simplify. Assume that all exponents are positive integers.

31. $x^a \cdot x^b$
32. $y^n \cdot y^{4n}$
33. $z^{x+2} \cdot z^{x-3}$

Find the value of n that makes each sentence true.

34. $x^{2n+3} \cdot x^{2n-3} = x^{12}$
35. $y^{5n-2} \cdot y^{-3n+4} = y^8$
36. $c^{4n-1} \cdot c^{n+2} = c^{6n-5}$

For each statement, tell whether it is true or false. If not true, give an example showing that it is not true.

37. For all real numbers x, $x^8 - x^5 = x^{8-5}$
38. An odd power of a negative number is always negative.

Mixed Review

Evaluate. *2.6, 2.8*

1. $16 - y$ for $y = -3$
2. $5x - 2y$ for $x = 2$ and $y = -6$

Solve. *3.4, 5.2*

3. $3x + 7 = 5x - 9$
4. $-3x + 12 < -15$
5. $3x - 6 > 4x - 2$
6. Mary and Bob bought new jackets. Mary paid $49. Her jacket cost $19 less than twice Bob's jacket. How much did Bob pay? *3.3*

6.2 Powers of Monomials

Objective	To simplify a power of a power and a power of a product

Suppose that a monomial such as a^3 is raised to the fourth power. The result, $(a^3)^4$, is called a *power of a power*. You can simplify $(a^3)^4$ as shown below.

$$(a^3)^4 = a^3 \cdot a^3 \cdot a^3 \cdot a^3 \quad \text{(Definition of exponent)}$$
$$= a^{3+3+3+3} \quad \quad \text{(Product of Powers)}$$
$$= a^{3 \cdot 4}$$
$$= a^{12}$$

The result is a as a factor 12 times. Similarly,

$$(x^5)^2 = x^5 \cdot x^5 = x^{5+5} = x^{5 \cdot 2} = x^{10}$$
$$(r^6)^3 = r^6 \cdot r^6 \cdot r^6 = r^{6+6+6} = r^{6 \cdot 3} = r^{18}$$

This suggests that to raise a power to a power, you multiply the exponents and keep the same base. In general,

$$(b^m)^n = \overbrace{b^m \cdot b^m \cdot \ldots \cdot b^m}^{n \text{ factors}} = \overbrace{b^{m+m+\ldots+m}}^{n \text{ terms}} = b^{mn}.$$

Power of a Power
For all real numbers b and all positive integers m and n,
$$(b^m)^n = b^{mn}.$$

EXAMPLE 1	Simplify. **a.** $(c^2)^5$ $\qquad\qquad\qquad\qquad$ **b.** $(y^3)^{10}$
Solutions	**a.** $(c^2)^5 = c^{2 \cdot 5} = c^{10}$ $\qquad$ **b.** $(y^3)^{10} = y^{3 \cdot 10} = y^{30}$

TRY THIS	Simplify. **1.** $(x^3)^3$ $\qquad$ **2.** $(a^{21})^2$

Now suppose that a product such as $2x$ is raised to the third power. The result, $(2x)^3$, is called a *power of a product*. You can simplify $(2x)^3$, as follows.

$$(2x)^3 = 2x \cdot 2x \cdot 2x = (2 \cdot 2 \cdot 2)(x \cdot x \cdot x) = 2^3 \cdot x^3 = 8x^3$$

Notice that both 2 and x are raised to the third power. This suggests that to find a power of a product, raise each factor to that power.

$$(ab)^m = \overbrace{(ab)(ab) \ldots (ab)}^{m \text{ factors}} = \overbrace{(a \cdot a \cdot \ldots \cdot a)}^{m \text{ factors}} \overbrace{(b \cdot b \cdot \ldots \cdot b)}^{m \text{ factors}} = a^m b^m.$$

Power of a Product
For all real numbers a and b and all positive integers m,
$$(ab)^m = a^m b^m.$$

Do not confuse $(2x)^3$ and $2x^3$. $(2x)^3$ means "$2x \cdot 2x \cdot 2x$," while $2x^3$ means "$2 \cdot x \cdot x \cdot x$."

EXAMPLE 2   Simplify.

a. $(-4c)^3$ b. $(-xy^2)^4$ c. $-4x\,(5x^3)^2$

Solutions   a. $(-4c)^3$ b. $(-xy^2)^4$ c. $-4x(5x^3)^2$
$= (-4)^3 c^3$ $= (-1x)^4 (y^2)^4$ $= -4x^1 \cdot 5^2 \cdot (x^3)^2$
$= -64c^3$ $= (-1)^4 x^4 y^{2 \cdot 4}$ $= -4 \cdot 25 \cdot x^1 \cdot x^6$
                      $= 1 \cdot x^4 y^8$, or $x^4 y^8$ $= -100 x^{1+6}$, or $-100x^7$

TRY THIS   Simplify.   **3.** $(-2a^4 b^6)^5$ **4.** $-y^2(4y^7)^2$

Classroom Exercises

Simplify.

1. $(a^2)^4$ **2.** $(y^3)^2$ **3.** $(c^5)^2$ **4.** $c^5 c^2$

5. $[-2(-1)]^2$ **6.** $-2(-1)^2$ **7.** $-[2(-1)]^2$ **8.** $(-2)^2(-1)^2$

9. $(cd)^2$ **10.** $(4x)^2$ **11.** $4(x)^2$ **12.** $-(2a)^3$

13. $(x^2y)^3$ **14.** $-(2xy)^4$ **15.** $(3b^2)^3$ **16.** $-(2a^2bc^3)^2$

Written Exercises

Simplify.

1. $(y^4)^3$ **2.** $(x^3)^5$ **3.** $y^4 \cdot y^3$ **4.** $x^3 \cdot x^5$

5. $(-3c)^2$ **6.** $-(3c)^2$ **7.** $(-3^2)^3$ **8.** $[(-3)^2]^3$

9. $(-r)^3$ **10.** $(-y)^6$ **11.** $-(c)^5$ **12.** $(xy)^4$

13. $(5y^3)^2$ **14.** $(-3c^4)^3$ **15.** $(a^2b)^4$ **16.** $(r^3s^2)^6$

17. $(-xy)^4$ **18.** $-(a^2b)^6$ **19.** $(x^2yz^3)^2$ **20.** $(-a^4b^2c)^4$

21. $(2a^4bc^2)^5$ **22.** $(-3rs^2c^3)^3$ **23.** $(-5x^2y^3z)^3$ **24.** $-(-6a^2b^2c^3)^2$

25. $x(2x^3)^2$ **26.** $4a(3a)^3$ **27.** $a^4(a^2b)^2$ **28.** $4x(-2xy)^3$

29. $3a(\frac{1}{3}a)^2$ **30.** $(-2x)^3(\frac{1}{2}x)^2$ **31.** $3c(-2cd)^3$ **32.** $(\frac{1}{2}x)^3(2x)^4$

33. $(2x^3)^3(3x^4)^2$ **34.** $(-x^2)^3(4x^2)^3$ **35.** $-3ab^3(a^2b)^4$ **36.** $0.05xy(2x^2y)^3$

Simplify, if possible. Then evaluate for $x = -1$ and $y = 3$.

37. $(x^2)^5 \cdot y^2$ **38.** $(xy)^2(x^3)^4$ **39.** $(2x^4y)^3$ **40.** $3xy(\frac{1}{3}xy)^2$

For the given conditions, tell whether x^n is positive, negative, or zero.

41. x is negative and n is even.   **42.** x is positive and n is odd.

43. x is zero and n is odd.   **44.** x is negative and n is odd.

For the given conditions, tell whether $(x^m)^n$ is positive, negative, or zero.

45. x is negative, m is odd, and n is even.   **46.** x is negative, m is odd, and n is odd.

For each sentence, find the value of a that makes it true.

47. $(x^4)^{2a-3} = x^4$ **48.** $x^{2a+6} = (x^{2a+1})^2$

49. $(y^{a+1})^5 = y^{3a+9}$ **50.** $(x^{3a+5})^2(x^a)^4 = x^{8a+12}$

Solve.

51. The exponent of a power of 2 is 3 more than the exponent of a power of 4. Find the exponents.

52. The exponent of a power of 3 is one more than twice the exponent of a power of 27. What are the exponents?

Mixed Review

1. Use the formula $A = \frac{1}{2}(b + c)h$ to find A for $b = 9$ cm, $c = 12$ cm, and $h = 14$ cm.   *1.4*

Simplify.   *2.9, 2.10*

2. $3x + 2y - x + y$ **3.** $4a + 3b + 2a - 2b$ **4.** $6x - 7(y - 4x) + 1$

5. Solve for a: $2a + 6 = 11$ *3.3*

6. Jackie bought $\frac{3}{4}$ yd of fabric for each stuffed animal she was making. To be safe, she bought an extra $\frac{1}{2}$ yd of fabric, for a total of $6\frac{1}{2}$ yd. How many stuffed animals did she plan to make?   *4.5*

6.3 Dividing Monomials

Objective

To divide monomials

You can divide the numerator and denominator of a fraction by the same nonzero number. For example,

$$\frac{12}{20} = \frac{\overset{1}{\cancel{4}} \cdot 3}{\underset{1}{\cancel{4}} \cdot 5} = \frac{3}{5} \qquad\qquad \frac{7}{14} = \frac{\overset{1}{\cancel{7}} \cdot 1}{\underset{1}{\cancel{7}} \cdot 2} = \frac{1}{2}$$

To divide monomials you can use the same cancellation property.

Factoring

Cancellation Property of Fractions
For all real numbers a, b, and c, such that $b \neq 0$ and $c \neq 0$,

$$\frac{a \cdot c}{b \cdot c} = \frac{a}{b}.$$

Now consider the quotient $\dfrac{a^5}{a^2}$, where $a \neq 0$.

$$\frac{a^5}{a^2} = \frac{\overbrace{\cancel{a} \cdot \cancel{a} \cdot a \cdot a \cdot a}^{5 \text{ factors}}}{\underbrace{\cancel{a} \cdot \cancel{a}}_{2 \text{ factors}}} = \overbrace{a \cdot a \cdot a}^{3 \text{ factors}} = a^3$$

Similarly, for $x \neq 0$ and $y \neq 0$,

$$\frac{x^4}{x^6} = \frac{\overset{1}{\cancel{x}} \cdot \overset{1}{\cancel{x}} \cdot \overset{1}{\cancel{x}} \cdot \overset{1}{\cancel{x}}}{x \cdot \underset{1}{\cancel{x}} \cdot \underset{1}{\cancel{x}} \cdot \underset{1}{\cancel{x}} \cdot \underset{1}{\cancel{x}} \cdot x} = \frac{1}{x^2} \text{ and } \frac{y^3}{y^3} = \frac{\overset{1}{\cancel{y}} \cdot \overset{1}{\cancel{y}} \cdot \overset{1}{\cancel{y}}}{\underset{1}{\cancel{y}} \cdot \underset{1}{\cancel{y}} \cdot \underset{1}{\cancel{y}}} = 1$$

These three cases suggest the following property for the *quotient of powers*, which you can use without having to write the factored forms.

Quotient of Powers
For all real numbers b, ($b \neq 0$), and all positive integers m and n,

if $m > n$, then	if $m < n$, then	if $m = n$, then
$\dfrac{b^m}{b^n} = b^{m-n}.$	$\dfrac{b^m}{b^n} = \dfrac{1}{b^{n-m}}.$	$\dfrac{b^m}{b^n} = \dfrac{b^m}{b^m} = 1.$
(Case 1)	(Case 2)	(Case 3)

EXAMPLE 1   Simplify.

a. $\dfrac{x^8}{x^5}$ $(x \neq 0)$ b. $\dfrac{y^9}{y^9}$ $(y \neq 0)$ c. $\dfrac{z}{z^5}$ $(z \neq 0)$

Plan   Use the three different cases of the Quotient-of-Powers Property.

Solutions   a. $\dfrac{x^8}{x^5} = x^{8-5} = x^3$ b. $\dfrac{y^9}{y^9} = 1$ c. $\dfrac{z}{z^5} = \dfrac{z^1}{z^5} = \dfrac{1}{z^{5-1}} = \dfrac{1}{z^4}$

by Case 1.   by Case 3.   by Case 2.

EXAMPLE 2   Simplify $\dfrac{-15a^2b^3}{5ab^8}$ $(a \neq 0,\ b \neq 0)$.

Solution $\dfrac{-15a^2b^3}{5ab^8} = \dfrac{-3 \cdot 5 \cdot a^2 \cdot b^3}{5 \cdot a^1 \cdot b^8} = \dfrac{-3a^{2-1}}{b^{8-3}} = \dfrac{-3a^1}{b^5} = \dfrac{-3a}{b^5}$

EXAMPLE 3   Simplify $\dfrac{18x^3y^4z}{27x^3y^2z^5}$ $(x \neq 0,\ y \neq 0,\ z \neq 0)$.

Solution $\dfrac{18x^3y^4z}{27x^3y^2z^5} = \dfrac{2 \cdot 9 \cdot x^3 \cdot y^4 \cdot z^1}{3 \cdot 9 \cdot x^3 \cdot y^2 \cdot z^5} = \dfrac{2y^{4-2}}{3z^{5-1}} = \dfrac{2y^2}{3z^4}$

TRY THIS   Simplify.

1. $\dfrac{a^3}{a^9}$ 2. $\dfrac{-13x^8y}{26x^4y^5}$ 3. $\dfrac{-24a^7bc^3}{36abc^6}$

It may be necessary to simplify the numerator or the denominator, or both, before using the Quotient-of-Powers Property.

EXAMPLE 4   Simplify $\dfrac{(3x^5y)^2}{6x^4y^3}$ $(x \neq 0,\ y \neq 0)$.

Solution $\dfrac{(3x^5y)^2}{6x^4y^3} = \dfrac{3^2 \cdot x^{5\cdot2} \cdot y^2}{6 \cdot x^4 \cdot y^3} = \dfrac{3^2 \cdot x^{10} \cdot y^2}{6 \cdot x^4 \cdot y^3} = \dfrac{3 \cdot 3 \cdot x^{10-4}}{3 \cdot 2 \cdot y^{3-2}} = \dfrac{3x^6}{2y}$

Notice that a quotient *in simplest form* contains no parentheses, each base appears just once, and numerical coefficients do not have a common factor (other than 1 or -1).

Classroom Exercises

Simplify. Assume that no variable is equal to zero.

1. $\dfrac{6^4}{6}$

2. $\dfrac{8^2}{8^3}$

3. $\dfrac{5^4}{5^4}$

4. $\dfrac{y^4}{y^8}$

5. $\dfrac{a^5}{a^5}$

6. $\dfrac{a^2b}{ab^2}$

7. $\dfrac{r^3s}{s^2t}$

8. $\dfrac{4xy^3}{8x^2y}$

Written Exercises

Simplify. Assume that no variable is equal to zero.

1. $\dfrac{5^3}{5}$

2. $\dfrac{7^2}{7^6}$

3. $\dfrac{x^3}{x^3}$

4. $\dfrac{9^{12}}{9^{10}}$

5. $\dfrac{z^2}{z^{10}}$

6. $\dfrac{x^2y}{xy}$

7. $\dfrac{c^2d^3}{c^3d}$

8. $\dfrac{3x^5}{5x^2}$

9. $\dfrac{5a^2b}{10a^2b}$

10. $\dfrac{6mn}{6m^2n}$

11. $\dfrac{-2r^2s}{18rs}$

12. $\dfrac{14x^2y}{14x^2y}$

13. $\dfrac{(7x)^2}{(7x)^5}$

14. $\dfrac{(9y)^3}{9y}$

15. $\dfrac{13xy}{26x^2y}$

16. $\dfrac{-5z^2}{15yz}$

17. $\dfrac{-18ab^2}{6a^2b^3}$

18. $\dfrac{-12x^2yz^3}{9xy^4z^3}$

19. $\dfrac{-4a^2b^3c}{-28abc}$

20. $\dfrac{16xy^2z^3}{18x^2y^2z^2}$

21. $\dfrac{(2a^2b)^3}{6ab^4}$

22. $\dfrac{4xy^2(-3x^2y)}{10x^3y}$

23. $\dfrac{(3r^2)^3(2rs)}{6rs}$

24. $\dfrac{5a^2b^2}{10b(2ab)^3}$

25. $\dfrac{(4x^5y^2)^2}{16x^{10}y^4}$

26. $\dfrac{-3ab(6a^2b^4)}{9a^3b^2}$

27. $\dfrac{(8 \cdot 10^2)^2}{16 \cdot 10^5}$

28. $\dfrac{(0.5)^8}{[(0.5)^2]^3}$

Simplify. Assume that no variable equals zero and that all exponents are positive integers.

29. $\dfrac{y^{3n}}{y^n}$

30. $\dfrac{x^ny^{2m}}{xy^m}$

31. $\dfrac{(3x^ny^{m-1})^2}{6x^ny^{m+2}}$

32. $\dfrac{7c^{2n}(2c)}{4c^n}$

Mixed Review

Which property of real numbers is illustrated?   *1.5*

1. $4(2 \cdot 6) = (4 \cdot 2)6$

2. $(7 + x)3 = 3(7 + x)$

3. $(4 + y) + z = 4 + (y + z)$

4. $(3 + a) + b = b + (3 + a)$

5. Barry's salary is 4 times Jack's salary. The difference of their salaries is $126. Find each boy's salary.   *4.2*

6.4 Negative Exponents

To simplify expressions with integral exponents
To evaluate monomials with integral exponents

Thus far, you have been working with positive exponents only. **Zero** and **negative exponents** can be defined by extending the Quotient of Powers Property. For example,

$$\frac{5^3}{5^3} = 5^{3-3} = 5^0 = 1$$

For this reason, mathematicians have made the following agreement.

Definition

Zero Exponent
For each nonzero real number b,

$$b^0 = 1. \qquad (0^0 \text{ is undefined.})$$

EXAMPLE 1   Simplify.

a. $4x^0$, $x \neq 0$ b. $(5m)^0$, $m \neq 0$

Solutions   a. $4x^0 = 4(1) = 4$ b. $(5m)^0 = 1$

Thus, $4x^0 = 4$ and $(5m)^0 = 1$.

TRY THIS   Simplify.   **1.** $(xy)^0$ **2.** $(7c^6)^0$

Next consider the quotient $\dfrac{6^2}{6^5}$.

You know that $\dfrac{6^2}{6^5} = \dfrac{6 \cdot 6}{6 \cdot 6 \cdot 6 \cdot 6 \cdot 6} = \dfrac{1}{6^3}$.

If $\dfrac{6^2}{6^5} = 6^{2-5} = 6^{-3}$, then by substitution $6^{-3} = \dfrac{1}{6^3}$.

Now suppose that the negative exponent appears in the denominator.

$$\frac{1}{4^{-3}} = \frac{1}{\frac{1}{4^3}} = 1 \div \frac{1}{4^3} = 1 \cdot \frac{4^3}{1} = 4^3$$

These cases suggest a definition for negative exponent.

Negative Exponent

For each nonzero real number b and for each positive integer n,

$$b^{-n} = \frac{1}{b^n} \text{ and } \frac{1}{b^{-n}} = b^n.$$

EXAMPLE 2 Simplify. Use positive exponents only. No variable equals zero.

a. $3^5 \cdot 3^{-8}$ b. $(ab^{-7})(-b^{-3})$

Solutions a. $3^5 \cdot 3^{-8} = 3^{5+(-8)} = 3^{-3} = \frac{1}{3^3} = \frac{1}{27}$

b. $(ab^{-7})(-b^{-3}) = -1(ab^{-7})(b^{-3}) = -ab^{-7+(-3)}$

$$= -ab^{-10} = \frac{-a}{b^{10}}$$

EXAMPLE 3 Evaluate $3x^{-4}$ for $x = -2$.

Solution $3x^{-4} = 3 \cdot \frac{1}{x^4} = \frac{3}{x^4} = \frac{3}{(-2)^4} = \frac{3}{16}$

TRY THIS 3. Simplify $(x^{-8}y^{-5})(x^{10}y^{-2})$. Use positive exponents only.

An expression such as $\dfrac{3x^{-5}}{7y^{-2}}$ can be simplified so that there are no negative exponents.

Use $\dfrac{a}{b} = \dfrac{a \cdot c}{b \cdot c}$. $\dfrac{3x^{-5}}{7y^{-2}} = \dfrac{3x^{-5} \cdot x^5 y^2}{7y^{-2} \cdot x^5 y^2}$.

Use $b^m \cdot b^n = b^{m+n}$. $= \dfrac{3x^{-5+5}y^2}{7x^5 y^{-2+2}}$

$= \dfrac{3x^0 y^2}{7x^5 y^0}$

Use $b^0 = 1$. $= \dfrac{3 \cdot 1 \cdot y^2}{7 \cdot x^5 \cdot 1}$, or $\dfrac{3y^2}{7x^5}$

This shows that $\dfrac{3x^{-5}}{7y^{-2}}$ is equivalent to $\dfrac{3y^2}{7x^5}$.

As a shortcut, many of the steps such as those shown above are often omitted, as in Example 4 on page 212.

EXAMPLE 4   Simplify $\dfrac{6x^{-4}y^2}{-3xy^{-5}}$, $x \neq 0$, $y \neq 0$. Use positive exponents only.

Plan   To write with positive exponents, use $a^{-n} = \dfrac{1}{a^n}$ and $\dfrac{1}{a^{-n}} = a^n$.

Solution   Write 6 as $-2(-3)$ and x as x^1.

$$\dfrac{6x^{-4}y^2}{-3xy^{-5}} = \dfrac{-2(-3)x^{-4}y^2}{-3x^1y^{-5}}$$

$$= \dfrac{-2y^2y^5}{x^1x^4} = \dfrac{-2y^7}{x^5}$$

EXAMPLE 5   Simplify $\left(\dfrac{2}{3}\right)^{-4}$.

Solution

$$\left(\dfrac{2}{3}\right)^{-4} = \dfrac{1}{\left(\dfrac{2}{3}\right)^4} = \dfrac{1}{\left(\dfrac{16}{81}\right)} = \dfrac{81}{16}$$

TRY THIS   **4.** Simplify $\dfrac{-5x^{-5}y^{-1}}{10x^2y^{-6}}$, $x \neq 0$, $y \neq 0$. Use positive exponents only.

In general, for all nonzero real numbers a and b, and all integers n,

$$\left(\dfrac{a}{b}\right)^{-n} = \left(\dfrac{b}{a}\right)^n.$$

The following properties hold for all integral exponents m and n.

Product of Powers	Quotient of Powers (b ≠ 0)	Power of a Power	Power of a Product
$b^m \cdot b^n = b^{m+n}$	$\dfrac{b^m}{b^n} = b^{m-n}$	$(b^m)^n = b^{mn}$	$(ab)^m = a^m b^m$

Classroom Exercises

Evaluate each expression for the given value of the variable.

1. $2a^{-1}$; $a = -5$ **2.** $-3n^4$; $n = -2$

Simplify. Use positive exponents only. No variable equals zero.

3. $-3x^0$ **4.** $(-3x)^0$ **5.** 3^{-2} **6.** $6^7 \cdot 6^{-8}$

7. $d^{-2} \cdot d^4$ **8.** $4a^{-5} \cdot 2a^3$ **9.** $3x^{-2}y \cdot 5xy^3$ **10.** $\left(\dfrac{1}{3}\right)^{-3}$

11. $\dfrac{(2y)^0}{(3y)^0}$ **12.** $\dfrac{4x^{-2}y^3}{-2xy^{-1}}$ **13.** $\dfrac{1}{2^{-3}}$ **14.** $\left(\dfrac{-12c^2}{3a^{-1}}\right)^{-2}$

Written Exercises

Evaluate each expression for the given value of the variable.

1. $2a^{-5}$; $a = 3$
2. y^{-2}; $y = 8$
3. $-5m^{-1}$; $m = -105$
4. $7n^{-9}$; $n = -1$
5. x^0; $x = -93$
6. $-5b^{-4}$; $b = -2$

Simplify. Use positive exponents only. Assume that no variable is equal to zero.

7. 4^{-3}
8. $5m^{-4}$
9. $-3a^0b$
10. $2m^{-5}n^3$
11. $m^{-3}m^{-8}$
12. $(-2x^{-3})(-3x^4)$
13. $(6y^{-1})(-xy)$
14. $(-4b^0)(-2ab^{-3})$
15. $\dfrac{8x}{4^0x^{-4}}$
16. $\dfrac{(7x)^0}{4x^0}$
17. $\dfrac{5a^{-2}}{15u^3}$
18. $\dfrac{8x^{-3}y^4}{-2xy^{-5}}$
19. $\left(\dfrac{1}{3}\right)^5$
20. $\left(-\dfrac{1}{4}\right)^2$
21. $\left(-\dfrac{1}{2}\right)^{-3}$
22. $\left(\dfrac{3}{4}\right)^{-2}$
23. $\dfrac{-16a^{14}b^{-6}}{-8a^{-10}b^2}$
24. $\dfrac{-6m^{-4}n^3}{2m^{-4}n^{-3}\cdot 5a^0}$
25. $\dfrac{8c^{-7}d^{10}}{12c^{-4}d^{-9}}$
26. $\left(\dfrac{6a^2b^3}{-2ab^{-4}}\right)^{-2}$

Solve each of the following for n.

27. $x^{-3n-6} = (x^3)^{n-6}$
28. $8^{-n+6}\cdot(8^2)^{-n} = (8^{4n})^{-1}$
29. $\left(\dfrac{a}{4}\right)^{-n}\cdot\left(\dfrac{a}{2}\right)^{2n} = a^0\ (a \neq 0)$
30. $x^{5n}\cdot x^{-2n} = \dfrac{1}{x^{-2}}\ (x \neq 0)$
31. $5^{6n-1}\cdot 5^{n+4} = (-5)^{2n}$
32. $\dfrac{1}{x^{3n}} = x^{2n}\cdot x^{-10}\ (x \neq 0)$

33. Show that $\left(\dfrac{a}{b}\right)^m = \dfrac{a^m}{b^m}$, $a \neq 0$, $b \neq 0$. (HINT: Rewrite $\left(\dfrac{a}{b}\right)^m$ as $(ab^{-1})^m$.)

34. Explain why $x^{-1} > 1$ if $0 < x < 1$.

Mixed Review

1. Simplify $8a - (-6 - 5a) - 2a$ 2.10

Evaluate.   1.3, 2.6, 2.8

2. $(3m)^3$ for $m = \dfrac{1}{2}$
3. $\dfrac{1}{3}x + 6x^2$ for $x = -6$
4. $(-a)^3$ for $a = -6$
5. $-m + 3n$ for $m = -5$ and $n = -2$

Solve.   3.3, 3.5

6. $\dfrac{x}{4} - 1 = 8$
7. $2x - (-2 + x) = 6$

6.5 Scientific Notation

Objective	To convert ordinary notation to scientific notation and vice versa

Scientific Notation is a compact way of writing very large and very small numbers. It enables you to see the magnitude of a number at a glance. The distance that light travels in one year is about 9,500,000,000,000 kilometers. In scientific notation this number is written as 9.5×10^{12}, which the eye can grasp quickly. The exponent 12 is a positive integer. However, the exponents used in scientific notation may be positive, negative, or zero.

Definition

A number is written in **scientific notation** when it is in the form

$$a \times 10^n,$$

where $1 \le a < 10$ and n is an integer.

Study the table below. Notice that for numbers greater than 10, the exponent is positive; for numbers between 0 and 1, the exponent is negative.

Number	Decimal-Point Shift	Scientific Notation
4 30,000,000	left 8 places	4.3×10^8
5 17 65	left 2 places	5.1765×10^2
0 0000 9 56	right 5 places	$\frac{9.56}{100,000} = 9.56 \times 10^{-5}$
0 04 71	right 2 places	$\frac{4.71}{100} = 4.71 \times 10^{-2}$

A number such as 1.432, between 1 and 10, is equal to 1.432×10^0. Also, $1 = 1 \times 10^0$ and $10 = 1 \times 10^1$.

EXAMPLE 1	Express each number in scientific notation.
	a. 8654.32 **b.** 0.00346
Solutions	**a.** $8654.32 = 8\,6\,5\,4.3\,2 = 8.65432 \times 10^3$
	b. $0.00346 = 0.0\,0\,3\,4\,6 = 3.46 \times 10^{-3}$

TRY THIS	Express each number in scientific notation.
	1. 0.00002013 **2.** 54179.82

To change a number from scientific notation to ordinary notation, perform the indicated multiplication by the power of 10, as in Example 2.

EXAMPLE 2   Express each number in ordinary notation.

a. 4.602×10^5 b. 3.76×10^{-6}

Solutions   a. 4.60200×10^5 b. 000003.76×10^{-6}

        $= 460{,}200$ $= 0.00000376$

TRY THIS   Express each number in ordinary notation.

3. 8.0032×10^4 **4.** 6.415×10^{-3}

A scientific calculator with an exponential shift key, $\boxed{\text{EE}}$ or $\boxed{\text{EXP}}$, can be used to perform multiplication and division of numbers written in scientific notation.

EXAMPLE 3   Simplify. Express the answer in ordinary notation.

a. $(5.2 \times 10^2)(8.6 \times 10^4)$ b. $(6.1 \times 10^{-2}) \div (4.5 \times 10^{-1})$

Solution   a. $5.2 \boxed{\text{EE}} 2 \boxed{\times} 8.6 \boxed{\text{EE}} 4 = 4.472 \quad 07 \longleftarrow 4.472 \times 10^7$

         In ordinary notation, $4.472 \times 10^7 = 44{,}720{,}000$.

       b. $6.1 \boxed{\text{EE}} \boxed{+/-} 2 \boxed{\div} 4.5 \boxed{\text{EE}} \boxed{+/-} 1 = 1.3556 \quad -01$

         In ordinary notation, $1.3556 \times 10^{-1} = 0.13556$.

To perform computations involving very large or very small numbers, first express the numbers in scientific notation. Then use a calculator.

$$\frac{(48{,}200{,}000)(0.0042)}{0.0000012} = \frac{(4.82 \times 10^7)(4.2 \times 10^{-3})}{1.2 \times 10^{-6}}, \text{ or}$$

$4.82 \boxed{\text{EE}} 7 \boxed{\times} 4.2 \boxed{\text{EE}} \boxed{+/-} 3 \boxed{\div} 1.2 \boxed{\text{EE}} \boxed{+/-} 6 \boxed{=} \quad 1.687 \quad 11$

So, the result is 1.687×10^{11}, or $168{,}700{,}000{,}000$.

Classroom Exercises

Express each number in scientific notation.

1. 463 **2.** 0.0034 **3.** 18×10^5 **4.** 0.513×10^{-5}

Express each number in ordinary notation.

5. 5.3×10^6 **6.** 7.24×10^{-4} **7.** 546×10^{-4} **8.** 0.025×10^6

Written Exercises

Express each number or measure in scientific notation.

1. 5,620,000   **2.** 0.0301   **3.** 5.002   **4.** 6,300

5. 0.0000067   **6.** 8   **7.** 91,420,000   **8.** 0.0000008

9. the speed of light (approximately 186,000 mi/s)

10. the wavelength of red light (approximately 0.00000068 m)

11. the wavelength of a TV signal (approximately 77,250,000 m)

12. the mass of one atom of oxygen (0.00000000000000000000000265 g)

Express each number in ordinary notation.

13. 3.1×10^{-4} **14.** 5.62×10^{7} **15.** 1×10^{-2} **16.** 8.04×10^{5}

17. 1×10^{3} **18.** 7.03×10^{-6} **19.** 2×10^{1} **20.** 4.6×10^{-3}

Simplify. Express the answer in ordinary notation.

21. $(4.6 \times 10^{3})(7.9 \times 10^{2})$

22. $(6.1 \times 10^{-3})(8.6 \times 10^{-2})$

23. $(8.8 \times 10^{-1}) \div (2.5 \times 10)$

24. $(2.25 \times 10^{2}) \div (9 \times 10^{-4})$

Simplify. Express the answer in scientific notation.

25. $\dfrac{(216,000,000)(0.00000168)}{0.00000084}$

26. $\dfrac{69,300,000}{(16,500)(0.0000015)}$

27. $\dfrac{(0.525)(7,820)}{22.5}$

28. $\dfrac{(7,500,000)(0.05)}{150,000,000}$

29. $\dfrac{(9,060,000)(0.00447)}{0.00042}$

30. $\dfrac{(0.000212)(0.588)}{57,700,000}$

Mixed Review

Evaluate for $x = -3$, $y = -1$, and $z = 4$.   **2.5, 2.6**

1. $-(x - y - z)$ **2.** $x^{2}yz$

3. Write an algebraic expression for 5 less than the product of 3 and x.   **4.1**

4. Solve: $\frac{1}{2}x + \frac{1}{4} = -\frac{3}{5}$ **4.5**

5. The degree measure of the vertex angle of an isosceles triangle is 20 less than twice the degree measure of each base angle of the triangle. What is the measure of each angle?   **4.4**

Application: The Earth's Hydrosphere

How many drops of water are there in the ocean?

You cannot know the exact answer, but you can get an idea of the size of the answer, or its *order of magnitude*. To estimate the number of drops of water in the hydrosphere, made up of the seas and the oceans, follow this plan.

1. Find the surface area of the earth in square meters (m^2).
2. Find the part of the surface area that is water in m^2.
3. Find the total volume of the water in the hydrosphere in m^3.
4. Divide the total volume by the volume of a drop of water to find the number of drops of water.

The first three exercises below help to estimate the total volume of the water. Use a scientific calculator for all the exercises (refer to page 215). Round answers to the nearest whole number.

1. The surface area of a sphere is given by the formula, $A = 4\pi r^2$, where r, the average radius of the earth, is about 6,370,000 m. Find the surface area of the earth. Use 3.1416 or the calculator key for π.

2. Since water covers approximately 70% of the earth, multiply your answer to Exercise 1 by 70% to find the surface area of the hydrosphere.

3. To find the total volume of the water in cubic meters, multiply your answer to Exercise 2 by 3,790 meters, the average depth of the earth's seas and oceans.

4. The volume of a large drop of water is about $5.0 \times 10^{-8} \, m^3$ (or 50 billionths of a cubic meter). Divide your answer to Exercise 3 by this volume to approximate how many drops of water there are in the oceans. Give your answer in scientific notation using as many digits as your calculator will show.

5. The *order of magnitude* of an estimate is indicated by the power of 10 when the estimate is written in scientific notation.
   Complete: The order of magnitude of the number of drops of water in the hydrosphere is __?__.

6.6 Simplifying Polynomials

To classify polynomials according to the number of terms
To simplify a polynomial and determine its degree
To write a polynomial in descending order and in ascending order

The sculpture shown here has the shape of two joined cubes. Its twelve faces are squares. If x and y represent the lengths of the sides of the large and small cube, respectively, then the total surface area can be represented by the *polynomial* $6x^2 + 6y^2$.

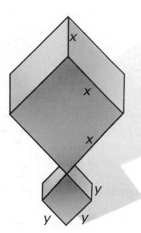

$6x^2$ and $6y^2$ are *monomials*.

A **polynomial** is a monomial or the sum of two or more monomials. The monomials in a polynomial are called *terms* of the polynomial. In the polynomial $5x^2 - 4x + 2$, the terms are $5x^2$, $-4x$, and 2.

Polynomials are classified according to their number of terms. A **binomial** has two terms and a **trinomial** has three terms.

Number of Terms	Name	Example
1	*monomial*	$-5x^3$
2	*binomial*	$a^2 - 2ab$
3	*trinomial*	$x^2 + 2x - 1$

Like terms are terms with the same variable(s) raised to the same power(s). A polynomial is *in simplest form* if no two of its terms are like terms.

EXAMPLE 1   Simplify.

   a. $3y^2 - 5y - y^2$ **b.** $5x^2 - 7x + 2$

Solutions   **a.** $3y^2 - 5y - y^2$ **b.** $5x^2 - 7x + 2$ has no like terms.
   $= 3y^2 - y^2 - 5y$ Thus, $5x^2 - 7x + 2$ is in simplest
   $= 2y^2 - 5y$ form.

TRY THIS   Simplify: **1.** $10y + 4y^2 - 5y^2$ **2.** $3x^2 + 2x^2 - 1$

The **degree of a monomial** is the sum of the exponents of all of its variables, as illustrated in the table below.

Monomial	-7	y	$6x^3y^2$	$-5a^4b^2c$
Degree	0	1	3 + 2, or 5	4 + 2 + 1, or 7

The **degree of a polynomial** is the same as the degree of its term with the greatest degree when the polynomial is in simplest form.

Polynomial	$8x^2 + 2x^3 + 1$			$9a^3b^2 + 6b^4$		$6 + 5c^2 - 3c^4 + c$			
Degree of terms	2	3	0	5	4	0	2	4	1
Degree of polynomial	3			5		4			

EXAMPLE 2   Simplify $3x^3 - 5x^2 + 6x^2 - 3x^3 - 7$. Then give the degree of the polynomial.

Solution $3x^3 - 5x^2 + 6x^2 - 3x^3 - 7 = (3x^3 - 3x^3) + (6x^2 - 5x^2) - 7$
$$= 0 + x^2 - 7$$
$$= x^2 - 7$$

The term with the greatest degree is x^2. Its degree is 2. Thus, the degree of the given polynomial is 2.

TRY THIS   3. Simplify $4y^2 - 6y + 7y^4 - y^2 + y^4$. Give the degree of the polynomial.

A polynomial in one variable is in **descending order** when the terms are in order from greatest to least degree. Thus, $7x^4 - 6x^3 + 4x + 2$ is in descending order.

EXAMPLE 3   Simplify $5x^4 + 7x - 1 - 3x^3 - 5x^4 - 3x + 2x^3$. Write the result in descending order.

Plan   First group terms in descending order. Then combine like terms.

Solution
$$5x^4 + 7x - 1 - 3x^3 - 5x^4 - 3x + 2x^3$$
$$= (5x^4 - 5x^4) + (-3x^3 + 2x^3) + (7x - 3x) - 1$$
$$= -x^3 + 4x - 1 \text{ (descending order)}$$

TRY THIS   4. Simplify $8x^5 - 6x^2 + 4x^4 + 3x^2 - 2x^5 + x^4 + 2x - 7$. Write the result in descending order.

Focus on Reading

To complete each sentence, write a letter from the column at the right.

1. $7 - 3x^2$ is a(n) __?__ .
2. The degree of the polynomial $6x^3 - 2x + 1$ is __?__ .
3. In $7x^3 - 2x - 1$, -1 is a(n) __?__ .
4. In $4x^2 - 3x + 1$, 2 is a(n) __?__ .
5. The degree of the monomial -1 is __?__ .
6. $9y^2 - 2y + 3$ is a(n) __?__ .
7. In the polynomial $3c^3 - 2c + 1$, c is the only __?__ .
8. $-7x^3y^4$ is a(n) __?__ .
9. The degree of the polynomial $7 - 4x$ is __?__ .
10. The __?__ of a monomial is the sum of the exponents of all of its variables.
11. The degree of the polynomial $7x^3 + 2x^2 - 7x$ is __?__ .

a. monomial
b. binomial
c. trinomial
d. 0
e. 1
f. 2
g. 3
h. constant
i. exponent
j. variable
k. degree

Classroom Exercises

Classify each polynomial as a monomial, a binomial, or a trinomial.

1. 4^2
2. $6a^4 - 2a^3$
3. $3y^2x^3$
4. $7x^2 - 3x^3 + 1$

Simplify. Then give the degree of the polynomial.

5. $4y^3 - 3y + 2y^2 - 5y^3 + y$
6. $-3a + 2a^2 - 7a + 6a^3 - a^2$

Give each polynomial in descending order and ascending order.

7. $2y^4 - 3y + 7y^3$
8. $3z^2 - z^4 + 7z$
9. $c^3 + 4 - c^2$
10. $-x + 2 - x^2$

Written Exercises

Tell whether the given expression is a polynomial.

1. $x - 2x^2 + 5$
2. $(0.5)^{-1}$
3. $n^2 + \frac{n}{2}$
4. $3y^2 - 3y^{-1}$

Classify each polynomial as a monomial, a binomial, or a trinomial.

5. $a^2 - b^2$
6. $2a + b - 3c$
7. $-6xy^4$
8. $-3x + 5y^2$

Simplify. Then give the degree of the polynomial.

9. $5y^3 - 3y^2 + 2y - 5y^3 + 1$
10. $3c + 2c^3 - 4c + 6c^2 + 5$
11. $8d^4 - 5d^3 + 4d^3 - 3d^4 - 5d^4$
12. $7 - 3y^4 + 2y^3 - y^4 + 5y^3 - 2y^4$

13. $7x^2 - 2x^3 - 4x^2 - x^3 + 3x + 1$
14. $-5z^2 - 2z + 4z^2 + 3z + z^2$
15. $3y^6 - 2y^4 + y^6 + 2y^4 + 3y + 7$
16. $x^4 - 2x + 5x^2 + 7x - x^4 + 2x^2$

Simplify. Write the result in descending order and in ascending order.

17. $7a + 2a^2 + 3a - 6$
18. $-5c + 1 - 4c^2 + 3c^2$
19. $3 + 7x^2 - 2x + 4x^2 - 1$
20. $-r^2 + 3r - 5 + 2r - 7r^2$
21. $7x^4 - 3x^2 + 2x^3 - x^4 - 2x^3$
22. $6y^5 - 4y^3 + y^4 - 7y + 1$
23. $-3 + 2r^4 + 2r - 6r^4 + 2r + 1$
24. $x^3 - 8x - 4x^2 + 8x + 3x^2 + 9x^3$
25. $-5a + 4a^3 - 3a^2 + 2 + 8a^3 - 9a + 5a - 6$
26. $-2 + 5x^2 - 4x - 3x^2 + x^2 + 7x + 2x^3 + 4$
27. $y^4 - 3y^3 - 8y + y^2 - 7y^3 + 9y + y^2 - 5 + 4y^4$

Simplify. (Exercises 28–32)

28. $7xy - 2yz + 3xz - 4yz + 4x - 7y$
29. $5b^2 - 6a^2 - 2b^2 + 4a^2 + 7a + 6b + 3a$
30. $2a^3b - 3ab^3 + 4a^3 - a^3b - 7ab^3$
31. $(-3a)(4b^2)(2a) + (2a^2)(4b^2) - (5ab^2)(2ab)$
32. $(2xy)(3x^2)(-x^2y) + (3y^2)(2x)(5x^4) + (x^2y)(-x^3y)$
33. Construct a polynomial of degree 3 with one variable and four terms.
34. Construct a trinomial of degree 5 with one variable.
35. Construct a monomial of degree 5 with two variables.
36. Solve $x(x^2 - 2x + 3) + 2x^2 + 3 = x(1 + x^2) + 6$.
37. Explain why "$x^3 + x^2 = x^5$ for all real values of x" is false.

Midchapter Review

Simplify. Use positive exponents only. No denominator equals zero. *6.1, 6.2, 6.3, 6.4*

1. $2y^4 \cdot y$
2. $(x^6)^2$
3. $-2x^0y^{-1}$
4. $4cd^2(6cd)$

5. $(ab^2)^3$
6. $(-2a^2bc)^4$
7. $6c^2d^3(-8bc)$
8. $0.5xy(-2x^7y^3)$

9. $\dfrac{y^3z}{yz^2}$
10. $\dfrac{-3ab^2}{6b^3c}$
11. $\dfrac{7x^{-1}}{14x^2}$
12. $5x\left(\dfrac{1}{5}x\right)^2$

13. $\dfrac{(5x^2)^3}{7x^4}$
14. $\left(\dfrac{4}{5}\right)^{-2}$
15. $\left(\dfrac{3xy}{2y}\right)^{-1}$
16. $\dfrac{15r^{-2}s^2}{5r^{-3}s^{-1}}$

Express each number in scientific notation. *6.5*

17. 32,000,000
18. 0.000017
19. 0.0065
20. 405,000,000,000

6.7 Addition and Subtraction of Polynomials

Objectives

To add and subtract polynomials
To write the indicated sum of polynomials in descending order.

The *perimeter* of a polygon is the sum of the lengths of its sides. To find the perimeter of this triangle, use vertical notation and add like terms.

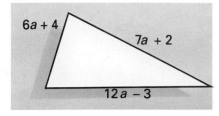

$$
\begin{array}{r}
6a + 4 \\
7a + 2 \\
\underline{12a - 3} \\
25a + 3
\end{array}
$$

The perimeter is $(25a + 3)$ units.

EXAMPLE 1   Add $7x^2 - 2x + 1$ and $4x^2 + 3x - 6$.

Plan   Write the sum. Then group like terms in descending order and simplify.

Solution $(7x^2 - 2x + 1) + (4x^2 + 3x - 6) = 7x^2 + 4x^2 - 2x + 3x + 1 - 6$

$= 11x^2 + x - 5$

EXAMPLE 2   Add $9y^3 - 7y + 8 + y^2$ and $7y - y^3 - 3y^4 - 3$.

Plan   When simplifying the sum, begin with the term with the greatest degree, $-3y^4$. Continue grouping like terms in descending order.

Solution $(9y^3 - 7y + 8 + y^2) + (7y - y^3 - 3y^4 - 3)$
$-3y^4 + 9y^3 - y^3 + y^2 - 7y + 7y + 8 - 3$
$-3y^4 + 8y^3 + y^2 + 5$

TRY THIS   1. Add $5x^2 + 7x^5 - 8$ and $-9x^2 + x - 2 - 6x^5$.

You can also use a vertical form to add polynomials.

EXAMPLE 3   Add. $(3x^5 - 2x^3 + 4x + 7) + (6x^3 - x^2 - 4x + 1)$

Solution
$$
\begin{array}{r}
3x^5 - 2x^3 \quad\;\; + 4x + 7 \\
\underline{+ 6x^3 - x^2 - 4x + 1} \\
3x^5 + 4x^3 - x^2 + 0 \;\; + 8, \text{ or } 3x^5 + 4x^3 - x^2 + 8
\end{array}
$$

TRY THIS   2. Add. $(5x^4 + 6x^3 - 3x^2 + x) + (2x^4 - x^3 - x^2 - x)$

Recall that $-a = -1 \cdot a$. This property is used in finding the opposite (additive inverse) of a polynomial.

EXAMPLE 4 Simplify $-(-5x^2 + 2x - 1)$.

Solution
$$-(-5x^2 + 2x - 1) = -1 \cdot (-5x^2 + 2x - 1) \longleftarrow -a = -1 \cdot a$$
$$= 5x^2 - 2x + 1 \longleftarrow \text{Distributive Property}$$

TRY THIS 3. Simplify $-(6x^3 - 4x^2 - 8x + 5)$.

Example 5 illustrates that the opposite of a polynomial is found by *changing the sign of each term* of the polynomial. That is,
$$-(x - 2) = -x + 2,$$
$$-(y^2 - y + 3) = -y^2 + y - 3, \quad \text{and}$$
$$-(a - b + c) = -a + b - c.$$

EXAMPLE 5 Subtract. $(5a^2 - 3a + 6) - (2a^2 - 3a - 2)$

Plan Use $a - b = a + (-b)$. (Definition of subtraction)
Add the opposite of $(2a^2 - 3a - 2)$ to $(5a^2 - 3a + 6)$.

Solution
$$(5a^2 - 3a + 6) - (2a^2 - 3a - 2) = (5a^2 - 3a + 6) + (-2a^2 + 3a + 2)$$
$$= 5a^2 - 2a^2 - 3a + 3a + 6 + 2$$
$$= \underbrace{3a^2} \quad \underbrace{+ 0} \quad \underbrace{+ 8}$$
$$= 3a^2 + 8$$

TRY THIS 4. Subtract. $(9y^3 + 4y - 3) - (8y^3 - 2y + 5)$

You can also use a vertical form in subtraction.

EXAMPLE 6 Subtract $0.2x^3 - 0.5x + 0.1$ from $0.4x^2 + 0.3x - 0.7$.

Plan "Subtract a from b" means add $(-a)$ to b.
Therefore, find the opposite of $0.2x^3 - 0.5x + 0.1$.
Add it to $0.4x^2 + 0.3x - 0.7$.

Solution
$$-(0.2x^3 - 0.5x + 0.1)$$
$$= -0.2x^3 + 0.5x - 0.1$$

$$\begin{array}{r} 0.4x^2 + 0.3x - 0.7 \\ -0.2x^3 \qquad\qquad + 0.5x - 0.1 \\ \hline -0.2x^3 + 0.4x^2 + 0.8x - 0.8 \end{array}$$

TRY THIS 5. Subtract $0.7x^4 - 0.3x^2 - 0.2$ from $0.2x^4 + 0.5x^2 - 0.1$.

Classroom Exercises

Add.

1. $5c^2 - 3c + 2$
$\underline{-4c^2 - c - 7}$

2. $-x^3 + 2x^2 + 1$
$\underline{ - 9x^2 - 2x + 3}$

3. $2b^4 - 3b^2 + 5b$
$\underline{ 6b^3 - 4b}$

Give the additive inverse of each polynomial.

4. $2x + 8$

5. $-y^3 - 6y + 1$

6. $3d^4 - 7d^2 + d - 1$

Simplify.

7. $-(3x - 2)$

8. $-(5x^4 - 7x^3 + 3x)$

9. $-(-6c^5 + 3c^3 + 1)$

10. Subtract: $(3c^2 - 7c + 2) - (c^2 + 8c + 5)$

Written Exercises

Add the given polynomials.

1. $5x^2 - 7x$ and $3x^2 + 2x$

2. $4y^2 + 6y + 1$ and $2y^2 + 3y - 2$

3. $-4a^2 - 9a + 6$ and $3a^2 - 2a + 5$

4. $x^2 - 7x + 2$ and $4x^2 + 2x - 9$

Add.

5. $(-3b^2 - 6b + 2) + (-4b^2 - b - 7)$

6. $(6a^4 - 7a^3 + a) + (5a^3 - 3a^2 - 2a)$

7. $(x^3 - 5x^4 + 2x^2 + x) + (-x^4 + 6x^2 - 5x + 2)$

Simplify.

8. $-(5c^2 - 3c)$ **9.** $-(y^3 - 3y^2 + 1)$ **10.** $-(-8t^2 + 3t)$ **11.** $-(2x^3 + 6x^2 + 3)$

Perform the indicated operations.

12. $(6x - 4) - (2x + 7)$

13. $(3y + 8) - (3y - 9)$ 17

14. $(7x^2 + 2x - 4) - (2x^2 - 2x + 6)$

15. $(5r^2 + 7r + 2) - (-5r^2 + 7r - 3)$

16. Subtract $x^2 - 3x + 2$ from $5x^2 + 4$.

17. Subtract $-x^2 - 4x$ from $-x^3 - x^2 - 9x$.

18. $(\frac{1}{2}x^2 + \frac{1}{4}x - \frac{1}{5}) + (-\frac{1}{4}x^2 - x + \frac{4}{5})$

19. $(\frac{2}{3}y^3 + \frac{1}{6}y - \frac{1}{4}) + (\frac{1}{3}y^3 - \frac{5}{8}y^2 - \frac{5}{6}y + \frac{1}{2})$

20. $0.5x^2 - 0.8x + 0.2) + (-0.9x^2 + 1.4x - 3.8)$

21. $(5.04x^3 - 6.2x^2 + 0.7) + (8.37x^3 - 4.9x^2 + 6.3x)$

22. $(0.6y^3 - 5.3y - 6.1) - (1.9y^3 + 4.9y^2 - 7.8y)$

23. $(8.5x^5 - 3.8x^3 + 2.7x) - (4.2x^4 + 3.8x^3 - 7.4x + 0.2)$

Express the perimeter of each figure as a polynomial in simplest form.

24.

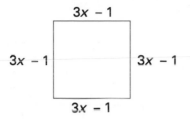

$3x - 1$

$3x - 1$ $3x - 1$

$3x - 1$

25.

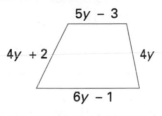

$5y - 3$

$4y + 2$ $4y$

$6y - 1$

26. Subtract the sum of $5y^2 - 3y + 2$ and $7y^3 + 2y - 1$ from $8y^4 - 7y^2 + 6y - 1$.

27. Subtract $6x^2y + xy^2$ from $3x^2y - 8y^3$ and add the difference to $x^2y - 5xy^2$.

Mixed Review

Simplify. *1.6, 2.2, 2.10, 6.1, 6.2, 6.3*

1. $-|7 - 9|$

2. $3(4x + 8)$

3. $-7(3a + 2b - 1)$

4. $-1(-5x - 2y + 3z)$

5. $-y - (6 + 3y)$

6. $-(2x + 4) - 5(x - 2)$

7. $7c - (2 + 6c - 5)$

8. $x^2 \cdot x^4$

9. $2y(-3y^2)$

10. $-x(-4xy^3)$

11. $(3a^2b)^3$

12. $\dfrac{4x^2y}{12xy^5}$

Application: Compound Interest

In January, Jackie started a savings account into which she deposited $100. Her bank pays 8% yearly interest compounded monthly according to this formula: $A = p(1 + r)^n$. Use your scientific calculator with these exercises to find how much money Jackie will have in her account at the end of the year.

1. To find r, divide the yearly rate of interest by the number of interest periods (12). Write your answer with as many places as your calculator will show.

2. Find A, the amount of the new balance, when p, the principal or amount deposited, is $100 and n, the number of interest periods per year, is 12. Here are the calculator steps:

   100 $\boxed{\times}$ $\boxed{(}$ 1.0066666 $\boxed{y^x}$ 12 $\boxed{)}$ $\boxed{=}$ 108.29986

   Round the answer to the nearest cent. How much money will Jackie have in her account at the end of the year?

3. How much money would she have if the bank only paid simple interest of 8% per year?

6.8 Multiplying a Polynomial by a Monomial

Objective	To multiply a polynomial by a monomial

The area of a rectangle is the product of its width and length. To find the product of $(a + 3)$ and $2a$, begin by multiplying a by $2a$.

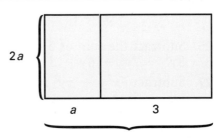

$2a$

a 3

$a + 3$

$$
\begin{array}{ll}
a \; + \; 3 & \text{Length} \\
\underline{ 2a} & \text{Width} \\
2a^2 + 6a & \text{Area}
\end{array}
$$

Thus, the area of the rectangle is $(2a^2 + 6a)$ square units.

EXAMPLE 1	Multiply $3x(4x - 1)$.
Solution	$3x(4x - 1) = (3x)(4x) + (3x)(-1) = 12x^2 - 3x$

EXAMPLE 2	Multiply $(3y^2 - y + 6)(-2y^2)$.
Solution	$(3y^2 - y + 6)(-2y^2) = (3y^2)(-2y^2) + (-1y)(-2y^2) + (6)(-2y^2)$
	$\qquad\qquad\qquad = -6y^4 + 2y^3 - 12y^2$

TRY THIS	Multiply: **1.** $9y^2(2y - 7)$ **2.** $y^4(-y - 2)$

Sometimes you may have to apply the Distributive Property within an expression.

EXAMPLE 3	Simplify $a^4 - 6a^2 - 4a^2(3a^2 - 7a + 2)$.
Solution	$a^4 - 6a^2 - 4a^2(3a^2 - 7a + 2)$
	$= a^4 - 6a^2 + (-4a^2)(3a^2) + (-4a^2)(-7a) + (-4a^2)(2)$
	$= a^4 - 6a^2 - 12a^4 + 28a^3 - 8a^2$
	$= a^4 - 12a^4 + 28a^3 - 6a^2 - 8a^2 = -11a^4 + 28a^3 - 14a^2$

TRY THIS	**3.** Simplify $a^3 + 2a^5 - 5a^4(4a - 7a^2 - 6)$.

Classroom Exercises

Multiply.

1. $3a(2a + 1)$
2. $(4x - 2)6x$
3. $5y(-3y - 9)$
4. $-x(4x^2 - 5x - 2)$
5. $(5t^2 - 3t + 4)2t$
6. $-6z^2(-3z^2 + 2z - 1)$

Simplify.

7. $5y^2 + 2y(y - 6)$
8. $3x^3 - (4x^2 + 3)5x$
9. $2(-5x^2 + 7) - 8x^2$

Written Exercises

Multiply.

1. $5y(3y - 2)$
2. $c(-4c + 2)$
3. $-r(-3r - 7)$
4. $3a(a^2 - 2a + 1)$
5. $-2x(x^2 + 4x - 1)$
6. $4c(2c^2 - c + 3)$
7. $x^2(7x^2 - 4x + 1)$
8. $(-3t^2 + 4t - 7)(-2t)$
9. $-a^2(3a^2 - a + 1)$
10. $4x(5x^2 + 3x - 2)$
11. $-2y^2(4y^3 - 3y^2 - y)$
12. $(-2x^2 + 3x - 1)(-3x^3)$
13. $2b^3(4b^2 - 3b + 1)$
14. $-3b^4(2b^2 - 6b + 2)$
15. $(-y^2 - 2y - 1)4y^3$

Express the area of each figure as a polynomial in simplest form.

16.

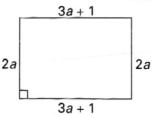

17.

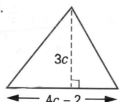

18.

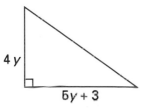

19.

Simplify.

20. $-3y^2 - 4y + 6 + 2(y^2 + 7y - 1)$
21. $-a^2 + 5a - 4 - 3(2a^2 - a - 5)$
22. $3x^2 + 2x(x - 5)$
23. $5y^2 + 2(y - 3) - 6y$
24. $4a^2 + 3a + (a + 7)2a$
25. $x^2 + 5x + 4 - 3x(-x + 1)$
26. $x^3 + (5x^2 - 6x - 1)x + 7x^2$
27. $3y^3 - 2y(4y^2 - 3y + 7) - 6y^2$

Multiply.

28. $5xy(x^2 + 2xy + y^2)$

29. $-3ab(a^2 - 2ab + b^2)$

30. $-2x^2y^2(3x^2 - xy + 4y^2)$

31. $-r^2s(r^2 + 2rs - 5s^2)$

32. $-2cd^2(3c^2d - 2c^2d^2 + cd^2)$

33. $(-2a^3 - 5ab + b^3)(3a^2b^2)$

34. $(a^3 + 2a^2b - ab^2 + 3b^3)(4ab)$

35. $-2xy(x^3 + 3x^2y - 5xy^2 + 4y^3)$

36. Explain in writing why $(x - 2)(x + 4) = (x - 2)x + (x - 2)4$, for all real numbers x is true.

37. Express in simplest polynomial form the total surface area of the rectangular solid below.

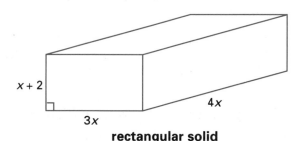

$x + 2$

$3x$

$4x$

rectangular solid

38. Add the product of m^3n^2 and $(5m^2 + 3mn + n^2)$ to the product of m^3n^2 and $(m^2 - 3mn + 2n^2)$.

39. Add the product of $3ab$ and $(a^2 - 5ab + 4b^2)$ to the product of $-2ab$ and $(6a^2 - 7ab - 8b^2)$.

Mixed Review

1. Evaluate $18a^3$ for $a = -\frac{2}{3}$.   **2.6**

Solve.   **4.5, 5.7**

2. $\frac{2}{3}y - \frac{1}{6} = \frac{5}{6}$

3. $|2a - 4| < 8$

4. Use the formula $p = 2l + 2w$ to find p if $l = 7.5$ in. and $w = 4.5$ in.   **1.4**

5. 6 is what percent of 24?   **4.7**

6. 12 is 75% of what number?   **4.7**

7. For the school play, the number of student tickets sold was 300 more than the number of adult tickets. Find the number of tickets of each type sold if the total number of tickets was 1,500.   **3.6**

6.9 Multiplying Binomials

To multiply two binomials
To multiply a trinomial by a binomial

A patio that measures 3 m by 5 m has an area of
3×5, or 15 m^2. Suppose the patio is to be expanded in two directions by a certain amount, say by
x meters. Then the new dimensions of the patio are
$(x + 3)$ m and $(x + 5)$ m. The area of the expanded
patio, in square meters, can be represented by the
product of two binomials, $(x + 3)(x + 5)$,

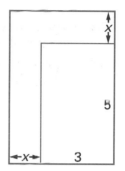

The Distributive Property is used twice in multiplying $(x + 3)$ by $(x + 5)$. In the horizontal multiplication below, $(x + 3)$ is first treated as a single
number.

Horizontal Multiplication   Vertical Multiplication

$(x + 3)(x + 5)$ or $\begin{pmatrix} x + 3 \\ x + 5 \end{pmatrix}$

$= (x + 3)x + (x + 3)5$

$= x^2 + 3x + 5x + 15$ $x^2 + 3x$

$= x^2 + 8x + 15$ $\underline{ 5x + 15}$

$x^2 + 8x + 15$

Thus, the area, in square meters, is represented by $x^2 + 8x + 15$.

Two binomials can be multiplied mentally by using the FOIL method.

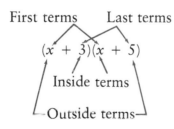

First terms   Last terms   First terms: x and x

$(x + 3)(x + 5)$ Outside terms: x and 5

Inside terms   Inside terms: 3 and x

Outside terms   Last terms: 3 and 5

Remember these four steps when you multiply two binomials.

First terms	Outside terms	Inside terms	Last terms
$x \cdot x$	$x \cdot 5$	$3 \cdot x$	$3 \cdot 5$
x^2	$5x$	$3x$	15
F	O	I	L

Then combine like terms: $x^2 + 8x + 15$.

EXAMPLE 1   Multiply: $(2x + 1)(7x - 4)$

Solution   F   O   I   L

$$(2x + 1)(7x - 4) = 2x(7x) + 2x(-4) + 1(7x) + 1(-4)$$
$$= 14x^2 - 8x + 7x - 4$$
$$= 14x^2 - x - 4$$

TRY THIS   Multiply: **1.** $(5y - 2)(2y + 4)$ **2.** $(a - 3)(a + 4)$

Some binomials contain more than one variable.

EXAMPLE 2   Multiply: $(5a - b)(-2a + b)$

Solution   F   O   I   L

$$(5a - b)(-2a + b) = 5a(-2a) + 5a(b) - b(-2a) - b(b)$$
$$= -10a^2 + 5ab + 2ab - b^2$$
$$-10a^2 + 7ab - b^2$$

TRY THIS   Multiply: **3.** $(6x - y)(-x - y)$

Focus on Reading

Use one of the expressions at the right below to complete each product.

1. $(x + 1)(x + 9) = x^2 + \underline{\ ?\ } + 9$

2. $(x - 3)(x + 4) = x^2 + x + \underline{\ ?\ }$

3. $(x - 2)(x - 8) = x^2 + \underline{\ ?\ } + 16$

4. $(3x - 7)(-2x + 5) = \underline{\ ?\ } + 29x - 35$

a. $-12x$ **e.** -12

b. $6x^2$ **f.** $9x$

c. $10x$ **g.** $-6x^2$

d. $-10x$

Classroom Exercises

Give the missing term in each product.

1. $(y + 3)(y + 2) = y^2 + 5y + \underline{\ ?\ }$ **2.** $(x - 4)(x + 7) = x^2 + 3x - \underline{\ ?\ }$

3. $(c - 9)(c - 1) = c^2 - 10c + \underline{\ ?\ }$ **4.** $(a - 8)(a - 3) = a^2 - \underline{\ ?\ } + 24$

5. $(x + 8)(x - 9) = x^2 - \underline{\ ?\ } - 72$ **6.** $(r - 3)(r + 7) = r^2 + \underline{\ ?\ } - 21$

7. $(3y + 2)(y - 4) = \underline{\ ?\ } - 10y - 8$ **8.** $(4x + 7)(5x - 1) = \underline{\ ?\ } + 31x - 7$

Multiply.

9. $(x + 2)(x + 4)$ **10.** $(y - 3)(y - 2)$ **11.** $(x + 2)(x - 1)$

12. $(a - 4)(a + 5)$ **13.** $(r - 8)(r - 3)$ **14.** $(c + 1)(c - 4)$

15. $(2x + 3)(x - 1)$ **16.** $(3y - 8)(2y - 3)$ **17.** $(4a + b)(3a - b)$

Written Exercises

Multiply.

1. $(x + 8)(x - 9)$
2. $(a + 5)(a + 7)$
3. $(y - 4)(y - 10)$
4. $(r + 5)(r + 5)$
5. $(c - 6)(c - 6)$
6. $(x + 8)(x - 8)$
7. $(2x + 5)(x + 1)$
8. $(3c + 4)(c + 5)$
9. $(y - 3)(2y - 4)$
10. $(3x + 4)(4x + 5)$
11. $(2y + 5)(3y + 1)$
12. $(2c - 3)(3c - 7)$
13. $(4x - 6)(2x + 1)$
14. $(3d - 7)(d + 7)$
15. $(r - 8)(2r + 5)$
16. $(3y + 5)(3y - 5)$
17. $(2y - 3)(y - 4)$
18. $(3x - 2)(3x - 2)$
19. $(x + 2y)(4x - y)$
20. $(3a + 2b)(a - b)$
21. $(r + s)(2r - 3s)$
22. $(7a + b)(3a - b)$
23. $(5y - z)(2y + 3z)$
24. $(4c - d)(-2c + d)$
25. $(x + 6)(x^2 + 4x - 1)$
26. $(2x - 1)(3x^2 - x + 4)$
27. $(3x - 2)(4x^2 - 1)$
28. $(5p - 1)(p^2 - 2p + 1)$
29. $(7y + 2)(2y^2 - 3y + 1)$
30. $(6a - 1)(3a^2 - a)$
31. $(x^2 - 2)(x^2 + 5)$
32. $(y^2 - 7)(y^2 - 4)$
33. $(c^2 + 2)(c^2 - 6)$
34. $(3x^2 - 1)(2x^2 + 5)$
35. $(4y^3 + 1)(4y^3 - 1)$
36. $(2c^3 - 3)(2c^3 - 3)$

Express the area of each figure as a polynomial in simplest form.

37.
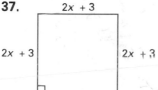

38.
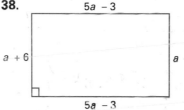

39.
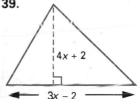

Simplify.

40. $(2x^4 - 3y)(4x^4 + 2y)$
41. $(3y^3 + 2x^2)(7y^3 - x^2)$
42. $(a + b)(x + y)$
43. $(a + b)(x - y)$
44. $(x^2 + y^2)(2x^2 - 3xy - y^2)$
45. $(a^2 - b^2)(7a^2 - 4ab + 6b^2)$
46. $(4x - 1)(4x + 1)(2x - 3)$
47. $(a + b + 3)(a + b - 3)$
48. Subtract the product of $(4y - 1)$ and $(3y + 2)$ from the product of $(6y - 5)$ and $(y - 8)$.

Mixed Review

1. Evaluate $x^2 - 5$ for $x = -9$. *2.8*

Solve. *3.1, 3.3, 5.2, 5.7*

2. $x - 8 = -52$
3. $2y + 7 = 1$
4. $\frac{a}{9} + 4 = -3$
5. $13 < 2x + 5$
6. $|x + 2| < -4$
7. $|x - 1| > 7$

6.10 Special Products

Objectives
To square a binomial
To find products of the form $(a + b)(a - b)$

To square a binomial means to multiply the binomial by itself.

Square of a Sum

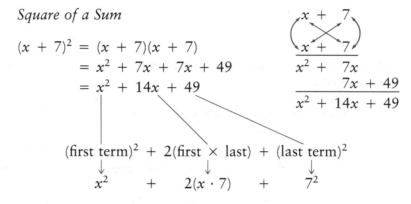

$$(x + 7)^2 = (x + 7)(x + 7)$$
$$= x^2 + 7x + 7x + 49$$
$$= x^2 + 14x + 49$$

$$\begin{array}{c} x + 7 \\ x + 7 \\ \hline x^2 + 7x \\ 7x + 49 \\ \hline x^2 + 14x + 49 \end{array}$$

(first term)^2 + 2(first × last) + (last term)^2
$$x^2 \quad + \quad 2(x \cdot 7) \quad + \quad 7^2$$

Square of a Difference

$$(3y - 5)^2 = (3y - 5)(3y - 5)$$
$$= 9y^2 - 15y - 15y + 25$$
$$= 9y^2 - 30y + 25$$

$$\begin{array}{c} 3y - 5 \\ 3y - 5 \\ \hline 9y^2 - 15y \\ - 15y + 25 \\ \hline 9y^2 - 30y + 25 \end{array}$$

(first term)^2 − 2(first × last) + (last term)^2
$$(3y)^2 \quad - \quad 2(3y \cdot 5) \quad + \quad 5^2$$

Notice that $(x + 7)^2 \neq x^2 + 7^2$,
and $(3y - 5)^2 \neq (3y)^2 - (5)^2$.

When you square a binomial the product always contains **three** terms.

In general, the **square of a binomial** can be expressed as a trinomial.

Square of a Binomial
$$(a + b)^2 = a^2 + 2ab + b^2$$
$$(a - b)^2 = a^2 - 2ab + b^2$$

The square of a binomial is the square of the first term, plus or minus twice the product of the two terms, plus the square of the last term.

EXAMPLE 1 Multiply.

a. $(x - 8)(x - 8)$ b. $(2y + 1)^2$

Solutions

a. $(x - 8)(x - 8)$
   $x^2 - 2(x \cdot 8) + 8^2$
   $x^2 - 16x + 64$

b. $(2y + 1)^2$
   $(2y)^2 + 2(2y \cdot 1) + 1^2$
   $4y^2 + 4y + 1$

TRY THIS Multiply: **1.** $(3x - 2)^2$
                        2. $(5a + 1)^2$

Now observe the result of multiplying *the sum and the difference* of the same two terms.

$$(x + 6)(x - 6) = x^2 - 6x + 6x - 36$$
$$= x^2 \qquad - \qquad 36$$

$$\text{(first term)}^2 \quad - \quad \text{(last term)}^2$$
$$\downarrow \qquad\qquad \downarrow$$
$$x^2 \qquad - \qquad 6^2$$

$$\begin{array}{r} x + 6 \\ x - 6 \\ \hline x^2 + 6x \\ -6x - 36 \\ \hline x^2 \qquad - 36 \end{array}$$

Notice that the product of the sum and difference of the same two terms results in an expression containing **two** terms.

In general, the **product** $(a + b)(a - b)$ can be expressed as a binomial.

Product of $(a + b)(a - b)$

$$(a + b)(a - b) = a^2 - b^2$$

The product of the sum and the difference of the same two terms is the square of the first term minus the square of the last term.

EXAMPLE 2 Multiply.

a. $(c - 1)(c + 1)$ b. $(4x - 3)(4x + 3)$ c. $(3x + 2y)(3x - 2y)$

Solutions

a. $(c - 1)(c + 1)$
   $= c^2 - 1^2$
   $= c^2 - 1$

b. $(4x - 3)(4x + 3)$
   $= (4x)^2 - 3^2$
   $= 16x^2 - 9$

c. $(3x + 2y)(3x - 2y)$
   $= (3x)^2 - (2y)^2$
   $= 9x^2 - 4y^2$

TRY THIS Multiply: **3.** $(2x + 2)(2x - 2)$
                        4. $(6x - 4)(6x + 4)$

Some equations contain products of binomials.

EXAMPLE 3   Solve $(x - 5)^2 = (x - 8)(x + 8)$.

Solution
$$(x - 5)^2 = (x - 8)(x + 8)$$
$$x^2 - 10x + 25 = x^2 - 64$$
$$-10x + 25 = -64 \quad \longleftarrow \text{Subtract } x^2 \text{ from each side.}$$
$$-10x = -89$$
$$x = 8.9$$

The check is left for you.

TRY THIS   5. Solve $(x - 2)(x + 2) = (x - 4)^2$.

Focus on Reading

Match each expression with one expression lettered a–e.

1. $(x + 6)^2$

2. $(x - 6)^2$

3. $(x + 6)(x - 6)$

4. $(6 - x)^2$

a. $x^2 + 36$

b. $x^2 - 36$

c. $x^2 + 6x + 36$

d. $x^2 - 12x + 36$

e. $x^2 + 12x + 36$

Classroom Exercises

Give the missing term in each product.

1. $(x + 1)^2 = x^2 + \underline{\ ?\ } + 1$

2. $(y - 4)^2 = y^2 - \underline{\ ?\ } + 16$

3. $(r + 5)(r - 5) = r^2 - \underline{\ ?\ }$

4. $(d - 2)(d + 2) = \underline{\ ?\ } - 4$

5. $(c + 9)(c + 9) = c^2 + \underline{\ ?\ } + 81$

6. $(y - 10)(y - 10) = y^2 - 20y + \underline{\ ?\ }$

7. $(p + q)(p - q) = \underline{\ ?\ } - q^2$

8. $(3 - x)(3 + x) = 9 - \underline{\ ?\ }$

9. $(1 + a)(1 + a) = 1 + 2a + \underline{\ ?\ }$

10. $(x + y)^2 = x^2 + \underline{\ \ ?\ \ } + y^2$

11. $(r - t)^2 = r^2 + \underline{\ \ ?\ \ } + t^2$

12. $(1 + 2b)^2 = 1 + 4b + \underline{\ \ ?\ \ }$

Multiply.

13. $(x + 5)^2$

14. $(y - 1)^2$

15. $(x + 3)(x + 3)$

16. $(a - 9)(a - 9)$

17. $(x + 2)^2$

18. $(5 - c)^2$

19. $(2x - 1)^2$

20. $(3y + 4)^2$

21. $(4c + 1)(4c - 1)$

22. $(3a - 7b)(3a + 7b)$

23. $(3x - 2y)(3x + 2y)$

24. $(9 + 4p)(9 - 4p)$

Written Exercises

Multiply.

1. $(y - 6)^2$
2. $(x + 2)^2$
3. $(c - 8)(c - 8)$
4. $(x - 3)(x + 3)$
5. $(y + 10)(y + 10)$
6. $(d - 4)(d + 4)$
7. $(r - 12)(r + 12)$
8. $(6 + y)(6 - y)$
9. $(7 + x)(7 - x)$
10. $(2x + 3)(2x - 3)$
11. $(7y + 1)(7y - 1)$
12. $(4c - 5)(4c + 5)$
13. $(10d - 2)(10d + 2)$
14. $(3r + 8)(3r - 8)$
15. $(1 + 6y)(1 - 6y)$
16. $(c + d)(c + d)$
17. $(2r - s)^2$
18. $(3y + 4z)(3y - 4z)$
19. $(2p - 3q)(2p + 3q)$
20. $(3a + 5b)^2$
21. $(7x + y)(7x - y)$
22. $(5x + 2y)^2$
23. $(4r + s)(4r + s)$
24. $(6a - b)^2$
25. $(3 - 5c)(5c + 3)$
26. $(3x + 2y)(2y + 3x)$
27. $(7x - y)(-y + 7x)$
28. $(x^2 + 2)^2$
29. $(y^2 - 5)^2$
30. $(z^2 + 1)(z^2 - 1)$
31. $(3x^2 - 2)^2$
32. $(5a^2 + 1)(5a^2 + 1)$
33. $(7y^3 + 2)(7y^3 - 2)$
34. $\left(y + \frac{1}{2}\right)^2$
35. $\left(x - \frac{1}{4}\right)^2$
36. $\left(a - \frac{1}{3}\right)\left(a + \frac{1}{3}\right)$
37. $(x - 0.1)^2$
38. $(a + 0.2)(a - 0.2)$
39. $(y + 0.5)^2$

Solve each equation.

40. $(x + 2)(x - 7) = (x - 4)^2$
41. $(x + 3)^2 = (x - 1)^2$
42. $(y + 5)(y - 5) = (y + 2)(y - 7)$
43. $a^2 = (a + 8)^2$
44. $(x + 4)^2 = (x + 2)(x - 4)$
45. $(y - 6)^2 = y^2$
46. $(x + 5)^2 - x^2 = 0$
47. $(2r - 4)(r + 5) = (2r + 5)(r - 1)$

Mixed Review

1. Evaluate $3x^2 - 6y$ for $x = -2$ and $y = 5$. *2.8*

Solve. *3.3, 3.5, 5.2, 5.6, 5.7*

2. $-\frac{2}{5}y + 42 = 36$
3. $3y - (4 - y) = 12$
4. $5y - 7 > 3y - 5$
5. $6x - 4 < -3 + 5x$
6. $|d| + 8 = 10$
7. $|4x + 2| < -7$
8. Graph the solution set: $8 + x < 12$ *and* $x \geq -2$ *5.4*

▰/Brainteaser

Maggie Mae buys pencils at 3 for 46¢. She sells them at 5 for 80¢.
How many pencils must she sell to make a profit of $1.00?

Chapter 6 Review

Key Terms

binomial   (p. 218)
Cancellation Property for Fractions   (p. 207)
degree of a monomial   (p. 219)
degree of a polynomial   (p. 219)
descending order   (p. 219)
FOIL method   (p. 229)
monomial   (p. 201)
negative exponent   (p. 211)
polynomial   (p. 218)

Power-of-a-Power Property   (p. 204)
Power-of-a-Product Property   (p. 205)
Product-of-Powers Property   (p. 201)
Quotient-of-Powers Property   (p. 207)
scientific notation   (p. 214)
square of a binomial   (p. 232)
trinomial   (p. 218)
zero exponent   (p. 210)

Key Ideas and Review Exercises

**6.1,
6.2**   To multiply powers with the same base, add the exponents and keep the same base.

Simplify.

1. $5x \cdot x^4$ **2.** $-6x \cdot 2x^2 \cdot 3x$ **3.** $0.5(6c^3d)$ **4.** $(3c^2d)(-7cd^4)$

5. $(x^4)^2$ **6.** $(3c^2)^3$ **7.** $(-xy^2z^3)^5$ **8.** $(5c^3)^2(2c)^2$

9. Explain why "$(x^2)^3 = (x^3)^2$ for all real numbers x" is true.

6.3   To simplify $\dfrac{b^m}{b^n}$ for any nonzero real number b and positive integers m and n, use the Quotient-of-Powers Property. See page 207.

Simplify.

10. $\dfrac{x^5}{x^2}$ **11.** $\dfrac{c^2d}{cd^3}$ **12.** $\dfrac{(4ab^2)^3}{2a^2b}$ **13.** $\dfrac{-2xy(x^3y^2)}{10x^4y^5}$

6.4   To simplify expressions with zero and negative exponents, use $b^0 = 1$, $b^{-n} = \dfrac{1}{b^n}$, $\dfrac{1}{b^{-n}} = b^n$, and $\left(\dfrac{a}{b}\right)^{-m} = \left(\dfrac{b}{a}\right)^m$ where a and b are nonzero real numbers and n is an integer.

Simplify. Use positive exponents only. No variable equals zero.

14. $5c^{-2}$ **15.** $\left(\dfrac{1}{3}\right)^{-3}$ **16.** $\dfrac{12x^{-1}y^{-2}}{-9xy^{-1}}$ **17.** $\left(\dfrac{3x^2y}{6y}\right)^{-2}$

18. Evaluate $\dfrac{(5y)^0}{y^{-2}}$ for $y = -4$.

6.5 To write a number in scientific notation, write it in the form $a \times 10^n$, where $1 \le a < 10$ and n is an integer.

Write each answer in scientific notation.

19. Find the number of seconds in a 24 h day.

20. Simplify $\dfrac{20.8(16,000,000)}{0.00004}$.

6.6, 6.7 To simplify a polynomial, combine like terms.

To write a polynomial in descending (ascending) order, arrange the terms in order from greatest to least (least to greatest) degree. See the definition of degree of a polynomial (Lesson 6.6).

To add polynomials, combine their like terms.

To subtract polynomials, add the opposite of the polynomial that is being subtracted to the other polynomial.

Simplify. Write the result in descending order and in ascending order. Give the degree of the polynomial.

21. $8x^2 + 7x - 5x^4 - 7x^2 + x$

22. $16y - 8y^5 + 3y^2 - 4y - y^2 + y^5$

Add or subtract.

23. $(2y^3 - 3y + 1) + (-2y^3 + 4y - 7)$

24. $(3x^2 - 7x + 2) + (+4x^2 + 3x + 5)$

25. Add $-2a^5 + 6a^3 - 3a + 1$ and $4a^4 - 6a^3 + 2a^2 - 8a$.

26. Subtract $c^3 - 5c$ from $c^4 - c^3 + 5c - 2$.

6.8, 6.9, 6.10 To multiply a polynomial by a monomial, multiply each term in the polynomial by the monomial.

To multiply two polynomials, multiply each term of the first polynomial by each term of the second. To multiply two binomials mentally, use the FOIL method (Lesson 6.9). Two special products are (1) the square of a binomial: $(a + b)^2 = a^2 + 2ab + b^2$, or $(a - b)^2 = a^2 - 2ab + b^2$, and (2) the product of the sum and difference of two terms: $(a + b)(a - b) = a^2 - b^2$.

Multiply.

27. $2y(3y^3 - 6y + 1)$

28. $(x + 8)(x - 7)$

29. $(2x + y)(3x + 4y)$

30. $(a - 5)(2a^2 + 3a - 1)$

31. $(y + 5)(y + 5)$

32. $(2a - 7)^2$

33. $(x - 3)(x + 3)$

34. $(y^2 + 6)(y^2 - 6)$

35. Simplify $-x^2 - 4x + (2x^2 + 3x - 1)5x$.

Chapter 6 Test

Classify each polynomial as a monomial, a binomial, or a trinomial.

1. $a + b - 1$ **2.** $4xy^2$ **3.** $2n + 5$ **4.** -100

Simplify, if possible. Assume that no denominator equals zero.

5. $4x \cdot x$ **6.** $-8y^2(-y^4)$ **7.** $(-a)^6$ **8.** $5c^2(2cd)(7cd^3)$

9. $(4a^3b)(-7ab^5)$ **10.** $(4x)^3$ **11.** $-(7xy^3)^2$ **12.** $(-2x^3y^2)^3$

13. $4c(-3c^2)^3$ **14.** $\dfrac{-5x^2y}{15xy^3}$ **15.** $9x^4yz^2\left(-\dfrac{1}{3}yz\right)$ **16.** $\dfrac{(2a^2b)^3}{(4ab^2)(3a)}$

Simplify. Use positive exponents only. Assume that no variable equals zero.

17. $6x^0$ **18.** $10^2 \cdot x^{-1}$ **19.** $\left(\dfrac{2}{3}\right)^{-4}$ **20.** $\dfrac{-12a^4b^{-3}c^0}{-6a^{-7}b^{-2}}$

21. Evaluate $6n^3$ for $n = -2$. **22.** Evaluate $-4t^{-2}$ for $t = 6$.

Express each number in scientific notation.

23. 0.000439 **24.** 52,400 **25.** 900,000 **26.** 0.084

27. Simplify $\dfrac{(186,000,000)(0.00000051)}{0.0034}$ and express the answer in scientific notation.

Simplify. Then give the degree of the polynomial.

28. $5c^3 - 7c^2 - 3c^3 + 2c - 2c^3$ **29.** $-4y^4 + 3y^3 + 6y - 3y^3 - 7y + 2$

30. Simplify $-3 + 7a^2 + 2a - 3a^2 + a^2 - 7a + 6a^3 - 4$.
Write the result in descending order and in ascending order.

Add or subtract.

31. $(7a^4 - 6a^3 + 1) + (3a^3 - 2a + 1)$ **32.** $(c^3 + 2c^2 - 5c) - (2c^3 + 4c - 1)$

33. Add $0.4x^2 - 0.3x + 0.1$ to $-0.9x^2 + 0.4x - 0.6$.

Multiply.

34. $2a^2(6a^2 - 4a - 2)$ **35.** $4x^2y(-3x^2y + xy - 9xy^2)$

36. $(x + 3)(x - 7)$ **37.** $(2x + 3)(5x + 1)$

38. $(a + 8)^2$ **39.** $(2x + 1)(2x - 1)$

40. $(x + 4)(x^2 - x + 3)$ **41.** $(r^2 - 2)^2$

42. Simplify. $-5c^2 - 7c + (c - 3)6c$ **43.** Simplify. $c^n \cdot c^{3n+2}$

44. Solve. $7 + x(x + 3) = x^2 - (5 - 4x)$

College Prep Test

Choose the one best answer to each question or problem.

1. The statement $(x + y)^2 = (x - y)^2$ is true if ___?___ .
(A) $x < y$ (B) $x > y$ (C) $x = y$
(D) $x = 0$ and $y = 0$
(E) $x = 1$ and $y = -1$

2. How many centimeters are there in 12 mm?
(A) 1,200   (B) 120   (C) 12
(D) 1.2   (E) 0.12?

3. One ft is what percent of one yd?
(A) $\frac{1}{3}\%$ (B) $\frac{2}{3}\%$ (C) 3%
(D) 300%   (E) $33\frac{1}{3}\%$

4. What is the area of the shaded region in the figure below?

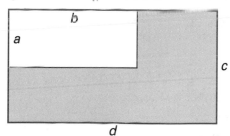

(A) $ab - cd$ (B) $cd - ab$
(C) ab (D) $ab + cd$
(F) $ac - bd$

5. If $0.6x = 4$, find $0.3x$.
(A) 0.4   (B) 1   (C) 2   (D) 2.4
(E) 0.8

6. Find the next term in the sequence: 0, 1, 3, 7, 15, 31, ___?___ .
(A) 42   (B) 52   (C) 62
(D) 63   (E) 73

7. If $1^m = 2^{m-1}$, then $m =$ ___?___ .
(A) -1 (B) 0   (C) 1   (D) 2
(E) none of these

8. Which expression is equivalent to $x^2 + y^2 + 18 - 11y$?
(A) $(x + y)^2 - 11y + 18$
(B) $(x + y - 9)(x + y - 2)$
(C) $(x + 18)(y - 11)$
(D) $y^2 + (x + 9)(x - 2)$
(E) $(y - 9)(y - 2) + x^2$

9. What is the perimeter of the figure below?

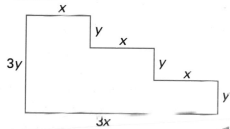

(A) $6x + 6y$ (B) $3(x + y)$
(C) $3xy$ (D) xy (E) None of these

10. If $0 < x < 1$, then what is true of x^{-1}?
(A) $x^{-1} < 0$ (B) $0 < x^{-1} < 1$
(C) $x^{-1} > 1$ (D) $x^{-1} = 0$
(E) It cannot be determined from the information given.

11. What part of a dollar is the value of 1 quarter, 1 dime, and 4 nickels?
(A) $.55   (B) $\frac{11}{20}$ (C) 50%
(D) $\frac{1}{55}$ (E) 5.5

12. If $0.00009 \times 0.02 = 1.8 \times 10^n$, then $n =$ ___?___ .
(A) -4 (B) -5 (C) -6
(D) -7 (E) -8

Simplify.

1. $16 - 2 \cdot 5$ *1.2*
2. $\left(\frac{2}{3}\right)\left(\frac{3}{4}\right) - \frac{1}{2}$
3. 2.8×10^4 *1.3*
4. $-|-3| \cdot |6|$ *2.2*
5. $-7 + (-9)$ *2.4*
6. $-6.8 + 6.8$
7. $6 - (-11)$ *2.5*
8. $-1.8 - 5.6$
9. $\frac{1}{2}(-16)$ *2.6*
10. $(-8)(2)^3$
11. $0 \div (-18)$ *2.7*
12. $-\frac{3}{4} \div \frac{6}{7}$
13. $3x - 5x$ *2.9*
14. $-4x + 2y - 7x - 9y$
15. $6(a + 3) - 4(2a - 1)$ *2.10*
16. $-2x^2y(-5xy^3)$ *6.1*
17. $(3c^2d)^4$ *6.2*
18. $5a(-2ab)^3$
19. $\frac{-2x^2y}{14xy^4}$ *6.3*
20. $\frac{(-2x^3)^2}{8x^5}$
21. $-3x^2 - 2x + 3 - x^2 + 6x$ *6.6*
22. Simplify $\frac{3a^0b^{-1}c}{15bc^{-3}}$. Use positive exponents only.   *6.6*

Evaluate.

23. $6.2n$ for $n = 4$ *1.1*
24. $\frac{x}{y}$ for $x = -5.5$ and $y = 2.7$
25. $16 - 3y$ for $y = 3$ *1.2*
26. $(4y)^2 - y$ for $y = 2$ *1.3*
27. $-x + y$ for $x = -7$ and $y = 4$ *2.5*

28. x^2y for $x = -2$ and $y = -3$ *2.6*
29. $\frac{6x^2}{y}$ for $x = 9$ and $y = 2$ *1.3*
30. $3x^{-2}$ for $x = 5$ *6.4*

Solve.

31. $-6 + a = 14$ *3.1*
32. $x + 9 = -12$
33. $-4y = 42$ *3.2*
34. $-\frac{3}{5}x = 51$
35. $\frac{x}{5} - 7 = -20$ *3.3*
36. $-4c + 3 = 17$
37. $3y - 4 = 28 - y$ *3.4*
38. $2(x + 9) = 5 - 7(2 + x)$ *3.5*

Graph the solution set.

39. $x - 7 < -2$ *5.1*
40. $2x + 3 > -7$ *5.2*
41. $-7y + 8 \le 2 - 6y$ *5.4*
42. $-3 < c < 1$
43. $|x - 7| \ge 3$ *5.7*
44. $|x + 2| < 4$
45. $|y - 3| < -5$

Add or subtract.

46. $(3t^2 - 5) + (-t^2 + 7 - 3)$ *6.7*
47. $(y^2 - y - 4) - (-2y^2 + y + 6)$

Multiply.

48. $3x(7x - 1)$ *6.8*
49. $(4y - 5)2y^2$
50. $(x + 8)(2x - 1)$ *6.9*
51. $(a - 6)(a - 10)$
52. $(y - 8)^2$ *6.10*
53. $(3x + 1)^2$
54. $(2x - 5)(2x + 5)$

Solve each problem.

55. Use the formula $A = s^2$ to find A if $s = 1.2$ cm.   *4.2*

56. Use the formula $p = 2l + 2w$ to find p if $l = 7$ m and $w = 5$ m.

57. Use the formula $V = lwh$ to find V if $l = 6$ in., $w = 9$ in., and $h = 2$ in.

58. After the temperature dropped $17°$, the thermometer read $-6°$. What did the thermometer read before the temperature dropped?   *3.6*

59. If Mr. Berensen travels at an average rate of 45 mi/h, how many hours must he travel to cover 105 mi?   *4.4*

60. The perimeter of a rectangular room is 72 ft. The width is $\frac{1}{3}$ of the length. Find the width and the length of the room.   *4.2*

61. Each leg of an isosceles triangle is 3 cm longer than the base. The perimeter of the triangle is 45 cm. Find the length of each side.

62. Use the formula $A = \frac{1}{2}(b + c)h$ to find the area A of a trapezoid if the height h is 12 cm and the bases b and c measure 7 cm and 10 cm, respectively.

63. Bill has 3 times as much money as Jim, and Jim has $8 less than Lynn. Together they have $268. How much money does each of them have?   *4.2*

64. The sum of two consecutive odd integers is -92. Find the integers.   *4.3*

65. Find three consecutive integers such that their sum, decreased by 60, is equal to the second integer.

66. Erika has half as many quarters as dimes. How many coins of each type does she have if the total number of coins is 4 more than the number of quarters?   *4.5*

67. This year Juan's earnings increased $\frac{2}{3}$ over last year's. This year he earned $605. How much did he earn last year?   *4.2*

68. After Bob lent $\frac{2}{5}$ of his pocket money to Marilee, he had $4.80 left. How much pocket money did he have at first?   *4.2*

69. Mrs. Danoff rented a car for $35 per day plus $0.12 per mile. How far can she travel in one day if she can spend at most $52, not including taxes or insurance?   *5.5*

70. Jason bought 5 pads of writing paper. The total was $3.79, but $0.24 of this was for tax. What was the price of each pad before the tax?   *4.8*

71. This year a book costs $1.90 less than twice what it cost last year. The book now costs $10. What did it cost last year?   *3.3*

72. The greater of two numbers is 6.8 more than 3 times the smaller. The difference between the two numbers is 21.6. Find the two numbers.   *4.2*

73. What number is 62% of 40?   *1.7*

74. Fourteen is what percent of 84?

75. Seventy-five is $62\frac{1}{2}$% of what number?

George R. Carruthers, Ph.D., is an astrophysicist who designs and builds instruments to study outer space which have been used in Apollo, Skylab, and space shuttle missions. He was the first to detect interstellar molecular hydrogen.

7.1 Introduction to Factoring

Objectives

To find the greatest common factor (GCF) of two or more integers
To find the greatest common factor (GCF) of two or more monomials
To find the missing factor, given a monomial and one of its factors

How can you arrange 36 square tiles to form a rectangle? The formula for the area of a rectangle is $A = lw$ (area − length × width), so look for two factors of 36.

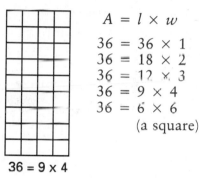

$$A = l \times w$$
$$36 = 36 \times 1$$
$$36 = 18 \times 2$$
$$36 = 12 \times 3$$
$$36 = 9 \times 4$$
$$36 = 6 \times 6$$
(a square)

36 = 9 x 4

There are five ways to arrange the tiles. In each product, 36 is said to be *factored*. To **factor an integer** means to express it as the product of two or more integers.

There are several ways to factor 36. For example,

$$36 = 1 \times 36 \qquad 36 = 2 \times 3 \times 6$$
$$36 = 4 \times 9 \qquad 36 = 2 \times 2 \times 3 \times 3$$

In $36 = 2 \times 2 \times 3 \times 3$, none of the factors can be factored further without using the factor 1. The only positive factors of 2 are 2 and 1; the only positive factors of 3 are 3 and 1. The numbers 2 and 3 are called *prime numbers*.

Definition

A **prime number** is an integer greater than 1 whose only positive factors are 1 and itself.

Other prime numbers are 5, 7, 11, 13, 17, 19, 23, 29, 31, and so on.

Definition

A **composite** number is a positive integer that has two or more positive factors other than 1.

Other composite numbers are 4, 6, 8, 9, 10, 12, 14, 15, and so on. The number 1 is neither prime nor composite.

A factorization such as $36 = 2 \times 2 \times 3 \times 3$ is called a **prime factorization** because all the factors are prime numbers.

EXAMPLE 1   Give the prime factorization of 90.

Plan   Choose two positive factors of 90. Continue factoring until all the factors are prime numbers.

Solution

Method 1	Method 2	Method 3
$90 = 45 \cdot 2$	$90 = 6 \cdot 15$	$90 = 30 \cdot 3$
$\quad = 9 \cdot 5 \cdot 2$	$\quad = 2 \cdot 3 \cdot 3 \cdot 5$	$\quad = 6 \cdot 5 \cdot 3$
$\quad = 3 \cdot 3 \cdot 5 \cdot 2$		$\quad = 3 \cdot 2 \cdot 5 \cdot 3$

Each method gives the same prime factors, but in a different order. In each case, 3 is a factor twice, and 5 and 2 are the other factors.

Thus, the prime factorization of 90 is $2 \cdot 3 \cdot 3 \cdot 5$, or $2 \cdot 3^2 \cdot 5$.

TRY THIS   1. Give the prime factorization of 100.

Example 1 illustrates that the prime factorization of an integer is *unique*. Only the order of the prime factors can differ.

A systematic way of finding the prime factorization of a positive integer is to divide by 2 as often as 2 is a factor, then by 3, and so on. You can use this method with your calculator. If a decimal appears in the display, return to the previous step. Then divide by the next larger prime number. Find the prime factorization of 660.

$660 \;\boxed{\div}\; 2 \;\boxed{=}\; 330$	$660 = 2 \cdot 330$
$330 \;\boxed{\div}\; 2 \;\boxed{=}\; 165$	$660 = 2 \cdot 2 \cdot 165$
$165 \;\boxed{\div}\; 3 \;\boxed{=}\; 55$	$660 = 2 \cdot 2 \cdot 3 \cdot 55$
$55 \;\boxed{\div}\; 5 \;\boxed{=}\; 11$	$660 = 2 \cdot 2 \cdot 3 \cdot 5 \cdot 11$

Thus, $660 = 2^2 \cdot 3 \cdot 5 \cdot 11$.

The integer 6 is a factor of *both* 30 and 12.

$$30 = 6 \cdot 5 \qquad 12 = 6 \cdot 2$$

Therefore, 6 is a **common factor** of 30 and 12. Notice that 6 is the *greatest common factor* of 30 and 12.

Definition   The **greatest common factor (GCF)** of two or more integers is the largest integer that is a factor of all the integers.

EXAMPLE 2   Find the GCF of 72 and 84.

Plan   To find the GCF of 72 and 84, factor both integers into primes. For each common factor of 72 and 84, compare its powers and choose the smaller power. The product of these powers is the GCF.

Solution
$$72 = 12 \cdot 6 = 2 \cdot 2 \cdot 3 \cdot 2 \cdot 3 = 2^3 \cdot 3^2$$
$$84 = 14 \cdot 6 = 2 \cdot 7 \cdot 2 \cdot 3 \quad = 2^2 \cdot 3 \cdot 7$$

smaller power of 2 $\longrightarrow$ 2^2 $\quad$ 3^1 $\longleftarrow$ smaller power of 3

So, the GCF of 72 and 84 is $2^2 \cdot 3$, or 12.

TRY THIS   2. Find the GCF of 36 and 90.

It may be necessary to find the GCF of two or more monomials whose factors are variables. The monomials x^3, x^2, and x^5 can be written as follows.

$$x^3 = x \cdot x \cdot x, \qquad x^2 = x \cdot x, \qquad x^5 = x \cdot x \cdot x \cdot x \cdot x$$

The product $x \cdot x$ is a common factor of these monomials. Thus, the GCF of x^3, x^2, and x^5 is x^2, the *smallest* power of x.

EXAMPLE 3   Find the GCF of $12x^4$, $-28x^3$, and $120x^2$.

Solution   Rewrite $-28x^3$ as $-1 \cdot 28 \cdot x^3$.

$$12x^4 = 2 \cdot 2 \cdot 3 \cdot x^4 \qquad\qquad = \quad\quad 2^2 \cdot 3 \cdot \quad x^4$$
$$-28x^3 = -1 \cdot 2 \cdot 2 \cdot 7 \cdot x^3 \qquad = -1 \cdot 2^2 \cdot 7 \cdot \quad x^3$$
$$120x^2 = 2 \cdot 2 \cdot 2 \cdot 3 \cdot 5 \cdot x^2 \qquad = \quad\quad 2^3 \cdot 3 \cdot 5 \cdot x^2$$

smallest power of 2 times smallest power of $x \longrightarrow 2^2 \cdot \quad\quad x^2$

Thus, $2^2 \cdot x^2$, or $4x^2$, is the GCF of $12x^4$, $-28x^3$, and $120x^2$.

TRY THIS   3. Find the GCF of $84y^3$, $98y^6$, and $-196y^5$.

Monomials such as $3a$ and $5b^2$ have no common factors other than 1. Thus, the GCF of $3a$ and $5b^2$ is 1.

Sometimes you need to find a missing factor, as in $x^3 \cdot \underline{} = x^7$. To do this, divide the given product by the given factor.

$$\frac{x^7}{x^3} = x^4 \qquad \text{Thus, the missing factor is } x^4. \qquad x^3 \cdot x^4 = x^7$$

EXAMPLE 4   Find the missing factor.

a. $a^5 \cdot \underline{\ ?\ } = a^9$ b. $\underline{\ ?\ } \cdot 5a = -30a^{10}$ c. $3a^3b^5 \cdot \underline{\ ?\ } = 24a^4b^7$

Solutions   a. $\dfrac{a^9}{a^5} = a^4$ b. $\dfrac{-30a^{10}}{5a} = -6a^9$ c. $\dfrac{24a^4b^7}{3a^3b^5} = 8ab^2$

So, the missing factors are a^4, $-6a^9$, and $8ab^2$, respectively.

TRY THIS   4. Find the missing factor for $13a^4b^7 \cdot \underline{\ \ \ } = 52\, a^9b^8$.

Classroom Exercises

Give the prime factorization of each number.

1. 4   **2.** 8   **3.** 6   **4.** 9   **5.** 14   **6.** 10
7. 15   **8.** 21   **9.** 12   **10.** 18   **11.** 20   **12.** 24

Give the GCF of each pair of monomials.

13. $2^5 \cdot 5^3$ and $2^3 \cdot 5^6$ **14.** $3^2 \cdot 7^3$ and $3^4 \cdot 7$ **15.** x^4 and x^3
16. $3x^4$ and $9x^3$ **17.** $5a^2$ and $3a^5$ **18.** $4n^7$ and $5t^3$

Find the missing factor.

19. $x^2 \cdot \underline{\ ?\ } = x^7$ **20.** $-a^3 \cdot \underline{\ ?\ } = -5a^7$ **21.** $3b^4 \cdot \underline{\ ?\ } = -12b^5$

Written Exercises

Give the prime factorization of each number.

1. 40   **2.** 16   **3.** 45   **4.** 42   **5.** 49   **6.** 51
7. 28   **8.** 32   **9.** 60   **10.** 180   **11.** 200   **12.** 360

Find the greatest common factor (GCF).

13. 12, 15   **14.** 8, 20   **15.** 20, 32   **16.** 27, 81   **17.** 30, 18   **18.** 36, 54
19. 81, 144   **20.** 45, 90   **21.** 18, 24   **22.** 26, 78   **23.** 34, 51   **24.** 48, 32
25. 4, 10, 6   **26.** 14, 21, 35   **27.** 12, 10, 15
28. 14, 15, 16   **29.** 6, 8, 4, 20   **30.** 18, 12, 24
31. 60, 48, 84, 12   **32.** $3x^3, 9x^5$ **33.** $6m^5, 8m^4$
34. $12a^3, 18a$ **35.** $24x^3, 33y^4$ **36.** $6x^2, 15x^3$
37. $14x^3, -21x^4$ **38.** $-30y^3, 20y$ **39.** $3x^3, 6x^2, -9x$
40. $4a^4m, 6a^3, 12a^2$ **41.** $6a^5, 8a^4, 2a^3$ **42.** $5a, -b^5, 8c^4$
43. $10y^3, 5y^2, 20y, -40y^2$ **44.** $4a^5, -12a^4, 28a^3$ **45.** $3x^3, 6x^4, 5x^2, 2x$

46. $6ab^2$, $6a^2$, $12ab^3$ **47.** $2m^3n$, $8m^2n^2$, $16m^2$ **48.** $3mn$, $6n$, $3m$

Find the missing factor.

49. $a^4 \cdot \underline{\qquad} = a^{10}$ **50.** $m^3 \cdot \underline{\qquad} = m^8$ **51.** $\underline{\qquad} \cdot n = b^7$

52. $\underline{\qquad} \cdot x^6 = x^{14}$ **53.** $7m^3 \cdot \underline{\qquad} = -21m^8$ **54.** $9m^4 \cdot \underline{\qquad} = 18y^{10}$

55. $\underline{\qquad} \cdot 4a^6 = -12a^{13}$ **56.** $4x^5 \cdot \underline{\qquad} = 32x^6$ **57.** $7c^3 \cdot \underline{\qquad} = 63c^5$

58. $8a^3b^7 \cdot \underline{\qquad} = 72a^9b^{10}$ **59.** $-6x^4y^6 \cdot \underline{\qquad} = 96x^4y^{12}$

60. $\underline{\qquad} \cdot 5xy^{10} = 75x^8y^{12}$ **61.** $5a^3b^4 \cdot \underline{\qquad} = -30a^6b^5$

62. $6a^2m^7 \cdot \underline{\qquad} = 24a^5m^9$ **63.** $\underline{\qquad} \cdot 3a^4m^6 = -39a^4m^7$

64. The monomial $45x^4y^3$ was factored into two factors. One factor was $-9xy^3$. What was the other factor?

65. The product of $4a^3b^5$ and what monomial is $80a^4b^6$?

66. A band director has a formation designed for 118 members, but 2 more members arrive. What are the possible rectangular formations?

67. An artist has 98 square tiles and wishes to make a rectangular design with at least 4 tiles in a column. What arrangements are possible?

68. Explain in writing why $2x^2$ is the greatest common factor of $(2xy)^2$ and $18x^6$.

In Exercises 69–72, use the formula for the area of a square, $A = s^2$, or the formula for the area of a rectangle, $A = lw$.

69. If the area of a rectangle is $72a^mb^{2n}$ and the length is $4a^2b^2$, what is the width?

70. If the area of a rectangle is $144x^{2a}y^{4b}$ and the width is $6x^{4a}y^{3b}$, what is the length?

71. If the area of a square is $36x^{4a}y^{6b}$, what is the length of each side?

72. If the area of a square is $81a^{8c}b^{12d}$, what is the length of each side?

Mixed Review

Simplify.   *1.6, 2.10, 6.2, 6.9*

1. $5(6a - 4)$ **2.** $4y + 6 - (8 - y)$ **3.** $3x - 7 - 5(x + 2)$

4. $(-4x^2y)^3$ **5.** $(3x - 2)(4x + 5)$ **6.** $(x + 5)(x^2 - 4x + 2)$

Solve.   *5.6, 5.7*

7. $|x| = 8$ **8.** $|x - 3| < 9$ **9.** $|x + 5| > 3$

10. The smaller of two numbers is 4 less than the greater. If the greater number is decreased by twice the smaller, the result is -10. Find the two numbers.   *4.2*

7.2 Greatest Common Monomial Factor

Objective   To factor out the greatest common monomial factor from a polynomial

The area of the large rectangle is

$$5x + 5y.$$

The Distributive Property can be used to rewrite the area as

$$5(x + y).$$

The Distributive Property can be used to multiply a polynomial having any number of addends by a monomial. For example,

$$2(x^2 - 3x - 5) = 2x^2 - 6x - 10.$$

The Distributive Property can also be used to factor polynomials. For example,

$$3x^2 - 9x + 6 \qquad 3(x^2 - 3x + 2).$$

The **GCF of a polynomial** is the greatest common factor of its terms.

EXAMPLE 1   Factor out the GCF from $5y^2 + 10y + 20$.

Plan   First find the GCF of the terms $5y^2$, $10y$, and 20.

$5y^2 = 5 \cdot y^2$, $10y = 5 \cdot 2y$, $20 = 5 \cdot 4$ The GCF is 5.

Write each term as a product of 5 and a monomial. Then use the Distributive Property.

Solution
$$5y^2 + 10y + 20 = 5(y^2) + 5(2y) + 5(4)$$
$$= 5(y^2 + 2y + 4)$$

EXAMPLE 2   Factor out the GCF from $t^5 - 8t^4 + t^3$.

Solution   The terms are $1t^5$, $-8t^4$, and $1t^3$.
The GCF of the numerical coefficients is 1.
The GCF of the variables is t^3, the smallest power of t.
Write each term as a product of t^3 and a monomial.
$$t^5 - 8t^4 + t^3 = t^3(t^2) + t^3(-8t) + t^3(1)$$
Thus, $t^5 - 8t^4 + t^3 = t^3(t^2 - 8t + 1)$.

TRY THIS   1. Factor out the GCF from $2t^4 + 4t^3 - 5t^2$.

Some terms include constants and variables as factors.

EXAMPLE 3	Factor out the GCF from $2b^4 - 10b^3 + 8b^2$.
Plan	The GCF of 2, -10, and 8 is 2.
	The GCF of b^4, b^3, and b^2 is b^2. The GCF of the polynomial is $2b^2$.
	Write each term as a product of $2b^2$ and a monomial. Then factor.
Solution	$2b^4 - 10b^3 + 8b^2 = 2b^2(b^2) + 2b^2(-5b) + 2b^2(4)$
	$\qquad\qquad\qquad\quad = 2b^2(b^2 - 5b + 4)$
EXAMPLE 4	Factor out the GCF from $24a^2b^5 - 8a^7b^6 + 12a^4b^3$.
Solution	The GCF of 24, -8, and 12 is 4.
	The GCF of a^2, a^7, and a^4 is a^2.
	The GCF of b^5, b^6, and b^3 is b^3. The GCF of the polynomial is $4a^2b^3$.
	Write each term as a product of $4a^2b^3$ and a monomial. Then factor.
	$24a^2b^5 - 8a^7b^6 + 12a^4b^3 = 4a^2b^3(6b^2) + 4a^2b^3(-2a^5b^3) + 4a^2b^3(3a^2)$
	$\qquad\qquad\qquad\qquad\qquad\quad = 4a^2b^3(6b^2 - 2a^5b^3 + 3a^2)$

TRY THIS	**2.** Factor out the GCF from $30x^5y + 12x^6y^2 - 6x^4y^4$.

Factoring can be used to simplify computational work with many area problems.

EXAMPLE 5	Find the area of the shaded region.
	Write the result in factored form.

Solution	First, by drawing two radii, you can see that the side of the square is $2r$.
	Area of shaded region = area of square − area of circle
	$\qquad\qquad A = 2r \cdot 2r - \pi r^2$
	$\qquad\qquad\quad = 4r^2 - \pi r^2$
	$\qquad\qquad\quad = r^2(4 - \pi)$

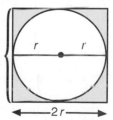

Sometimes the GCF of a polynomial is 1 as in $5t^2 - 12t + 3$.

Classroom Exercises

State the GCF of each polynomial.

1. $3x^2 - 6$ 2. $5a - 10$ 3. $3y - 15$ 4. $x^3 + x^2$
5. $5x^3 - 2x^2$ 6. $3x^4 - x^2$ 7. $3x^2 + 9x$ 8. $4x^3 + 12x$
9. $7a^2 - 14a + 21$ 10. $3x^3 + 2x^2 + 4x$
11. $4a^2 - 2a + 16$ 12. $3a^4 - 9a^2 + 120$

Factor out the GCF from each polynomial.

13. $3x(x^2) + 3x(5x) + 3x(7)$ 14. $2x^2(5x^2) - 2x^2(7x) + 2x^2(9)$
15. $5x(2x^2) + 5x(7x) - 5x(3)$ 16. $4a^2(3a^2) - 4a^2(13a) - 4a^2(11)$
17. $m^3 + 5m^2 - 8m$ 18. $5x^3 - 15x^2 + 10x$
19. $14y^2 + 28y - 7$ 20. $15t^4 - 20t^2 + 25t$

Written Exercises

Factor out the GCF from each polynomial. If the GCF is 1, just write
the polynomial.

1. $2x^2 - 8x - 6$ 2. $3a^2 + 9a - 15$ 3. $5t^2 - 15t + 25$
4. $5b^2 + 35b - 60$ 5. $4x^2 - 12x - 36$ 6. $3a^2 + 7a + 2$
7. $28y^2 - 20y - 24$ 8. $30y^2 - 35y - 45$ 9. $2x^2 + 11x - 4$
10. $2x^2 - 10x + 12$ 11. $8a^2 + 16a + 8$ 12. $12x^2 - 10x - 12$
13. $6x^2 - 21x - 12$ 14. $18a^2 + 21a - 9$ 15. $4b^2 + 26b - 14$
16. $2x^2 + 10x - 28$ 17. $5b^2 + 12b - 60$ 18. $5y^2 - 45y - 110$
19. $a^3 + 3a^2 - a$ 20. $2y^3 - y^2 + y$ 21. $m^4 - 3m^3 - 7m^2$
22. $7r^4 - 2r^3 + 8$ 23. $a^6 - a^4 - 2a^2$ 24. $y^7 - 2y^6 + 20$
25. $9a^3 - 3a^2 + 6a$ 26. $4x^3 - 12x^2 + 16x$ 27. $3a^2 - 21a$
28. $4x^4 - 24x^2$ 29. $5r^2 - 36$ 30. $6a^3 - 18a^2 - 24a$
31. $4y^3 - 20y^2 + 24y$ 32. $7y^3 - 21y^2 + 14y$ 33. $9x^5 + 81x^3 - 27x$
34. $51p^2q + 3pq$ 35. $3x^3 - 33x^2 + 84x$ 36. $6z^3 - 3z^2 - 30z$
37. $5a^5 - b^5$ 38. $42r - 14r^3$ 39. $2y^3 - 4y^2 - 48y$
40. $x^4 - 9x^2$ 41. $6f^2 - 15f^3$ 42. $n^2 + 5n + 7$
43. $2t^3 - 128t^5$ 44. $3x^2 + 21x^4$ 45. $8a^2 + b^2 + ab$
46. $ab^2 - ab - 72a$ 47. $8a^4 + 4a^3 - 12a^2$ 48. $st^2 - st - 20s$

Write a formula in factored form for the area of each shaded region.

49.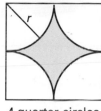

4 quarter-circles
in a square

50.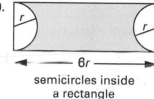

←———— 6r ————→

semicircles inside
a rectangle

51.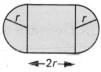

←2r→

square with
semicircle ends

Factor out the GCF from each polynomial.

52. $8a^3b + 12a^4b^3 - 4ab^2$

53. $6x^2y^3 - 20x^4y^5 + 36x^7y^6$

54. $14m^4n^7 + 21m^3n^8 - 35m^9n^6$

55. $8x^9y^4 - 20x^7y^8 + 12x^5y^9$

56. $100a^{10}b^4 - 50a^8b^8 + 75a^6b^9$

57. $35c^4d^2 + 45c^3d^3 - 50c^2d^4$

58. $x^{n+3} + x^n$

59. $2y^{n+1} + 4y^n$

60. $4p^{n-1} + 6p^{n+1}$

61. $9w^{2n} + 21w^{2n+1}$

62. $t^{3n+21} + 2t^{2n+14}$

63. $3r^{9n-27} - 13r^{6n-18}$

Mixed Review

Solve. **3.4, 5.2, 5.6**

1. $3x - 4 = -x + 20$ **2.** $3x - 4 < 5x + 8$ **3.** $|8 - 2b| = 10$

Simplify. Use positive exponents only. Assume that no variable equals zero. **6.2, 6.3, 6.9, 6.10**

4. $(-2x^4y^2)^2$ **5.** $\dfrac{16a^4b}{-8a^3b^9}$ **6.** $(x + 5)(x + 8)$ **7.** $(x + 7)(x - 7)$

Brainteaser

There is a legend that the man who invented the game of chess taught it to the king. The king was so pleased that he offered to give the man anything he wished as payment. "All I wish for payment, sire, is the amount of grain that it would take to do the following. Place one grain of wheat on the first square of this chessboard. Then place two grains on the second, four grains on the third, and so on so that each square has twice as many as the previous square."

1. How many grains of wheat should be on the last square?

2. How many grains of wheat should the man receive altogether?

3. Suppose that you use pennies instead of grains of wheat. For which square will the payment reach more than one billion dollars?

7.3 Factoring Trinomials: $x^2 + bx + c$

Objective

To factor trinomials of the form $x^2 + bx + c$

The product of two binomials is usually a trinomial. For example,

$$(x + 3)(x - 2) = x^2 + x - 6.$$

To factor a trinomial means to express it as a product of two binomials. Thus, factoring can be thought of as undoing the result of multiplication; that is, to factor $x^2 + x - 6$ is to rewrite it as $(x + 3)(x - 2)$.

To factor a trinomial, the FOIL method of multiplying can be used in reverse. For example, to factor $x^2 - 2x - 48$, the first step is to think of x^2 as $x \cdot x$ and write

$$x^2 - 2x - 48 = (x \qquad)(x \qquad).$$

Now examine the sign of the constant term, -48. Since the sign of the constant term is negative, the sign of the second terms in the binomials must be opposites. Thus you can write

$$x^2 - 2x - 48 = (x + \quad)(x - \quad).$$

Apply the guess and check strategy to find the numbers needed to complete the binomial factors. However, the FOIL method does tell us that the product of those numbers must be -48 and their sum must be -2.

Guess	Check	Result
1. $4, -12$	$4 \cdot -12 = -48;\ 4 + -12 = -8$	Does not work.
2. $8, -6$	$8 \cdot -6 = -48;\ 8 + -6 = 2$	Does not work.
3. $-8, 6$	$-8 \cdot 6 = -48;\ -8 + 6 = -2$	It works.

The numbers are -8 and 6. The binomial factors can be completed.

$$x^2 - 2x - 48 = (x + 6)(x - 8)$$

The FOIL method indicates which signs to choose in factoring $x^2 + bx + c$. If the constant term c is negative, then the second terms in the binomial factors will have opposite signs.

On the other hand, if the constant term c is positive, then the second terms in the binomial factors must have the same sign, both negative or both positive.

$$(x - 4)(x - 6) = x^2 - 10x + 24 \qquad (x + 7)(x + 2) = x^2 + 9x + 14$$

same sign   positive   same sign   positive
(negative)   constant   (positive)   constant

EXAMPLE 1   Factor $x^2 - 13x + 40$.

Solution   **Trial 1**
Try -10 and -4 as factors of 40: $(x - 10)(x - 4)$.

Check: $(x - 10)(x - 4) = x^2 - 4x - 10x + 40$
$$= x^2 - 14x + 40$$

This combination does *not* work.
$$x^2 - 14x + 40 \neq x^2 - 13x + 40$$

Trial 2
Try -5 and -8 as factors of 40: $(x - 5)(x - 8)$.

Check: $(x - 5)(x - 8) = x^2 - 8x - 5x + 40$
$$= x^2 - 13x + 40$$

This combination *works*, so $x^2 - 13x + 40 = (x - 5)(x - 8)$.

TRY THIS   1. Factor $x^2 + 11x + 24$.
2. Factor $x^2 - 15x + 56$.

By now you may have discovered an easier way to factor a polynomial of the form $x^2 + bx + c$, where the coefficient of x^2 is 1. Examples 1 and 2 suggest a pattern. Look for two numbers whose product is c and whose sum is b.

$x^2 - 2x - 48 = (x - 8)(x + 6)$
        Product: $8(6) = -48$
         Sum: $-8 + 6 = -2$

$x^2 - 13x + 40 = (x - 5)(x - 8)$
        Product: $-5(-8) = 40$
         Sum: $-5 + (-8) = -13$

EXAMPLE 2   Factor $x^2 - x - 20$.

Solution $x^2 - x - 20 = x^2 - 1x - 20$

Try factors of -20. Check to see whether their sum is -1.

$-20 = -10(2)$	$-10 + 2 = -8$	Sum is *not* -1.
$-20 = -4(5)$	$-4 + 5 = 1$	Sum is *not* -1.
$-20 = 4(-5)$	$4 + (-5) = -1$	Sum *is* -1.

So, $x^2 - x - 20 = (x + 4)(x - 5)$.

TRY THIS   3. Factor $x^2 - 2x - 24$.

To factor a trinomial of the form $x^2 + bx + c$, look for binomial factors $(x + r)(x + s)$ such that $r \cdot s = c$ and $r + s = b$.

If c is *negative*, then r and s have *opposite signs*.

If c is *positive* and b is *negative*, then r and s are *both negative*.

If c is *positive* and b is *positive*, then r and s are *both positive*.

Classroom Exercises

For each trinomial, predict the signs contained in its binomial factors. State all possible factors of the constant term.

1. $x^2 + 5x + 6$

2. $a^2 + a - 20$

3. $y^2 + 9y + 14$

4. $y^2 - 2y - 35$

5. $t^2 - 19t + 34$

6. $s^2 + s - 16$

7. $b^2 + 5b + 4$

8. $k^2 - k - 30$

9. $j^2 + 5j - 14$

Factor each trinomial.

10. $x^2 - 5x + 4$

11. $x^2 - x - 6$

12. $a^2 + 6a + 5$

Written Exercises

Factor each trinomial.

1. $x^2 + 3x - 4$

2. $y^2 + 2y - 15$

3. $a^2 - 9a + 14$

4. $b^2 - 4b - 21$

5. $r^2 + r - 6$

6. $x^2 - 10x + 9$

7. $t^2 - 2t - 24$

8. $a^2 - a - 42$

9. $y^2 - 9y + 22$

10. $s^2 - 11s + 28$

11. $b^2 - 6b - 27$

12. $m^2 - 10m + 25$

13. $x^2 + 7x + 12$

14. $t^2 + 10t + 24$

15. $y^2 - 18y + 17$

16. $a^2 - 11a - 60$

17. $x^2 - 16x + 48$

18. $m^2 - 6m - 40$

19. $y^2 + 17y + 72$

20. $y^2 - 16y + 64$

21. $a^2 + 15a + 54$

22. $x^2 - 15x + 44$

23. $c^2 - c - 56$

24. $w^2 - 3w - 54$

25. The formula for the area of a rectangle is $A = lw$. Find possible algebraic expressions for l and w if $A = x^2 + 13x + 36$.

26. The formula for the area of a parallelogram is $A = bh$. Find possible algebraic expressions for b and h if $A = x^2 - 3x - 10$.

27. The formula for the area of a square is $A = s^2$. Find a possible algebraic expression for s if $A = x^2 - 8x + 16$.

28. The formula for the area of a triangle is $A = \frac{1}{2}bh$. Find possible algebraic expressions for b and h if $A = \frac{1}{2}(x^2 - 11x + 30)$.

Factor. Assume that a, b, c, d, e, and n are positive integers.

29. $x^2 + dx + ex + de$ **30.** $x^2 - dx - cx + dc$ **31.** $x^2 + nx + 3x + 3n$

32. $a^{10n} + 3a^{5n} - 130$ **33.** $x^{6a} + 21x^{3a} + 108$ **34.** $-98 - 3t^{4d} + t^{8d}$

35. $y^{6b} + 27y^{3b} + 180$ **36.** $a^{4c} + 17a^{2c} - 38$ **37.** $t^{8n} - 27t^{4n} - 160$

Mixed Review

Simplify.   *1.2, 1.3, 6.6*

1. $3.8 + 4.1 \times 2.3$ **2.** $1.8(4.4 - 1.6)$

3. 4^3 **4.** 2^5 **5.** $(4 \cdot 3)^2$ **6.** $3^3 + 3^2 + 3^4$

7. $8x^2 + 3x + 4x - 2x^2 - 8$ **8.** $9y^3 - 3y + 8y^2 - 2y^3 - y + 2y^2$

Application: Gas Mileage

Anita is planning to tour the Northwest and needs to estimate her gasoline costs. To make this estimate, she writes a proportion.

$$\frac{\text{miles traveled on one gallon}}{\text{one gallon of gasoline}} = \frac{\text{total miles for the trip}}{\text{total gallons needed}}$$

Anita knows that her car usually travels about 23 miles on one gallon of gasoline. Since she plans a trip of about 3,500 miles, Anita substitutes the known values into the proportion and solves for the total number of gallons g.

$$\frac{23}{1} = \frac{3500}{g} \quad \longleftarrow \quad \text{If } \frac{a}{b} = \frac{c}{d}, \text{ then } ad = bc.$$
$$23g = 3500$$
$$g = \frac{3500}{23}$$

1. Use your calculator to find the total numbers of gallons of gasoline, rounded to the nearest gallon.

2. If the average price for gasoline is \$1.17/gal, what is Anita's total cost for gasoline?

3. If the average price falls to \$1.13/gal, how much less will Anita's total cost be?

4. If her car only averages 21 mi/gal, how many more gallons will Anita need?

5. Len budgets \$50 for fuel for his vacation trip of 1500 miles. His car averages 32 mi/gal. If gasoline costs \$1.20 gal, has he budgeted enough?

7.4 Factoring Trinomials: $ax^2 + bx + c$

Objectives

To factor trinomials of the form $ax^2 + bx + c$, where $a > 1$

For the trinomial $ax^2 + bx + c$, the signs of b and c give clues for finding the binomial factors, if there are any. To determine the binomial factors of a trinomial such as $3x^2 - 14x + 8$, trial factors must include pairs of factors of $3x^2$ as well as of 8.

EXAMPLE 1   Factor $3x^2 - 14x + 8$.

Plan   Note that b is negative (-14) and c is positive (8).
So, the trial factors of 8 must both be negative.

Solution   **Trial 1**
Try $3x$ and x as factors of $3x^2$; -4 and -2 as factors of 8.

$$(3x - 4)(x - 2) = 3x^2 - 6x - 4x + 8 = 3x^2 - 10x + 8$$

This combination does *not* work: $3x^2 - 10x + 8 \neq 3x^2 - 14x + 8$

Trial 2
Interchange the factors -4 and -2. Try -2 and -4.

$$(3x - 2)(x - 4) = 3x^2 - 12x - 2x + 8 = 3x^2 - 14x + 8.$$

This combination *works* so $3x^2 - 14x + 8 = (3x - 2)(x - 4)$.

EXAMPLE 2   Factor $4x^2 - x - 5$.

Solution   The trial factors of -5 must have opposite signs.

Trial 1
Try $2x$ and $2x$ as factors of $4x^2$; -5 and 1 as factors of -5.

$$(2x - 5)(2x + 1) = 4x^2 + 2x - 10x - 5 = 4x^2 - 8x - 5$$

This combination does *not* work: $4x^2 - 8x - 5 \neq 4x^2 - x - 5$.

Trial 2
Try $4x$ and $1x$ as factors of $4x^2$ and keep -5 and 1 as factors of -5.

$$(4x - 5)(1x + 1) = 4x^2 + 4x - 5x - 5 = 4x^2 - 1x - 5.$$

This combination *works* so $4x^2 - x - 5 = (4x - 5)(x + 1)$.

TRY THIS   1. Factor $4x^2 - 2x - 6$.   2. Factor $5x^2 + 7x - 6$.

It may be necessary to try several combinations before finding the correct pair of binomial factors.

EXAMPLE 3   Factor $6x^2 + 7x - 24$.

Solution   **Trial 1**
Try $6x$ and x as factors of $6x^2$; 6 and -4 as factors of -24.

$$(6x + 6)(x - 4) = 6x^2 - 24x + 6x - 24 = 6x^2 - 18x - 24$$

This combination does *not* work: $6x^2 - 18x - 24 \neq 6x^2 + 7x - 24$.

Trial 2
Interchange the factors of 6 and -4. Try -4 and 6.

$$(6x - 4)(x + 6) = 6x^2 + 36x - 4x - 24 = 6x^2 + 32x - 24$$

This combination does *not* work: $6x^2 + 32x - 24 \neq 6x^2 + 7x - 24$

Trial 3
Try $2x$ and $3x$ as factors of $6x^2$; -3 and 8 as factors of -24.

$$(2x - 3)(3x + 8) = 6x^2 + 16x - 9x - 24 = 6x^2 + 7x - 24$$

This combination *works*. So $6x^2 + 7x - 24 = (2x - 3)(3x + 8)$.

TRY THIS   **3.** Factor $4x^2 - 12x - 7$.   **4.** Factor $10x^2 - 19x + 6$.

Some trinomials cannot be factored into two binomials. For example, the only possible binomial factors of $2x^2 + 3x + 5$ are shown below.

$$(2x + 1)(x + 5) = 2x^2 + 11x + 5 \neq 2x^2 + 3x + 5$$
$$(2x + 5)(x + 1) = 2x^2 + 7x + 5 \neq 2x^2 + 3x + 5$$

A polynomial that cannot be factored into polynomials of lower degree is said to be an **irreducible polynomial**. Thus, $2x^2 + 3x + 5$ is an irreducible trinomial.

Classroom Exercises

For each trinomial $ax^2 + bx + c$, state all possible factors of a and of c.

1. $8x^2 + 14x - 15$ **2.** $10a^2 - 11a - 6$ **3.** $6t^2 + 31t - 35$
4. $14a^2 - 55a + 21$ **5.** $12t^2 - 3t - 20$ **6.** $18x^2 + 39x + 20$
7. $16m^2 + 34m - 15$ **8.** $27x^2 + 6x - 8$ **9.** $20x^2 + 88x - 9$
10. $4y^2 + 13y - 35$ **11.** $6a^2 - 43a + 72$ **12.** $15y^2 - y - 2$

Factor each trinomial.

13. $2x^2 + x - 1$ **14.** $3a^2 + 13a - 10$ **15.** $6m^2 + m - 1$

16. $9y^2 + 3y - 2$ **17.** $6y^2 - 17y + 12$ **18.** $21x^2 + 5x - 6$

Written Exercises

Factor each trinomial. If not possible, write *irreducible*.

1. $2x^2 + 5x - 3$ **2.** $3a^2 + 10a + 3$ **3.** $5x^2 - 11x + 2$

4. $3y^2 + 2y - 5$ **5.** $2b^2 - 5b + 3$ **6.** $3a^2 - 7a - 6$

7. $4f^2 - 7f + 2$ **8.** $2x^2 - x - 6$ **9.** $10a^2 + 13a - 3$

10. $2x^2 - x - 15$ **11.** $3b^2 - b - 2$ **12.** $6y^2 - 7y + 3$

13. $6y^2 + 5y - 6$ **14.** $4a^2 - 11a - 3$ **15.** $6a^2 + a - 3$

16. $3x^2 + 3x - 4$ **17.** $6x^2 - 7x - 5$ **18.** $4b^2 + 4b - 3$

19. $6t^2 - t - 15$ **20.** $27t^2 - 12t - 7$ **21.** $4x^2 - 12x + 9$

22. $28a^2 - 15a + 2$ **23.** $8m^2 + 34m + 35$ **24.** $2t^2 - 17t + 30$

25. $15a^2 - 9a - 6$ **26.** $3x^2 + 17x + 40$ **27.** $36c^2 + 12c - 35$

28. $4a^2 + 17a - 15$ **29.** $2b^2 - b - 45$ **30.** $14y^2 - 39y + 10$

31. $8t^2 + 42t + 49$ **32.** $8y^2 + 45y - 18$ **33.** $10a^2 - 91a + 9$

34. $10 - t - 3t^2$ **35.** $16 - 34a - 15a^2$ **36.** $8 - 26m + 21m^2$

37. $18 - 3x - 10x^2$ **38.** $9 + 6y - 8y^2$ **39.** $20 + 44b - 15b^2$

40. $18 - 9y - 35y^2$ **41.** $8x^2 - 35x + 12$ **42.** $2x^2 - 5x - 3$

43. $8x^2 - 10x + 3$ **44.** $14t^2 - 57t - 27$ **45.** $40d^2 + 39d - 40$

46. Write an explanation of how to factor $8x^2 + 31x - 4$.

Factor each polynomial. Simplify each factor of the product.

47. $4(a + 3)^2 - 6(a + 3) - 10$

48. $12(t - 1)^2 + 8(t - 1) - 15$

49. If $8x^2 + (3b - 1)x + 45 = (4x - 5)(2x - 9)$, what is the value of b?

Mixed Review

Solve and check.   *3.1, 3.3, 3.5, 4.1, 4.5, 4.6*

1. $15 = -6 + x$ **2.** $z - 4 = -3$ **3.** $x + \frac{3}{4} = 4$

4. $4y - 8 = 12$ **5.** $8 - \frac{1}{3}x = 10$ **6.** $0.3b - 2.6 = 5.3$

7. $-3(2 - 5x) = 3(4 - 3x)$ **8.** $-6(6 - 4y) + 3y = (y - 4)5$

9. Five less than twice a number is 13 less than 3 times the number. Find the number.   *4.2*

7.5 Two Special Cases of Factoring

Objectives
To factor the difference of two squares
To factor a perfect-square trinomial

Let a^2 and b^2 represent areas of two squares. The shaded region at the right represents the *difference* of the two squares, where b^2 is subtracted from a^2. Now see how the region is separated into two parts (I and II) and reassembled, as shown below.

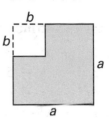

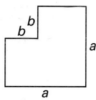 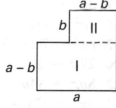 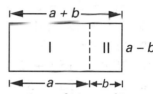

Then, $a^2 - b^2 = a(a - b) + b(a - b) = (a + b)(a - b)$
Region I + Region II

This formula can be used to factor binomials of the form $a^2 - b^2$.

Difference of Two Squares

$$a^2 - b^2 = (a + b)(a - b)$$

EXAMPLE 1 Factor $a^2 - 16$.

Plan Since 16 is the square of 4, factor $a^2 - 16$ as $a^2 - 4^2$.

Solution $a^2 - 16 = a^2 - 4^2 = (a + 4)(a - 4)$

TRY THIS   1. Factor $y^2 - 36$.   2. Factor $x^2 - 81$.

Sometimes both the coefficients and the variables are perfect squares.

EXAMPLE 2 Factor each of the following.
a. $144b^2 - 49y^2$ b. $(x - 3)^2 - 25y^2$

Solution
a. $144b^2 - 49y^2$
$= (12b)^2 - (7y)^2$
$= (12b + 7y)(12b - 7y)$

b. $(x - 3)^2 - 25y^2$
$= (x - 3)^2 - (5y)^2$
$= (x - 3 + 5y)(x - 3 - 5y)$

EXAMPLE 3   The figure at the right shows a square inside a square. Write a formula for the shaded region. Then evaluate for $r = 6.2$ and $t = 4.3$.

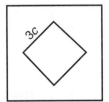

Solution   The area of the shaded region is $(3r)^2 - (2t)^2$.

$$(3r)^2 - (2t)^2 = (3r + 2t)(3r - 2t)$$
$$= (18.6 + 8.6)(18.6 - 8.6)$$
$$= 272 \text{ square units}$$

TRY THIS   3. Factor $25a^2 - 100b^2$.   4. Factor $(a + 4)^2 - 64b^2$.

Write a formula for each shaded region.

5. 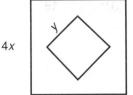   6.

Since $(a + b)^2 = a^2 + 2ab + b^2$ and $(a - b)^2 = a^2 - 2ab + b^2$, the resulting trinomials are called *perfect-square trinomials*. To factor a perfect square trinomial, you must first recognize its form: *square of the first term ± twice the product of the two terms + square of the second term.*

Perfect Square Trinomials

$a^2 + 2ab + b^2 = (a + b)^2$ $a^2 - 2ab + b^2 = (a - b)^2$

EXAMPLE 4   Determine whether $4x^2 - 12x + 9$ is a perfect square trinomial. If so, factor the trinomial.

Solution   Express the first and last terms as squares.

$$4x^2 - 12x + 9 = (2x)^2 - 12x + (3)^2$$

Check whether the middle term is $2(2x \cdot 3)$ or $-2(2x \cdot 3)$.

$$-12x = -2(2x \cdot 3) ✔$$
So, $4x^2 - 12x + 9 = (2x)^2 - 2(2x \cdot 3) + (3)^2$, a perfect square.
$$4x^2 - 12x + 9 = (2x - 3)^2$$

TRY THIS   7. Determine whether $9x^2 + 42x + 49$ is a perfect square trinomial. If so, factor the trinomial.

Classroom Exercises

Express as the square of a monomial.

1. 100
2. $16c^2$
3. $36b^2$
4. $49y^2$
5. $81w^2$
6. $144k^2$

Factor as the difference of two squares.

7. $(3x)^2 - (4y)^2$
8. $(4a)^2 - (11y)^2$
9. $(5t)^2 - (8j)^2$
10. $t^2 - 4$
11. $a^2 - 1$
12. $36 - x^2$

Tell how to fill the blank so that the trinomial will be a perfect square.

13. $(2x)^2 + \underline{\ ?\ } + (5)^2$
14 $(5x)^2 \ \underline{\ ?\ } + (3)^2$
15. $(a)^2 + \underline{\ ?\ } + (3b)^2$

Written Exercises

Factor.

1. $a^2 - 25$
2. $m^2 - 49$
3. $t^2 - 36$
4. $100 - y^2$
5. $25 - r^2$
6. $f^2 - 81$
7. $9 - g^2$
8. $9k^2 - 64$
9. $49u^2 - 25$
10. $25b^2 - 4$
11. $49 - 16y^2$
12. $1 - 64r^2$
13. $4e^2 - 1$
14. $9w^2 - 64$
15. $144 - h^2$

Determine whether the given trinomial is a perfect square. If so, factor it.

16. $x^2 + 8x + 16$
17. $m^2 - 8m + 49$
18. $y^2 + 12y + 36$
19. $t^2 - 4t + 4$
20. $k^2 - 14k + 49$
21. $a^2 - 12a + 9$
22. $4x^2 + 4x + 1$
23. $9a^2 - 6a + 1$
24. $25x^2 - 12x + 1$
25. $25a^2 + 30a + 4$
26. $16y^2 - 12y + 1$
27. $49u^2 - 14u + 1$

Factor.

28. $121a^2 - 169b^2$
29. $49t^2 - 225y^2$
30. $25x^2 - 196y^2$
31. $256a^2 - 225b^2$
32. $(2a + 5)^2 - 121r^2$
33. $4y^2 - (2x - 5)^2$
34. $36a^2 - 60ab + 25b^2$
35. $81t^2 + 90tv + 25v^2$
36. $4p^2 - 44pq + 121q^2$
37. $49r^2 + 42rt + 9t^2$
38. $9k^2 - 30kh + 25h^2$
39. $4y^2 + 28yx + 49x^2$

40. Find an algebraic expression for the length of a side of a square of area $25p^2 + 110pq + 121q^2$. What is the length for $p = 5$ and $q = 4$?

41. Find an algebraic expression for the length of a side of a square of area $9a^2 - 24ab + 16b^2$. What is the length for $a = 5$ and $b = 3$?

Write a formula in factored form for the area of each shaded region. Then evaluate for the given values of the variables. Use 3.14 for π. Give answers to the nearest integer.

42.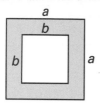

$a = 10$ and $b = 6$

43.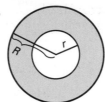

$R = 12$ and $r = 5$

44.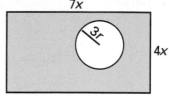

$r = 5$ and $x = 8$

Factor as the difference of two squares. Then simplify.

45. $(5t + 6)^2 - (t - 3)^2$

46. $(x - y)^2 - (4x + 3y)^2$

47. Express $(a + b)^4 - 81$ as the product of three factors.

48. There is a shortcut for mentally squaring any two-digit number ending in 5. Notice the pattern in the following examples.

$$(65)^2 = 6(6 + 1)100 + 25 = 6(7)(100) + 25 = 4{,}225$$
$$(85)^2 = 8(8 + 1)100 + 25 = 8(9)(100) + 25 = 7{,}225$$

Explain this shortcut by letting $10t + 5$ represent any two-digit number ending in 5, where $1 \le t \le 9$. (HINT: $(10t + 5)^2 = ?$)

Midchapter Review

Find the greatest common factor (GCF). *7.1*

1. 12, 22

2. 15, 27

3. 15, 18, 30

Find the missing factor. *7.1*

4. $x^3 \cdot \underline{\ ?\ } = x^6$

5. $9a^2 \cdot \underline{\ ?\ } = 36a^8$

6. $5x^2y^3 \cdot \underline{\ ?\ } = 60x^5y^6$

Factor out the GCF from each polynomial. *7.2*

7. $3a^2 - 9a + 15$

8. $15x^4 - 20x^2 + 10$

9. $8a^4b^2 - 48a^2b^3 + 4a^3b$

Factor each polynomial. If not possible, write *irreducible*. *7.3, 7.4, 7.5*

10. $x^2 - 2x - 15$

11. $a^2 + a - 20$

12. $t^2 + 8t + 7$

13. $2a^2 + 3a - 5$

14. $6x^2 - 11x + 4$

15. $16t^2 - 1$

16. $9a^2 - 25$

17. $a^2 + 6a + 8$

18. $4t^2 - 20t + 25$

7.6 Combined Types of Factoring

Objectives

To factor polynomials completely
To factor polynomials by grouping terms

The polynomial $3x^2 - 27$ can be factored in two steps.

$$3x^2 - 27 = 3(x^2 - 9) \qquad \text{3 is the GCF.}$$
$$= 3(x + 3)(x - 3) \quad \text{Each factor is irreducible.}$$

When a polynomial is factored into irreducible polynomials that have no common factor, then it is *factored completely*.

Steps in Factoring Completely	Examples
1. Look for the GCF.	$8t^4 - 32t^3 + 40t = 8t(t^3 - 4t - 5)$
2. Look for special cases.	
a. difference of two squares	$4x^2 - 9y^2 = (2x)^2 - (3y)^2$
	$\qquad\qquad = (2x + 3y)(2x - 3y)$
b. perfect-square trinomial	$x^2 + 8x + 16 = x^2 + 8x + 4^2$
	$\qquad\qquad = (x + 4)^2$
3. If a trinomial is not a perfect square, look for two different binomial factors.	$6x^2 + 11x - 10 = (2x + 5)(3x - 2)$

EXAMPLE 1

Factor $8x^3 + 12x^2 + 4x$ completely.

Solution

1. The GCF is $4x$.
$$8x^3 + 12x^2 + 4x = 4x(2x^2 + 3x + 1)$$

2. $2x^2 + 3x + 1$ can be factored into binomials.
$$2x^2 + 3x + 1 = (2x + 1)(x + 1)$$

So, $8x^3 + 12x^2 + 4x = 4x(2x + 1)(x + 1)$.

TRY THIS

1. Factor $6x^3 + 14x^2 + 8x$.

The factoring in Example 2 uses the GCF, as well as the special case of the difference of two squares, applied twice.

EXAMPLE 2

Factor $3x^5 - 243x$ completely.

Solution

$$3x^5 - 243x = 3x(x^4 - 81) \quad \longleftarrow \text{GCF: } 3x$$
$$= 3x[(x^2)^2 - 9^2)]$$
$$= 3x(x^2 + 9)(x^2 - 9) = 3x(x^2 + 9)(x + 3)(x - 3)$$

EXAMPLE 3   Factor $2m^2 - 20mn + 50n^2$ completely.

Plan   Factor out 2, the GCF. Then factor the trinomial into a perfect square.

Solution
$$2m^2 - 20mn + 50n^2 = 2(m^2 - 10mn + 25n^2)$$
$$= 2[m^2 - 2(m)(5n) + (5n)^2]$$
$$= 2(m - 5n)^2$$

TRY THIS   2. Factor $5x^4y - 80x^2y^3$ completely.

To be factorable, a polynomial need not be a binomial or a trinomial. In the polynomial $x(r + s) + y(r + s)$, notice that $r + s$ is common to each product. So, $r + s$ can be factored from the polynomial.

$$x(r + s) + y(r + s) \text{ can be factored as } (x + y)(r + s).$$

Sometimes the possibility of factoring this way is less obvious, as in $5x - 5y + ax - ay$. However, 5 is common to the first two terms and a is common to the last two terms. This suggests grouping those terms to find a common binomial factor. This method of factoring is called **factoring by grouping.**

EXAMPLE 4   Factor $5x - 5y + ax - ay$.

Plan   Group the terms in either of the two ways shown to factor out the common monomial factor.

Solution

Method 1	Method 2
$(5x - 5y) + (ax - ay)$	$(5x + ax) + (-5y - ay)$ ⟵ $-y$ is common
$5(x - y) + a(x - y)$	$x(5 + a) - y(5 + a)$ to the last
	two terms.
$(5 + a)(x - y)$	$(x - y)(5 + a)$

TRY THIS   3. Factor $2a - 4c + ax - 2cx$.

Focus on Reading

1. When is a polynomial factored completely?
2. One factor of a perfect square trinomial is $(a - 2b)$. What is the other factor?
3. Give an example of a binomial that has three factors.
4. Give an example of a polynomial having a common binomial factor.

Classroom Exercises

Indicate whether each of the following can be factored (1) as the product of two different binomials, (2) as a perfect square trinomial, (3) as the difference of two squares, or (4) by grouping.

1. $x^2 - 25$
2. $x^2 - 8x + 12$
3. $x^2 + 6x + 9$
4. $ax + ay + 3x + 3y$
5. $x^2 - 20x - yx + 20y$
6. $4a^2 - 121r^2$

State the GCF, if there is one other than 1.

7. $3x^2 + 3x - 6$
8. $2a^2 - 2a - 12$
9. $3y^2 - 27$
10. $2a^3 - 8a^2$
11. $12x^2 + 20x - 8$
12. $5a^2 + 15a + 10$
13. $3y^3 + 12y^2 - 15y$
14. $5t^3 - 20t$
15. $9x^2y - 36y$

16–24. Factor the polynomials in Classroom Exercises 7–15 completely.

Written Exercises

Factor completely.

1. $2x^2 + 10x + 8$
2. $5x^2 - 10x - 15$
3. $2a^2 - 14a + 24$
4. $6a^3 + 3a^2 - 18a$
5. $3y^3 + 15y^2 + 12y$
6. $4a^3 - 12a^2 - 16a$
7. $3x^2 - 75$
8. $5y^3 - 20y$
9. $98 - 2a^2$
10. $2a^2 + 48a - 50$
11. $3x^2 + 12x + 12$
12. $2x^3 + 12x^2 + 18x$
13. $9p^2 + 33pq - 12q^2$
14. $9a^2 - 9b^2$
15. $6x^2 - 18xy - 60y^2$
16. $2a^2 - 6ab - 20b^2$
17. $50y^2 - 98x^2$
18. $8a^2 - 24ab + 18b^2$
19. $8m^2 - 18mn - 26n^2$
20. $8x^2 + 14xy - 30y^2$
21. $8a^2 - 8ab + 2b^2$
22. $8a + 8b + ca + cb$
23. $2x + 2y + bx + by$
24. $ac + bc + 5a + 5b$
25. $5ax + 3bx + 5ay + 3by$
26. $a^2 + ac - 7a - 7c$
27. $tr - 3r + st - 3s$
28. $ax^2 - 9a + bx^2 - 9b$
29. $p^2y - 25y - 2p^2 + 50$
30. $x^2a + x^2b - 16a - 16b$
31. $12r^2 - 45r - 12$
32. $48t^3 - 24t^2 + 3t$
33. $-3f^2 - 6f + 24$
34. $6x^2y - 39xy - 210y$
35. $288a - 50a^3$
36. $a^3b - ab^3$
37. $30s^3 + 22s^2 - 28s$
38. $x^3 - 6x^2y - 5xy^2$
39. $20y^3 - 6y^2 - 8y$
40. $ax^2 - 9a + bx^2 - 9b$
41. $x^2m + x^2 - 4m - 4$
42. $2x^3 - 8y^2x + 4x^2 - 16y^2$
43. $-4a^4y - 64a^2y^3 + 12a^3y^2 + 192ay^4$
44. $45x^2y - 5x^4y - 45xy^2 + 5x^3y^2$
45. $a^4 - (a - 2)^2$
46. $(r^2 - 1)^2 - (r - 1)^2$
47. $3(2x - s)^2 + 5(2x - s) - 12$
48. $x(x + 1)(4x - 5) - 6(x + 1)$
49. $4x^2 - 25y^2 + 2x - 5y$
50. $(x^2 - 5)^2 - 7(x^2 - 5) + 12$
51. Factor $64a^4 + 1$ by writing it as $(64a^4 + 16a^2 + 1) - 16a^2$, the difference of two squares.

Mixed Review

Solve. *3.2, 4.5, 5.4*

1. $\frac{3}{5}x - 3 = \frac{4}{3}x$

2. $3a - 2(3 - a) = 2a + 9$

3. $3.2y - 1.7y = 3(0.02y + 13)$

4. $8 - 2x \geq 10 - (4x - 8)$

Simplify. *6.2, 2.10, 6.7*

5. $(p^3r)^7$

6. $(-2ab^3)^4$

7. $(5a^2b^3c^4)^3$

8. $(-3p^4q^3r^5)^3$

9. $-(-3a^2 - 4a + 6)$

10. $9a - 3b - (7a + b - 10)$

11. $(8x^3 + 3x^2 - 8) - (-x^3 - 2x^2 + 9)$

12. $(14a^4 - 12a^2 + 8) - (15a^3 - 12a^2 + 4a)$

Application: *Commission Sales*

Example

Jill works as a salesperson in an appliance store. She earns $140 per week plus a commission of 15% on the selling price of the television sets she sells. Find the total of Jill's television sales, s, if she earns $260 for the week.

Solution

Let s = the amount of sales needed.

Regular salary plus commission equals total earned.

$$
\begin{array}{rcll}
140 \quad + \quad 15\% \text{ of } s & = & 260 & \\
140 + 0.15s & = & 260 & \longleftarrow 15\% \text{ of } s \text{ means } 0.15s. \\
100(140 + 0.15s) & = & 100 \cdot 260 & \longleftarrow \text{Multiply each side} \\
100 \cdot 140 + 100 \cdot 0.15s & = & 26{,}000 & \quad\quad \text{by the LCM, 100.} \\
14{,}000 + 15s & = & 26{,}000 & \\
15s & = & 12{,}000 & \\
s & = & 800 &
\end{array}
$$

Thus, Jill must sell $800 worth of television sets.

1. Diego is paid $165 a week plus a 10% commission on all camera sales. How much must his sales be for him to earn a total of $215 for the week?

2. Janell earns only a 30% commission of her total sales. What must her total sales be to earn $270?

3. Mary earns $175 a week plus a 2% commission on each car she sells. What must her total sales be to have total earnings of $355?

7.7 Solving Quadratic Equations by Factoring

To solve quadratic equations by factoring
To solve cubic equations by factoring

Recall that the Property of Zero for Multiplication states that the product of any number and 0 is 0.

$$\text{If } a = 0 \ or \ b = 0, \text{ then } a \cdot b = 0.$$

The converse of the Property of Zero for Multiplication is also true.

$$\text{If } a \cdot b = 0, \text{ then } a = 0 \ or \ b = 0.$$

You can use the words *if and only if* to combine a conditional and its converse.

Zero-Product Property
For all real numbers a and b, $ab = 0$ if and only if $a = 0$ or $b = 0$.

EXAMPLE 1   Solve $(x - 5)(2x + 6) = 0$.

Plan   By the Zero-Product Property, if $(x - 5)(2x + 6) = 0$, then $x - 5 = 0$ or $2x + 6 = 0$. Solve each of these equations.

Solution

$(x - 5)(2x + 6) = 0$

$x - 5 = 0 \ or \ 2x + 6 = 0$
$\qquad x = 5 \qquad\qquad 2x = -6$
$\qquad\qquad\qquad\qquad\quad x = -3$

Check   For $x = 5$:

$(x - 5)(2x + 6) = 0$
$(5 - 5) \ [2(5) + 6] \overset{?}{=} 0$
$0 \cdot 16 \overset{?}{=} 0$
$0 \quad = 0 \ \text{True}$

For $x = -3$:

$(x - 5)(2x + 6) = 0$
$(-3 - 5) \ [2(-3) + 6] \overset{?}{=} 0$
$-8 \cdot 0 \overset{?}{=} 0$
$0 \ - 0 \ \text{True}$

So, the solutions of $(x - 5)(2x + 6) = 0$ are 5 and -3.

TRY THIS   1. Solve $(x + 4)(3x - 15) = 0$.

In Example 1, the solution set of $(x - 5)(2x + 6) = 0$ is $\{-3, 5\}$. If the factors are multiplied, the equation becomes $2x^2 - 4x - 30 = 0$. You can check by substitution that this equation has the same solution set, $\{-3, 5\}$.

Equations such as $2x^2 - 4x - 30 = 0$ are called *quadratic equations*.

Definition

A **quadratic equation** is an equation that can be written in the form $ax^2 + bx + c = 0$, where a, b, and c are real numbers and $a \neq 0$.

Some quadratic equations can be solved by factoring the polynomial and then applying the Zero-Product Property, as shown in Example 2.

EXAMPLE 2   Solve $3m^2 + 13m - 10 = 0$.

Solution

Factor.	$3m^2 + 13m - 10 = 0$
Set each factor equal to 0.	$(3m - 2)(m + 5) = 0$
Solve for m.	$3m - 2 = 0 \ \ or \ \ m + 5 = 0$

$$3m = 2 \qquad m = -5$$
$$m = \frac{2}{3}$$

Check: For $m = \frac{2}{3}$:

$$3m^2 + 13m - 10 = 0$$
$$3\left(\frac{2}{3}\right)^2 + 13\left(\frac{2}{3}\right) - 10 \stackrel{?}{=} 0$$
$$3\left(\frac{4}{9}\right) + \frac{26}{3} - 10 \stackrel{?}{=} 0$$
$$\frac{4}{3} + \frac{26}{3} - 10 \stackrel{?}{=} 0$$
$$\frac{30}{3} - 10 \stackrel{?}{=} 0$$
$$10 - 10 \stackrel{?}{=} 0$$
$$0 = 0 \ \ True$$

For $m = -5$:

$$3m^2 + 13m - 10 = 0$$
$$3(-5)^2 + 13(-5) - 10 \stackrel{?}{=} 0$$
$$3(25) - 65 - 10 \stackrel{?}{=} 0$$
$$75 - 65 - 10 \stackrel{?}{=} 0$$
$$10 - 10 \stackrel{?}{=} 0$$
$$0 = 0 \ \ True$$

So, the solution set of $3m^2 + 13m - 10 = 0$ is $\left\{\frac{2}{3}, -5\right\}$

TRY THIS   2. Solve $2a^2 - 7a - 4 = 0$.

A quadratic equation has at most two solutions, or **roots**. If the polynomial of a quadratic equation is a perfect square, then its factors will be the same. In this case, there will be only one root.

EXAMPLE 3   Solve $4a^2 - 12a + 9 = 0$.

Solution

$$4a^2 - 12a + 9 = 0$$
$$(2a - 3)(2a - 3) = 0$$
$$2a - 3 = 0 \quad \text{or} \quad 2a - 3 = 0$$
$$2a = 3 \qquad\qquad 2a = 3$$
$$a = \frac{3}{2} \qquad\qquad a = \frac{3}{2} \qquad \text{The check is left for you.}$$

So, the solution set of $4a^2 - 12a + 9 = 0$ is $\left\{\frac{3}{2}\right\}$.

TRY THIS   **3.** Solve $16y^2 + 24y + 9 = 0$.

In Example 3, the solution $\frac{3}{2}$ is called a **double root** since $2a - 3$ appears twice as a factor.

The equation $y^3 - 9y = 0$ is a *third-degree* or **cubic equation**. To solve this cubic equation, extend the Zero-Product Property to three factors.

$$a \cdot b \cdot c = 0 \text{ if and only if } a = 0 \text{ or } b = 0 \text{ or } c = 0.$$

EXAMPLE 4   Solve $y^3 - 9y = 0$.

Solution

Factor out the GCF.	$y^3 - 9y = 0$
	$y(y^2 - 9) = 0$
Factor $y^2 - 9$.	$y(y + 3)(y - 3) = 0$
Set each factor equal to 0.	$y = 0 \text{ or } y + 3 = 0 \text{ or } y - 3 = 0$
Solve each equation.	$y = 0 \qquad\qquad y = -3 \qquad\qquad y = 3$

The solution set is $\{-3, 0, 3\}$.

TRY THIS   **4.** Solve $x^3 - 36x = 0$.

Focus on Reading

1. Give another name for the *solutions* of an equation.
2. What is the degree of the equation $x^2 - 12x + 20 = 0$?
3. How does a cubic equation differ from a quadratic equation?
4. When will a quadratic equation have a double root?
5. Can the equation $ax^2 + bx + c = 0$ be quadratic if b equals 0?

Classroom Exercises

Find the solution set of each equation.

1. $(x - 2)(x + 1) = 0$ **2.** $(x + 5)(x - 6) = 0$ **3.** $(x - 9)(x - 2) = 0$
4. $(x - 8)(x - 8) = 0$ **5.** $x(x - 7) = 0$ **6.** $x(x + 7) = 0$
7. $(2x - 6)(x - 5) = 0$ **8.** $x(2x + 1)(x - 4) = 0$ **9.** $x(x + 5)(3x - 1) = 0$
10. $x^2 + 4x - 5 = 0$ **11.** $x^2 + 2x - 3 = 0$ **12.** $2x^2 - 5x + 3 = 0$

Written Exercises

Find the solution set of each equation.

1. $(x - 2)(x - 3) = 0$ **2.** $(x + 4)(x + 1) = 0$ **3.** $p^2 - 2p - 3 = 0$
4. $r^2 + 9r + 20 = 0$ **5.** $a^2 - 16 = 0$ **6.** $y^2 - 144 = 0$
7. $x^2 - 12x = 0$ **8.** $2t^2 - 3t - 2 = 0$ **9.** $3x^2 - 5x - 2 = 0$
10. $m^2 + 7m = 0$ **11.** $2m^2 - m - 1 = 0$ **12.** $3t^2 - 8t - 3 = 0$
13. $4a^2 + a = 0$ **14.** $3y^2 - 7y + 2 = 0$ **15.** $x^2 - 49 = 0$
16. $x^2 + 7x - 44 = 0$ **17.** $4x^2 + 3x - 1 = 0$ **18.** $y^2 + 7y + 10 = 0$
19. $3x^2 + 19x - 14 = 0$ **20.** $5y^2 - 46y + 9 = 0$ **21.** $2g^2 - 15g + 7 = 0$
22. $7a^2 - 52a + 21 = 0$ **23.** $9x^2 - 12x + 4 = 0$ **24.** $4b^2 - 25 = 0$
25. $4a^2 + 23a - 6 = 0$ **26.** $3t^2 - 22t - 16 = 0$ **27.** $2a^2 + 3a - 20 = 0$
28. $4x^2 + 32x + 64 = 0$ **29.** $3t^2 + 29t + 40 = 0$ **30.** $6x^2 + 37x - 35 = 0$
31. $6y^2 + 19y + 8 = 0$ **32.** $9y^2 + 78y + 169 = 0$ **33.** $x^3 - 36x = 0$
34. $5t^3 - 125t = 0$ **35.** $4a^3 - 16a = 0$ **36.** $3t^3 + 4t^2 + t = 0$
37. $2x^3 + 3x^2 - 2x = 0$ **38.** $2y^3 - 5y^2 + 3y = 0$ **39.** $16t^3 - 56t^2 + 49t = 0$
40. $a^3 - 9a^2 + 20a = 0$ **41.** $5y^3 - 605y = 0$ **42.** $6b^3 - 19b^2 + 10b = 0$
43. $x^5 - 20x^3 + 64x = 0$ **44.** $36a^4 - 85a^2 + 9 = 0$ **45.** $8t^4 - 18t^2 = 0$
46. $4x^5 - 13x^3 + 9x = 0$ **47.** $b^5 - 29b^3 + 100b = 0$ **48.** $3a^5 - 39a^3 + 108a = 0$
49. $8b^5 - 58b^3 + 50b = 0$ **50.** $t^5 - 10t^3 + 9t = 0$ **51.** $2y^6 - 100y^4 + 98y^2 = 0$
52. Solve $x^2 - 14x + 49 - 16y^2 = 0$ for x in terms of y.

Mixed Review

Multiply.   *6.9, 6.10, 4.4*

1. $(2x - 3)(3x - 1)$ **2.** $(x - 3)(2x^2 + 7x - 1)$ **3.** $(3y + 5)(2y^2 - 3y - 4)$
4. $(a - b)(a + b)$ **5.** $(5t + 7)(5t - 7)$ **6.** $(2n - 11)(2n - 11)$
7. The length of a rectangle is 2 more than 3 times the width. The
perimeter of the rectangle is 36. Find the length and the width.   *4.4*

Application: Boiling Point of Water

If you live in Houston and like your break-
fast soft-boiled egg cooked for four minutes,
you will have to adjust the timing when you
go camping near Denver, the "mile-high
city."

In Houston, where the altitude is approximately at sea level, water boils when it
reaches a temperature of 100°C or 212°F.

In Denver, where the altitude is about 5,280
feet above sea level, there is less atmospheric
pressure. So water boils at a lower temperature. This means that you have to cook an
egg longer at the higher altitude to obtain
the same degree of "doneness."

It is the temperature, and not the boiling,
that determines how fast food cooks. Since
the temperature of water remains the same
after it reaches the boiling point, water that is boiling vigorously
doesn't cook eggs any faster than water that is boiling gently.

A convenient rule-of-thumb for campers who often cook foods at
different altitudes is that the boiling point of water decreases about
1°C for each 1,000 -foot increase in altitude.

Exercises

1. Estimate the boiling point of water in Celsius degrees in Denver.
   Round your answer to the nearest degree.

2. If the boiling point of water is about 98°C in Mountain City, what is
   the approximate altitude there?

3. Estimate the boiling point of water at a location that has an altitude
   of 7,000 feet.

4. Find out the altitude of your city or town. What boiling point will
   the rule-of-thumb predict for this altitude? Perform an experiment to
   determine the temperature in Celsius degrees at which water boils in
   the area where you live. Compare your experimental result with the
   estimate.

7.8 Standard Form of a Quadratic Equation

Objectives   To write quadratic equations in standard form
To solve word problems involving quadratic equations

The quadratic equation $3x^2 + 14x - 5 = 0$ is in **standard form** because

1. the polynomial, $3x^2 + 14x - 5$, is set equal to zero, and

2. the terms $3x^2$, $14x$, and -5 are in descending order of exponents.

Notice also that the coefficient of the square term is positive.

EXAMPLE 1   Write $x^2 - 18 = 7x$ in standard form.

Solution

$$x^2 - 18 = 7x$$

Subtract $7x$ from each side. $x^2 - 18 - 7x = 0$
Arrange terms in descending order. $x^2 - 7x - 18 = 0$

EXAMPLE 2   Solve $11x = -x^2 - 28$. Check the solutions.

Plan   Add $1x^2$ to each side so that the coefficient of the x^2 term will be positive. Then write the equation in standard form and solve.

Solution

$$11x = -1x^2 - 28$$

Add $1x^2$ to each side. $1x^2 + 11x = -28$
Add 28 to each side. $1x^2 + 11x + 28 = 0$ ⟵ standard form
Factor. $(x + 7)(x + 4) = 0$
Set each factor equal to 0. $x + 7 = 0$ *or* $x + 4 = 0$
Solve for x. $x = -7$ $x = -4$

Check   For $x = -7$:   For $11x = -4$:

$$11x = -x^2 - 28$$ $$11x = -x^2 - 28$$
$$11(-7) \stackrel{?}{=} -(-7)^2 - 28$$ $$11(-4) \stackrel{?}{=} -(-4)^2 - 28$$
$$-77 \stackrel{?}{=} -49 - 28$$ $$-44 \stackrel{?}{=} -16 - 28$$
$$-77 = -77 \quad \text{True}$$ $$-44 = -44 \quad \text{True}$$

The roots are -7 and -4. So the solution set is $\{-7, -4\}$.

TRY THIS   1. Solve $x^2 = 30 - x$. Check the solutions.

In the next two examples, it is more convenient to have the polynomial on the right side of the equation and 0 on the left side.

EXAMPLE 3   Solve $-x^2 = 7x$.

Solution

$$-x^2 = 7x$$

Add x^2 to each side. $0 = x^2 + 7x$
Factor out the GCF, x. $0 = x(x + 7)$
Set each factor equal to 0. $x = 0$ *or* $x + 7 = 0$
Solve. $x = 0$ $x = -7$

The roots are 0 and -7. The check is left for you.

So, the solution set is $\{-7, 0\}$.

EXAMPLE 4   Solve $6 - 11x = 2x^2$.

Plan   The x^2 term is on the right and its coefficient is positive. Write the equation in standard form with the polynomial on the right and 0 on the left side of the equation. Solve by factoring.

Solution
$$6 - 11x = 2x^2$$
$$0 = 2x^2 + 11x - 6$$
$$0 = (2x - 1)(x + 6)$$
$$2x - 1 = 0 \ or \ x + 6 = 0$$
$$x = \tfrac{1}{2} \qquad\qquad x = -6$$

Check   For $x = \tfrac{1}{2}$:   For $x = -6$:

$$6 - 11x = 2x^2 \qquad\qquad 6 - 11x = 2x^2$$
$$6 - 11\left(\tfrac{1}{2}\right) \stackrel{?}{=} 2\left(\tfrac{1}{2}\right)^2 \qquad 6 - 11(-6) \stackrel{?}{=} 2(-6)^2$$
$$6 + 66 \stackrel{?}{=} 2(36)$$
$$6 - 5\tfrac{1}{2} \stackrel{?}{=} 2\left(\tfrac{1}{4}\right) \qquad\qquad 72 = 72 \ \text{True}$$
$$\tfrac{1}{2} = \tfrac{1}{2} \ \text{True}$$

The roots are $\tfrac{1}{2}$ and -6. So, the solution set is $\left\{\tfrac{1}{2}, -6\right\}$.

TRY THIS   2. Solve $22x - 5x^2 = 8$.

Sometimes a word problem will lead to a quadratic equation. A quadratic equation may have two different roots.

EXAMPLE 5　The square of a number is 12 less than 8 times the number. Find the number.

What are you to find?　　A number

What is given?　　The square of the number is 12 less than 8 times the number.

Choose a variable. What does it represent?　　Let x = the number.

Write an equation.　　*Square of x*　　is 12 less than *8 times x*.

$$x^2 = 8x - 12$$

Solve the equation.

$$x^2 - 8x + 12 = 0$$
$$(x - 6)(x - 2) = 0$$
$$x - 6 = 0 \; or \; x - 2 = 0$$
$$x = 6 \qquad\qquad x = 2$$

Check in the original problem.　　Is the square of 6, which is 36, 12 less than 8 times 6? Yes, because $36 = 8(6) - 12 = 48 - 12$.

Is the square of 2, which is 4, 12 less than 8 times 2? Yes, because $4 = 8(2) - 12 = 16 - 12$.

State the answer.　　There are two answers, 6 and 2.

EXAMPLE 6　The product of a number and 3 more than twice the number is 44. Find the number.

Solution　Let x = the number. The *product* of x and *3 more than twice x* is 44.

$$x(2x + 3) = 44$$
$$2x^2 + 3x = 44$$
$$2x^2 + 3x - 44 = 0$$
$$(2x + 11)(x - 4) = 0$$
$$2x + 11 = 0 \qquad or \quad x - 4 = 0$$
$$2x = -11 \qquad\qquad x = 4$$
$$x = -\frac{11}{2}$$

Check　Show that both $-\frac{11}{2}$ and 4 are correct answers.

TRY THIS　3. The product of a number and 7 less than 3 times the number is 20.

Classroom Exercises

State each equation in standard form with a positive coefficient for the square term.

1. $x^2 = 4x - 3$ **2.** $-a^2 = 13a$ **3.** $-14 - a^2 - 9a$

4. $-t^2 - 5t = 4$ **5.** $p^2 = 11p - 30$ **6.** $4 = d^2$

7. $5 + g^2 = -6g$ **8.** $8x = -x^2$ **9.** $4x - x^2 = 0$

10–18. Solve the equations in Exercises 1–9.

Written Exercises

Solve each equation.

1. $13y = -y^2 - 40$ **2.** $-x^2 = -3x$ **3.** $5c = -c^2$

4. $8x = -x^2 - 16$ **5.** $21 + 4m^2 = m^2$ **6.** $10 - 3u = u^2$

7. $x^2 = 8x + 20$ **8.** $2y = -y^2$ **9.** $-4a + 4 = -a^2$

10. $64 = b^2$ **11.** $8 - 10a = 3a^2$ **12.** $4k^2 = 9$

13. $n^2 - 3n = 28$ **14.** $2x^2 + 15 = -11x$ **15.** $3a^2 = -5a + 2$

16. $5x - 25 = -2x^2$ **17.** $49 = 25t^2$ **18.** $3a^2 - 4 = a$

19. $31x + 42 = -4x^2$ **20.** $12x^2 = 13x + 35$ **21.** $-2b = 3 - 8b^2$

22. $-10 = 7y - 12y^2$ **23.** $21 = 11x + 6x^2$ **24.** $10x^2 - 6 = -11x$

25. Write an explanation of how to solve the equation $4x^3 + 9x = 15x^2$.

Solve each problem.

26. The square of a number is 6 less than 5 times the number. Find the numbers.

27. The product of a number and 5 more than twice the number is 75. Find the numbers.

28. The sum of the square of a number and 6 times the number is 40. Find the numbers.

29. Six less than 5 times the square of a number is the same as the number. Find the numbers.

30. Twice the square of a number is 15 less than 11 times the number. Find the numbers.

31. Three times the square of a number is 5 less than 16 times the number. Find the numbers.

32. The product of 1 more than twice a number and 3 less than 4 times the same number is 25. Find the numbers.

Solve each equation.

33. $(3a - 4)(2a + 3) = (a - 1)(5a + 4)$ **34.** $6(x + 2)^2 - 5(x + 2) = 6$
35. $(y + 4)(3y - 2) = -y - 14$ **36.** $-13x^2 + 36 = -x^4$
37. Solve for x: $x^2 - cx = ac - ax$

Mixed Review

Simplify.   *2.10, 6.2, 6.8, 6.9*

1. $3x - [4 - (2 - x)]$ **2.** $(-4a^2)^3$ **3.** $(3x - 2)(4x - 3)$
4. $(x + 2)(x^2 - 4x + 3)$ **5.** $(x - 5)(x + 2) - (x^2 + 5x)$ **6.** $(2a + 3)^2$

Solve.   *7.7*

7. $x^2 - 2x = 0$ **8.** $16x^2 - 1 = 0$ **9.** $x^2 - 6x + 5 = 0$
10. The sum of three consecutive even integers is 48. Find the integers.   *4.3*

Brainteaser

1. When simplified, the product,

$$\left(1 - \tfrac{1}{3}\right)\left(1 - \tfrac{1}{4}\right)\left(1 - \tfrac{1}{5}\right)\left(1 - \tfrac{1}{6}\right) \cdots \left(1 - \tfrac{1}{n}\right),$$

becomes which of the following?

a. $\dfrac{1}{n}$ b. $\dfrac{2}{n}$ c. $\dfrac{2(n - 1)}{n}$ d. $\dfrac{3}{n(n + 1)}$

2. When simplified, the product,

$$\left(1 + \tfrac{1}{3}\right)\left(1 + \tfrac{1}{4}\right)\left(1 + \tfrac{1}{5}\right)\left(1 + \tfrac{1}{6}\right) \cdots \left(1 + \tfrac{1}{m}\right),$$

becomes which of the following?

a. $\dfrac{4}{m}$ b. $\dfrac{m + 1}{m}$ c. $\dfrac{m + 1}{3}$ d. $\dfrac{m + 1}{3m}$

3. Simplify.

$$\left[1 - \left(\tfrac{1}{3}\right)^2\right]\left[1 - \left(\tfrac{1}{4}\right)^2\right]\left[1 - \left(\tfrac{1}{5}\right)^2\right]\left[1 - \left(\tfrac{1}{6}\right)^2\right] \cdots \left[1 - \left(\tfrac{1}{n}\right)^2\right]$$

7.9 Problem Solving: Using Quadratic Equations

Objectives   To solve consecutive integer problems involving quadratic equations
To solve area problems involving quadratic equations

Some problems lead to quadratic equations. They can be solved by solving their corresponding equations.

EXAMPLE 1   Find two consecutive odd integers such that the square of the second, decreased by the first, is 14.

What are you to find?	Two consecutive odd integers
What is given?	The square of the second integer, decreased by the first integer, is 14.
Choose a variable.	Let x = the first odd integer.
What does it represent?	Then $x + 2$ = the second odd integer.

Write an equation.
$$(x + 2)^2 - x = 14$$
$$x^2 + 4x + 4 - x = 14$$
$$x^2 + 3x - 10 = 0$$
$$(x + 5)(x - 2) = 0$$
$$x + 5 = 0 \quad or \quad x - 2 = 0$$
$$x = -5 \qquad\qquad x = 2 \quad \underleftarrow{\quad} \text{ Not odd}$$
$$x + 2 = -3 \qquad x + 2 = 4 \qquad \text{integers}$$

Check in the original problem.   Are -5 and -3 consecutive odd integers? Yes.

Does the square of -3, decreased by -5, equal 14? Yes, because
$$(-3)^2 - (-5) = 9 + 5 = 14$$

State the answer.   The consecutive odd integers are -5 and -3.

EXAMPLE 2   The product of the first and third of three consecutive integers is 1 less than 8 times the second. Find the three integers.

Solution   Let x, $x + 1$, and $x + 2$ represent the three consecutive integers. Use the given information to write an equation.

Product of 1st and 3rd is 1 less than 8 times 2nd.

$$x(x + 2) = 8(x + 1) - 1$$

$$x^2 + 2x = 8x + 8 - 1$$
$$x^2 - 6x - 7 = 0$$
$$(x - 7)(x + 1) = 0$$
$$x - 7 = 0 \ or \ x + 1 = 0$$
$$x = 7 \qquad x = -1$$
$$x + 1 = 8 \qquad x + 1 = 0$$
$$x + 2 = 9 \qquad x + 2 = 1$$

Check   Are 7, 8, and 9 consecutive integers?   Yes.

Is the product of 7 and 9 equal to 1 less than 8 times 8?
 Yes, because $7(9) = 8(8) - 1$, or $63 = 64 - 1$

Are -1, 0, and 1 consecutive integers?   Yes.

Is the product of -1 and 1 equal to 1 less than 8 times 0?
 Yes, because $-1(1) = 8(0) - 1$, or $-1 = 0 - 1$

Thus, there are two groups of such integers: $7, 8, 9$ and $-1, 0, 1$.

TRY THIS   1. The product of the first and second of three consecutive integers is 22 more than 5 times the third. Find the three integers.

Only positive solutions of an equation can represent measurements such as the length and width of a rectangle, as shown in Example 3.

EXAMPLE 3   The area of a rectangle is 48 cm². The length is 4 cm less than twice the width. Find the length and width.

What are you to find?   length and width of a rectangle

Draw and label a figure.

$A = lw$ w

l

What is given?   length = 4 cm less than 2 times width
area = 48 cm²

Choose a variable.   Let x = the width.

What does it represent?   Then $2x - 4$ = the length.

Write an equation. $A = lw$
$48 = (2x - 4)x$

Solve the equation. $48 = 2x^2 - 4x$
$0 = 2x^2 - 4x - 48$
$0 = 2(x - 6)(x + 4)$
$x - 6 = 0 \ or \ x + 4 = 0$
$x = 6 \qquad x = -4$

Check in the original problem.

If $x = 6$, the width is 6 cm and the length is $2(6) - 4$, or 8 cm. Does $A = lw = 48$? Yes.

Reject -4. A width must be a positive number.

State the answer.

The width is 6 cm and the length is 8 cm.

EXAMPLE 4 A rectangular patio is 6 m long and 4 m wide. The area of the patio is to be increased by 39 m² by increasing the length and width by the same amount. Find the amount by which each side must be increased.

Solution Let $t =$ the amount of increase of each side.
Then $t + 6 =$ the new length and
$t + 4 =$ the new width.

$$A = 6 \cdot 4 + 39 \qquad t + 4$$
$$t + 6$$

New area $=$ original area $+$ increase in area
$(t + 6)(t + 4) = \quad 6 \cdot 4 \quad + \quad 39$

$t^2 + 10t + 24 = 24 + 39$
$t^2 + 10t - 39 = 0$
$(t + 13)(t - 3) = 0$
$t + 13 = 0 \quad or \quad t - 3 = 0$
$\qquad t = -13 \qquad\qquad t = 3$

Check Since the amount of increase must be a positive number, reject -13.

If each side is increased by 3 m, the new width is 7 m and the new length is 9 m. Is the new area 39 m² more than the original area?

Yes, since $9(7) = 39 + 6(4)$, or $63 = 39 + 24$.

Thus, each side is increased by 3 m.

TRY THIS 2. The area of a rectangle is 36 cm². The length is 3 cm less than 3 times the width. Find the width and length.

Classroom Exercises

Let n, $n + 2$, and $n + 4$ represent three consecutive odd integers. Write an algebraic expression for each of the following. Do not simplify.

1. the product of the first two consecutive integers
2. the square of the second integer decreased by twice the third integer
3. the sum of the squares of the second and the third integers
4. the product of the first and the third integers, decreased by the second integer

Give, in simplest form, an algebraic expression for the area of each rectangle with the given length and width.

5. length: $w + 5$
   width: w
6. width: w
   length: $2w - 3$
7. width: $w + 1$
   length: $w + 2$
8. width: $w - 5$
   length: $w + 5$
9. Find two consecutive even integers whose product is 120.
10. Find two consecutive odd integers whose product is 143.

Written Exercises

Solve each problem.

1. Find two consecutive even integers whose product is 48.
2. Find two consecutive odd integers whose product is 63.
3. Find two consecutive even integers such that the square of the second, decreased by the first, is 58.
4. Find two consecutive odd integers such that the square of the second, increased by the first, is 88.
5. Find two consecutive odd integers such that the sum of their squares is 34.
6. Find two consecutive even integers such that the sum of their squares is 52.
7. The width of a rectangle is 3 in. less than the length. The area is 54 in². Find the length and width.
8. The length of a rectangle is 4 yd more than the width. The area is 60 yd². Find the length and width.
9. The length of a rectangle is 3 cm more than twice its width. The area is 44 cm². Find its dimensions.
10. The length of a rectangle is 5 m more than 3 times its width. Find the dimensions if the area is 42 m².
11. Find three consecutive odd integers such that the square of the second integer, increased by the first, is 54.
12. Find four consecutive integers such that the sum of the squares of the first and the third integers is 130.

13. Find three consecutive even integers such that the product of the first and the third integers is 20 more than 5 times the second.

14. If each of the dimensions of a 7 ft by 10 ft rectangle is increased by the same amount, the area is increased by 38 ft². Find the amount of increase in each dimension.

15. A movie screen measures 8 m by 6 m. Each dimension is to be increased by the same amount to increase the area by 72 m². Find the amount of increase in each dimension.

16. Find three consecutive integers such that the product of all three, decreased by the cube of the first, is 33.

17. A room has dimensions 11 ft by 12 ft. A rug with area 90 ft² is placed in the center of the room leaving bare edges of the same width all the way around. Find the dimensions of the rug.

18. A photograph, 14 in. by 11 in., is to have a white border of uniform width around it. The total area of the picture, including the border, is 270 in². Find the width of the border.

19. Squares 2 in. wide are cut out from the corners of a square sheet of metal. The sides of the remaining sheet are then turned up to form an open box. The volume of the box is 32 in³. Find the original length of each side of the square.

Mixed Review

Evaluate. *1.1, 1.2, 1.3*

1. $n - 3.5$ for $n = 14.1$

2. $\frac{x}{12}$ for $x = 4.8$

3. $27 - 5y$ for $y = 6$

4. $m(n - 3) - (m - 2)$ for $m = -2$ and $n = -1$

5. $3a^2 - 4a$ for $a = 8$

6. $\frac{x^2 - y^2}{(x - y)^2}$ for $x = 6$ and $y = 3$

Simplify. *6.1, 6.2*

7. $3y \cdot y^6$

8. $-5a^4(2a^3)$

9. $(6x^3y^2)(-3xy^4)$

10. $(y^6)^2$

11. $-(a^5)^3$

12. $(-2ab^2c^4)^5$

13. $(3c^4)^3(2c^2)^4$

14. $-m^2(m^3n)^4$

15. John has 6 more quarters than dimes. He has 18 coins in all. Find the number of coins of each type. *4.2*

Problem Solving Strategies

Organizing the Possibilities

In some problems you need to keep track of possibilities. One way to help manage a large number of possibilities is to list or diagram the possibilities in a systematic way. Organizing the possibilities can help you make sure you have them all and that you have not counted the same one twice.

Example

A rock band wants to add a new twist to its act by featuring a different duet in each song of a performance. How many songs will the 5-member band need to play so that each member sings one duet with every other member? Start by representing each member with the letters *A–E* to make it easier to list duets. Next, list all possible duets on a chart. Begin with all duets that include band member *A*, then those that include *B*, then *C*, and so on. Then cross out any repeats, such as *AB* and *BA*.

With *A*	With *B*	With *C*	With *D*	With *E*
AB	B̶A̶	C̶A̶	D̶A̶	E̶A̶
AC	BC	C̶B̶	D̶B̶	E̶B̶
AD	BD	CD	D̶C̶	E̶C̶
AE	BE	CE	DE	E̶D̶

Since each of the 5 band members can be in 4 duets, there are 4(5), or 20 possible duets. But half of these 20 are repeats, so there are only 10 different duets. The band must play 10 songs.

Solve each problem.

1. As head of a dance club with a membership of 8 girls and 8 boys, you are planning a "Mix-Up" Dance at which each boy has 1 complete dance with each girl. How many dances must you allow for?

2. Four teams play basketball at the same time in 2 adjacent gyms. After each game, each team plays a different team. What is the fewest number of games that will allow each team to play each other team the same number of times and allow each team to play in each gym the same number of times?

3. An organizer for the teams in Exercise 2 wants them to play 3 games each and to play a different team each time. He does not want a team to play all 3 of its games in the same gym. Show that such a schedule is impossible.

4. How much money would it take to display all the possible combinations that can be made using 3 different denominations at one time from these 5 coins: half-dollar, quarter, dime, nickel, penny? Each combination must have a different monetary value.

Mixed Problem Solving

As you work Exercises 1, 2, 3, 5, 6, 7, and 12, apply the strategy of *Estimating Before Solving.* For each problem, write an estimate (including the units) of the final answer before you begin to solve the problem.

If your final answer is not close to your estimate, think about how you might improve your estimating skills.

1. Find the perimeter and the area of a square with each side 8.7 cm.

2. Find the area of a triangle with a base of 8.3 cm and altitude 4.8 cm.

3. Willa has saved $290 in two years. She saved 4 times as much the first year as she saved the second year. How much did she save each year?

4. Find the perimeter of a triangle if the perimeter, decreased by 5 cm, is the same as 43 cm decreased by 7 times the perimeter.

5. For the February opera, 2,452 people attended. This audience was $\frac{4}{5}$ as large as the October audience. How many attended the opera in October?

6. Sue lives $2\frac{1}{2}$ miles from school. She walks at the rate of 3 mi/h. How long does it take her to walk to school?

7. Luis drove 234 mi at an average rate of 52 mi/h. If he stopped for a 40-min lunch break, how long did the trip take?

8. The length of a rectangle is 12 cm more than 3 times the width. The perimeter is 96 cm. Find the length and width.

9. A triangle has a perimeter of 76 cm. The first side is 8 cm longer than the second side. The third side is 5 cm longer than the second side. Find the length of each side.

10. One side of a triangle is 3 cm shorter than the second side. The remaining side is 8 cm longer than the second side. The perimeter is 95 cm. Find the length of each side.

11. Forty-eight students are separated into two groups. The first group is 3 times as large as the second. How many students are in each group?

12. On a video game, Wilma and Alex scored 2,895 points. Wilma's score was 2 times Alex's score. Find their scores.

13. The vertex angle of an isosceles triangle measures 16 more than twice a base angle. Find the measure of each angle of the triangle.

14. One typist worked 8 h longer than a second. A third typist worked 3 h less than the second. How long did each typist work if together they worked 95 h?

15. Last month George earned $620 more than this month. He earned a total of $5,420 for the two months. Find his earnings for each month.

16. Find three consecutive integers if 3 times the square of the smallest equals the product of the other two.

Key Terms

composite number   (p. 243)
cubic equation   (p. 269)
difference of two squares   (p. 259)
double root   (p. 269)
factoring by grouping   (p. 264)
greatest common factor (GCF)   (p. 244)
irreducible polynomial   (p. 257)
perfect square trinomial   (p. 260)

prime factorization   (p. 244)
prime number   (p. 243)
quadratic equation   (p. 268)
quadratic polynomial   (p. 268)
roots   (p. 268)
standard form of a quadratic
  equation   (p. 272)
Zero-Product Property   (p. 267)

Key Ideas and Review Exercises

7.1   To find the greatest common factor (GCF) of two or more monomials, factor the integers into primes. Then multiply the smallest powers of prime numbers and of variables that are common to the monomials. To find a missing factor, divide the product by the given factor.

Find the greatest common factor (GCF).

1. 18, 45

2. $30a^3$, $35a^2$

3. $72b^5$, $135b$, $54ab^2$

Find the missing factor.

4. $a^6 \cdot \underline{\ ?\ } = a^{12}$

5. $-5n^4 \cdot \underline{\ ?\ } = 20n^{10}$

6. $8a^3b^2 \cdot \underline{\ ?\ } = 64a^6b^8$

7.2   To factor out the greatest common monomial factor from a polynomial, find the GCF of the terms. Then use the Distributive Property to factor out the GCF.

Factor out the GCF from each polynomial.

7. $5x^2 - 15x + 20$

8. $a^5 + a^3 - 3a^2$

9. $3x^4 - 9x^3 + 27x$

7.3   To factor trinomials of the form $x^2 + bx + c$, find binomial factors $(x + r)(x + s)$ such that $r \cdot s = c$ and $r + s = b$.

Factor each trinomial.

10. $x^2 - 8x + 15$

11. $a^2 + 3a - 28$

12. $y^2 + 14y + 24$

7.4   To factor trinomials of the form $ax^2 + bx + c$, where $a > 1$, form trial binomial factors using factors of ax^2 for the first terms and factors of c for the second terms. Then multiply the binomials to check that the middle term is bx.

Factor each trinomial.

13. $3a^2 - 11a + 10$ **14.** $10a^2 + a - 3$ **15.** $6x^2 + 17x + 12$
16. $2a^2 + 13a + 15$ **17.** $2m^2 - 7m + 5$ **18.** $4a^2 - 20a + 25$

7.5 To factor the difference of two squares, use $a^2 - b^2 = (a + b)(a - b)$.
To factor a perfect square trinomial, use
$a^2 + 2ab + b^2 = (a + b)^2$ or $a^2 - 2ab + b^2 = (a - b)^2$.

Factor.

19. $x^2 - 400$ **20.** $y^2 + 18y + 81$ **21.** $36y^2 - 25$
22. $a^2 + 8a + 16$ **23.** $x^2 - 12x + 36$ **24.** $9x^2 + 30xy + 25y^2$

7.6 To factor a polynomial by grouping, look for the GCF in pairs of terms. Factor out the GCF. Then factor out the common binomial.

Factor by grouping.

25. $5x + ax - 5y - ay$ **26.** $ax + ay + bx + by$ **27.** $x^2y - 25y - 3x^2 + 75$
28. $xm + xb + tm + bt$ **29.** $ta + 6t + a^2 + 6a$ **30.** $x^2m + x^2 - 4m - 4$
31. $ax + ay + 3x + 3y$ **32.** $ax + bx - ay - by$ **33.** $2axy - 2ay + 3bx - 3b$

7.6 To factor a polynomial completely, first factor out any GCF greater than 1. Continue factoring until polynomial factors are irreducible.

Factor completely.

34. $2a^2 + 2a - 12$ **35.** $24x^2 + 4x - 8$ **36.** $100a^2 - 4b^2$

7.7, 7.8, To solve quadratic equations that are in standard form, factor the poly-
7.9 nomial and apply the Zero-Product Property.

Solve each equation or problem.

37. $a^2 + 8a + 15 = 0$ **38.** $t^2 - 196 = 0$ **39.** $y - 15 = -6y^2$

40. If a number is multiplied by 5 more than twice that number, the result is 12. Find the number.

41. Find three consecutive integers such that the square of the third integer is 9 times the first integer.

42. Find the solution of $(3y - 6)^2$ $12(3y - 6) + 36 = 0$

43. The square of a number is 24 more than twice the number. Find the number.

Give the prime factorization of each number.

1. 48   **2.** 81   **3.** 250

Find the greatest common factor (GCF).

4. 27, 45   **5.** $18y^3, -24y$ **6.** $x^4, 27x^2, 36x^3$

Find the missing factor.

7. $a^5 \cdot \underline{\quad?\quad} = a^{10}$ **8.** $-4x^4 \cdot \underline{\quad?\quad} = 24x^9$ **9.** $\underline{\quad?\quad} \cdot 5b^3c^7 = -20b^7c^{12}$

Factor out the GCF from each trinomial.

10. $5x^2 - 20x - 15$ **11.** $a^4 - 5a^3 + 6a$ **12.** $18a^3b^4 - 30a^4b^3 - 24a^4b^2$

Factor each polynomial completely.

13. $x^2 - 6x - 7$ **14.** $a^2 + 7a + 12$ **15.** $y^2 - 6y + 5$

16. $a^2 + 9a - 90$ **17.** $4a^2 + 7a - 2$ **18.** $18t^2 - 15t + 3$

19. $a^2 - 100$ **20.** $9x^2 - 30xy + 25y^2$ **21.** $6ax - 3bx + 2ay - by$

22. $2x^2 - 28x + 98$ **23.** $81x^2 - 9$ **24.** $24a^3 + 28a^2 + 8a$

25. $2x^3 + 4x^2 - 30x$ **26.** $x^3y - 36xy^3$ **27.** $x^3 - 9xy^2 - x^2 + 9y^2$

Solve each equation.

28. $x^2 - 7x + 12 = 0$ **29.** $a^2 - 16a = 0$ **30.** $3 + 5t = 2t^2$

Solve each problem.

31. The square of a number is 4 more than 3 times the number. Find the number.

32. If 4 times a number is added to the square of the number, the result is 21. Find the number.

33. The area of a wedding photograph is 300 cm². The length is 5 cm longer than the width. Find the length and width.

34. Find three consecutive even integers if the product of the first and the second integers is 8 more than 10 times the third integer.

Factor each polynomial completely. (Exercises 35–36)

35. $x^{6a} - 11x^{3a} + 30$

36. $32a^4 - 1,250b^4$

37. Solve the equation $x^5 - 17x^3 + 16x = 0$ for all values of x.

Choose the one best answer to each question or problem.

1. The sum of an even number and an odd number is __?__ .
   (A) always composite
   (B) always prime
   (C) always even
   (D) always odd
   (E) always divisible by 3

2. If $5a - 15 = 40$, then $a - 3 =$ __?__
   (A) 11   (B) 5   (C) 8   (D) 40
   (E) 3

3. The symbol $\begin{vmatrix} a & b \\ c & d \end{vmatrix}$ means $ad - bc$.
   What is the value of x^2 if $\begin{vmatrix} x & 3 \\ 3 & x \end{vmatrix} = 0$?
   (A) -9 (B) 9   (C) 3
   (D) -3 (E) 0

4. If r, s, and t are positive numbers such that $3r = 4s$ and $2s = 5t$, arrange the numbers in order from least to greatest.
   (A) r, t, s (B) t, s, r (C) r, s, t
   (D) s, r, t (E) t, r, s

5. $ACIG$ is a square. $AB = 6$ cm and $HI = 5$ cm.
   The area of the shaded region is 75 cm^2. What is the area of $BCFE$?
   (A) 25 cm^2
   (B) 121 cm^2
   (C) 61 cm^2
   (D) 66 cm^2
   (E) 46 cm^2

6. The perimeter of a rectangle is given by the formula $p = 2l + 2w$, where l is the length and w is the width. If $3a - 2$ represents the width and $18a + 12$ represents the perimeter, then the length is __?__ .
   (A) $6a + 3$ (B) $6a + 8$
   (C) $12a + 16$ (D) $15a + 14$
   (E) $15a + 10$

7. If $0.5a + 1.5 = 3.0$, find the value of $3a - 10$.
   (A) 3   (B) -3 (C) 17
   (D) 1   (E) -1

8. Six consecutive odd integers are given. The sum of the first three integers is 3. What is the sum of the last three?
   (A) 21   (B) 0   (C) 9
   (D) 4   (E) 3

9. If $x - 5 = 2$ and $x^2 - y^2 = 0$, then $y =$ ___
   (A) 7   (B) -7 (C) 7 or -7
   (D) 49   (E) -49

10. If the roots of the equation $(x - 5)(2x + c) = 0$ are integers, then c cannot equal ___ .
    (A) -6 (B) -4 (C) 0
    (D) 5   (E) 10

11. When is $(x - y)^2 - x^2 + y^2$ true?
    (A) Always   (B) Never
    (C) Sometimes   (D) only with decimals   (E) It cannot be determined from the information given.

12. A rectangle has a width of 8 cm and a length of 10 cm. If the length and width are each increased by 2 cm, what is the percent increase in the area of the rectangle?
    (A) $33\frac{1}{3}\%$ (B) 50% (C) 80%
    (D) 120% (E) 150%

Belinda Campos is a champion at the game of billiards. To be a winner, she must judge the force and direction of her shots carefully. As she hits the ball, Belinda also uses her knowledge of angles and reflections.

8.1 Simplifying Rational Expressions

Objectives
To find the values, if any, for which rational expressions are undefined
To simplify rational expressions
To evaluate rational expressions

An expression such as $\dfrac{5}{x+5}$ is called a *rational expression*. A **rational expression** is a polynomial or the quotient of two polynomials.

Each of the following expressions is a rational expression.

$$\frac{3x}{10} \qquad \frac{2x-5}{x^2-3x+5} \qquad 2a \qquad \frac{0}{3x+2} \qquad x^2-9$$

A rational expression is undefined when the denominator is equal to 0.

EXAMPLE 1 For what value or values of the variable is the given rational expression undefined?

  a. $\dfrac{a-3}{3a+9}$ b. $\dfrac{5x+2}{x^2-7x+12}$

Plan Find the values of the variable that will make the denominator 0.

Solutions

  a. Let $3a+9=0$.
  $$3a=-9$$
  $$a=-3$$

  Thus, $\dfrac{a-3}{3a+9}$ is undefined for $a=-3$.

  b. Let $x^2-7x+12=0$.
  $$(x-4)(x-3)=0$$
  $$x-4=0 \; or \; x-3=0$$
  $$x=4 \; or \qquad x=3$$

  Thus, $\dfrac{5x+2}{x^2-7x+12}$ is undefined for $x=4$ and for $x=3$.

TRY THIS

1. For what value or values of the variable is the rational expression $\dfrac{6x-4}{x^2-10x+25}$ undefined?

In Example 1a, if a is replaced by -3, then the numerator of $\dfrac{a-3}{3a+9}$ is $-3-3$, or -6. The denominator is 0. Use a calculator to find $\dfrac{-6}{0}$. What does the display show?

Assume that if a value of a variable causes a denominator in an expression to be zero, then the expression is undefined for that value.

EXAMPLE 2   Simplify $\dfrac{18a^2}{12a}$.

Solution $\dfrac{18a^2}{12a} = \dfrac{2 \cdot 3 \cdot 3 \cdot a \cdot a}{2 \cdot 2 \cdot 3 \cdot a}$

$= \dfrac{\overset{1}{\cancel{2}} \cdot \overset{1}{\cancel{3}} \cdot 3 \cdot \overset{1}{\cancel{a}} \cdot a}{\underset{1}{\cancel{2}} \cdot 2 \cdot \underset{1}{\cancel{3}} \cdot \underset{1}{\cancel{a}}} = \dfrac{3a}{2}$, or $\dfrac{3}{2}a$

TRY THIS   **2.** Simplify $\dfrac{30x^4}{36x^2}$.

A rational expression is said to be *simplified* when it is written as a polynomial or as a quotient of polynomials with 1 as the greatest common factor (GCF) of the numerator and denominator.

EXAMPLE 3   Simplify $\dfrac{(a + 3)(a + 4)}{(a - 3)(a + 4)}$.

Solution $\dfrac{(a + 3)(a + 4)}{(a - 3)(a + 4)} = \dfrac{(a + 3)\overset{1}{\cancel{(a + 4)}}}{(a - 3)\underset{1}{\cancel{(a + 4)}}}$

$= \dfrac{(a + 3)1}{(a - 3)1}$

$= \dfrac{a + 3}{a - 3}$

EXAMPLE 4   Simplify $\dfrac{x^2 + 2x - 15}{2x^2 - 7x + 3}$.

Plan   Factor the numerator and the denominator. Then divide out the common factors.

Solution $\dfrac{x^2 + 2x - 15}{2x^2 - 7x + 3} = \dfrac{(x - 3)(x + 5)}{(2x - 1)(x - 3)}$ ⟵ The GCF is $x - 3$.

$= \dfrac{\overset{1}{\cancel{(x - 3)}}(x + 5)}{(2x - 1)\underset{1}{\cancel{(x - 3)}}}$

$= \dfrac{1(x + 5)}{(2x - 1)1}$ ⟵ The GCF is now 1.

$= \dfrac{x + 5}{2x - 1}$

TRY THIS   **3.** Simplify $\dfrac{2x^2 - 5x - 12}{x^2 - 11x + 28}$.

EXAMPLE 5 Simplify $\dfrac{3x^3 - 12x}{6x^4 - 12x^3}$.

Solution
$$\dfrac{3x^3 - 12x}{6x^4 - 12x^3} = \dfrac{3x(x^2 - 4)}{6x^3(x - 2)}$$
$$= \dfrac{3x(x + 2)(x - 2)}{6x^3(x - 2)} \quad \longleftarrow \text{The GCF is } 3x(x - 2).$$
$$= \dfrac{\overset{1}{\cancel{3x}}(x + 2)(\overset{1}{\cancel{x - 2}})}{\underset{2x^2}{\cancel{6x^3}}(\underset{1}{\cancel{x - 2}})}$$
$$= \dfrac{x + 2}{2x^2} \quad \longleftarrow \text{The GCF is now 1.}$$

EXAMPLE 6 Evaluate the rational expression $\dfrac{2x^2 - 5}{x^2 - 3x + 9}$ for $x = -2$.

Solution
$$\dfrac{2x^2 - 5}{x^2 - 3x + 9} = \dfrac{2(-2)^2 - 5}{(-2)^2 - 3(-2) + 9}$$
$$= \dfrac{2(4) - 5}{4 + 6 + 9}$$
$$= \dfrac{8 - 5}{19}, \text{ or } \dfrac{3}{19}$$

Thus, the value of the given rational expression for $x = -2$ is $\dfrac{3}{19}$

TRY THIS 4. Simplify $\dfrac{10x^4 + 40x^3}{2x^3 - 32x}$.

Classroom Exercises

For what values of the variable is the rational expression undefined?

1. $\dfrac{10m}{m - 3}$ 2. $\dfrac{x - 6}{y}$ 3. $\dfrac{7a}{a - 4}$ 4. $\dfrac{10}{5 - y}$

5. $\dfrac{8 - x}{6 - x}$ 6. $\dfrac{m - 3}{3 - m}$ 7. $\dfrac{x - 4}{2x - 10}$ 8. $\dfrac{3 - y}{y^2 - 9}$

Simplify, if possible. If not possible, write NP.

9. $\dfrac{110}{225}$ 10. $\dfrac{a}{a^6}$ 11. $\dfrac{-52y^2}{39y^2}$ 12. $\dfrac{10m^{15}}{22m^5}$

13. $\dfrac{x + 4}{(x + 4)(x - 3)}$ 14. $\dfrac{(5x - 3)(x + 9)}{(x + 1)(5x - 3)}$ 15. $\dfrac{9x - 2}{2x + 9}$ 16. $\dfrac{x^3 + x^2}{2x^3 - 2x}$

Written Exercises

For what value or values of x is the rational expression undefined?

1. $\dfrac{x-3}{2x+6}$

2. $\dfrac{-12}{5x-10}$

3. $\dfrac{x}{2x-8}$

4. $\dfrac{x-14}{3x-15}$

5. $\dfrac{x}{x^2+5x+6}$

6. $\dfrac{x-3}{x^2+3x-4}$

7. $\dfrac{4x+5}{x^2-4x+3}$

8. $\dfrac{x+7}{x^2-25}$

Simplify, if possible. If not possible, write NP.

9. $\dfrac{14k}{21}$

10. $-\dfrac{9}{33}x$

11. $\dfrac{42t}{70t}$

12. $-\dfrac{15x}{25x^3}$

13. $\dfrac{2x-10}{x-5}$

14. $\dfrac{a-6}{a^2-6a}$

15. $\dfrac{y^2-49}{y^2+4y-21}$

16. $\dfrac{2a+6}{3a-15}$

17. $\dfrac{a^2+3a-10}{2a^2+11a+5}$

18. $\dfrac{2x^2-x-1}{2x^2-5x+3}$

19. $\dfrac{2y^2-y}{2y^2-5y-3}$

20. $\dfrac{m^2+4m}{m^2+m-12}$

21. $\dfrac{x^2-7x+18}{x^2-12x+27}$

22. $\dfrac{2a^2+7a-4}{a^2-16}$

23. $\dfrac{3m^2-9m-30}{6m-30}$

24. $\dfrac{5a-20}{a^2-4a}$

25. $\dfrac{t-3}{8.96t-26.88}$

26. $\dfrac{3m^2+21m-54}{0.341m-3.069}$

Evaluate for the given value of the variable.

27. $\dfrac{3a-5}{2a+1}$ for $a=-1$

28. $\dfrac{5x-3}{x^2-3}$ for $x=-2$

29. $\dfrac{m^2-9}{3m+5}$ for $m=3$

Simplify, if possible.

30. $\dfrac{3a^4+7a^3-20a^2}{6a^4-7a^3-5a^2}$

31. $\dfrac{2p^3-14p^2+20p}{4p^4-8p^3-60p^2}$

32. $\dfrac{a^3+10a^2+25a}{a^5-3a^4-40a^3}$

33. $\dfrac{3y^3-15y^2-12y}{6y^3-42y^2}$

34. $\dfrac{3a^3-a^2-14a}{2a^4+3a^3-2a^2}$

35. $\dfrac{3x^2+18x-21}{15x^2-15}$

36. $\dfrac{2x^3-4x^2-6x}{4x^4-12x^3-16x^2}$

37. $\dfrac{3x^3+24x^2+48x}{9x^4-144x^2}$

38. $\dfrac{2a^2-ab-3b^2}{2a-3b}$

39. $\dfrac{a^3b^7(2x^2+9x-5)}{a^2b^9(2x^2+7x-15)}$

40. $\dfrac{a^3b^4(y^2+7y+10)}{a^6b^2(y^2+y-20)}$

41. $\dfrac{m^2n(2x^2-8x+6)}{mn^2(12x-36)}$

42. Write an explanation of how to determine the values of the variable for which a rational expression is undefined. Give an example of a rational expression that is always defined and an example of a rational expression that is undefined for certain values of the variable.

43. The area of a certain rectangle is represented by $x^2 + 2x - 3$ and its length by $x - 1$. Find its width.

44. The area of a certain rectangle is represented by $x^2 - 9$ and its width by $x - 3$. Find its length.

The volume of the cube at the right is determined by multiplying the area of its square base by its height. The total surface area of the cube is determined by multiplying the area of one face by 6.

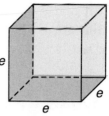

45. Find an expression for the volume of the cube.

46. Find an expression for the total surface area of the cube.

47. Find the quotient of the total surface area divided by the volume.

48. Find the value of the quotient in Exercise 47 for $e = 4$.

The volume of the right circular cylinder at the right is $\pi r^2 h$ and its surface area is $2\pi r^2 + 2\pi rh$.

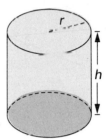

49. Find the quotient of the volume of the cylinder divided by its surface area.

50. Find the value of the quotient of Exercise 49 for $r = 3$ and $h = 8$.

Simplify.

51. $\dfrac{x^4 - 13x^2 + 36}{x^3 + x^2 - 6x}$

52. $\dfrac{9p^6 - 145p^4 + 16p^2}{3p^2 + 11p - 4}$

53. $\dfrac{50y^6 - 58y^4 + 8y^2}{30y^2 + 18y - 12}$

54. $\dfrac{x^4 - 10x^2 + 9}{3x^2 - 27}$

55. $\dfrac{a^2 + 4ab - 21b^2}{a^2 + 7ab - 3a - 21b}$

56. $\dfrac{ax^2 - ay^2 + 3x^2 - 3y^2}{ax - ay + 3x - 3y}$

Mixed Review

Multiply. *6.9, 6.10*

1. $(2x + 1)(x - 3)$

2. $(2y - 3)(3y + 5)$

3. $(m - 1)(3m + 5)$

4. $(x - 9)(x + 9)$

5. $(y - 3)(y + 3)$

6. $(3a + 4)(3a - 4)$

7. $(2m + 5)(m - 3)$

8. $(2b + 3)^2$

9. $(3a - 1)^2$

Simplify. *6.1, 6.2, 6.3*

10. $(-3x^2)^4$

11. $(-2x^2y)(5x^5y^4)$

12. $\dfrac{-18a^5b}{12ab^8}$

Find the solution set. *7.9*

13. $x^2 - 9 = 0$

14. $x^2 + 2x - 3 = 0$

15. $2x^3 - 7x^2 - 15x = 0$

16. Use the formula $A = \frac{1}{2}h(b + c)$ to find the area A of a trapezoid, where $b = 14$ cm, $c = 18$ cm, and $h = 8$ cm. *1.4*

8.2 Simplifying Rational Expressions: Convenient Form

Objective

To simplify rational expressions by writing polynomials in convenient form

To simplify $\dfrac{14 + a - 3a^2}{-3a + 2 - 2a^2}$, it is necessary first to factor both the numerator and denominator. To get the polynomial $14 + a - 3a^2$ in a more convenient form, follow these steps.

1. Write in descending order of the exponents.

$$-3a^2 + a^1 + 14, \text{ or } -3a^2 + a + 14$$

2. Factor out -1 in order to obtain a first coefficient that is positive.

$$-1(3a^2 - a - 14)$$

The convenient form of $14 + a - 3a^2$ is $-1(3a^2 - a - 14)$. The denominator $-3a + 2 - 2a^2$ can also be written in convenient form following the same two steps.

EXAMPLE 1

Simplify $\dfrac{a - 3}{9 - a^2}$.

Plan

The numerator, $a - 3$, is already in convenient form. The denominator, $9 - a^2$, is not. Rewrite the denominator in convenient form.

$$9 - a^2 = -1a^2 + 9 = -1(a^2 - 9)$$

Solution

$$\frac{a - 3}{9 - a^2} = \frac{a - 3}{-1(a^2 - 9)}$$

$$= \frac{a - 3}{-1(a + 3)(a - 3)} = \frac{\overset{1}{\cancel{(a - 3)}}}{-1(a + 3)\underset{1}{\cancel{(a - 3)}}} = \frac{1}{-(a + 3)}$$

TRY THIS

1. Simplify $\dfrac{c^2 - 36}{-c - 6}$.

The following expressions are equivalent.

$$-\frac{x}{y} \qquad \frac{-x}{y} \qquad \frac{x}{-y}$$

Thus, $\dfrac{1}{-(a + 3)}$ in Example 1 can also be written as $-\dfrac{1}{a + 3}$, or as $\dfrac{-1}{a + 3}$. Although any one of the three forms, $-\dfrac{x}{y}, \dfrac{-x}{y}, \dfrac{x}{-y}$ is acceptable, the form $-\dfrac{x}{y}$ is used most frequently.

EXAMPLE 2   Simplify $\dfrac{14 + a - 3a^2}{-3a + 2 - 2a^2}$.

Plan   Rewrite the numerator and denominator in convenient form.

Solution

$$\dfrac{14 + a - 3a^2}{-3a + 2 - 2a^2} = \dfrac{-3a^2 + a + 14}{-2a^2 - 3a + 2}$$

$$= \dfrac{-1(3a^2 - a - 14)}{-1(2a^2 + 3a - 2)}$$

$$= \dfrac{\overset{1}{-\cancel{1}}(3a - 7)\overset{1}{\cancel{(a + 2)}}}{\underset{1}{-\cancel{1}}(2a - 1)\underset{1}{\cancel{(a + 2)}}} = \dfrac{3a - 7}{2a - 1}$$

TRY THIS   2. Simplify $\dfrac{25 + 4x^2 - 20x}{15 - x - 2x^2}$.

Focus on Reading

Determine which polynomials are in convenient form. Explain.

1. $3x^2 - 5x + 2$
2. $-4x^2 - 3x + 1$
3. $-1(x^2 - 7x - 12)$
4. List the steps for putting $-4 + 5x - x^2$ in convenient form.
5. List two other forms for expressing $-\dfrac{x + 5}{2x - 7}$.

Classroom Exercises

Give each expression in convenient form.

1. $-5x - 2$
2. $-x^2 + 9$
3. $25 - m^2$
4. $-2x^2 + 8x$
5. $-x^2 + 4x + 12$
6. $42 + y - y^2$
7. $-c^2 + 8c + 20$
8. $6 - x - 2x^2$

Simplify.

9. $\dfrac{9 - x}{3x - 27}$
10. $\dfrac{a - 2}{6 - 3a}$
11. $\dfrac{a - 4}{16 - a^2}$
12. $\dfrac{x^2 - 5x + 6}{3 - x}$

Written Exercises

Simplify.

1. $\dfrac{x-5}{25-x^2}$

2. $\dfrac{8-b}{3b-24}$

3. $\dfrac{a+6}{36-a^2}$

4. $\dfrac{a-1}{1-a^2}$

5. $\dfrac{x^2-7x+10}{5-x}$

6. $\dfrac{18-3x}{x^2-36}$

7. $\dfrac{x^2-x-2}{2-x}$

8. $\dfrac{x^2-3x}{9-x^2}$

9. $\dfrac{x-4}{12+x-x^2}$

10. $\dfrac{8-x}{x^2-6x-16}$

11. $\dfrac{2-c}{c^2-11c+18}$

12. $\dfrac{5-2b}{2b^2-b-10}$

13. $\dfrac{12-x-x^2}{2x^2+5x-12}$

14. $\dfrac{2a^2-5a-3}{4+7a-2a^2}$

15. $\dfrac{p^2-8p-20}{-p^2+12p-20}$

16. $\dfrac{16-y^2}{y^2-5y+4}$

17. $\dfrac{-2b^2-b+6}{b^2-2b-8}$

18. $\dfrac{4k-12}{-9+6k-k^2}$

19. $\dfrac{x^2+x-30}{36-x^2}$

20. $\dfrac{13x-15-2x^2}{2x^2-x-3}$

21. $\dfrac{2m^2+8m-64}{28-3m-m^2}$

22. $\dfrac{42+a-a^2}{2a^2+10a-12}$

23. $\dfrac{3x^2-3x-60}{96-6x^2}$

24. $\dfrac{3x^3-12x^2+9x}{18x-6x^2}$

25. $\dfrac{m^8p^6(y^2+9y+20)}{m^{11}p^5(-4-y)}$

26. $\dfrac{18x-6x^2}{2x^4+x^3-15x^2}$

27. $\dfrac{14-17s-6s^2}{3s^3-20s^2+12s}$

28. $\dfrac{-x^3-2x^2+15x}{x^4+2x^3-15x^2}$

29. $\dfrac{6a^3+10a^2}{100a-36a^3}$

30. $\dfrac{a^3+6a^2-4a-24}{-a^3+2a^2+36a-72}$

31. $\dfrac{x^2-6x+9-4y^2}{2y+3-x}$

32. $\dfrac{2-(x+y)-(x+y)^2}{x+y+2}$

Mixed Review

Solve each equation or inequality.   3.2, 3.4, 3.5, 4.5, 5.6, 5.7

1. $15-(7-x)=10$

2. $-7x-2(3-4x)=-15$

3. $7y-12=3y+4$

4. $-6a+15=12-9a$

5. $\frac{3}{4}a=\frac{5}{2}$

6. $\frac{2}{3}x-\frac{1}{3}=\frac{1}{4}x+\frac{1}{5}$

7. $|3x-4|=12$

8. $|5x+4|\le 7$

9. $|x+8|>16$

10. $|x+8|<16$

8.3 Multiplying Rational Expressions

Objective	To multiply rational expressions

Multiplying rational expressions is similar to multiplying fractions.

$$\frac{2}{3} \cdot \frac{4}{5} = \frac{2 \cdot 4}{3 \cdot 5} = \frac{8}{15} \qquad \frac{2}{x} \cdot \frac{y}{5} = \frac{2 \cdot y}{x \cdot 5} = \frac{2y}{5x}$$

Rule for Multiplying Rational Expressions

If $\frac{a}{b}$ and $\frac{c}{d}$ are rational expressions, $b \neq 0$ and $d \neq 0$, then

$$\frac{a}{b} \cdot \frac{c}{d} = \frac{a \cdot c}{b \cdot d}.$$

EXAMPLE 1   Multiply $\frac{3}{10} \cdot \frac{15x}{9}$.

Plan   Write the numerator and denominator of the product in factored form. Then use the Cancellation Property of Fractions.

Solution   Use the Rule for Multiplying Rational Expressions.

$$\frac{3}{10} \cdot \frac{15x}{9} = \frac{3 \cdot 15x}{10 \cdot 9}$$

Factor the numerator and the denominator.

$$= \frac{3 \cdot 3 \cdot 5 \cdot x}{2 \cdot 5 \cdot 3 \cdot 3}$$

Use the Cancellation Property of Fractions (Lesson 6.3).

$$= \frac{\overset{1}{\cancel{3}} \cdot \overset{1}{\cancel{3}} \cdot \overset{1}{\cancel{5}} \cdot x}{2 \cdot \underset{1}{\cancel{5}} \cdot \underset{1}{\cancel{3}} \cdot \underset{1}{\cancel{3}}}$$

$$= \frac{x}{2}$$

TRY THIS   1. Multiply $\frac{6}{10x} \cdot \frac{5}{2}$.

The Cancellation Property can be used *before* multiplying.

$$\frac{3}{10} \cdot \frac{15x}{9} = \frac{3}{2 \cdot 5} \cdot \frac{3 \cdot 5 \cdot x}{3 \cdot 3}$$

$$= \frac{\overset{1}{\cancel{3}}}{2 \cdot \underset{1}{\cancel{5}}} \cdot \frac{\overset{1}{\cancel{3}} \cdot \overset{1}{\cancel{5}} \cdot x}{\underset{1}{\cancel{3}} \cdot \underset{1}{\cancel{3}}}$$

$$= \frac{1}{2} \cdot \frac{x}{1} = \frac{1 \cdot x}{2 \cdot 1} = \frac{x}{2}$$

The same procedure can be used to multiply all rational expressions.

EXAMPLE 2 Multiply.

a. $\dfrac{6x^4}{5y^7} \cdot \dfrac{3y^5}{8x}$ b. $\dfrac{a + 5}{6a + 24} \cdot \dfrac{4a + 16}{a + 3}$

Plan   Factor numerators and denominators. Divide out the common factors. Then multiply.

Solutions

a. $\dfrac{6x^4}{5y^7} \cdot \dfrac{3y^5}{8x}$

$= \dfrac{\overset{1}{\cancel{2}} \cdot 3 \cdot \overset{x^3}{\cancel{x^4}}}{5 \cdot \underset{y^2}{\cancel{y^7}}} \cdot \dfrac{3\overset{1}{\cancel{y^5}}}{\underset{1}{\cancel{2}} \cdot 2 \cdot 2 \cdot \underset{1}{\cancel{x}}}$

$= \dfrac{3x^3 \cdot 3}{5y^2 \cdot 4}$

$= \dfrac{9x^3}{20y^2}$

b. $\dfrac{a + 5}{6a + 24} \cdot \dfrac{4a + 16}{a + 3}$

$= \dfrac{a + 5}{6(a + 4)} \cdot \dfrac{4(a + 4)}{a + 3}$

$= \dfrac{(a + 5)}{\underset{3}{\cancel{6}}\underset{}{\cancel{(a + 4)}}} \cdot \dfrac{\overset{2}{\cancel{4}}\overset{1}{\cancel{(a + 4)}}}{a + 3}$

$= \dfrac{(a + 5) \cdot 2}{3 \cdot (a + 3)}$

$= \dfrac{2(a + 5)}{3(a + 3)}, \text{ or } \dfrac{2a + 10}{3a + 9}$

EXAMPLE 3 Multiply $\dfrac{x^2 + 13x + 42}{x^2 - 3x - 40} \cdot \dfrac{x - 8}{x + 6}$.

Plan   Factor numerators and denominators. Divide out the common factors. Then multiply.

Solution $\dfrac{(x + 7)(x + 6)}{(x - 8)(x + 5)} \cdot \dfrac{x - 8}{x + 6}$

$= \dfrac{(x + 7)\overset{1}{\cancel{(x + 6)}}}{\underset{1}{\cancel{(x - 8)}}(x + 5)} \cdot \dfrac{\overset{1}{\cancel{x - 8}}}{\underset{1}{\cancel{x + 6}}}$

$= \dfrac{x + 7}{x + 5}$

TRY THIS   2. Multiply $\dfrac{a^2 - 81}{a^2 - 7a + 12} \cdot \dfrac{a - 4}{a - 9}$.

Sometimes the first step in multiplying rational expressions is to express one or more factors in convenient form.

EXAMPLE 4 Multiply $\dfrac{6a^2b^3}{10 - 2y} \cdot \dfrac{y^2 - y - 20}{4ab^8}$.

Plan First rewrite $10 - 2y$ in convenient form. Factor out -2 rather than -1: $10 - 2y = -2y + 10 = -2(y - 5)$.

Solution
$$\dfrac{6a^2b^3}{10 - 2y} \cdot \dfrac{y^2 - y - 20}{4ab^8} = \dfrac{6a^2b^3}{-2(y - 5)} \cdot \dfrac{(y + 4)(y - 5)}{4ab^8}$$

$$= \dfrac{\overset{3a}{\cancel{6a^2b^3}}}{\underset{1}{-2\cancel{(y - 5)}}} \cdot \dfrac{(y + 4)\cancel{(y - 5)}^{1}}{\underset{2b^5}{\cancel{4ab^8}}}$$

$$= \dfrac{3a(y + 4)}{-4b^5}, \text{ or } -\dfrac{3a(y + 4)}{4b^5}$$

TRY THIS 3. Multiply $\dfrac{9xy^4}{y^2 - 2y - 24} \cdot \dfrac{6 - y}{12x^4y^2}$.

Rational expressions can be used to solve problems.

EXAMPLE 5 Find the area of the rectangle shown at the right.

Use the formula for the area of a rectangle, $A = lw$, where l is the length and w is the width.

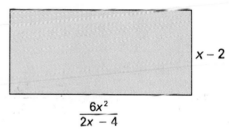

$x - 2$

$\dfrac{6x^2}{2x - 4}$

Plan Substitute the given dimension into the area formula. For convenience, write $x - 2$ as $\dfrac{x - 2}{1}$.

Solution
$A = lw$

$A = \dfrac{6x^2}{2x - 4} \cdot (x - 2)$

$A = \dfrac{6x^2}{2(x - 2)} \cdot \dfrac{x - 2}{1}$

$A = \dfrac{\overset{3}{\cancel{6x^2}}}{\underset{1}{2\cancel{(x - 2)}}} \cdot \dfrac{\cancel{x - 2}^{1}}{1} = 3x^2$ Thus, the area can be represented as $3x^2$.

TRY THIS 4. Find the area of the rectangle with length $\dfrac{9x - 6}{7x^3}$ and width $\dfrac{1}{3x - 2}$.

Classroom Exercises

Multiply.

1. $\dfrac{2}{3} \cdot \dfrac{5}{7}$

2. $\dfrac{8}{15} \cdot \dfrac{5}{12}$

3. $\dfrac{y}{9} \cdot \dfrac{7}{x}$

4. $\dfrac{x^3}{2} \cdot \dfrac{2}{x^5}$

5. $\dfrac{3}{y^4} \cdot \dfrac{y^5}{6}$

6. $\dfrac{a^3}{10} \cdot \dfrac{5}{a^2}$

7. $\dfrac{3x^7}{4y^5} \cdot \dfrac{2y^6}{3x^8}$

8. $\dfrac{5a^3}{b^7} \cdot \dfrac{b^9}{15a}$

9. $\dfrac{x-3}{4(x+2)} \cdot \dfrac{8(x+2)}{x-1}$

10. $\dfrac{12(a-2)}{a-3} \cdot \dfrac{a-3}{6(a+5)}$

11. $\dfrac{a^3(x+1)}{x-4} \cdot \dfrac{x-4}{a^5}$

12. $\dfrac{3a+6}{a^2-4a+3} \cdot \dfrac{3-a}{a+2}$

Written Exercises

Multiply.

1. $\dfrac{9}{11} \cdot \dfrac{5}{8}$

2. $\dfrac{3}{14} \cdot \dfrac{35}{33}$

3. $\dfrac{6a}{5} \cdot \dfrac{a^2}{7}$

4. $\dfrac{3x^3}{14y^2} \cdot \dfrac{7y}{15x}$

5. $\dfrac{-4a^5}{9b^2} \cdot \dfrac{12b^5}{22a^6}$

6. $\dfrac{6m}{15n^4} \cdot \dfrac{30n^8}{9m^7}$

7. $\dfrac{a-3}{2} \cdot \dfrac{2a+10}{6}$

8. $\dfrac{p+1}{5} \cdot \dfrac{3}{-2p-2}$

9. $\dfrac{3x-12}{5y^2z} \cdot \dfrac{25yz^2}{x-4}$

10. $\dfrac{y+1}{21} \cdot \dfrac{14}{y+1}$

11. $\dfrac{-5x}{7x-14} \cdot \dfrac{3x-6}{15}$

12. $\dfrac{x-1}{5} \cdot \dfrac{x-1}{2}$

13. $\dfrac{-3a^2b}{c} \cdot \dfrac{1-c}{c-1}$

14. $\dfrac{x-7}{x+4} \cdot (x-7)$

15. $(y+5) \cdot \dfrac{y-5}{55+11y}$

16. $\dfrac{-(2p+3q)}{8} \cdot \dfrac{6}{-2p+3q}$

17. $\dfrac{35}{6y+8z} \cdot \dfrac{9y+12z}{7}$

18. $\dfrac{-a-b}{3x-1} \cdot \dfrac{12-36x}{9a+9b}$

19. $\dfrac{x^2+7x+12}{x+5} \cdot \dfrac{5x+25}{x+4}$

20. $\dfrac{a-7}{a-6} \cdot \dfrac{a^2-5a-6}{3a-21}$

21. $\dfrac{5y+30}{y^2-2y-3} \cdot \dfrac{y-3}{y+6}$

22. $(x+4) \cdot \dfrac{2x+2}{4x^2+8x-32}$

23. $\dfrac{4a-24}{4a^2+18a-10} \cdot (2a-1)$

24. $(3m-6) \cdot \dfrac{2m+4}{9m^2-36}$

25. $\dfrac{4a^3b^5}{x^2-9} \cdot \dfrac{6-2x}{6a^4b^2}$

26. $\dfrac{x^2-5x+4}{10p^3q^2} \cdot \dfrac{15p^6q}{2x-2}$

27. $\dfrac{5-5x}{10b^2c} \cdot \dfrac{5b^6c}{x^2-1}$

28. $\dfrac{24x^4y^3}{4m-12} \cdot \dfrac{9-m^2}{18x^7y^4}$

29. $\dfrac{y^2-y-30}{9ab^8} \cdot \dfrac{3ab^7}{18-3y}$

30. $\dfrac{15a^5b}{7-x} \cdot \dfrac{3x-21}{30a^2b^6}$

31. $\dfrac{2x^2-13x+20}{3x^2-10x-8} \cdot \dfrac{-3-x}{2x^2+x-15}$

32. $\dfrac{3x^2+20xy-7y^2}{x^2+5xy-14y^2} \cdot \dfrac{6y^2-xy-x^2}{3x^2+3xy-y^2}$

33. $\dfrac{x^2 - y^2}{3x^2 - 21xy + 30y^2} \cdot \dfrac{75y^2 - 3x^2}{x^2 - 2xy + y^2}$

34. $\dfrac{a^2 - ad - 6d^2}{2a^2 + 11ad + 5d^2} \cdot \dfrac{a^2 + 9ad + 20d^2}{a^2 + 6ad + 8d^2}$

35. $\dfrac{10 - 3x - x^2}{x - 5} \cdot \dfrac{4x - 8}{2x^2 - 8x + 8}$

36. $\dfrac{3t^3 - 14t^2 + 8t}{20 + 3t - 2t^2} \cdot \dfrac{16t^2 + 34t - 15}{24t^2 - 25t + 6}$

37. $\dfrac{3 - x}{x^2 - 2x - 15} \cdot \dfrac{x^2 - 4x - 5}{x^2 - x - 6}$

38. $\dfrac{2y^2 + 9y - 5}{2y^2 + 5y - 3} \cdot \dfrac{y^2 + y - 6}{y^2 + 7y + 10}$

39. $\dfrac{16 - x^2}{x^2 + 7x + 12} \cdot \dfrac{2x^2 + 3x - 9}{x^2 - 5x + 4}$

40. $\dfrac{2a^2 + 7a - 4}{a^3 - 16a} \cdot \dfrac{8 - 2a}{10a - 5}$

41. Use the formula $d = rt$ to find the distance traveled in t hours at a rate of r mi/h, given that $r = \dfrac{x - 5}{5}$ and $t = \dfrac{15}{13x - 65}$.

42. The formula for the volume of a rectangular solid is given by $V = lwh$, where l is the length, w is the width, and h is the height. Find the volume of the rectangular solid at the right. Give your answer in simplified form.

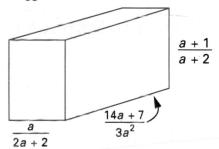

The formula for the volume of a cube is $V = e^3$, where e is the length of one edge of the cube. Find the volume for the given length of an edge. Give your answer in simplified form.

43. $e = \dfrac{2x - 1}{3}$

44. $e = \dfrac{a}{a + 1}$

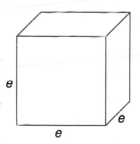

Mixed Review

Write an algebraic expression for each word description. *1.1*

1. 15 more than Myra's age m

2. 35 less than the cost c

3. the cost, in dollars, of m pounds of apples at $.74 per pound

4. $2\frac{1}{2}$ times the regular team score s

Translate each problem into an equation and solve. *4.2*

5. Raul has 18 tapes. He has 6 fewer tapes than twice the number Marcia has. Find the number of tapes Marcia has.

6. The selling price of a pair of skis is $250. The selling price is $20 less than twice the cost. Find the cost.

8.4 Dividing Rational Expressions

Objective

To divide rational expressions

You know that $\frac{2}{3} \div \frac{3}{5} = \frac{2}{3} \cdot \frac{5}{3}$. Since $\frac{5}{3}$ is the reciprocal of $\frac{3}{5}$, $\frac{2}{3} \div \frac{3}{5}$ equals $\frac{2}{3}$ times the reciprocal of $\frac{3}{5}$.

Dividing rational expressions is similar to dividing fractions. That is,

$$\frac{a}{b} \div \frac{c}{d} \text{ equals } \frac{a}{b} \text{ times the } \textit{reciprocal} \text{ of } \frac{c}{d}.$$

Rule for Dividing Rational Expressions

If $\frac{a}{b}$ and $\frac{c}{d}$ are rational expressions, $b \neq 0$, $c \neq 0$, and $d \neq 0$, then

$$\frac{a}{b} \div \frac{c}{d} = \frac{a}{b} \cdot \frac{d}{c}.$$

EXAMPLE 1

Divide: $\dfrac{12x^5}{15y^4} \div \dfrac{6x^2}{5y}$

Plan

Multiply $\dfrac{12x^5}{15y^4}$ by the reciprocal of $\dfrac{6x^2}{5y}$.

Solution

$$\frac{12x^5}{15y^4} \div \frac{6x^2}{5y} = \frac{12x^5}{15y^4} \cdot \frac{5y}{6x^2}$$

$$= \frac{\overset{2}{\cancel{12}}\overset{x^3}{\cancel{x^5}}}{\underset{3}{\cancel{15}}\underset{y^3}{\cancel{y^4}}} \cdot \frac{\overset{1}{\cancel{5}}\overset{1}{\cancel{y}}}{\underset{1}{\cancel{6}}\underset{1}{\cancel{x^2}}} = \frac{2x^3}{3y^3}$$

EXAMPLE 2

Divide: $\dfrac{6x + 24}{7x - 49} \div \dfrac{3x - 6}{x - 7}$

Solution

$$\frac{6x + 24}{7x - 49} \div \frac{3x - 6}{x - 7} = \frac{6x + 24}{7x - 49} \cdot \frac{x - 7}{3x - 6}$$

$$= \frac{\overset{2}{\cancel{6}}(x + 4)}{7\cancel{(x - 7)}} \cdot \frac{\cancel{x - 7}}{\cancel{3}(x - 2)} = \frac{2(x + 4)}{7(x - 2)}, \text{ or } \frac{2x + 8}{7x - 14}$$

TRY THIS

1. Divide: $\dfrac{16a - 32}{21a + 21} \div \dfrac{4a + 12}{7a + 7}$

Sometimes expressions contain both multiplication and division. If there are no parentheses, multiply or divide in order from left to right. Write the reciprocal of a rational expression only if it immediately follows a division symbol.

EXAMPLE 3 Simplify $\dfrac{x + 2}{x - 3} \cdot \dfrac{(x - 3)(x - 4)}{x} \div \dfrac{(x + 2)(x - 4)}{x^2}$.

Plan To divide by the third expression, multiply by its reciprocal.

Solution
$$\frac{x + 2}{x - 3} \cdot \frac{(x - 3)(x - 4)}{x} \cdot \frac{x^2}{(x + 2)(x - 4)}$$

$$= \frac{\overset{1}{\cancel{x + 2}}}{\underset{1}{\cancel{x - 3}}} \cdot \frac{\overset{1}{\cancel{(x - 3)}}\overset{1}{\cancel{(x - 4)}}}{\underset{}{\cancel{x}}} \cdot \frac{x^2}{\underset{1}{\cancel{(x + 2)}}\underset{1}{\cancel{(x - 4)}}} = x$$

EXAMPLE 4 Simplify $\dfrac{x^2 + 3x - 10}{8x^4} \div \dfrac{x^2 - 8x + 12}{12x^3} \cdot \dfrac{x - 6}{3x^2 + 15x}$.

Plan To divide by the second expression, multiply by its reciprocal.

Solution
$$\frac{x^2 + 3x - 10}{8x^4} \cdot \frac{12x^3}{x^2 - 8x + 12} \cdot \frac{x - 6}{3x^2 + 15x}$$

$$= \frac{\cancel{(x + 5)}\cancel{(x - 2)}}{\underset{2x^2}{\cancel{8x^4}}} \cdot \frac{\overset{}{\cancel{12x^3}}}{\underset{1}{\cancel{(x - 6)}}\underset{1}{\cancel{(x - 2)}}} \cdot \frac{\overset{}{\cancel{x - 6}}}{\underset{1}{\cancel{3x}}\underset{1}{\cancel{(x + 5)}}} = \frac{1}{2x^2}$$

TRY THIS 2. Simplify $\dfrac{x^2 + 12x + 27}{4x^3 - 28x^2} \div \dfrac{x + 3}{x^2 - 13x + 42} \cdot \dfrac{24x^6}{x^2 + 3x - 54}$.

Classroom Exercises

Give the reciprocal.

1. 9

2. $\dfrac{1}{a - 3}$

3. $x + 11$

4. $\dfrac{4b^3}{b^2 - 7b + 6}$

Divide.

5. $\dfrac{3}{8} \div \dfrac{4}{5}$

6. $\dfrac{5}{6} \div \dfrac{7}{8}$

7. $\dfrac{1}{3} \div \dfrac{5}{6}$

8. $\dfrac{-8}{9} \div \dfrac{2}{3}$

9. $\dfrac{3}{8} \div 3$

10. $\dfrac{a}{b} \div \dfrac{3a^2}{4}$

11. $\dfrac{x^2}{3y} \div \dfrac{6x}{4y^3}$

12. $\dfrac{a + b}{2} \div \dfrac{a - b}{4}$

13. $\dfrac{x^2 - 1}{y + 2} \div \dfrac{(x - 1)^2}{y - 2}$

14. $\dfrac{a^2 - 49}{5a^7b^6} \div \dfrac{a^2 + 4a - 21}{15ab^2}$

Written Exercises

Divide.

1. $\dfrac{7}{9} \div \dfrac{2}{5}$

2. $\dfrac{6}{11} \div \dfrac{-8}{9}$

3. $\dfrac{9x}{14} \div \dfrac{7x^2}{2}$

4. $\dfrac{m^2}{p^2} \div \dfrac{p^4}{m^4}$

5. $\dfrac{3ab^2}{-4st} \div \dfrac{6b^3t}{5a}$

6. $\dfrac{(-x)^4}{y^3} \div \dfrac{-x^4}{y}$

7. $\dfrac{y}{3x} \div \dfrac{2y^2}{9}$

8. $\dfrac{2m}{m+2} \div (m+2)$

9. $\dfrac{n^2}{n+1} \div (n-1)$

10. $\dfrac{x-7}{3} \div \dfrac{x+7}{6}$

11. $\dfrac{a+1}{a} \div \dfrac{-3a-3}{ab}$

12. $\dfrac{5x+10}{x} \div \dfrac{x+2}{y}$

13. $\dfrac{a^2-2a-8}{a^2-16} \div \dfrac{4a+12}{a+4}$

14. $\dfrac{3a+21}{16} \div \dfrac{a^2-49}{4a-8}$

15. $\dfrac{x^2-16}{y-2} \div \dfrac{2x+8}{7y-14}$

16. $\dfrac{x^2+3x-18}{m^5} \div \dfrac{2x+12}{m^8}$

17. $\dfrac{4x^5}{x-7} \div \dfrac{16x^7}{3x^2-21x}$

18. $\dfrac{3x+21}{7x^5} \div \dfrac{3x^2+21x}{14x^2}$

19. $\dfrac{18a^5b^4}{5a-10a^2} \div \dfrac{24a^4b^6}{6a-3}$

20. $\dfrac{36-x^2}{3x^4y^3} \div \dfrac{4x-24}{15x^5y}$

21. $\dfrac{15-5m}{6m^3n^3} \div \dfrac{m^2-9}{14m^4n^2}$

22. $\dfrac{x^2-10x+25}{x+1} \div \dfrac{2x^2-10x}{x^2+x}$

23. $\dfrac{x^2-16}{6x} \div \dfrac{5x-20}{3x^2-15x}$

24. $\dfrac{x^2+2x-15}{x+3} \div \dfrac{x^2+7x+10}{x-2}$

25. $\dfrac{x-5}{x^2+3x-10} \div \dfrac{9x^2}{3x^2-6x}$

26. $\dfrac{x^2+10x+24}{3x^2+12x} \div (x^2+3x-18)$

27. $\dfrac{x^2-2x-15}{5x^2+15x} \div (x^2-6x+5)$

28. $\dfrac{x^2-y^2}{6x} \div \dfrac{x^2y+xy^2}{3x^2y^2}$

29. $\dfrac{4x^2-25y^2}{2x^2y+5xy^2} \div \dfrac{6x^2-15xy}{9x^2y^2}$

30. $\dfrac{3(x+y)^2}{x-y} \div 6(x+y)$

31. $\dfrac{x-y}{x+y} \div \dfrac{5x^2-5y^2}{3x-3y}$

32. $\dfrac{x^2+2x+1}{3x} \div (x+1)$

33. $\dfrac{a^3-6a^2+8a}{5} \div \dfrac{2a-4}{10a-40}$

34. $\dfrac{5x^2y^3}{2x+6} \cdot \dfrac{x^2-16}{20x^7y} \div \dfrac{x+4}{x^2-2x-15}$

35. $\dfrac{k^2+8k+15}{12k^2} \cdot \dfrac{9k^3}{k+2} \div \dfrac{4k+12}{k^2+2k}$

36. $\dfrac{a^2-2a-15}{a^7b^2} \div \dfrac{a^2-25}{16a^7b^3} \cdot \dfrac{4a-24}{3a+9}$

37. $\dfrac{b^2-3b}{b^6} \div \dfrac{b^2+b-12}{b^7} \cdot \dfrac{6b^2+24b}{4b^2}$

38. $\dfrac{a^2 + 4a - 21}{a^2 + a - 20} \div \dfrac{a^2 + 8a + 7}{a^2 + 6a + 5}$

39. $\dfrac{2x^3 + 6x^2 - 20x}{15 - 2x - x^2} \div \dfrac{4x^2 + 24x - 64}{6x^2 - 54}$

40. $\dfrac{2x^2 + 5x + 3}{x^2 + 9x + 14} \div \dfrac{2x^2 - 3x - 9}{x^2 + 6x - 7}$

41. $\dfrac{3a^2 - a - 2}{a^2 - 3a} \div \dfrac{3a^2 + 11a + 6}{a^3}$

42. $\dfrac{9y^2 - b^2}{15y^2 + 6by} \div \dfrac{3y^2 + 2by - b^2}{25y^2 - 4b^2}$

43. $\dfrac{6a^2 + 11ab - 10b^2}{a^8} \div \dfrac{2a^2 + 11ab + 15b^2}{a^5 + 3a^4b}$

44. $\dfrac{xy - xz - x^2}{xyz} \cdot \dfrac{x^2y^2z^3}{yx - zx} \div x^3$

45. $\dfrac{2a^3}{2a + b} \div \dfrac{10a^2}{4a^2 + 4ab + b^2} \cdot \dfrac{12a + 3b}{2a^2 + ab}$

46. $\dfrac{a^2 - 5a + 6}{a^2 + 3a} \cdot \dfrac{a^2 + 2a - 3}{a^2 + 4a + 3} \div \dfrac{2a^2 - 3a - 2}{2a^2 + a - 1}$

47. $\dfrac{x^2 - 2x - 8}{x^3 - 9x} \div \dfrac{x^2 - 16}{x^2 + 3x} \cdot \dfrac{2x^2 - 7x - 4}{2x^2 + 5x + 2}$

A formula for the height of a rectangular solid is $h = \dfrac{V}{B}$, where V is the volume of the solid and B is the area of its rectangular base. Find an expression for the height of the rectangular solid.

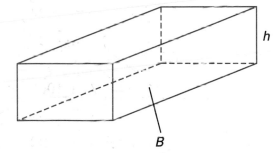

48. volume: $8x^3 + 8x^2$
area of base: $8x^2$

49. volume: $9x^3 + 45x^2 + 54x$
area of base: $9x^2 + 18x$

50. volume: $21x^2y + 105xy$
width of base: $7x$
length of base: $3y$

51. volume: $5x^2 + 5xy + 20x^2 + 20x$
width of base: $5x$
length of base: $x + 1$

Mixed Review

Solve each equation or inequality. *5.2, 5.7, 7.8*

1. $x^2 + x - 12 = 0$

2. $x^2 + 2x - 15 = 0$

3. $a^2 + 6a - 7 = 0$

4. $x^2 - 25 = 0$

5. $a^2 - 7a - 8 = 0$

6. $x^2 - 5x = 0$

7. $-6x + 8 \geq 20$

8. $15 - 3y < 45$

9. $|x - 1| \leq 3$

8.5 Adding and Subtracting Rational Expressions: Like Denominators

Objective

To add and subtract rational expressions with like denominators

One pizza weighs m ounces and another weighs n ounces. Each of the 2 pizzas will be divided evenly among 8 people. How much pizza will each person get? Each person will get $\frac{1}{8}$ of each pizza.

In all, the fraction of both pizzas received by each person is $\frac{m}{8} + \frac{n}{8}$. How can this be expressed as a single rational expression?

To answer this question, recall that two fractions are added or subtracted in the manner shown below.

$$\frac{4}{7} + \frac{2}{7} = \frac{4 + 2}{7} = \frac{6}{7} \qquad\qquad \frac{5}{7} - \frac{2}{7} = \frac{5 - 2}{7} = \frac{3}{7}$$

This suggests that an expression for each person's share of the pizzas is $\frac{m + n}{8}$ ounces.

Rule for Adding and Subtracting Rational Expressions

If $\frac{a}{b}$ and $\frac{c}{b}$ are rational expressions, $b \neq 0$, then

$$\frac{a}{b} + \frac{c}{b} = \frac{a + c}{b} \text{ and } \frac{a}{b} - \frac{c}{b} = \frac{a - c}{b}.$$

EXAMPLE 1   Add or subtract.

   a. $\dfrac{7x}{4} + \dfrac{6x}{4}$ 　　　　 b. $\dfrac{5}{y} + \dfrac{6}{y}$ 　　　　 c. $\dfrac{4x}{x - 3} - \dfrac{3x}{x - 3}$

Plan   Use $\dfrac{a}{b} + \dfrac{c}{b} = \dfrac{a + c}{b}$ or $\dfrac{a}{b} - \dfrac{c}{b} = \dfrac{a - c}{b}$.

Solutions

a. $\dfrac{7x}{4} + \dfrac{6x}{4}$
$= \dfrac{7x + 6x}{4} = \dfrac{13x}{4}$

b. $\dfrac{5}{y} + \dfrac{6}{y}$
$= \dfrac{5 + 6}{y} = \dfrac{11}{y}$

c. $\dfrac{4x}{x - 3} - \dfrac{3x}{x - 3}$
$= \dfrac{4x - 3x}{x - 3} = \dfrac{x}{x - 3}$

TRY THIS   1. Subtract $\dfrac{7x}{2x + 3} - \dfrac{5x}{2x + 3}$.

The Rule for Adding Fractions can be extended to include three or more addends as illustrated in the next example.

EXAMPLE 2 Add or subtract.

a. $\dfrac{7a}{3} + \dfrac{4a}{3} + \dfrac{10a}{3}$

b. $\dfrac{3x}{2x-10} - \dfrac{9}{2x-10} + \dfrac{4-2x}{2x-10}$

Solutions

a. $\dfrac{7a}{3} + \dfrac{4a}{3} + \dfrac{10a}{3}$

$= \dfrac{7a + 4a + 10a}{3}$

$= \dfrac{\overset{7a}{\cancel{21a}}}{\underset{1}{\cancel{3}}}$

$= 7a$

b. $\dfrac{3x}{2x-10} - \dfrac{9}{2x-10} + \dfrac{4-2x}{2x-10}$

$= \dfrac{3x - 9 + (4-2x)}{2x-10}$

$= \dfrac{3x - 9 + 4 - 2x}{2x - 10}$

$= \dfrac{\overset{1}{\cancel{x-5}}}{2\underset{1}{(\cancel{x-5})}} = \dfrac{1}{2}$

EXAMPLE 3 Add $\dfrac{x^2}{x^2 - 7x + 12} + \dfrac{18 - 3x}{-x^2 + 7x - 12}$.

Plan Write $-x^2 + 7x - 12$ in convenient form: $-1(x^2 - 7x + 12)$.

Solution

$\dfrac{x^2}{x^2 - 7x + 12} + \dfrac{18 - 3x}{-1(x^2 - 7x + 12)}$

$= \dfrac{x^2}{x^2 - 7x + 12} - \dfrac{18 - 3x}{x^2 - 7x + 12} \quad \longleftarrow \dfrac{a}{-b} = -\dfrac{a}{b}$

$= \dfrac{x^2 - (18 - 3x)}{x^2 - 7x + 12}$

$= \dfrac{x^2 - 18 + 3x}{x^2 - 7x + 12}$

$= \dfrac{x^2 + 3x - 18}{x^2 - 7x + 12}$

$= \dfrac{(x + 6)\overset{1}{\cancel{(x-3)}}}{\underset{1}{\cancel{(x-3)}}(x - 4)} = \dfrac{x + 6}{x - 4}$

TRY THIS

2. Subtract $\dfrac{-x^2}{-x^2 + x + 56} - \dfrac{17x - 72}{x^2 - x - 56}$.

3. Add $\dfrac{x}{x^2 + 2x} + \dfrac{2}{x^2 + 2x}$.

EXAMPLE 4 Find the perimeter of the rectangle at the right.

Plan Add the lengths of the four sides.

Solution

$$\frac{3x + 6}{3} + \frac{3x + 6}{3} + \frac{2x}{3} + \frac{2x}{3}$$

$$= \frac{(3x + 6) + (3x + 6) + 2x + 2x}{3}$$

$$= \frac{3x + 6 + 3x + 6 + 2x + 2x}{3}$$

$$= \frac{10x + 12}{3} \longleftarrow \text{simplified form}$$

Thus, a rational expression for the perimeter is $\frac{10x + 12}{3}$.

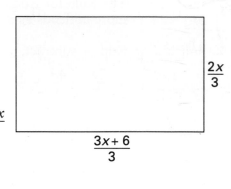

$\frac{2x}{3}$

$\frac{3x + 6}{3}$

TRY THIS 4. Find the perimeter of a rectangle with length $\frac{4y + 2}{9}$ and width $\frac{5y}{9}$.

Classroom Exercises

Add or subtract.

1. $\frac{2}{7} + \frac{3}{7}$

2. $\frac{7}{10} - \frac{3}{10}$

3. $\frac{5y}{8} + \frac{y}{8}$

4. $\frac{14}{15a} - \frac{4}{15a}$

5. $\frac{-3}{5y} + \frac{2}{5y}$

6. $\frac{6}{11m} + \frac{1}{-11m}$

7. $\frac{1}{b - 1} - \frac{b}{b - 1}$

8. $\frac{a}{a + 1} - \frac{2}{1 + a}$

9. $\frac{x}{9} + \frac{2x}{9} + \frac{3x}{9}$

10. $\frac{m^2}{m - 1} - \frac{2m}{m - 1} - \frac{1}{1 - m}$

Written Exercises

Add or subtract.

1. $\frac{8a}{5} + \frac{3a}{5}$

2. $\frac{2x^2}{7} + \frac{4x^2}{7}$

3. $\frac{7x^3}{3} - \frac{x^3}{3}$

4. $\frac{b}{9} - \frac{10b}{9}$

5. $\frac{4}{x^2} - \frac{2}{x^2}$

6. $\frac{12}{a} + \frac{5}{a}$

7. $\frac{9}{2x} + \frac{3}{2x}$

8. $\frac{10}{3b} - \frac{8}{3b}$

9. $\frac{6}{x - 1} - \frac{-5}{x - 1}$

10. $\frac{7}{2 - y} + \frac{5}{2 - y}$

11. $\frac{a}{a - 4} + \frac{4}{4 - a}$

12. $\frac{t}{t + 1} - \frac{1}{1 + t}$

13. $\frac{x + 3}{4} + \frac{x - 1}{4}$

14. $\frac{2y}{3} - \frac{y - 1}{3}$

15. $\frac{a + 9}{a} + \frac{8}{a}$

16. $\frac{3n}{2p} - \frac{n + 2}{2p}$

17. $\dfrac{5b}{21} + \dfrac{2b}{21} + \dfrac{8b}{21}$

18. $\dfrac{2}{a} + \dfrac{3}{a} - \dfrac{4}{a}$

19. $\dfrac{5y}{2y - 3} - \dfrac{3y}{2y - 3}$

20. $\dfrac{6x}{x - 4} + \dfrac{2x}{4 - x}$

21. $\dfrac{3x}{4x - 20} - \dfrac{15}{4x - 20}$

22. $\dfrac{2a^2}{a - 1} + \dfrac{2}{1 - a}$

23. $\dfrac{x^2}{4x - 12} + \dfrac{9}{12 - 4x}$

24. $\dfrac{x - y}{x + y} + \dfrac{2x + y}{x + y}$

25. $\dfrac{3a}{a^2 + 6a} + \dfrac{18}{a^2 + 6a}$

26. $\dfrac{a}{a^2 - 9a + 18} - \dfrac{6}{a^2 - 9a + 18}$

27. $\dfrac{2a}{a^2 - 8a + 12} - \dfrac{4}{a^2 - 8a + 12}$

28. $\dfrac{3x}{x^2 - 25} - \dfrac{x}{x^2 - 25} + \dfrac{x + 15}{x^2 - 25}$

29. $\dfrac{x^2}{2x - 6} + \dfrac{5x}{2x - 6} - \dfrac{24}{2x - 6}$

30. $\dfrac{2x}{2x^2 - 3x - 20} + \dfrac{5}{2x^2 - 3x - 20}$

31. $\dfrac{3x}{3x^2 + 10x - 8} - \dfrac{2}{3x^2 + 10x - 8}$

32. $\dfrac{x^2}{x^2 - 7x + 10} - \dfrac{4x + 5}{x^2 - 7x + 10}$

33. $\dfrac{2x^2}{x^2 - 6x - 16} - \dfrac{6 - x}{x^2 - 6x - 16}$

34. $\dfrac{16y^2 - 7}{5y^2 + 26y - 24} - \dfrac{9y^2 - 9}{-5y^2 - 26y + 24}$

35. $\dfrac{2b^2}{3b - 6c} + \dfrac{7bc}{-3b + 6c} + \dfrac{6c^2}{3b - 6c}$

Find the perimeters of the figures shown.

36.

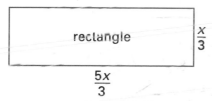

37.

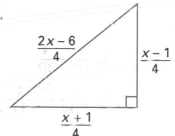

38.

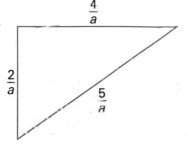

39.

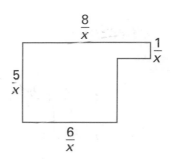

Add or subtract.

40. $\dfrac{7ax + 4a - 2b}{ay^2 - by^2 + 3ay - 3by + 2a - 2b} + \dfrac{-6ax - bx - 2b}{ay^2 - by^2 + 3ay - 3by + 2a - 2b}$

Add or subtract.

41. $\dfrac{x^2}{x - 6 - 2y} - \dfrac{12x - 36}{x - 6 - 2y} - \dfrac{4y^2}{x - 6 - 2y}$

42. $\dfrac{a^2x}{ax^2 - bx^2 + cx^2} - \dfrac{2abx - b^2x}{ax^2 - bx^2 + cx^2} - \dfrac{c^2x}{ax^2 - bx^2 + cx^2}$

Midchapter Review

For what values of the variable is the rational expression undefined?   *8.1*

1. $\dfrac{a - 5}{a - 3}$

2. $\dfrac{32}{3 - x}$

3. $\dfrac{m + 3}{m - 2}$

4. $\dfrac{t - 1}{t^2 - 2t - 15}$

5. $\dfrac{a + 1}{a^2 - 9}$

6. $\dfrac{4x - 8}{x^2 - 2x + 1}$

Simplify each rational expression, if possible.   *8.1, 8.2*

7. $\dfrac{36a^6b^4}{-14ab^6}$

8. $\dfrac{3p - 18}{2p - 12}$

9. $\dfrac{a^2 + 3a}{2a^2 + 7a + 3}$

10. $\dfrac{y - 3}{9 - y^2}$

11. $\dfrac{9 - a}{a^2 - 10a + 9}$

12. $\dfrac{x^2 + 7x + 10}{20 - 5x^2}$

Multiply.   *8.3*

13. $\dfrac{-15a^6}{9b^3} \cdot \dfrac{24b^6}{20a^7}$

14. $\dfrac{9y^2}{4 - 2y} \cdot \dfrac{5y - 10}{21y}$

Divide.   *8.4*

15. $\dfrac{-(x - 2)}{y} \div \dfrac{3x - 6}{y^2}$

16. $\dfrac{12 - 4m}{18x^5y^3} \div \dfrac{m^2 - 9}{20x^3y}$

Add or subtract.   *8.5*

17. $\dfrac{7a}{4} - \dfrac{3a}{4} + \dfrac{5a + 6}{4}$

18. $\dfrac{a^2}{3a + 12} - \dfrac{16}{3a + 12}$

8.6 Adding and Subtracting: Unlike Denominators

Objective

To add and subtract rational expressions with unlike monomial denominators

The fractions $\frac{10}{12}$ and $\frac{5}{6}$ are *equivalent*, that is, they have the same value.

$$\frac{10}{12} = \frac{5 \cdot 2}{6 \cdot 2} = \frac{5}{6}$$

The above steps can be reversed.

$$\frac{5}{6} = \frac{5 \cdot 2}{6 \cdot 2} = \frac{10}{12}$$

Notice that multiplying the numerator and denominator of $\frac{5}{6}$ by 2 does not change the value of the fraction $\frac{5}{6}$. This suggests the following alternate version of the *Cancellation Property*.

Multiplicative Identity Property for Rational Expressions

For all real numbers a, b, and c, if $b \neq 0$ and $c \neq 0$, then $\frac{a}{b} = \frac{a \cdot c}{b \cdot c}$.

The expression $\frac{5}{6} + \frac{1}{4}$ has unlike denominators. To write $\frac{5}{6} + \frac{1}{4}$ as a single fraction, begin by expressing it as a sum of two equivalent fractions with like denominators. Use the Multiplicative Identity Property.

$$\frac{5}{6} + \frac{1}{4} = \frac{5 \cdot 2}{6 \cdot 2} + \frac{1 \cdot 3}{4 \cdot 3} = \frac{10}{12} + \frac{3}{12} = \frac{10 + 3}{12} = \frac{13}{12}$$

In this example, the denominator 12 is the *least common multiple* of 6 and 4, which is also called the *least common denominator* (LCD) of the fractions.

The procedure for adding rational expressions with unlike denominators is the same as that just shown for fractions. Always begin by finding the LCD.

EXAMPLE 1

Add $\frac{3a}{20} + \frac{a}{6}$.

Plan

Factor the denominators into prime factors. Find the number of times each prime factor must occur.

Solution $20 = 2 \cdot 2 \cdot 5$ $6 = 2 \cdot 3$

The LCD will have each of 2, 3, and 5 as its prime factors at least once. Since one denominator, 20, has 2 as a factor *twice*, the LCD must also have 2 as a factor twice. The LCD is $2 \cdot 2 \cdot 3 \cdot 5$, or 60.

$$\frac{3a}{20} + \frac{a}{6} = \frac{3a}{2 \cdot 2 \cdot 5} + \frac{a}{2 \cdot 3}$$

needs 3   needs 2 and 5

$$= \frac{3a \cdot 3}{2 \cdot 2 \cdot 5 \cdot 3} + \frac{a \cdot 2 \cdot 5}{2 \cdot 3 \cdot 2 \cdot 5}$$

$$= \frac{9a}{60} + \frac{10a}{60}$$

$$= \frac{9a + 10a}{60} = \frac{19a}{60}$$

EXAMPLE 2   Subtract and add $\dfrac{1}{2x^3} - \dfrac{5}{6x} + \dfrac{2}{3x^2}$.

Solution   First, find the prime factors of each denominator.

$$2x^3 = 2 \cdot x \cdot x \cdot x \qquad 6x = 2 \cdot 3 \cdot x \qquad 3x^2 = 3 \cdot x \cdot x$$

There are at most three x's, one 3, and one 2 in any denominator. The LCD is $2 \cdot 3 \cdot x \cdot x \cdot x$, or $6x^3$.

$$\frac{1}{2x^3} - \frac{5}{6x} + \frac{2}{3x^2} = \frac{1}{2 \cdot x \cdot x \cdot x} - \frac{5}{2 \cdot 3 \cdot x} + \frac{2}{3 \cdot x \cdot x}$$

needs 3   needs $x \cdot x$ needs $2 \cdot x$

$$= \frac{1 \cdot 3}{2 \cdot x \cdot x \cdot x \cdot 3} - \frac{5 \cdot x \cdot x}{2 \cdot 3 \cdot x \cdot x \cdot x} + \frac{2 \cdot 2 \cdot x}{3 \cdot x \cdot x \cdot 2 \cdot x}$$

$$= \frac{3}{6x^3} - \frac{5x^2}{6x^3} + \frac{4x}{6x^3} = \frac{3 - 5x^2 + 4x}{6x^3}, \text{ or } -\frac{5x^2 - 4x - 3}{6x^3}$$

This result cannot be simplified further.

TRY THIS   1. Add and subtract $\dfrac{3}{4y^4} + \dfrac{5}{2y^2} - \dfrac{1}{8y}$.

The next example illustrates the process for adding or subtracting rational expressions that contain binomials in the numerators.

EXAMPLE 3   Subtract $\dfrac{5a + 4}{9a} - \dfrac{3a - 1}{12a}$.

Solution $9a = 3 \cdot 3 \cdot a$ $12a = 2 \cdot 2 \cdot 3 \cdot a$
The LCD is $2 \cdot 2 \cdot 3 \cdot 3 \cdot a$, or $36a$.

$$\dfrac{5a + 4}{9a} - \dfrac{3a - 1}{12a}$$

$$= \dfrac{(5a + 4) \cdot 2 \cdot 2}{3 \cdot 3 \cdot a \cdot 2 \cdot 2} - \dfrac{(3a - 1) \cdot 3}{2 \cdot 2 \cdot 3 \cdot a \cdot 3}$$

$$= \dfrac{20a + 16}{36a} - \dfrac{9a - 3}{36a}$$

$$= \dfrac{20a + 16 - (9a - 3)}{36a}$$

$$= \dfrac{20a + 16 - 9a + 3}{36a} = \dfrac{11a + 19}{36a}$$

The result cannot be simplified further.

TRY THIS   2. Subtract $\dfrac{2y - 1}{14y} - \dfrac{-3y - 2}{8y^2}$.

Focus on Reading

Suppose that two or more rational expressions are being added. Determine whether each statement is *always true*, *sometimes true*, or *never true*. Justify your answer.

1. The LCD is the product of the denominators.
2. The LCD is the sum of the denominators.
3. The factors of each denominator are also factors of the LCD.
4. The factors of the LCD are also factors of each denominator.

Classroom Exercises

Find the LCD of the fractions or rational expressions.

1. $\dfrac{5}{7} + \dfrac{3}{2 \cdot 5}$

2. $\dfrac{3}{2 \cdot 3 \cdot 5} - \dfrac{5}{2 \cdot 3 \cdot 3}$

3. $\dfrac{1}{3 \cdot 5 \cdot 5} + \dfrac{7}{2 \cdot 3 \cdot 5}$

4. $\dfrac{8m}{3 \cdot 5} + \dfrac{13m}{2 \cdot 3 \cdot 3 \cdot 5}$

5. $\dfrac{3x - 4}{2x^2} - \dfrac{4x - 1}{3x^3}$

6. $\dfrac{3q - 1}{2 \cdot 3 \cdot 3 \cdot 7} - \dfrac{5q + 2}{2 \cdot 2 \cdot 5}$

7. $\dfrac{3x + 2}{5} + \dfrac{2x - 1}{15}$

8. $\dfrac{2x - 1}{3a} + \dfrac{x}{6a} + \dfrac{x - 4}{2a}$

9. $\dfrac{3}{2a^2} - \dfrac{4}{a^3} + \dfrac{5}{7a}$

Add or subtract.

10. $\dfrac{3a}{15} + \dfrac{a}{3}$

11. $\dfrac{3k}{10} - \dfrac{2k}{5} + \dfrac{k}{2}$

12. $\dfrac{x}{12} - \dfrac{3x}{2} + \dfrac{x}{18}$

13. $\dfrac{2}{21x} + \dfrac{5}{7x} - \dfrac{1}{3x}$

14. $\dfrac{8}{9a} + \dfrac{7}{15a^2} + \dfrac{1}{a^3}$

15. $\dfrac{2x+1}{3} - \dfrac{x-1}{2}$

16. $\dfrac{1}{6a} - \dfrac{1}{4a} + \dfrac{1}{3a}$

17. $\dfrac{3}{b} + \dfrac{5}{2b} - \dfrac{11}{6b}$

18. $\dfrac{3x-5}{4} + \dfrac{5x-3}{3}$

Written Exercises

Add and subtract as indicated.

1. $\dfrac{5x}{14} + \dfrac{x}{7}$

2. $\dfrac{a}{2} - \dfrac{3a}{10}$

3. $\dfrac{2b}{9} + \dfrac{5b}{21}$

4. $\dfrac{3x}{5} - \dfrac{4x}{15}$

5. $\dfrac{5a}{8} + \dfrac{a}{6}$

6. $\dfrac{5b}{4} - \dfrac{3b}{10}$

7. $\dfrac{2k}{3} + \dfrac{5k}{6}$

8. $\dfrac{m}{5} + \dfrac{3m}{10} + \dfrac{m}{2}$

9. $\dfrac{x}{12} + \dfrac{x}{3} + \dfrac{5}{6}$

10. $\dfrac{5x}{12} + \dfrac{x}{4} - \dfrac{x}{6}$

11. $\dfrac{11}{14a} - \dfrac{3}{7a} + \dfrac{1}{2a}$

12. $\dfrac{1}{3x^2} - \dfrac{2}{15x^3} + \dfrac{2}{5x}$

13. $\dfrac{7}{4m^2} + \dfrac{2}{8m} + \dfrac{1}{2m^3}$

14. $\dfrac{6y}{5} + \dfrac{3y}{4} + \dfrac{y}{10}$

15. $\dfrac{7}{4x^3} - \dfrac{5}{6x} + \dfrac{1}{3x^2}$

16. $\dfrac{3}{5x^3} + \dfrac{7}{10x} - \dfrac{5}{2x^2}$

17. $\dfrac{2y+7}{4y} + \dfrac{2y-1}{3y}$

18. $\dfrac{2x-5}{5x} - \dfrac{x+2}{4x}$

19. $\dfrac{a+1}{3a} + \dfrac{2a+3}{6a}$

20. $\dfrac{3x-1}{4} - \dfrac{5x+1}{6}$

21. $\dfrac{b-2}{9} + \dfrac{2b-1}{4}$

22. $\dfrac{x+2}{3x} - \dfrac{x+4}{4x}$

23. $\dfrac{2x-3}{6} + \dfrac{2}{3} - \dfrac{4x+1}{2}$

24. $\dfrac{4y-3}{7} - \dfrac{2y+1}{14} + \dfrac{3y-4}{2}$

25. $\dfrac{2a-1}{3a} + \dfrac{5a+4}{2a} + \dfrac{a-7}{2a}$

26. $\dfrac{b+3}{8b} + \dfrac{4b-3}{4b} - \dfrac{b-3}{2b}$

27. $\dfrac{2k-1}{15} - \dfrac{3k}{5} + \dfrac{3k-1}{2}$

28. $\dfrac{7}{24b} + \dfrac{2b-3}{6b} + \dfrac{b+2}{4b}$

29. $\dfrac{7y-2}{6} - \dfrac{y}{5} + \dfrac{3y-2}{10}$

30. $\dfrac{2z-1}{9z} - \dfrac{3z+4}{3z} + \dfrac{3z-1}{4z}$

31. $\dfrac{5x-1}{6} + \dfrac{2x-1}{4} + \dfrac{4-x}{3}$

32. $\dfrac{2a-1}{5} - \dfrac{a+3}{3} + \dfrac{a+4}{10}$

33. Write in your own words how to find the LCD of two rational expressions.

34. Write in your own words how to add or subtract rational expressions with unlike denominators.

Find the perimeters of the figures shown.

35.

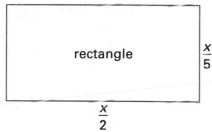

rectangle $\dfrac{x}{5}$

$\dfrac{x}{2}$

36.

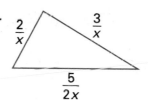

$\dfrac{2}{x}$ $\dfrac{3}{x}$

$\dfrac{5}{2x}$

37.

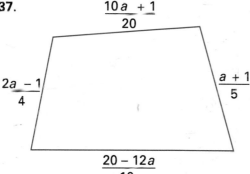

$\dfrac{10a+1}{20}$

$\dfrac{2a-1}{4}$

$\dfrac{a+1}{5}$

$\dfrac{20-12a}{10}$

38.

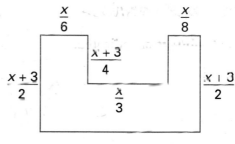

$\dfrac{x}{6}$ $\dfrac{x}{8}$

$\dfrac{x+3}{4}$

$\dfrac{x+3}{2}$ $\dfrac{x+3}{2}$

$\dfrac{x}{3}$

Simplify.

39. $\dfrac{x-y}{3xy} + \dfrac{2x+y}{4x} + \dfrac{3x+2y}{6y}$

40. $\dfrac{a+3}{4a} - \dfrac{a+2}{3a^2} + \dfrac{a-4}{12a^2}$

41. $\dfrac{3a^2-4a+6}{4a} + \dfrac{3a-1}{5a} + \dfrac{a^2}{10a}$

42. $\dfrac{y-x}{7y} + \dfrac{x^2+3xy+y^2}{14xy} + \dfrac{3x-y}{4x}$

43. $\left(\dfrac{5a}{6} - \dfrac{1}{3}\right) \div \dfrac{4-25a^2}{12}$

44. $\left(\dfrac{2}{b} - \dfrac{1}{a}\right) \cdot \dfrac{bax+bay}{2ax+2ay-bx-by}$

Mixed Review

Multiply. *6.9, 8.3*

1. $(3x-1)(2x+5)$

2. $(4y+3)(2y-1)$

3. $(a-5)(a+5)$

4. $(3m+4)(3m-4)$

5. $(2x-t)(3x+2t)$

6. $(3m+4p)(2m-p)$

7. $\dfrac{4a^7}{9b^3} \cdot \dfrac{-2a}{5b^2}$

8. $\dfrac{(-3a^2)^4}{5b^2} \cdot \dfrac{a^3}{-2b^4}$

9. $\dfrac{9x^3y}{7xy^3} \cdot \dfrac{3x^4y}{5x^2y^7}$

Simplify. *2.10*

10. $5a - [3 - 2a(5 - 2a)]$

11. $15x - 3[x - (10 - 2x)]$

8.7 Adding and Subtracting: Polynomial Denominators

Objectives	To add and subtract rational expressions with unlike polynomial denominators
	To add and subtract a polynomial and a rational expression

Sums and differences of rational expressions may contain denominators that are polynomials.

EXAMPLE 1   Add $\dfrac{6}{a-2} + \dfrac{5}{a-4}$.

Plan   Find the LCD. Then replace the two rational expressions with equivalent expressions that have the LCD as the denominator.

Solution   The denominators $a - 2$ and $a - 4$ are irreducible. That is, their factored forms are $1 \cdot (a - 2)$ and $1 \cdot (a - 4)$. The LCD is $(a - 2)(a - 4)$.

$$\underset{\text{needs } a - 4}{\dfrac{6}{a-2}} + \underset{\text{needs } a - 2}{\dfrac{5}{a-4}}$$

$$= \dfrac{6 \cdot (a-4)}{(a-2) \cdot (a-4)} + \dfrac{5 \cdot (a-2)}{(a-4) \cdot (a-2)}$$

$$= \dfrac{6a - 24}{(a-2)(a-4)} + \dfrac{5a - 10}{(a-4)(a-2)}$$

$$= \dfrac{11a - 34}{(a-2)(a-4)} \quad \longleftarrow \text{THINK: Can the numerator be factored?}$$

Since the numerator and denominator have no common factors, the answer, in simplified form, is written as either $\dfrac{11a - 34}{(a-2)(a-4)}$ or $\dfrac{11a - 34}{a^2 - 6a + 8}$.

EXAMPLE 2   Subtract $(a + 2) - \dfrac{a - 1}{2a - 3}$.

Plan   Write $a + 2$ as $\dfrac{a+2}{1}$. Then find the LCD.

Solution   The binomial $2a - 3$ is irreducible. The LCD is $1 \cdot (2a - 3)$, or $2a - 3$.

$$(a + 2) \qquad \frac{a - 1}{2a - 3}$$

$$= \frac{(a + 2)}{1} - \frac{a - 1}{2a - 3}$$

needs $2a - 3$

$$= \frac{(a + 2) \cdot (2a - 3)}{1 \cdot (2a - 3)} - \frac{a - 1}{2a - 3}$$

$$= \frac{2a^2 + a - 6}{2a - 3} - \frac{a - 1}{2a - 3}$$

$$= \frac{(2a^2 + a - 6) - (a - 1)}{2a - 3}$$

$$= \frac{2a^2 + a - 6 - a + 1}{2a - 3}$$

$$= \frac{2a^2 - 5}{2a - 3} \qquad \longleftarrow \; 2a^2 - 5 \text{ is irreducible and } 2a - 3$$
$$\text{is irreducible.}$$

The numerator and denominator are both irreducible, and they have no common factor. The answer, in simplified form, is $\frac{2a^2 - 5}{2a - 3}$.

TRY THIS   1. Subtract $\frac{x - 2}{x - 9} - \frac{x + 4}{x + 5}$.

In the next two examples, it is convenient to change the form of one of the denominators in order to find the LCD.

EXAMPLE 3   Add $\frac{4x}{5x - 25} + \frac{2}{5 - x}$.

Plan   Use $\frac{a}{-b} = \frac{-a}{b}$ in order to obtain $\frac{2}{5 - x}$ in a more convenient form.

Solution
$$\frac{4x}{5x - 25} + \frac{2}{5 - x}$$

$$= \frac{4x}{5(x - 5)} + \frac{2}{1(x - 5)} \qquad \longleftarrow \; 5 - x = -1(-5 + x) = -1(x - 5)$$

$$= \frac{4x}{5(x - 5)} + \frac{-2}{1(x - 5)} \qquad \longleftarrow \; \frac{a}{-b} = \frac{-a}{b}$$
$$\text{needs } 5$$

$$= \frac{4x}{5(x - 5)} + \frac{-2 \cdot 5}{(x - 5) \cdot 5} \qquad \longleftarrow \; 4x + (-2 \cdot 5) = 4x + (-10)$$

$$= \frac{4x - 10}{5(x - 5)}, \text{ or } \frac{2(2x - 5)}{5(x - 5)}, \text{ or } \frac{4x - 10}{5x - 25}$$

EXAMPLE 4 Add and subtract $\dfrac{-2y - 10}{y^2 - 11y + 28} + \dfrac{1}{y - 4} - \dfrac{y + 1}{7 - y}$.

Solution

$$\dfrac{-2y - 10}{y^2 - 11y + 28} + \dfrac{1}{y - 4} - \dfrac{y + 1}{7 - y}$$

$$= \dfrac{-2y - 10}{(y - 4)(y - 7)} + \dfrac{1}{y - 4} - \dfrac{y + 1}{-1(y - 7)}$$

$$= \dfrac{-2y - 10}{(y - 4)(y - 7)} + \dfrac{1}{y - 4} - \dfrac{-(y + 1)}{1(y - 7)} \quad \longleftarrow \dfrac{a}{-b} = \dfrac{-a}{b}$$

$$= \dfrac{-2y - 10}{(y - 4)(y - 7)} + \dfrac{1 \cdot (y - 7)}{(y - 4) \cdot (y - 7)} - \dfrac{-(y + 1) \cdot (y - 4)}{(y - 7) \cdot (y - 4)}$$

$$= \dfrac{(-2y - 10) + (y - 7) - [-(y^2 - 3y - 4)]}{(y - 4)(y - 7)}$$

$$= \dfrac{-2y - 10 + y - 7 + (y^2 - 3y - 4)}{(y - 4)(y - 7)} \quad \longleftarrow -(-y^2) = y^2$$

$$= \dfrac{y^2 - 4y - 21}{(y - 4)(y - 7)} \quad \longleftarrow \text{The numerator is factorable.}$$

$$= \dfrac{(y + 3)(y - 7)^{1}}{(y - 4)(y - 7)_{1}}$$

$$= \dfrac{y + 3}{y - 4}$$

TRY THIS **2.** Subtract and add $\dfrac{9 - 12y}{y^2 + 3y - 18} - \dfrac{y + 2}{y + 6} + \dfrac{-4y}{3 - y}$.

Classroom Exercises

Give the LCD for each sum or difference.

1. $\dfrac{3}{x - 2} + \dfrac{-2}{x + 1}$ **2.** $\dfrac{5}{2a + 1} - \dfrac{6}{a + 3}$ **3.** $\dfrac{3}{a - 1} + \dfrac{2}{a + 5}$

4. $2 - \dfrac{4}{x}$ **5.** $15 - \dfrac{2}{m}$ **6.** $\dfrac{4}{x} + 1$

7. $(x + 3) + \dfrac{7}{x - 2}$ **8.** $(a + 2) - \dfrac{2a}{a + 1}$ **9.** $\dfrac{5}{a - 9} + \dfrac{3}{a(a - 9)}$

Add or subtract.

10. $\dfrac{3}{x - 2} + \dfrac{2}{x}$ **11.** $5 - \dfrac{1}{a + 5}$ **12.** $\dfrac{2x}{x^2 - 25} - \dfrac{10}{5 - x}$

Written Exercises

1–9. Find the sum or difference for Classroom Exercises 1–9.

Add and subtract as indicated.

10. $\dfrac{x+5}{x+2} + \dfrac{4}{x}$

11. $\dfrac{5}{x} - \dfrac{2x-1}{x+1}$

12. $3 - \dfrac{4b-1}{2b}$

13. $\dfrac{x}{x-1} + 2$

14. $(a+3) + \dfrac{a-4}{3a-2}$

15. $\dfrac{x+4}{x-3} + (x-2)$

16. $\dfrac{2}{b-4} - \dfrac{8}{b^2-4b}$

17. $\dfrac{y}{y-3} - \dfrac{9}{y^2+3y}$

18. $\dfrac{3x-4}{x^2-16} + \dfrac{2}{4-x}$

19. $\dfrac{9x+14}{x^2+7x} + \dfrac{x}{x+7}$

20. $\dfrac{a}{a-6} - \dfrac{a+30}{a^2-6a}$

21. $\dfrac{4}{x-6} - \dfrac{3}{x^2-2x-24}$

22. $\dfrac{3}{a-2} - \dfrac{12}{a^2-4} + \dfrac{2}{a+2}$

23. $\dfrac{44}{a^2-7a-18} + \dfrac{3}{a-9} + \dfrac{4}{a+2}$

24. $\dfrac{2}{z-5} + \dfrac{4}{z^2+2z-35} + \dfrac{1}{z+7}$

25. $\dfrac{3}{a-4} + \dfrac{2}{2-a} + \dfrac{2}{a^2-6a+8}$

26. $\dfrac{x-1}{x-4} - \dfrac{2x-3}{x^2+x-20}$

27. $\dfrac{14-a^2}{a^2-9a+20} + \dfrac{a+6}{a-5}$

28. $\dfrac{-24}{a^2-7a+10} - \dfrac{a+3}{5-a}$

29. $\dfrac{3b+1}{b^2-25} - \dfrac{2b+1}{5-b}$

30. $\dfrac{3x-1}{x-4} + \dfrac{2x+1}{x^2-16}$

31. $\dfrac{x+1}{x^2-5x+6} + \dfrac{x+4}{x-3}$

32. $\dfrac{x^2+2}{x^2-5x+4} - \dfrac{x-2}{x-1}$

33. $\dfrac{a^2-22}{a^2-9a+20} - \dfrac{a-2}{a-5}$

34. $\dfrac{m^2-8}{m^2-8m+12} - \dfrac{m+1}{m-6}$

35. $\dfrac{3}{2y^2-5y-12} - \dfrac{y+1}{2y+3} + \dfrac{y-5}{y-4}$

36. $(4x-3) - \dfrac{x^2+4}{2x+1}$

37. $(3x+4) - \dfrac{2x^2-x-1}{5x-2}$

38. $(x^2-x+1) - \dfrac{x^3+1}{x+1}$

39. $\dfrac{-3a-9}{a^2-7a+10} + \dfrac{a+3}{a-5} + \dfrac{3}{a-2}$

40. $\dfrac{2}{12+a-a^2} - \dfrac{5}{a^4-25a^2+144}$

41. $x^2+16 + \dfrac{5}{x-4} + \dfrac{4}{x+4}$

Mixed Review

Solve. *5.6*

1. $|x| = 4$

2. $|x-2| = 8$

3. $|x+3| = 5$

4. $|2x-1| = 13$

5. Find two consecutive integers whose sum is 89. *4.3*

6. One number is 8 more than twice another. Represent the numbers. *4.1*

8.8 Dividing Polynomials

Objectives	To divide polynomials by monomials and binomials

You know that when one whole number is divided by another, there may be a nonzero remainder, as illustrated below for $53 \div 13$.

$$53 \div 13 = \frac{53}{13} = 4 + \frac{1}{13} \quad \longleftarrow \quad \frac{\text{dividend}}{\text{divisor}} = \text{quotient} + \frac{\text{remainder}}{\text{divisor}}$$

Another way to express the division example above is shown below.

$$53 = 4 \cdot 13 + 1 \quad \longleftarrow \quad \text{dividend} = \text{quotient} \cdot \text{divisor} + \text{remainder}$$

If the remainder happens to be zero, then the quotient and divisor are *factors* of the dividend.

$$52 \div 13 = 4, \text{ or } 52 = 4 \cdot 13 \quad \longleftarrow \quad \text{dividend} = \text{quotient} \cdot \text{divisor}$$

You can also divide polynomials.

EXAMPLE 1   Divide $(16x^4 - 12x^3 + 8x^2) \div (4x^2)$.

Plan   Think of the quotient as $\dfrac{16x^4 - 12x^3 + 8x^2}{4x^2}$ and use the Rule for Adding and Subtracting Rational Expressions.

Solution

$$\frac{16x^4 - 12x^3 + 8x^2}{4x^2}$$

Divide each term of the numerator by $4x^2$.

$$= \frac{16x^4}{4x^2} - \frac{12x^3}{4x^2} + \frac{8x^2}{4x^2}$$

Simplify each term. $= 4x^2 - 3x + 2$

Thus, the quotient is $4x^2 - 3x + 2$, with a zero remainder.

TRY THIS   1. Divide $(6y^5 + 9y^8 - 21y^6) \div (3y^3)$.

In Example 1, the divisor $4x^2$ was a *monomial*. To understand the division of a polynomial by a *binomial* such as $2x - 5$, it is helpful to think of the steps of a numerical example such as $807 \div 32$ as shown at the top of page 321 where Step 2 is described.

Step 2

Bring down 7, the next digit of the dividend.

$$\begin{array}{r} 25 \\ 32\overline{)807} \\ 64 \\ \hline 167 \\ 160 \\ \hline 7 \end{array}$$

Divide. $32\overline{)167}$ with 5 above

Multiply. $5 \cdot 32 = 160$

Subtract. $167 - 160 = 7$ — nonzero remainder

Check: $25 \cdot 32 + 7 = 807$ True

quotient $\cdot$ divisor $+$ remainder $=$ dividend

So, the quotient is 25 and the remainder is 7.

EXAMPLE 2 Divide $(6x^2 - 9x - 12)$ by $(2x - 5)$.

Plan First rewrite as $2x - 5\overline{)6x^2 - 9x - 12}$. Then repeat the *divide-multiply-subtract* steps shown for the numerical example until a remainder is obtained.

Solution $2x - 5\overline{)6x^2 - 9x - 12}$

Step 1

Divide. $2x\overline{)6x^2}$ with $3x$ above

Multiply. $3x(2x - 5) = 6x^2 - 15x$

$$\begin{array}{r} 3x \\ 2x - 5\overline{)6x^2 - 9x - 12} \\ 6x^2 - 15x \\ \hline 6x \end{array}$$

Subtract. $(6x^2 - 9x) - (6x^2 - 15x)$
$= 6x^2 - 9x - 6x^2 + 15x$
$= 6x$

Step 2

Bring down -12.

Divide. $2x\overline{)6x}$ with 3 above

Multiply. $3(2x - 5) = 6x - 15$

Subtract. $(6x - 12) - (6x - 15) = 3$

$$\begin{array}{r} 3x + 3 \\ 2x - 5\overline{)6x^2 - 9x - 12} \\ 6x^2 - 15x \quad\downarrow \\ \hline 6x - 12 \\ 6x - 15 \\ \hline 3 \end{array}$$

nonzero remainder

Check $(3x + 3)(2x - 5) + 3 = (6x^2 - 9x - 15) + 3 = 6x^2 - 9x - 12$

quotient $\cdot$ divisor $+$ remainder $=$ dividend

Thus, the quotient is $3x + 3$ and the remainder is 3.

The answer may also be represented as $3x + 3 + \dfrac{3}{2x - 5}$.

The division of Example 2 can be performed using a more compact form, as shown below.

$$
\begin{array}{r}
3x + 3 \\
2x - 5 \overline{)6x^2 - 9x - 12} \\
\underline{6x^2 - 15x} \\
6x - 12 \\
\underline{6x - 15} \\
3
\end{array}
$$

EXAMPLE 3   Divide $(x^3 - 5x + 2)$ by $(x - 2)$.

Plan   Rewrite as $x - 2\overline{)x^3 + 0x^2 - 5x + 2}$. Then proceed with the *divide-multiply-subtract* cycle.

Solution
$$
\begin{array}{r}
x^2 + 2x - 1 \\
x - 2 \overline{)x^3 + 0x^2 - 5x + 2} \\
\underline{x^3 - 2x^2} \\
2x^2 - 5x \\
\underline{2x^2 - 4x} \\
-x + 2 \\
\underline{-x + 2} \\
0 \quad \longleftarrow \text{ zero remainder}
\end{array}
$$

Check $(x^2 + 2x - 1)(x - 2) = (x^3 + 2x^2 - x) + (-2x^2 - 4x + 2)$
$$= x^3 - 5x + 2$$

quotient · divisor = dividend

TRY THIS   2. Divide $(8x^3 - 12x^2 - 4)$ by $(2x - 1)$.

Classroom Exercises

Divide.

1. $2x^2\overline{)-8x^3}$ **2.** $-3x^2\overline{)-27x^4}$ **3.** $5x^3\overline{)15x^3}$ **4.** $-6x\overline{)12x^3}$

Divide.

5. $(9x^3 - 15x^2 + 27x) \div (3x)$ **6.** $(a^3 - 6a^2 + a - 6) \div (a - 6)$

Written Exercises

Divide and check.

1. $(30a^5 + 12a^3 - 16a^2) \div (2a)$
2. $(24t^8 - 12t^6 + 18t^4) \div (6t^2)$
3. $(24n^3 - 18n^2 + 36n) \div (6n)$
4. $(18b^4 - 24b^3 - 6b^2) \div (-3b^2)$
5. $(3x^2 - 5x - 2) \div (x - 2)$
6. $(10x^2 - 39x - 27) \div (5x + 3)$
7. $(3y^2 + 5y - 5) \div (y + 2)$
8. $(8a^2 - 22a + 3) \div (4a - 1)$

Divide.

9. $(6a^2 - 5a - 2) \div (2a - 3)$
10. $(15y^2 + 13y - 6) \div (3y - 1)$
11. $(12x^2 - 11x - 8) \div (3x + 1)$
12. $(12a^2 - 9a - 30) \div (4a + 5)$
13. $(12t^2 - 15t - 14) \div (4t + 3)$
14. $(4t^2 - 12t - 7) \div (2t + 1)$
15. $(10y^2 + 2y - 12) \div (2y - 2)$
16. $(12x^2 - x - 23) \div (3x - 4)$
17. $(6x^3 - x^2 - 8x + 4) \div (3x - 2)$
18. $(12a^3 - a^2 + 3a - 1) \div (4a + 1)$
19. $(6t^3 - 5t^2 + 16t - 5) \div (3t - 1)$
20. $(6y^3 + 14y^2 - 10y + 9) \div (2y + 6)$
21. $(4a^2 + 4a + 10) \div (2a - 1)$
22. $(4x^3 - 44x + 24) \div (x - 6)$
23. $(3t^3 + 16t^2 + 11) \div (3t + 4)$
24. $(4b^3 - 59b - 48) \div (2b + 6)$

25. Factor $a^3 - 13a - 12$ given that $a + 3$ is one of its factors.
26. Factor $a^3 - 8a^2 + 19a - 12$ completely, given that $a - 1$ is one of its factors.

27. Factor $8a^3 - 27$ given that $2a - 3$ is one of its factors.
28. Divide $(x^{3c} + 3x^{2c} - x^{2c+1} - 3x^{c+1} + 2) \div (x^c + 3)$.
29. Find the value of k for which $2x + 1$ is a factor of $2x^3 - 7x^2 + kx + 3$.

Mixed Review

Multiply. *6.9*

1. $(x + 3)(x + 5)$
2. $(2x - 1)(x + 7)$
3. $(x - 5)(x + 5)$

Simplify. *8.1, 8.2*

4. $\dfrac{x^2 - x - 6}{x^2 + x - 2}$
5. $\dfrac{2x + 8}{6x - 6}$
6. $\dfrac{x^2 - 25}{x^2 + 4x - 5}$

7. $\dfrac{5 - 5x}{x^2 + 6x - 7}$
8. $\dfrac{36 - x^2}{x^2 + 4x - 12}$
9. $\dfrac{3x^2 + 3x - 6}{6x^2 - 6}$

10. A triangle has angles measuring 48 and 52. What is the measure of the third angle of the triangle? *4.2*

11. The length of a rectangle is 5 yd more than 3 times the width. The perimeter is 90 yd. Find the length and the width of the rectangle. *4.2*

Problem Solving Strategies

Testing Conditions

Problems have conditions that affect which outcomes are reasonable. Testing different numbers can help you discover the conditions.

Example

A box of My-Grain cereal lists the ingredients in decreasing order by weight: oats, wheat, brown sugar, sugar, coconut oil, malt flavoring, salt, baking soda. What is the smallest possible percent of grain (oats and wheat) that could be in the cereal?

Think:

The total of the percents by weight of the ingredients must equal 100%. Find the minimum percent for the first 2 ingredients.

Try some possible percents for the 8 ingredients, and each time try to make the percents for the first 2 items smaller.

(1) 30%, 25%, 15%, 10%, 5%, 5%, 5%, 5%
(2) 20%, 20%, 15%, 15%, 10%, 10%, 5%, 5%
(3) 15%, 15%, 15%, 15%, 15%, 15%, 5%, 5%

These examples suggest that the more there is of other ingredients, the less there will be of grain. But there can't be more of any other ingredient than there is of either grain. Therefore, the minimum for the first 2 items—the grains—is reached when each of the 8 items is the same percent. Under these conditions, each item would be $\frac{100}{8}$%, or 12.5% of the total. So, the cereal must contain *at least* 12.5% oats and 12.5% wheat for a total of 25% grain.

Exercises

Solve each problem, if possible.

1. Jolly O cereal has the same ingredients list as MyGrain but the sugars account for 30% of the cereal. What is the minimum percent of grain in Jolly O?

2. Kim had an 89% average for 3 tests. If there was no extra credit for any test, what is the lowest score she could have received for any of the 3 tests?

3. Mark claims that he walked straight for 5 mi, turned, and walked straight again for 3 mi, and then turned and walked 1 mi straight back to his starting point. Could Mark have done this?

8.9 Complex Rational Expressions

Objective

To simplify complex fractions and complex rational expressions

The indicated division, $5 \div 6$, can be written as a fraction.

$$5 \div 6 = \frac{5}{6}$$

The division of two fractions can be written as a complex fraction.

$$\frac{3}{5} \div \frac{2}{3} = \frac{\dfrac{3}{5}}{\dfrac{2}{3}}$$

Definition

A **complex fraction** is a fraction that has at least one fraction in its numerator, denominator, or in both its numerator and denominator.

A complex fraction can be simplified by multiplying its numerator and denominator by the common denominator of the two fractions in its numerator and denominator.

EXAMPLE 1

Simplify $\dfrac{\dfrac{3}{5}}{\dfrac{2}{3}}$.

Plan

Find the LCD of $\frac{3}{5}$ and $\frac{2}{3}$. Then use the rule $\frac{a}{b} = \frac{a \cdot c}{b \cdot c}$.

Solution

The LCD of $\frac{3}{5}$ and $\frac{2}{3}$ is $3 \cdot 5$. Multiply by $3 \cdot 5$.

$$\frac{\dfrac{3}{5}}{\dfrac{2}{3}} = \frac{\dfrac{3}{5} \cdot 3 \cdot 5}{\dfrac{2}{3} \cdot 3 \cdot 5} \qquad \longleftarrow \frac{a}{b} = \frac{a \cdot c}{b \cdot c} \text{ (Divide out common factors.)}$$

$$= \frac{3 \cdot 3 \cdot 1}{2 \cdot 1 \cdot 5} \text{, or } \frac{9}{10}$$

TRY THIS

Simplify $\dfrac{\dfrac{4}{7}}{\dfrac{4}{5}}$.

The rational expression $\dfrac{\dfrac{4}{5} - \dfrac{3}{y}}{\dfrac{5y}{6}}$ is a complex rational expression.

Definition	A **complex rational expression** is a rational expression that has at least one rational expression in its numerator, denominator, or both numerator and denominator.

A complex rational expression can be simplified in the same way as a complex fraction.

EXAMPLE 2 Simplify $\dfrac{\dfrac{p}{14}}{\dfrac{p}{2} - \dfrac{3}{7}}$.

Plan Find the LCD of $\dfrac{p}{14}$, $\dfrac{p}{2}$, and $\dfrac{3}{7}$. Then, use the rule $\dfrac{a}{b} = \dfrac{a \cdot c}{b \cdot c}$.

Solution Multiply the numerator and denominator of the complex rational expression by 14, the *LCD* of $\dfrac{p}{14}$, $\dfrac{p}{2}$, and $\dfrac{3}{7}$.

$$\dfrac{\dfrac{p}{14}}{\dfrac{p}{2} - \dfrac{3}{7}} = \dfrac{\dfrac{p}{14} \cdot 14}{\left(\dfrac{p}{2} - \dfrac{3}{7}\right) \cdot 14} \quad \longleftarrow \dfrac{a}{b} = \dfrac{a \cdot c}{b \cdot c}$$

$$= \dfrac{\dfrac{p}{\cancel{14}} \cdot \overset{1}{\cancel{14}}}{\dfrac{p}{\cancel{2}} \cdot \overset{7}{\cancel{14}} - \dfrac{3}{\cancel{7}} \cdot \overset{2}{\cancel{14}}} \quad \longleftarrow (a - b)c = ac - bc$$

$$= \dfrac{p}{7p - 6} \quad \longleftarrow \text{ simplified form}$$

TRY THIS 2. Simplify $\dfrac{\dfrac{x}{12}}{\dfrac{5}{6} + \dfrac{x}{4}}$.

EXAMPLE 3 Simplify $\dfrac{1 - \dfrac{1}{n} - \dfrac{30}{n^2}}{1 - \dfrac{36}{n^2}}$.

Solution The *LCD* is n^2.

326 Chapter 8 Rational Expressions

$$\frac{1 - \dfrac{1}{n} - \dfrac{30}{n^2}}{1 - \dfrac{36}{n^2}} = \frac{n^2\left(1 - \dfrac{1}{n} - \dfrac{30}{n^2}\right)}{n^2\left(1 - \dfrac{36}{n^2}\right)} \quad\longleftarrow\; \frac{a}{b} = \frac{c \cdot a}{c \cdot b}$$

$$= \frac{n^2 \cdot 1 - \cancel{n}^2 \cdot \dfrac{1}{\cancel{n}_1} - \cancel{n}^2 \cdot \dfrac{30}{\cancel{n^2}_1}}{n^2 \cdot 1 - \cancel{n}^2 \cdot \dfrac{36}{\cancel{n^2}_1}} \quad\longleftarrow \text{Distributive Property}$$

$$= \frac{n^2 - n - 30}{n^2 - 36} \quad\longleftarrow \text{THINK: Can the numerator or}$$

$$= \frac{\cancel{(n-6)}(n+5)}{(n+6)\cancel{(n-6)}_1} = \frac{n+5}{n+6} \quad\begin{array}{l}\text{the denominator}\\\text{be factored?}\end{array}$$

EXAMPLE 4 Simplify $\dfrac{x - 1 + \dfrac{4}{x+3}}{\dfrac{4}{x+3} - 2}$.

Solution

$$\frac{x - 1 + \dfrac{4}{x+3}}{\dfrac{4}{x+3} - 2} = \frac{(x+3)\left[(x-1) + \dfrac{4}{x+3}\right]}{(x+3)\left[\dfrac{4}{x+3} - 2\right]}$$

$$= \frac{(x + 3 \cdot (x-1) + \cancel{(x+3)} \cdot \dfrac{4}{\cancel{x+3}_1}}{\cancel{(x+3)} \cdot \dfrac{4}{\cancel{x+3}_1} - (x+3) \cdot 2}$$

$$= \frac{(x+3)(x-1) + 4}{4 - 2(x+3)}$$

$$= \frac{x^2 + 2x - 3 + 4}{4 - 2x - 6}$$

$$= \frac{x^2 + 2x + 1}{-2x - 2}$$

$$= \frac{\cancel{(x+1)}(x+1)}{-2\cancel{(x+1)}_1} = \frac{x+1}{-2}, \text{ or } -\frac{x+1}{2}$$

TRY THIS 3. Simplify $\dfrac{\dfrac{x+5}{x-2} - 6}{7 - \dfrac{1}{x-2}}$.

Classroom Exercises

Find the LCD that you would use to simplify each complex expression.

1. $\dfrac{\frac{2}{7}}{\frac{3}{5}}$

2. $\dfrac{\frac{x}{6}}{\frac{3x}{6}}$

3. $\dfrac{x + \frac{1}{3}}{5 - \frac{1}{9}}$

4. $\dfrac{\frac{a}{9}}{\frac{a}{2} + \frac{a}{18}}$

5. $\dfrac{8 + \frac{1}{5}}{4\frac{1}{4}}$

6. $\dfrac{1\frac{2}{7}}{2\frac{5}{21}}$

7. $\dfrac{2a + \frac{1}{3}}{\frac{7}{15} + \frac{a}{5}}$

8. $\dfrac{1 + \frac{1}{n} - \frac{6}{n^2}}{1 - \frac{4}{n^2}}$

9–16. Simplify Classroom Exercises 1–8 above.

Written Exercises

Simplify.

1. $\dfrac{\frac{3}{16}}{\frac{4}{7}}$

2. $\dfrac{\frac{1}{5} + \frac{2}{9}}{\frac{5}{9} + \frac{3}{5}}$

3. $\dfrac{\frac{x}{5}}{\frac{x}{2} - \frac{1}{10}}$

4. $\dfrac{\frac{3t}{7} + \frac{1}{14}}{\frac{t}{2} + \frac{5}{7}}$

5. $\dfrac{6 - \frac{3}{4}}{8 + \frac{5}{8}}$

6. $\dfrac{10\frac{2}{3}}{11\frac{1}{9}}$

7. $\dfrac{2a + \frac{1}{6}}{\frac{a}{6} + \frac{2}{3}}$

8. $\dfrac{5a + \frac{1}{2}}{7a + \frac{1}{2}}$

9. $\dfrac{\frac{6}{m} - \frac{2}{9}}{\frac{1}{3} + \frac{4}{m^2}}$

10. $\dfrac{\frac{7}{2} - \frac{3}{b}}{\frac{5}{b^2} + \frac{11}{14}}$

11. $\dfrac{\frac{8}{x^2} - \frac{3}{x}}{\frac{11}{x} + \frac{1}{x^2}}$

12. $\dfrac{1 - \frac{5}{m} + \frac{4}{m^2}}{1 - \frac{16}{m^2}}$

13. $\dfrac{3 + \frac{6}{a} - \frac{9}{a^2}}{6 - \frac{6}{a^2}}$

14. $\dfrac{4 - \frac{8}{x} - \frac{60}{x^2}}{2 - \frac{18}{x^2}}$

15. $\dfrac{-2 - \frac{4}{y} + \frac{30}{y^2}}{4 - \frac{100}{y^2}}$

16. $\dfrac{\frac{3}{m - 8} + 4}{2 + \frac{1}{m - 8}}$

17. $\dfrac{3 + \frac{2}{a - 1}}{4 - \frac{3}{a + 1}}$

18. $\dfrac{5 - \frac{2}{x - 3}}{6 + \left(\frac{-1}{x + 5}\right)}$

19. $\dfrac{\frac{2}{a - 2} + \frac{7}{a^2 - 4}}{\frac{5}{a + 2} + \frac{6}{a - 2}}$

20. $\dfrac{\frac{4}{a^2 + 4a} - \frac{3}{a}}{\frac{2}{a + 4} + \frac{4}{a}}$

21. $\dfrac{\frac{3}{x} - \frac{12}{x^2 + 2x}}{\frac{2}{x + 2} - \frac{1}{x}}$

$$\dfrac{\dfrac{3}{x-5}+\dfrac{-2}{x+3}}{\dfrac{4}{x^2-2x-15}+\dfrac{1}{x+3}}$$

$$\dfrac{\dfrac{-3}{a+5}-\dfrac{2}{a-2}}{\dfrac{4}{a^2+3a-10}+\dfrac{5}{a+5}}$$

$$\dfrac{\dfrac{2x+4}{x+8}-\dfrac{x-1}{x-2}}{\dfrac{x^2-49}{x^2+6x-16}}$$

$$\dfrac{1-\dfrac{13}{x^2}+\dfrac{36}{x^4}}{\dfrac{1}{x^2}-\dfrac{1}{x^3}-\dfrac{6}{x^4}}$$

$$\dfrac{1-\dfrac{34}{x^2}-\dfrac{225}{x^4}}{1-\dfrac{8}{x}+\dfrac{15}{x^2}}$$

In Exercises 27 and 28, S represents the area of the figure's surface and V represents its volume. Find the quotient $\dfrac{S}{V}$ for each figure and simplify.

Sphere

$S = 4\pi r^2$

$V = \dfrac{4}{3}\pi r^3$

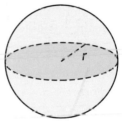

Right circular cone

$S = \pi r^2 + \pi r l$

$V = \dfrac{1}{3}\pi r^2 h$

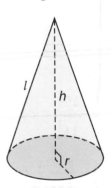

Mixed Review

Simplify. Then evaluate for the given value of the variable. *1.7*

1. $3(3x - 18) + 6x - 1$ for $x = 3$

2. $6s - (10 - s) + 18$ for $s = -4$

3. $-4(6 - 4a) - (2a - 10)$ for $a = 2$

4. $x - 3(2 - x) - (1 - x)$ for $x = -2$

Solve. *3.2, 3.3, 3.4, 3.5, 4.5, 4.6*

5. $16x - 3 = -2x - 3 + 17x$

6. $8x - 3(2 - 3x) = -2(2x - 1)$

7. $\dfrac{3}{5}a = 9$

8. $\dfrac{5}{3}x - 3 = 4$

9. $\dfrac{1}{2} + \dfrac{1}{3}x = \dfrac{4}{6}$

10. $1.3x + 0.05 = 0.31$

Chapter 8 Review

Key Terms

complex fraction   (p. 325)
complex rational expression   (p. 326)
least common denominator (LCD)
   (p. 311)
least common multiple (LCM)
   (p. 311)
Multiplicative Identity Property for
   Rational Expressions   (p. 311)

rational expression   (p. 289)
Rule for Adding and Subtracting Rational
   Expressions   (p. 306)
Rule for Dividing Rational Expressions
   (p. 302)
Rule for Multiplying Rational Expressions
   (p. 297)

Key Ideas and Review Exercises

**8.1,
8.2**   To find the value(s), if any, for which a rational expression is undefined, set
   the denominator equal to 0 and solve the equation.

   To simplify a rational expression, factor the numerator and denominator. If
   necessary, rewrite the numerator and denominator in convenient form. Then
   divide out the common factor(s), noting all restrictions on the variables.

1. For what value or values of x is the expression undefined?

$$\frac{3x - 2}{2x^2 + 5x - 3}$$

Simplify.

2. $\dfrac{36t^5}{14t}$

3. $\dfrac{x^2 + 3x + 2}{x^2 - x - 6}$

4. $\dfrac{49 - a^2}{a + 7}$

5. $\dfrac{x - 5}{10 + 3x - x^2}$

8.3   To multiply two rational expressions, factor the numerators and denominators, divide out common factors, and multiply.

Multiply.

6. $\dfrac{12a^2b^4}{5 - a} \cdot \dfrac{a^2 - 25}{3ab^3}$

7. $\dfrac{x^2 - 3x + 2}{x + 3} \cdot \dfrac{5x + 15}{x^2 + 4x - 5}$

8.4   To divide two rational expressions, multiply the first expression by the reciprocal of the second expression.

Divide.

8. $\dfrac{36a^7b^3}{27 - 3a^2} \div \dfrac{12a^5b^4}{5a + 15}$

9. $\dfrac{x^2 + 7x + 12}{x^2 - 16} \div \dfrac{x^2 + 4x - 21}{x - 4}$

8.5 To add or subtract rational expressions with like denominators, use $\dfrac{a}{b} + \dfrac{c}{b} = \dfrac{a + c}{b}$ or $\dfrac{a}{b} - \dfrac{c}{b} = \dfrac{a - c}{b}$.

Add or subtract.

10. $\dfrac{2a}{a - 4} - \dfrac{8}{a - 4}$

11. $\dfrac{2x}{x^2 + 7x + 10} + \dfrac{10}{x^2 + 7x + 10}$

8.6, To add or subtract rational expressions with unlike denominators, find the
8.7 LCD. Then use the Multiplicative Identity Property to write equivalent expressions with like denominators.

Add or subtract.

12. $\dfrac{3}{10x^2} + \dfrac{7}{15x^3}$

13. $\dfrac{b + 2}{18} + \dfrac{3b - 1}{9} - \dfrac{b - 1}{6}$

14. $\dfrac{25}{5 - m} - \dfrac{5m}{m^2 - 25}$

15. $\dfrac{35}{x^2 + x - 12} - \dfrac{5}{x - 3} + \dfrac{7}{x + 4}$

16. Explain how to add or subtract a polynomial and a rational expression Use $(x - 2) + \dfrac{6}{x + 3}$ as an illustration.

8.8 To divide a polynomial by a monomial, divide each term of the polynomial by the monomial.

To divide a polynomial by a binomial, arrange the terms in descending order of exponents. If there is a missing term in the dividend, insert the term with a coefficient of 0. Then divide as in Examples 2 and 3 in Lesson 8.8.

Divide.

17. $(36t^4 - 18t^3 + 12t) \div (6t)$

18. $(4x^3 - 19x + 15) \div (2x - 3)$

8.9 To simplify a complex fraction or complex rational expression, multiply the numerator and the denominator of the expression by the LCD of all the terms.

Simplify.

19. $\dfrac{\dfrac{3t}{5} - \dfrac{2}{10}}{\dfrac{2t}{20} + \dfrac{5}{4}}$

20. $\dfrac{1 + \dfrac{2}{n} - \dfrac{15}{n^2}}{1 - \dfrac{25}{n^2}}$

For what values of the variable is the rational expression undefined?

1. $\dfrac{y - 3}{3y + 6}$

2. $\dfrac{x + 4}{6 - x}$

3. $\dfrac{m + 3}{m^2 + 7m + 6}$

Simplify.

4. $\dfrac{-54t^7}{6t^2}$

5. $\dfrac{6a^2 + a - 2}{4a^2 + 4a - 3}$

6. $\dfrac{8a^3 - 4a^4}{5a^3 - 10a^2}$

Multiply.

7. $\dfrac{5a^5}{3b^6} \cdot \dfrac{4a^2}{7b^7}$

8. $\dfrac{x^2 + 6x - 7}{x + 3} \cdot \dfrac{4x + 12}{x - 1}$

9. $\dfrac{3 - a}{a^2 + 3a - 4} \cdot \dfrac{a^2 - 1}{a - 3}$

10. Divide. $\dfrac{a^2 + 2a - 15}{a^2 - 9} \div \dfrac{a^2 + 4a - 5}{3a - 9}$

11. Simplify. $\dfrac{x^2 + 4x + 3}{4x^4y^3} \div \dfrac{x^2 - 1}{12x^5y} \cdot \dfrac{x^2 - 6x + 5}{6x^2 + 18x}$

Add or subtract.

12. $\dfrac{3x}{x + 5} + \dfrac{15}{x + 5}$

13. $\dfrac{-5}{18a^5} + \dfrac{7}{12a^3}$

14. $\dfrac{3t - 2}{2} + \dfrac{5t - 7}{7} - \dfrac{3t}{14}$

15. $(a + 5) - \dfrac{2}{a - 2}$

16. $\dfrac{x + 3}{x + 5} + \dfrac{4x - 2}{x^2 - x - 30}$

17. $\dfrac{-6}{x - 3} + \dfrac{18}{x^2 - 9} + \dfrac{3}{x + 3}$

Divide.

18. $(36m^6 - 45m^3 + 81m^2) \div (9m^2)$

19. $(6x^3 + 7x^2 - 5x + 15) \div (2x - 1)$

Simplify.

20. $\dfrac{\dfrac{2}{3} - \dfrac{1}{2}}{\dfrac{1}{5} + \dfrac{1}{10}}$

21. $\dfrac{1 - \dfrac{4}{x} - \dfrac{5}{x^2}}{1 - \dfrac{8}{x} + \dfrac{15}{x^2}}$

22. Factor $27x^3 - 8$ if one of its factors is $3x - 2$.

23. Simplify $\dfrac{\dfrac{2}{x + 1} + \dfrac{-3}{x - 3}}{\dfrac{5}{x^2 - 2x - 3} + \dfrac{1}{x + 1}}$.

In each Exercise, you are to compare a quantity in Column 1 with a quantity in Column 2. Write the letter of the correct answer from these choices.

A—The quantity in Column 1 is greater than the quantity in Column 2.
B—The quantity in Column 2 is greater than the quantity in Column 1.
C—The quantity in Column 1 is equal to the quantity in Column 2.
D—The relationship cannot be determined from the given information.

NOTE: Information centered over both columns refers to one or both of the quantities to be compared.

Sample Question and Answer	Answer: C, because
Column 1 $\qquad$ **Column 2** $x \neq 0$ and $y \neq 0$ $\dfrac{1}{x} - \dfrac{1}{y}$ $\qquad\qquad$ $\dfrac{y - x}{xy}$	$\dfrac{1}{x} - \dfrac{1}{y} = \dfrac{1}{x} + \dfrac{-1}{y}$ $= \dfrac{1 \cdot y}{x \cdot y} + \dfrac{-1 \cdot x}{y \cdot x}$ $= \dfrac{1y - 1x}{xy}$, or $\dfrac{y - x}{xy}$

	Column 1	Column 2
	$a \neq 0, b \neq 0$	
1.	$\dfrac{1}{a} + \dfrac{1}{b}$	$\dfrac{a + b}{ab}$
	$c > b > a > 0$	
2.	$\dfrac{a}{b}$	$\dfrac{c}{a}$
	$-4 < x < 0$	
3.	$\dfrac{1}{x^2}$	$\dfrac{1}{x^3}$
	$a = -100$	
4.	$\dfrac{a^8}{a^3}$	$\dfrac{a^7}{a}$
	$z = \dfrac{1}{x + y}, x > 0, y > 0$	
5.	$\dfrac{m}{z}$	$mx + my$

	Column 1	Column 2
	The 15 small rectangles below have the same length and width. The large rectangle has length x and width y.	

	Column 1	Column 2
6.	$\dfrac{7xy}{15}$	area of the shaded region
	$\dfrac{5}{a} = \dfrac{7}{b}$ and $a > 0, b > 0$	
7.	a	b
	$\dfrac{1}{4} + \dfrac{2}{x} + \dfrac{2}{3} = \dfrac{13}{12}$	
8.	x	3

Cumulative Review (Chapters 1–8)

Choose the one best answer.

1. Compute $(-3)^2 \cdot 2^3$.   *6.2*
   (A) 36   (B) -72 (C) 72
   (D) 48   (E) None of these

2. Solve $-6 \leq 9 + 5x$.   *5.2*
   (A) $x \leq -3$ (B) $x \leq 3$
   (C) $x \geq 3$ (D) $x \geq -3$
   (E) None of these

3. Simplify $(2a - 3)^2$.   *6.10*
   (A) $4a^2 + 12a + 9$
   (B) $4a^2 - 12a + 9$
   (C) $4a^2 + 6a - 9$
   (D) $4a^2 - 6a + 9$
   (E) None of these

4. Simplify.   *2.10*
   $-3(2x - 4) + 2(6 - x)$
   (A) $-4x$ (B) $-8x$
   (C) $-4x + 24$
   (D) $-8x + 24$
   (E) None of these

5. Multiply $-4x^3y^5(-6xy^2)$.   *6.1*
   (A) $24x^4y^7$ (B) $24x^3y^7$
   (C) $-24xy^{11}$ (D) $24xy^{10}$
   (E) None of these

6. Solve $|3x - 5| = 13$.   *5.6*
   (A) -6 (B) $-\frac{8}{3}, 6$
   (C) $\frac{8}{3}, 6$ (D) -3
   (E) None of these

In Exercises 7 and 8, what property is illustrated?

7. $-8 + 10 = 10 + (-8)$ *1.5*
   (A) Assoc Prop for Add
   (B) Comm Prop for Add
   (C) Add Inverse Prop
   (D) Rule of Subt
   (E) None of these

8. $-9a \cdot 1 = -9a$ *1.7*
   (A) Add Identity Prop
   (B) Closure Prop for Mult
   (C) Mult Identity Prop
   (D) Distr Prop
   (E) None of these

Evaluate.

9. a^2 for $a = -\frac{1}{3}$ *2.6*

10. $4x^3$ for $x = -2$

11. $2m - 3n + 6$ for $m = 3$ and   *2.8*
    $n = -2$

12. $-3a^2bc^3$ for $a = -1$, $b = 2$,   *2.6*
    and $c = -2$

13. $\dfrac{x + 12}{2x}$ for $x = 4$ *8.1*

14. $\dfrac{x^2 - 2}{x}$ for $x = -5$

Solve each equation or inequality.

15. $|x - 3| \leq 4$ *5.7*

16. $|x - 10| > 7$

17. $|3x + 4| \leq 17$

18. $a - 15 = -8$ *3.1*

19. $3y + 8 - y = -2 + y$ *3.4*

20. $9x = -45$ *3.2*

21. $y - \frac{1}{5} = \frac{7}{6}$ *3.1*

22. $5(2x - 3) = 5x + 50$ *3.5*

23. $|x - 3| = 8$ *5.6*

24. $2x^2 - 7x - 4 = 0$ *7.7*

25. $m^2 - 14m = 0$

26. $5 + 14t = 3t^2$

Factor.

27. $x^2 - 6x - 7$ *7.3*

28. $6x^2 - x - 2$ *7.4*

29. $m^2 - 36$ *7.5*

30. $5y^2 + 30y + 40$ *7.6*

31. $6x^3 + 28x^2 - 10x$

32. $25x^2 - 81y^2$ *7.5*

Simplify.

33. $8x^3 - 2x^2 + 3x - 4x^3 + x^2$ *6.6*

34. $-8 + 2y^4 - 3y^3 - y^4 + 6y^3 - 5y^4$

35. $3x - 2(8 - 9x)$ *2.10*

36. $-(8a^3 + 6 - 7a^2) - (a^2 + 5)$ *6.7*

37. $(-3x^2y^3)^2$ *6.2*

38. $\dfrac{18a^4b^6}{-6ab^7}$ *6.3*

39. $(8x^4y^5)(-4xy^7)$ *6.1*

Write an algebraic expression.

40. $12x$ increased by 4   *1.1*

41. $4x$ decreased by 9

42. 9 times $6x$

43. 23 divided by x

Solve each problem.

44. Use $p = 2l + 2w$ to find p for $l = 8$ cm and $w = 12$ cm.   *1.4*

45. Use $A = 4s^2$ to find A for $s = 8$ m.

46. Find two consecutive integers whose sum is 87.   *4.3*

47. Find three consecutive odd integers whose sum is 57.

48. The second of three numbers is 2 less than 3 times the first. The third is 8 more than twice the first. If 4 times the second is decreased by the third, the result is 8 times the first. Find the numbers.   *4.2*

49. The length of a rectangle is 5 m less than 6 times the width. The perimeter is 74 m. Find the length and the width.   *4.4*

50. The length of a rectangle is 10 m more than 3 times the width. The perimeter is 180 m. Find the length and the width.

51. The larger of two numbers is 9 less than twice the smaller. The sum of the numbers is 36. Find the two numbers.   *4.2*

52. A team won 16 games and lost 4 games. The number of games won is what percent of the games played?   *4.7*

53. The selling price of a VCR is $420. The profit is 40% of the cost. Find the cost.   *4.8*

54. A college bookstore makes a profit of $4 on each book sold. How many books must be sold to make a total profit of at least $1,000?

55. The degree measure of the vertex angle of an isosceles triangle is 39 more than that of a base angle. Find the measure of each angle of the triangle.   *4.4*

56. Find the area of a trapezoid if the height is 8.3 cm and the bases are 5.4 cm and 6.6 cm.   *1.4*

57. Eighty students are separated into two groups. The second group is 7 times as large as the first. How many students are in each group?   *4.2*

58. In a collection of 30 nickels and quarters, there are twice as many nickels as quarters. Find the number of coins of each type.

Susan Butcher has won the sled dog race over the Iditarod Trail in Alaska four times. Only one other person has done this! In 1990, she and her champion dogs completed the 1,158 miles from Anchorage to Nome in a little over 11 days, a record time.

9.1 Rational Equations

Objective   To solve equations containing rational expressions

An equation such as $\frac{4}{x} + \frac{1}{2x} = \frac{1}{3}$ is called a **rational equation** because it contains one or more rational expressions. To solve a rational equation, first multiply each side of the equation by the least common denominator of the fractions.

EXAMPLE 1   Solve $\frac{4}{x} + \frac{1}{2x} = \frac{1}{3}$.

Plan   Multiply each side of the equation by the LCD, $2 \cdot x \cdot 3$, or $6x$.

Solution

$$\frac{4}{x} + \frac{1}{2x} = \frac{1}{3} \qquad \text{Check:} \qquad \frac{4}{x} + \frac{1}{2x} = \frac{1}{3}$$

$$6x\left(\frac{4}{x} + \frac{1}{2x}\right) = 6x \cdot \frac{1}{3} \qquad\qquad \frac{4}{\frac{27}{2}} + \frac{1}{2\left(\frac{27}{2}\right)} \stackrel{?}{=} \frac{1}{3}$$

$$6x \cdot \frac{4}{x} + 6x \cdot \frac{1}{2x} = 6x \cdot \frac{1}{3} \qquad\qquad \frac{8}{27} + \frac{1}{27} \stackrel{?}{=} \frac{1}{3}$$

$$24 + 3 = 2x$$

$$27 = 2x \qquad\qquad\qquad\qquad \frac{9}{27} \stackrel{?}{=} \frac{1}{3}$$

$$x = \frac{27}{2}, \text{ or } 13\frac{1}{2} \qquad\qquad \frac{1}{3} = \frac{1}{3} \text{ True}$$

Thus, the solution is $\frac{27}{2}$.

TRY THIS   1. Solve $\frac{3}{5x} + \frac{2}{x} = \frac{1}{2}$.

Sometimes, when you multiply by the LCD, you obtain a quadratic equation. Such an equation may have more than one root. Then, you need to check each root in the *original equation* to see whether it is a *solution* of the original equation.

EXAMPLE 2   Solve $\frac{a + 7}{a - 3} = \frac{9}{a} + \frac{30}{a^2 - 3a}$.

Plan   Factor $a^2 - 3a$.
Then multiply each side of the equation by the LCD.

Solution   Factor.

$$\frac{a + 7}{a} = \frac{9}{3} + \frac{30}{a(a - 3)}$$

Multiply by $a(a - 3)$.

$$a(a - 3)\frac{a + 7}{a - 3} = a(a - 3)\left[\frac{9}{a} + \frac{30}{a(a - 3)}\right]$$

$$\overset{1}{\cancel{a(a - 3)}}\frac{a + 7}{\cancel{a - 3}}_1 = \overset{1}{\cancel{a}}(a - 3)\frac{9}{\cancel{a}}_1 + \overset{1}{\cancel{a}}\overset{1}{\cancel{(a - 3)}}\frac{30}{\underset{1}{\cancel{a}}\underset{1}{\cancel{(a - 3)}}}$$

$$a(a + 7) = (a - 3)9 + 30$$
$$a^2 + 7a = 9a - 27 + 30$$
$$a^2 - 2a - 3 = 0$$

Factor.

$$(a - 3)(a + 1) = 0$$
$$a - 3 = 0 \ or \ a + 1 = 0$$
$$a = 3 \ or \qquad a = -1$$

Checks

Substitute 3 for a in the *original* equation.

$$\frac{a + 7}{a - 3} = \frac{9}{a} + \frac{30}{a^2 - 3a}$$

$$\frac{3 + 7}{3 - 3} \overset{?}{=} \frac{9}{3} + \frac{30}{3^2 - 3 \cdot 3}$$

$$\frac{10}{0} \overset{?}{=} \frac{9}{3} + \frac{30}{0}$$

The symbols $\frac{10}{0}$ and $\frac{30}{0}$ are undefined. Therefore, 3 is not a solution of the original equation.

Substitute -1 for a in the *original* equation.

$$\frac{a + 7}{a - 3} = \frac{9}{a} + \frac{30}{a^2 - 3a}$$

$$\frac{-1 + 7}{-1 - 3} \overset{?}{=} \frac{9}{-1} + \frac{30}{(-1)^2 - 3(-1)}$$

$$\frac{6}{-4} \overset{?}{=} -9 + \frac{30}{1 + 3}$$

$$-\frac{6}{4} \overset{?}{=} -9 + \frac{30}{4}$$

$$-\frac{6}{4} \overset{?}{=} \frac{-36}{4} + \frac{30}{4}$$

$$-\frac{6}{4} = -\frac{6}{4} \ \text{True}$$

Thus, -1 is the only solution of the original equation.

TRY THIS

2. Solve $\dfrac{6}{x} + \dfrac{x + 4}{x - 2} = \dfrac{12}{x^2 - 2x}$.

In Example 2, 3 is a solution of the *derived* equation, $a^2 - 2a - 3 = 0$. However, 3 is not a solution of the original equation. In this case, 3 is called an *extraneous solution*, or *extraneous root*.

An **extraneous solution** is a solution of a derived equation that is not a solution of the original equation.

EXAMPLE 3   Solve $\dfrac{-17}{x^2 + 5x - 6} = \dfrac{x + 2}{x + 6} + \dfrac{3}{1 - x}$.

Solution   Factor $x^2 + 5x - 6$ in the denominator.

$$\frac{-17}{(x+6)(x-1)} = \frac{x+2}{x+6} + \frac{3(-1)}{x-1} \quad \longleftarrow \text{Put } 1 - x \text{ in convenient form.}$$

$$\frac{-17}{(x+6)(x-1)} = \frac{(x+2)}{(x+6)} + \frac{-3}{x-1} \quad \longleftarrow \text{The LCD is } (x+6)(x-1).$$

$$\overset{1}{\cancel{(x+6)}}\overset{1}{\cancel{(x-1)}}\frac{-17}{\underset{1}{\cancel{(x+6)}}\underset{1}{\cancel{(x-1)}}} = (x+6)(x-1)\left[\frac{x+2}{x+6} + \frac{-3}{x-1}\right]$$

$$-17 = \cancel{(x+6)}(x-1)\frac{x+2}{\underset{1}{\cancel{x+6}}} + (x+6)\cancel{(x-1)} \cdot \frac{-3}{\underset{1}{\cancel{x-1}}}$$

$$-17 = (x-1)(x+2) + (x+6)(-3)$$
$$-17 = x^2 + 2x - 1x - 2 - 3x - 18$$
$$-17 = x^2 - 2x - 20$$
$$0 = x^2 - 2x - 3$$

Factor.
$$0 = (x-3)(x+1)$$
$$x - 3 = 0 \ or \ x + 1 = 0$$
$$x = 3 \qquad\qquad x = -1 \qquad \text{The check is left to you.}$$

EXAMPLE 4 The sum of a number and its reciprocal is $\frac{13}{6}$. Find the number and its reciprocal.

Solution Let x = the number. Then $\frac{1}{x}$ = the reciprocal of the number.

$$x + \frac{1}{x} = \frac{13}{6} \quad \longleftarrow \text{Number} + \text{reciprocal} = \frac{13}{6}$$

$$6x\left[x + \frac{1}{x}\right] = 6x\left(\frac{13}{6}\right)$$

$$6x \cdot x + 6x \cdot \frac{1}{x} = 13x$$
$$6x^2 + 6 = 13x$$
$$6x^2 - 13x + 6 = 0$$
$$(3x - 2)(2x - 3) = 0$$
$$3x - 2 = 0 \ or \ 2x - 3 = 0$$
$$3x = 2 \qquad\qquad 2x = 3$$
$$x = \frac{2}{3} \qquad\qquad x = \frac{3}{2}$$

If $x = \frac{2}{3}$, then $\frac{1}{x} = \frac{3}{2}$. If $x = \frac{3}{2}$, then $\frac{1}{x} = \frac{2}{3}$.

Check $\frac{2}{3}$ and $\frac{3}{2}$ are reciprocals since $\frac{2}{3} \times \frac{3}{2} = 1$. Also, $\frac{2}{3} + \frac{3}{2} = \frac{4}{6} + \frac{9}{6} = \frac{13}{6}$.

Thus, the number and its reciprocal are $\frac{2}{3}$ and $\frac{3}{2}$, or $\frac{3}{2}$ and $\frac{2}{3}$.

EXAMPLE 5   The denominator of a fraction is 1 less than twice the numerator. If the numerator and denominator are each increased by 3, the resulting fraction simplifies to $\frac{3}{4}$. Find the original fraction.

Solution   Let a = the numerator of the original fraction.
Then $2a - 1$ = the denominator of the original fraction.

The original fraction is $\frac{a}{2a - 1}$.

If 3 is added to the original numerator and denominator, the resulting fraction is equal to $\frac{3}{4}$.

$$\frac{a + 3}{(2a - 1) + 3} = \frac{3}{4}$$

$$\frac{a + 3}{2a + 2} = \frac{3}{4}$$

$$\frac{a + 3}{2(a + 1)} = \frac{3}{2 \cdot 2} \quad \longleftarrow \text{LCD} = 2 \cdot 2(a + 1)$$

$$2 \cdot \overset{1}{\cancel{2}}(\overset{1}{\cancel{a + 1}})\left[\frac{a + 3}{\underset{1}{\cancel{2}}(\underset{1}{\cancel{a + 1}})}\right] = \overset{1}{\cancel{2}} \cdot \overset{1}{\cancel{2}}(a + 1)\left[\frac{3}{\underset{1}{\cancel{2}} \cdot \underset{1}{\cancel{2}}}\right]$$

$$2(a + 3) = (a + 1)3$$
$$2a + 6 = 3a + 3$$
$$6 = a + 3$$
$$3 = a$$

Original fraction $= \dfrac{a}{2a - 1} = \dfrac{3}{2 \cdot 3 - 1} = \dfrac{3}{6 - 1} = \dfrac{3}{5}$

Check   The denominator of $\frac{3}{5}$ is 1 less than twice the numerator. If the numerator and the denominator are each increased by 3, the new fraction simplifies to $\frac{3}{4}$.

$$\frac{3 + 3}{5 + 3} = \frac{6}{8} = \frac{3}{4}$$

Thus, the original fraction is $\frac{3}{5}$

TRY THIS   3. The denominator of a fraction is 3 less than 3 times the numerator. If the numerator and denominator are each increased by 4, the resulting fraction simplifies to $\frac{1}{2}$. Find the original fraction.

Classroom Exercises

State the LCD for the denominators of each rational equation.

1. $\dfrac{1}{2} - \dfrac{1}{x} = \dfrac{1}{8}$

2. $\dfrac{3}{y} - \dfrac{2}{5y} = 13$

3. $\dfrac{2}{t^2 - 9} + \dfrac{5}{t - 3} = \dfrac{4}{t + 3}$

4. $\dfrac{6}{x^2 - 3x - 28} = \dfrac{3}{x - 7} - \dfrac{2}{x + 4}$

Solve. Check the extraneous solutions.

5. $\dfrac{1}{x} - \dfrac{1}{4} = \dfrac{1}{12}$

6. $\dfrac{2}{a + 1} + \dfrac{1}{a - 1} = 1$

Write algebraic representations for the fractions described below.

7. The numerator of a fraction is twice the denominator.

0. The denominator of a fraction is 4 less than 3 times the numerator.

Written Exercises

Solve. Check for extraneous solutions.

1. $\dfrac{1}{2} - \dfrac{1}{x} = \dfrac{1}{3}$

2. $\dfrac{5}{2y} + \dfrac{1}{12} = \dfrac{3}{y}$

3. $\dfrac{1}{2x} - \dfrac{1}{3x} = 1$

4. $\dfrac{5}{6} = \dfrac{1}{n} + \dfrac{2}{3n}$

5. $\dfrac{5}{y + 3} = \dfrac{1}{y + 3} + 3$

6. $\dfrac{1}{3x + 6} + 2 = \dfrac{3}{x + 2}$

7. $\dfrac{2}{n^2 - n} + 1 = \dfrac{2}{n - 1}$

8. $\dfrac{1}{x} + \dfrac{2}{x + 1} = \dfrac{7}{x^2 + x}$

9. $\dfrac{1}{x - 4} = \dfrac{3}{x + 4} - \dfrac{2}{x^2 - 16}$

10. $\dfrac{2}{y^2 - 9} = \dfrac{4}{y + 3} - \dfrac{5}{y - 3}$

11. $\dfrac{6}{n^2 - 3n - 28} + \dfrac{2}{n + 4} = \dfrac{3}{n - 7}$

12. $\dfrac{4}{x^2 - 2x - 15} = \dfrac{2}{5 - x} + \dfrac{1}{x + 3}$

13. $\dfrac{5}{a^2 - 2a - 24} = \dfrac{2}{6 - a} + \dfrac{3}{a + 4}$

14. $\dfrac{1}{x - 5} + \dfrac{3}{x - 2} = \dfrac{4}{x^2 - 7x + 10}$

15. $\dfrac{2y - 1}{y^2 - 9y + 20} = \dfrac{4}{4 - y} + \dfrac{7}{y - 5}$

16. $\dfrac{-20}{a^2 - 4a - 45} = \dfrac{2}{a - 9} + \dfrac{a + 3}{a + 5}$

17. $\dfrac{x + 5}{x - 4} = \dfrac{3}{x} + \dfrac{36}{x^2 - 4x}$

18. $\dfrac{16}{x^2 - 4x} = \dfrac{2}{x} + \dfrac{x}{x - 4}$

19. $\dfrac{13}{x^2 - 4} + \dfrac{x}{2 - x} = \dfrac{-2}{x + 2}$

20. $\dfrac{x + 1}{x - 3} = \dfrac{3}{x} + \dfrac{12}{x^2 - 3x}$

Sometimes, none of the solutions of a derived equation is a solution of the original equation. In that case, the original equation has no solution. Solve and check.

21. $\dfrac{6}{3y - 2} + \dfrac{6y}{9y^2 - 4} = \dfrac{1}{3y + 2}$

22. $\dfrac{x}{x - 2} = \dfrac{1}{x} + \dfrac{4}{x^2 - 2x}$

23. $\dfrac{n}{n - 2} = \dfrac{4}{n + 3} + 1$

24. $\dfrac{3}{9 - 4x^2} - \dfrac{2}{3 + 2x} = \dfrac{2x}{9 - 4x^2}$

The formula at the right refers to a convex lens and the way it forms an inverted image of a given object.

$$\dfrac{1}{D} + \dfrac{1}{d} = \dfrac{1}{F}$$

Here, D is the distance from the lens to the object; d is the distance from the lens to the image; and F is the distance from the lens to a point called the *focus*. F is called the *focal length* of the lens.

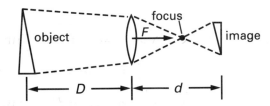

25. Find F for $D = 18$ cm and $d = 12$ cm.

26. Find d for $D = 10$ cm and $F = 3$ cm.

27. The sum of a number and its reciprocal is $\frac{25}{12}$. Find the number.

28. Find two consecutive integers if the sum of their reciprocals is $\frac{11}{30}$.

29. The denominator of a fraction is 2 less than twice the numerator. If the numerator is decreased by 2 and the denominator is increased by 3, the resulting fraction simplifies to $\frac{1}{3}$. Find the original fraction.

Solve and check.

30. $\dfrac{5}{x^2 + 2x - 24} - \dfrac{2}{4x - x^2} = \dfrac{4}{x^2 + 6x}$

31. $\dfrac{1}{x^2 + 5x + 6} = \dfrac{2}{x^2 - x - 6} - \dfrac{3}{9 - x^2}$

Mixed Review

State the correct property for each equation.   *1.5, 1.6, 1.7*

1. $a + 6 = 6 + a$

2. $3 + (b + 9) = (3 + b) + 9$

3. $7(a + 6) = 7a + 7 \cdot 6$

4. $1 \cdot x = x$

Simplify.   *6.2, 6.10, 8.2, 8.3*

5. $(-3x^2y^4)^3$

6. $(x + 3)^2$

7. $\dfrac{a - 3}{9 - a^2}$

8. $\dfrac{36a^4b^2}{9x - 27} \cdot \dfrac{9 - x^2}{12ab^5}$

9.2 Ratios and Proportions

Objective   To solve proportions

A **ratio** is a comparison of two numbers by division. The equation $\frac{7}{2} = \frac{x}{3}$ states that two ratios are equal. Such an equation is called a *proportion*.

Definition

A **proportion** is an equation that states that two ratios are equal.

$$\frac{a}{b} = \frac{c}{d}, \ b \neq 0 \text{ and } d \neq 0 \quad \text{or} \quad a{:}b = c{:}d$$

In this proportion, a and d are the **extremes**; b and c are the **means**.

EXAMPLE 1   Identify the extremes and the means of the proportion $\frac{7}{2} = \frac{x}{3}$. Then solve for x.

Solution   The extremes are 7 and 3. The means are 2 and x.

A proportion such as $\frac{7}{2} = \frac{x}{3}$ can be solved by multiplying each side of the equation by the LCM of the denominators, $2 \cdot 3$.

$$\overset{1}{2} \cdot 3 \cdot \frac{7}{\underset{1}{2}} = 2 \cdot \overset{1}{3} \cdot \frac{x}{\underset{1}{3}}$$

$$3 \cdot 7 = 2 \cdot x$$

$$21 = 2x$$

$$10\tfrac{1}{2} = x, \text{ or } x = 10\tfrac{1}{2}$$

TRY THIS   1. Identify the extremes and the means of the proportion $\frac{x}{9} = \frac{4}{5}$. Then solve for x.

Proportion Property

For all real numbers a, b, c, and d where $b \neq 0$, $d \neq 0$, if $\frac{a}{b} = \frac{c}{d}$, then $ad = bc$. That is, the product of the extremes equals the product of the means.

The Proportion Property provides another method for solving proportions.

EXAMPLE 2 Solve $\dfrac{2}{x} = \dfrac{3}{x + 6}$.

Plan Use the Proportion Property: product of extremes = product of means.

Solution

$$\dfrac{2}{x} = \dfrac{3}{x + 6} \qquad \text{Check:} \qquad \dfrac{2}{x} = \dfrac{3}{x + 6}$$

$$2(x + 6) = x \cdot 3$$
$$2x + 12 = 3x \qquad\qquad\qquad \dfrac{2}{12} \overset{?}{=} \dfrac{3}{12 + 6}$$
$$12 = x$$
$$x = 12 \qquad\qquad\qquad\qquad \dfrac{1}{6} \overset{?}{=} \dfrac{3}{18}$$

$$\dfrac{1}{6} = \dfrac{1}{6} \text{ True}$$

Thus, 12 is the solution of the proportion.

TRY THIS 2. Solve $\dfrac{4}{a} = \dfrac{6}{a + 3}$.

In solving a proportion, you may need to solve a quadratic equation.

EXAMPLE 3 Solve $\dfrac{y - 6}{7} = \dfrac{1}{y}$.

Plan Use the fact that product of extremes = product of means.

Solution

$$(y - 6)y = 7 \cdot 1$$
$$y^2 - 6y = 7$$
$$y^2 - 6y - 7 = 0$$

Factor. $\qquad (y - 7)(y + 1) = 0$

$$y - 7 = 0 \quad \text{or} \quad y + 1 = 0$$
$$y = 7 \qquad\qquad\quad y = -1$$

The checks are left for you. Both 7 and -1 make the proportion true.

Thus, the solutions are 7 and -1

TRY THIS 3. Solve $\dfrac{1}{x} = \dfrac{(x + 5)}{24}$.

Many practical problems involve ratio and proportion. Some of these are illustrated in the next three examples.

EXAMPLE 4 A recipe for $3\frac{1}{2}$ dozen muffins requires 700 g of flour. How many dozens of muffins can be made using 800 g of flour? (THINK: 800 g is a little more than 700 g, so the answer must be a little more than $3\frac{1}{2}$.)

Solution Let x = the number of dozens of muffins using 800 g of flour.

$$\frac{3\frac{1}{2}}{700} = \frac{x}{800}$$

Calculator Steps:

3.5 $\boxed{\times}$ 800 $\boxed{\div}$ 700 $\boxed{=}$ 4

$$\frac{7}{2} \cdot 800 = 700 \cdot x$$
$$2,800 = 700x$$
$$4 = x$$

(THINK: 4 is a little more than $3\frac{1}{2}$, so the answer is reasonable.)

Check The ratios $\frac{3\frac{1}{2}}{700}$ and $\frac{4}{800}$ are equal, since $3\frac{1}{2} \times 800 = 2,800$ and $4 \times 700 = 2,800$.
Thus, 4 dozen muffins can be made.

EXAMPLE 5 A recent poll found that 7 out of 8 people use No-Cavit toothpaste. How many people can be expected to use this brand in a city of 40,000?

Solution *7 out of 8* means $\frac{7}{8}$. Let x = the number of people who can be expected to use No-Cavit in a city of 40,000.

$$\frac{7}{8} = \frac{x}{40,000}$$
⟵ No-Cavit users
⟵ total number of people

$7 \cdot 40,000 = 8 \cdot x$ **Calculator Steps:**
$280,000 = 8x$
$35,000 = x$ 7 $\boxed{\times}$ 40,000 $\boxed{\div}$ 8 $\boxed{=}$ 35,000

The check is left for you.

In a city of 40,000 people, 35,000 can be expected to use No-Cavit.

TRY THIS 4. A recipe for $2\frac{1}{2}$ dozen cookies requires 400 g of flour. How many dozens can be made using 600 g of flour?

Some problems involving *ratios* can be solved without writing proportions. If two numbers are in a given ratio, they can be represented in terms of a single variable.

This figure shows two angles whose measures are in a ratio of 4:5.

Two angles are **supplementary** if the sum of their degree measures is 180.

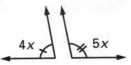

$4x$ $5x$

EXAMPLE 6	Find the measures of two supplementary angles if they are in a ratio of 4:5.
Solution	Let $4x$ = measure of one angle. Let $5x$ = measure of second angle.

$4x + 5x = 180$ ⟵ Sum of measures of supplementary angles is 180.
$$9x = 180$$
$$x = 20$$

Then, $4x = 80$ and $5x = 100$.

Check The ratio $\frac{80}{100}$ equals $\frac{4}{5}$. The angles are supplementary, because
$80 + 100 = 180$.

Thus, the degree measures of the angles are 80 and 100.

TRY THIS 5. Find the measures of two supplementary angles if they are in a ratio of 2:1.

Focus on Reading

Which equation is *not* equivalent to the others in the group? Explain.

1. a. $\dfrac{8}{3} = \dfrac{y}{9}$ **b.** $\dfrac{72}{3} = y$ **c.** $9y = 24$ **d.** $8 \cdot 9 = 3 \cdot y$

2. a. $\dfrac{3}{x} = \dfrac{4}{x-2}$ **b.** $4(x-2) = 3x$ **c.** $3(x-2) = 4x$ **d.** $-6 = x$

Classroom Exercises

Identify the extremes and means of each proportion. Then use the Proportion Property to write an equivalent equation without fractions.

1. $\dfrac{n}{5} = \dfrac{3}{4}$ **2.** $\dfrac{4}{x} = \dfrac{3}{5}$ **3.** $\dfrac{x}{7} = \dfrac{x-2}{10}$ **4.** $\dfrac{3}{x} = \dfrac{5}{2x-3}$

Solve.

5. $\dfrac{n}{3} = \dfrac{4}{7}$ **6.** $\dfrac{3}{a-2} = \dfrac{4}{a}$ **7.** $\dfrac{x-1}{3} = \dfrac{x}{4}$ **8.** $\dfrac{8}{n} = \dfrac{n}{18}$

Written Exercises

Identify the extremes and the means of each proportion.

1. $\dfrac{5}{2} \diagup \dfrac{10}{x}$
2. $\dfrac{9}{12} = \dfrac{36}{n}$
3. $\dfrac{x}{3} = \dfrac{7}{4}$
4. $\dfrac{10}{m} = \dfrac{52}{13}$

5. $\dfrac{3}{n+6} = \dfrac{2}{n}$
6. $\dfrac{x+3}{5} = \dfrac{x-2}{4}$
7. $\dfrac{n}{3} = \dfrac{2}{n-5}$
8. $\dfrac{x}{2} = \dfrac{2}{x+3}$

9–12. Solve the proportions in Written Exercises 1–4.

Solve.

13. $\dfrac{x}{5} = \dfrac{3}{7}$
14. $\dfrac{11}{x} = \dfrac{3}{1}$
15. $\dfrac{4}{n} = \dfrac{5}{9}$
16. $\dfrac{8}{3} = \dfrac{m}{7}$

17. $\dfrac{2}{x-3} = \dfrac{5}{x}$
18. $\dfrac{x}{3} - 1 = \dfrac{x+1}{5}$
19. $\dfrac{n}{3} = \dfrac{n+4}{7}$
20. $\dfrac{1}{n-3} = \dfrac{3}{n-5}$

21. $\dfrac{x}{2} = \dfrac{30}{x-4}$
22. $\dfrac{12}{x} = \dfrac{x+4}{1}$
23. $\dfrac{n}{4} = \dfrac{10}{n-3}$
24. $\dfrac{y}{3} = \dfrac{56}{y+2}$

25. $\dfrac{8}{x} = \dfrac{x}{2}$
26. $\dfrac{n}{3} = \dfrac{1}{12n}$
27. $\dfrac{y-5}{4} = \dfrac{y+3}{3}$
28. $\dfrac{m}{2} = \dfrac{36}{m+6}$

29. $\dfrac{x}{3} = \dfrac{6}{2x}$
30. $\dfrac{12}{y} = \dfrac{y}{12}$
31. $\dfrac{2x}{3} = \dfrac{16}{x+2}$
32. $\dfrac{1}{y} = \dfrac{6y-1}{1}$

33. If 6 out of 8 people use Clean-White toothpaste, how many people out of 60,000 can be expected to use Clean-White toothpaste?

34. Sal uses 4 skeins of yarn to make 3 scarfs. How many skeins of yarn will he need to make 15 scarfs?

35. $\dfrac{3}{x+2} = \dfrac{x-8}{13}$
36. $\dfrac{2}{n-3} = \dfrac{n-4}{1}$
37. $\dfrac{9}{m-5} = \dfrac{m+7}{-3}$
38. $\dfrac{b+2}{3} = \dfrac{13}{b-8}$

39. $\dfrac{n}{n+3} = \dfrac{n}{2}$
40. $\dfrac{y}{y+4} = \dfrac{y}{10}$
41. $\dfrac{n+3}{n-1} = \dfrac{5n}{2}$
42. $\dfrac{2x+2}{x+1} = \dfrac{x-2}{1}$

43. A recipe for making bran muffins requires 1,600 g of flour to make 40 muffins. How many muffins can be made using 1,000 g of flour?

44. Mr. Carmelito used 15 gallons of gasoline to drive 450 mi. How far can he drive on a full tank of 20 gallons of gasoline?

45. Find the measures of two supplementary angles if their measures are in a ratio of 7:2.

46. Find the measures of two supplementary angles if their measures are in a ratio of 1:3.

47. Find the measures of two complementary angles if their measures are in a ratio of 5:13. (Recall that two angles are complementary if the sum of their measures is 90.)

48. The area of a rectangle is 300 in². The sides are in the ratio 3:4. Find the perimeter of the rectangle.

49. If $3x = 4y$, find the ratio $y:x$.

50. If $pq = rs$, find the ratio $r:q$.

Mixed Review

Solve. *3.3, 5.6, 7.7*

1. $3x - 2 = -23$ **2.** $|3x + 1| = 16$ **3.** $a^2 - 6a = 0$ **4.** $x^2 - 16 = 0$

Multiply. *8.3*

5. $(a - 1) \cdot \dfrac{5a + 15}{a^2 + 2a - 3}$

6. $\dfrac{x^2 - 9}{4x + 20} \cdot \dfrac{x^2 - 25}{x^2 - 8x + 15}$

Divide. *8.4*

7. $\dfrac{a^2 - 9a + 20}{4a - a^2} \div \dfrac{a^2 + 2a - 35}{a}$

8. $\dfrac{18x^4 y^2}{a^2 + 4a - 5} \div \dfrac{6xy^4}{a^2 - 4a + 3}$

9. The larger of two numbers is 8 more than 4 times the other. Their sum is 113. Find the two numbers. *4.2*

Application: Direct Variation

A visitor to a sheep ranch asked a sheepherder how he could count the sheep so quickly. The herder answered, "Oh, it's easy. I just count the legs and divide by four!" This old joke may not describe an efficient way to count sheep, but it is an example of *direct variation*. The ratio of the number of legs to the number of heads is always 4:1.

In a **direct variation**, the ratio of y to x is always the same. If y *varies directly* as x, then

$$\frac{y}{x} = k, \text{ or } y = kx \text{ where } k \text{ is constant.}$$

Solve.

1. A conservationist catches 650 deer, tags them, and releases them. Later she catches 216 deer and finds that 54 of them are tagged. Estimate how many deer are in the forest. Use this proportion.

$$\frac{\text{Total tagged}}{\text{Total in forest}} = \frac{\text{Sample with tags}}{\text{Sample caught}}$$

(Assume that the number of tagged deer caught *varies directly* as the number of deer later caught.)

2. A game warden catches 125 fish, tags them, and puts them back in the lake. Later, he catches 65 fish and finds that 13 of them are tagged. How many fish are in the lake? Assume that the number of tagged fish caught *varies directly* as the number of fish later caught.

3. Emil's hourly earnings *vary directly* as the number of hours worked. For working 45 h, the earnings are $168.75. Find his earnings for 35 h of work.

9.3 Literal Equations

Objectives

To solve a literal equation or formula for one of its variables

To evaluate a formula for one of its variables, given the value(s) of its other variables(s)

Simple interest on money invested can be expressed by the formula

$$i = prt,$$

where i is the amount of interest, p is the principal, r is the rate of interest, and t is the time in years. The formula $i = prt$ can also be solved for one of the other variables. For example, you can solve for r by dividing each side of the equation by pt.

$$i = prt$$

$$\frac{i}{pt} = \frac{\overset{1}{\cancel{p}}r\overset{1}{\cancel{t}}}{\underset{1}{\cancel{p}}\underset{1}{\cancel{t}}}$$

$$\frac{i}{pt} = r, \text{ or } r = \frac{i}{pt}$$

A formula contains more than one variable. Similarly, a *literal equation* such as $ax + b = 10c$ contains more than one letter or variable. In a **literal equation** any variable can be expressed in terms of the others.

EXAMPLE 1   Solve $ax + b = 10c$ for x.

Plan   Solve for x in the same way you would solve the equation $2x + 18 = 16$.

Solution

$ax + b = 10c$	THINK: $2x + 18 = 16$
$ax + b - b = 10c - b$	$2x + 18 - 18 = 16 - 18$
$ax = 10c - b$	$2x = -2$
$x = \dfrac{10c - b}{a}$	$x = -1$

TRY THIS   1. Solve $ax - 3b = 8c$ for a.

To solve an equation for a variable that appears in more than one term, get all of those terms by themselves on one side of the equation.

EXAMPLE 2 Solve $ax = 4c - bx$ for x.

Plan Add bx to each side.

Solution

$$ax = 4c - bx$$
$$ax + bx = 4c - bx + bx$$
Factor out x. $\quad ax + bx = 4c$
Divide each side by $(a + b)$. $\quad x(a + b) = 4c$
$$x = \frac{4c}{a + b}$$

TRY THIS 2. Solve $ay = xy + 6c$ for y.

An important formula in banking is $A = p + prt$. The formula is used to find: (1) the amount of money in an account after interest has been credited, or (2) the total amount due on a loan including the interest.

EXAMPLE 3 Solve $A = p + prt$ for t. Then find the time t in years, for principal $p = \$500$, amount $A = \$560$, and rate $r = 6\%$ per year.

Plan First solve for t.

Solution Subtract p from each side. $\qquad A = p + prt$
$$A - p = p - p + prt$$
Divide each side by pr. $\qquad A - p = prt$
$$\frac{A - p}{pr} = t$$

Now find t by substituting 560 for A, 500 for p, and 0.06 for r.

$$t = \frac{A - p}{pr}$$

$$= \frac{560 - 500}{500(0.06)}$$

Calculator Steps:

560 $\boxed{-}$ 500 $\boxed{=}$ $\boxed{\div}$ 500 $\boxed{\div}$ .06 $\boxed{=}$

$$= \frac{60}{30} = 2$$

Thus, $t = \dfrac{A - p}{pr}$, and $t = 2$ years for the given values of A, p, and r.

TRY THIS 3. Solve $A = p + prt$ for p. Then find the principal, p, when the amount $A = \$399$, the rate $r = 7\%$ per year, and the time $t = 2$ years.

EXAMPLE 4   Solve $\frac{1}{a} = \frac{5}{b} + \frac{3}{c}$ for b.

Solution   Multiply by the LCD, abc.

$$abc \cdot \frac{1}{a} = abc \cdot \frac{5}{b} + abc \cdot \frac{3}{c}$$

$$\not{a} \cdot b \cdot c \cdot \frac{1}{\not{a}} = a \cdot \not{b} \cdot c \cdot \frac{5}{\not{b}} + a \cdot b \cdot \not{c} \cdot \frac{3}{\not{c}}$$

$$bc = 5ac + 3ab$$

Subtract $3ab$. $bc - 3ab = 5ac$

Factor out b. $b(c - 3a) = 5ac$

$$b = \frac{5ac}{c - 3a}$$

EXAMPLE 5   A formula for the area of a trapezoid is

$$A = \tfrac{1}{2}h(b + c).$$

Solve this formula for c. Then find c for $A = 70$, $b = 6$, and $h = 10$.

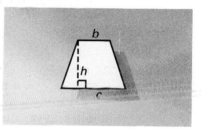

Solution   Multiply each side by 2.

Use the Distributive Property.
Subtract bh from each side to get ch alone.
Divide each side by h.

$$A = \tfrac{1}{2}h(b + c)$$
$$2A = h(b + c)$$
$$2A = bh + ch$$
$$2A - bh = ch$$
$$\frac{2A - bh}{h} = c$$

Substitute 70 for A, 6 for b and 10 for h.

$$c = \frac{2A - bh}{h}$$
$$= \frac{2 \cdot 70 - 6 \cdot 10}{10}$$
$$= \frac{140 - 60}{10}$$
$$= \frac{80}{10}, \text{ or } 8$$

Thus, $c = \frac{2A - bh}{h}$, and $c = 8$ for the given values of A, h, and b.

TRY THIS   4. Solve $\frac{2}{x} = \frac{5}{2y} - \frac{3}{z}$ for z.

Classroom Exercises

Solve for *x*.

1. $ax = 3$

2. $x + b = c$

3. $x - a = b$

4. $ax = b$

5. $\dfrac{x}{a} = b$

6. $-5 = ax$

7. $x + r = s$

8. $-4 = \dfrac{x}{t}$

9. $ax - b = 6$

10. $-n = 12x + 5$

11. $ax - 3c = 2x$

12. $\dfrac{1}{x} = \dfrac{a}{b}$

Written Exercises

Solve for *x*.

1. $bx = 5$

2. $x - e = f$

3. $x + 2c = b$

4. $-ax = c$

5. $\dfrac{x}{y} = z$

6. $\dfrac{2}{x} = \dfrac{a}{c}$

7. $\dfrac{r}{s} = \dfrac{3}{x}$

8. $-5 = \dfrac{1}{cx}$

9. $6x + b = c$

10. $ax - b = c$

11. $n = ax + m$

12. $px - q = -r$

13. $ax + bx = c$

14. $c = ax - bx$

15. $ax = c + bx$

16. $ax = 4c - 3x$

17. $bx = 36 - dx$

18. $mx = d + rx$

19. $cx = dx + 18$

20. $7ax = 16 - cx$

21. $\dfrac{x}{3} = \dfrac{a}{2} + \dfrac{t}{6}$

22. $\dfrac{h}{5} + \dfrac{h}{3} = \dfrac{x}{15}$

23. $\dfrac{x}{5b} = \dfrac{k}{j}$

24. $\dfrac{x}{y} - g = v$

25. The formula for the perimeter of a rectangle is $p = 2l + 2w$. Solve for *l*. Then find *l* for $p = 49.4$ cm and $w = 6.3$ cm.

26. The formula for the perimeter of a model of a certain racetrack is $p = 4r + 2\pi r$. Solve for *r*. Then find *r* for $p \approx 30.84$.

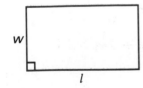

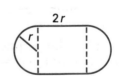

Solve for *x*.

27. $-6x + c = -3x - 14c$

28. $16a - 5bx = bx - 4$

29. $kx - cd = 4e + f$

30. $5ax + b = 80ax - c$

31. $px + q = rx - 6p$

32. $-4a + 2bx = 12a + 10bx$

33. $\dfrac{1}{a} + \dfrac{1}{b} = \dfrac{1}{x}$

34. $v = \dfrac{x - t}{s}$

35. Give an example of a literal equation and write in your own words a step-by-step description of how to solve it.

Solve each equation for the variable indicated.

36. $a^2 - ax + 12 = 4x - 7a$ for x

37. $rx + 2sx = r^2 - 7rs - 18s^2$ for x

38. $\dfrac{rs}{a} + \dfrac{st}{b} = 1$ for s

39. $s = \dfrac{a - ar^2}{1 - r}$ for a

40. $W = -G\left(c - \dfrac{Q}{m}\right)$ for Q

41. $ry^2 - b^2r - ty^2 + b^2t = y^2 - b^2$ for r

42. $a_1 = b\left(\dfrac{a_2}{b} + 4\right)$ for a_2

43. $V = \dfrac{A}{x_1} - \dfrac{B}{x_2}$ for x_2

Midchapter Review

Solve. Check for extraneous solutions.   *9.1, 9.2*

1. $\dfrac{2}{3} - \dfrac{5}{x} = \dfrac{1}{4}$

2. $\dfrac{1}{y} - \dfrac{2}{3y} = 2$

3. $\dfrac{3a - 1}{a^2 - a - 12} = \dfrac{5}{a + 3} - \dfrac{6}{4 - a}$

4. $\dfrac{3y - 1}{y - 4} = \dfrac{3}{y^2 - 16} + \dfrac{3}{y + 4}$

5. $\dfrac{x}{12} = \dfrac{3}{x}$

6. $\dfrac{y - 5}{6} = \dfrac{y - 1}{3}$

7. $\dfrac{a + 4}{-5} = \dfrac{2}{a - 3}$

8. $\dfrac{n}{3} = \dfrac{150}{2n}$

Solve for x.   *9.3*

9. $ax - 3 = 5b$

10. $n = \dfrac{x}{y}$

11. $bx - c = ax$

12. $\dfrac{x}{4} = \dfrac{a}{3} + \dfrac{b}{6}$

13. The sum of a number and its reciprocal is $\dfrac{61}{30}$. Find the number.   *9.1*

14. The formula for the perimeter of a rectangle is $p = 2l + 2w$. Solve for w. Then find w for $p = 62$ cm and $l = 7$ cm.   *9.3*

▰/Brainteaser

A young boy could not yet tell time but was counting the number of times the grandfather clock chimed. At 3:40 in the afternoon he told his mother that the clock had chimed 34 times. If the clock chimes the number of times of the hour on the hour and once on the half hour, what time was it when the boy began counting the chimes?

9.4 Problem Solving: Motion Problems

Objective	To solve motion problems

Motion problems involve three variables: distance, rate, and time where distance = rate × time, or $d = rt$. The formula $d = rt$ can be solved for either r or t.

$$r = \frac{d}{t} \qquad \text{or} \qquad t = \frac{d}{r}$$

Each form of the distance formula is useful in solving problems.

EXAMPLE 1 *Traveling in Opposite Directions*
Two cyclists leave at the same time from the same point and travel in opposite directions. The rate of one cyclist is 7 km/h less than the rate of the other cyclist. After 10 h, the cyclists are 530 km apart. Find the rate of each cyclist.

Solution Let x = the rate of the faster cyclist. Then $x - 7$ = the rate of the slower cyclist

Make a sketch. Also, make a table to represent the distance traveled by each cyclist. Then write an equation and solve it.

	Rate	Time	Distance ($d = r \cdot t$)
Faster cyclist	x	10	$10x$
Slower cyclist	$x - 7$	10	$10(x - 7)$, or $10x - 70$

$$\underset{\text{faster cyclist}}{\text{distance of}} + \underset{\text{slower cyclist}}{\text{distance of}} = \underset{\text{apart}}{\text{total distance}}$$

$$
\begin{aligned}
10x \quad + \quad 10x - 70 \quad &= \quad 530 \\
20x &= 600 \\
x &= 30 \text{ (faster rate: 30 km/h)} \\
\text{So, } x - 7 &= 23 \text{ (slower rate: 23 km/h)}
\end{aligned}
$$

Check The rates differ by 7 km/h. After 10 h, are the cyclists 530 km apart? Yes, since $(10 \cdot 30) + (10 \cdot 23) = 300 + 230 = 530$.

Thus, the two rates are 30 km/h and 23 km/h.

TRY THIS 1. Two cars leave at the same time from the same point and travel in opposite directions. The rate of one car is 4 km/h more than the rate of the other car. After 6 h, the cars are 624 km apart. Find the rate of each car.

EXAMPLE 2 *Traveling in Same Direction*
Rae Marie and Fred were practicing for a long-distance boat race. Rae Marie started first and rowed at the rate 12 km/h. One hour later Fred left from the same point and rowed in the same direction at 16 km/h. How many hours did he row before he caught up with Rae Marie?

Solution Let x = number of hours that Rae Marie rowed.

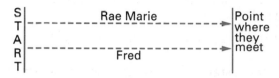

Then $x - 1$ = number of hours that Fred rowed.

	Rate	Time	Distance ($d = rt$)
Rae Marie	12	x	$12x$
Fred	16	$x - 1$	$16(x - 1)$, or $16x - 16$

Rae Marie's distance = Fred's distance
$$12x = 16x - 16$$
$$16 = 4x$$
$$x = 4 \quad \longleftarrow \text{ Rae Marie's time}$$
$$x - 1 = 3 \quad \longleftarrow \text{ Fred's time}$$

The check is left for you.

Thus, Fred rowed 3 h before he caught up with Rae Marie.

EXAMPLE 3 *Going and Returning at Different Rates*
Larry, Judy, and their daughters drove to the ski slope at 70 km/h. After a snowstorm, they managed to drive home at 40 km/h. It took 2 h longer to return home than it took going to ski. How long did it take for them to get home?

Solution Let x = number of hours that it took to go.

Distances are equal.

Then $x + 2$ = number of hours that it took to return.

	Rate	Time	Distance ($d = rt$)
Going	70	x	$70x$
Returning	40	$x + 2$	$40(x + 2)$, or $40x + 80$

$$\text{distance going} = \text{distance returning}$$
$$70x = 40x + 80$$
$$30x = 80$$
$$x = \frac{80}{30}, \text{ or } 2\frac{2}{3} \quad \longleftarrow \text{ time going}$$
$$\text{So, } x + 2 = 4\frac{2}{3}. \quad \longleftarrow \text{ time returning}$$

The check is left for you.

Thus, it took $4\frac{2}{3}$ h for them to return home.

EXAMPLE 4 *Traveling Different Distances in the Same Time*
It took Peter the same amount of time to drive 325 km as it took Mary to drive 275 km. Peter's speed was 10 km/h more than Mary's speed. How fast did each drive?

Solution Let x = Mary's rate in kilometers per hour.
Then $x + 10$ = Peter's rate in kilometers per hour.
Since the distances are given, represent the time in terms of distance and rate.

	Rate	Time $\left(t = \frac{d}{r}\right)$	Distance
Mary	x	$\dfrac{275}{x}$	275
Peter	$x + 10$	$\dfrac{325}{x + 10}$	325

$$\text{Peter's time} = \text{Mary's time}$$
$$\frac{325}{x + 10} = \frac{275}{x}$$
$$325x = 275(x + 10)$$
$$325x = 275x + 2{,}750$$
$$50x = 2{,}750$$
$$x = 55 \quad \longleftarrow \text{ Mary's rate}$$
$$\text{So, } x + 10 = 65 \quad \longleftarrow \text{ Peter's rate}$$

The check is left for you.

Thus, Peter's rate was 65 km/h and Mary's rate was 55 km/h.

TRY THIS 2. Sue and Tim drove for the same amount of time. Sue's rate was 52 km/h and Tim's rate was 42 km/h. Sue drove 40 km farther than Tim. How far did each drive?

Classroom Exercises

Use one of the formulas, $d = rt$, $r = \frac{d}{t}$, or $t = \frac{d}{r}$ to find the indicated value. (Exercises 1–4)

1. rate: 50 km/h
   time: 4 h
   distance: _____?_____

2. distance: 300 km
   rate: 60 km/h
   time: _____?_____

3. distance: 40 km
   time: 5 h
   rate: _____?_____

4. rate: 24 km/h
   time: 1.5 h
   distance: _____?_____

5. Bob drives 60 km/h for x hours. What is an expression for the distance traveled?

6. Carlotta drives 55 km/h for $(x + 2)$ hours. What is an expression for the distance traveled?

7. Pierre drove 680 km at a rate of $(y + 10)$ km/h. Write an expression for the time that he spent traveling.

8. Two jets left from the same airport at the same time. One flew east at 600 km/h. The other flew west at 900 km/h. In how many hours were they 6,000 km apart?

Written Exercises

Solve each problem.

1. Two cyclists left from the same place at the same time and rode in opposite directions. One cyclist rode 5 km/h faster than the other. After 6 h, the cyclists were 78 km apart. How fast did each travel?

2. Two cars left at the same time and traveled in opposite directions from the same starting point. One car traveled 20 km/h faster than the other car. After 7 h the cars were 910 km apart. Find each car's rate.

3. Bea ran along a bicycle path at 6 km/h. One hour later, Roberto left from the same point and ran along the same path at 9 km/h. How many hours did he run before he caught up with Bea?

4. Nathan started out in his car at the rate of 42 km/h. Two hours later, Joelle left from the same point driving along the same road at 80 km/h. How long did it take her to catch up to Nathan?

5. The Smith family drove to the beach at 75 km/h. They returned later, in heavy traffic, at 50 km/h. The return trip took 2 h longer than the trip to the beach. How long did it take to get home?

6. Bart drove to a family reunion at the rate of 70 km/h. A few days later, the return trip took 1 h less because he drove at 80 km/h. How long did it take him to get home?

7. Miguel biked 14 km in the same amount of time that Linda hiked 10 km. Miguel's rate was 4 km/h more than Linda's. How fast did each travel?

8. Chuck drove 240 km in the same amount of time that Millie drove 190 km. Chuck drove 20 km/h faster than Millie. How fast did each drive?

9. Two cars drove away from the same place at the same time in opposite directions. One car drove 12.5 km/h faster than the other. After 4 h, the cars were 570 km apart. Find each car's rate.

10. Carol started running at 7 km/h. One half-hour later, Roberto left from the same point and ran along the same path at 9 km/h. How many hours did he run before he caught up with Carol?

11. Two trains left at the same time from the same station and traveled in the same direction. The first train averaged 65 km/h and the second train averaged 85 km/h. How long did it take the faster train to get 200 km ahead of the slower train?

12. Two cars traveled in opposite directions from the same starting point. The rate of one car was 18 km/h faster than the rate of the other car. After 2 h 20 min, the cars were 428 km apart. Find each car's rate.

An aircraft carrier and a destroyer left the same port at 7:00 A.M. and sailed in the same direction. The destroyer traveled at a rate of 36 km/h and the carrier traveled at a rate of 24 km/h. At what time were they 300 km apart?

Eight minutes after a bank was robbed, the police started a chase to pursue the thief. The thief was driving at 80 km/h while the police were driving at 95 km/h. How long did it take the police to catch up with the thief?

Two trucks started toward each other at the same time from towns x km apart. One truck averaged y km/h and the other z km/h. Express algebraically the number of hours before they reached each other.

Tony started driving at the rate of q km/h. Then r hours later, Mary left from the same point driving along the same road at s km/h. Assume that $s > q$. Express algebraically the number of hours before Mary caught up with Tony.

Mixed Review

Multiply.   *6.4, 6.8, 6.9*

1. $3a^7b^2(-2a^{-2}b)$

2. $-4a^3b^{-4}(-3a^2b^3)$

3. $-3(x^4 + 2x^2 - 3x)$

4. $-5a^2b(a^3b - 3ab^2 - 2a^2b)$

5. $(2x - 1)(x + 8)$

6. $(3x - 1)(3x + 1)$

7. $(a - 1)(a^2 - 2a + 3)$

8. $(a + b)(3x - 2y)$

9. The length of a rectangle is 8 cm more than 4 times the width. The perimeter is 123 cm. Find the length and the width.   *4.4*

10. Maria has 14 coins, all in dimes and quarters. The number of dimes is 2 fewer than 3 times the number of quarters. How many coins of each type are there?   *4.2*

9.5 Problem Solving: Work Problems

Objective   To solve work problems

If Linda Sue can paint her room in 6 h, it takes 1 h to paint $\frac{1}{6}$ of the room and 3 h to paint $\frac{3}{6}$, or $\frac{1}{2}$, of the room. The part of work done in 5 h is $\frac{5}{6}$.

$$5 \quad \cdot \quad \frac{1}{6} \quad = \quad \frac{5}{6}$$

$$\underset{\substack{\text{time} \\ \text{worked}}}{} \cdot \underset{\substack{\text{rate of} \\ \text{work}}}{} = \underset{\substack{\text{part of work} \\ \text{completed}}}{}$$

This suggests a formula for solving work problems.

time · rate = part of work completed: $t \cdot r = w$, or $w = rt$

EXAMPLE 1   Frank can type a report in 5 h. What part can he type in 2 h? in 3 h? in n h?

Solution   To type the report in 5 h means $\frac{1}{5}$ of the report can be typed each hour. That is, $r = \frac{1}{5}$.

$w = rt$: In 2 h, $w = \frac{1}{5} \cdot 2 = \frac{2}{5}$ ⟵ $\frac{2}{5}$ of the report can be typed.

In 3 h, $w = \frac{1}{5} \cdot 3 = \frac{3}{5}$ ⟵ $\frac{3}{5}$ of the report can be typed.

In n h, $w = \frac{1}{5} \cdot n = \frac{n}{5}$ ⟵ $\frac{n}{5}$ of the report can be typed.

Thus, Frank can type $\frac{2}{5}$ of the report, $\frac{3}{5}$ of the report, and $\frac{n}{5}$ of the report in the given numbers of hours.

TRY THIS   1. Mary can wallpaper a room in 8 h. What part of the room can she wallpaper in 2h? in 5 h? in x h?

Sometimes two or more people work together to complete a job. Suppose, in Example 1, Frank did $\frac{2}{5}$ of the job and Gail did $\frac{3}{5}$ of the job. Then, together, they completed the job. So, $\frac{2}{5} + \frac{3}{5} = 1$.

EXAMPLE 2   Kim takes 6 days to prepare a boat for use. Dick takes 8 days to prepare the same boat for use. How long will it take to prepare the boat if they work together? (THINK: Will the number of days be less than 6 or more than 6?)

Plan   Let x = number of days Kim and Dick work together. Make a table to represent the part of the job completed by each person.

Solution

	rate	×	time	=	work
	Part of job done in 1 day		Number of days working together		Part of job completed
Kim	$\frac{1}{6}$		x		$\frac{1}{6}x = \frac{x}{6}$
Dick	$\frac{1}{8}$		x		$\frac{1}{8}x = \frac{x}{8}$

Kim's part + Dick's part = the whole job

$$\frac{x}{6} + \frac{x}{8} = 1$$

$$24\left(\frac{x}{6} + \frac{x}{8}\right) = 24 \cdot 1$$

$$24 \cdot \frac{x}{6} + 24 \cdot \frac{x}{8} = 24$$

$$4x + 3x = 24$$

$$7x = 24$$

$$x = \frac{24}{7}, \text{ or } 3\frac{3}{7} \quad \longleftarrow \text{ number of days to prepare the boat}$$

Check   In $3\frac{3}{7}$ days, will Kim and Dick complete the job?

Yes, since in $3\frac{3}{7}$ days, Kim will do $\frac{1}{6} \cdot \frac{24}{7}$, or $\frac{4}{7}$ of the job; Dick will do $\frac{1}{8} \cdot \frac{24}{7}$, or $\frac{3}{7}$ of the job, and $\frac{4}{7} + \frac{3}{7} = 1$.

Thus, the job will take $\frac{24}{7}$ days, or $3\frac{3}{7}$ days, if Kim and Dick work together.

TRY THIS   2. Dan paints a house in 6 days. It takes Joan 9 days to paint the same house. How long will it take them to paint the house if they work together?   **days**

Suppose that Kim can complete a job in x days, then $\frac{1}{x}$ is the rate (the part she can complete in 1 day). In 2 days, she can complete $\frac{2}{x}$ of the job; in n days she can complete $\frac{n}{x}$ of the job.

EXAMPLE 3   Sue and Ed can clean their house in 7 h. It takes Sue 15 h to do the job alone. How long would it take Ed to do the job alone?

Solution   Let x = number of hours it would take Ed to do the job alone.

	Part of job done in 1 h	Number of hours working together	Part of job completed
Sue	$\frac{1}{15}$	7	$\frac{1}{15} \cdot 7 = \frac{7}{15}$
Ed	$\frac{1}{x}$	7	$\frac{1}{x} \cdot 7 = \frac{7}{x}$

$$\text{Sue's part} + \text{Ed's part} = 1$$
$$\frac{7}{15} + \frac{7}{x} = 1$$
$$15x\left(\frac{7}{15} + \frac{7}{x}\right) = 15x \cdot 1$$
$$7x + 105 = 15x$$
$$105 = 8x$$
$$x = \frac{105}{8}, \text{ or } 13\frac{1}{8}$$

The check is left for you. Ed would take $13\frac{1}{8}$ h to do the job alone.

EXAMPLE 4   Working together, Jodi and her father can deliver the Sunday papers in 3 h. It takes Jodi $1\frac{1}{2}$ times as long to deliver the papers alone. How long would it take each of them to deliver the papers alone?

Solution   Let x = number of hours it would take the father alone.

Then $\frac{3}{2}x$ = number of hours it would take Jodi alone.

	Part of job done in 1 h	Number of hours working together	Part of job completed
Father	$\frac{1}{x}$	3	$\frac{1}{x} \cdot 3 = \frac{3}{x}$
Jodi	$\frac{1}{\frac{3}{2}x} = \frac{2}{3x}$	3	$\frac{2}{3x} \cdot 3 = \frac{2}{x}$

$$\text{Father's part} + \text{Jodi's part} = 1 \longrightarrow \frac{3}{x} + \frac{2}{x} = 1$$

The solution of this equation and the check are left for you.

It would take the father 5 h and Jodi $7\frac{1}{2}$ h to do the job alone.

Classroom Exercises

Maria can write a computer program in 12 h. What part can she write in:

1. 1 h? **2.** 3 h? **3.** 5 h? **4.** x h?

Kris takes 5 days to construct the set for the school play. Susan takes 7 days to construct the same set. Solve Exercises 5–9 based on this information.

5. What part of the job can Kris do in 2 days?

6. What part of the job can Susan do in 6 days?

7. What part of the job can Kris do in $3\frac{1}{2}$ days?

8. What part of the job can Susan do in $4\frac{1}{3}$ days?

9. How long will it take to construct the set if they work together?

10. It takes Pam 5 h to complete a job. It takes Uri 10 h to complete the same job. How long will it take them to complete the job if they work together?

Written Exercises

Juan can paint his room in 8 h. What part of the room can he paint in:

1. 3 h? **2.** 4 h? **3.** 6 h? **4.** n h?

Solve.

5. Mike takes 12 h to clean the basement. Jackie takes 14 h to clean the same basement. How long will it take them to clean the basement together?

6. A large pump can empty a pool in 8 h. A smaller pump can empty the pool in 10 h. How long will it take both pumps working together?

7. One machine can complete an order in 16 h while another machine takes 22 h to complete the same order. How long will it take both machines working together to complete the same order?

8. Working together, Audrey and Bill can address invitations in 5 h. If it takes Audrey 8 h to do it alone, how long would it take Bill to do the job alone?

9. It takes José 28 h to wallpaper two rooms of a house. Together José and Carol can finish the job in 16 h. How long would it take Carol to do the job alone?

10. Together Kathy and Mark can do their holiday baking in 5 h. If it takes Kathy 9 h to do the job alone, how long would it take Mark to do the job alone?

11. Working together, Anita and Dawn can install all the windows in a house in 7 days. It takes Anita twice as long as Dawn to install the windows alone. How long would it take each of them to install the windows alone?

12. Jack and his son can build a house in 8 months. It takes the son twice as long as it takes his father to build the house alone. How long would it take each to do it alone?

13. One pipe can fill a pool in 8 h. A second pipe can do it in 7 h, and a third pipe can do it in 9 h. How long would it take to fill the pool if all three pipes are used?

14. Working together, Mel, Roz, and Abner can clean the Teen Center in 6 h. It takes Mel 18 h to do all the cleaning alone, and Roz 20 h to do it alone. How long would it take Abner to do it alone?

15. To clean the house, it would take Candy 6 h, Joe 7 h, and Jennifer 4 h. How long would it take to do the job if they all worked together?

16. To do a job alone, it takes Hannah 2 h. It takes Andy 1 h longer than Hannah, and it takes Bob 3 times as long as Hannah. How long would it take to do the job if they worked together?

17. A swimming pool can be filled by a pipe in 18 h and emptied by an outlet pipe in 24 h. How long will it take to fill the empty pool if the outlet pipe is mistakenly left open at the same time as the inlet pipe is opened?

18. Sandy and her little brother can clean the snow off the driveway in $1\frac{1}{2}$ h if they work together. It takes her little brother twice as long as it takes Sandy to do it alone. How long does it take each of them to do it alone?

19. It takes Dennis 16 h to plow a field. After he worked for 6 h, Dawn began to help him. Together they finished the job in 2 more hours. How long would it take Dawn to do the job alone?

20. It takes Charles 12 h to clean his apartment. After he has worked 4 h, he is joined by Marie, and they finish cleaning in $2\frac{1}{2}$ more hours. How long would it take Marie to clean the apartment alone?

Mixed Review

Factor completely. *7.2, 7.4, 7.5, 7.6*

1. $5x - 20$

2. $3a^2 + 15a$

3. $2x^2 - 5x - 3$

4. $x^2 - 16$

5. $4y^2 - 49$

6. $a^2x^2 - x^2 - 4a^2 + 4$

Simplify each rational expression. *8.1, 8.2*

7. $\dfrac{48x^6y^4}{-20xy^6}$

8. $\dfrac{5n - 20}{8n - 32}$

9. $\dfrac{x - 4}{16 - x^2}$

9.6 Dimensional Analysis

Objective	To convert from one unit of measurement to another using dimensional analysis

The equation 3 ft = 1 yd states the relationship of feet to yards. By treating "ft" and "yd" as factors, this equation can be expressed in two ways as a fraction that is equal to 1.

Divide each side by 1 yd.   Divide each side by 3 ft.

$$3 \text{ ft} = 1 \text{ yd} \qquad\qquad 3 \text{ ft} = 1 \text{ yd}$$

$$\frac{3 \text{ ft}}{1 \text{ yd}} = 1 \qquad\qquad\qquad 1 = \frac{1 \text{ yd}}{3 \text{ ft}}$$

Such fractions are used in converting one unit of measurement to another. The fractions are called **conversion fractions** or *conversion factors*. Their use in computations is called **dimensional analysis**.

To convert 29 ft to yards, multiply 29 ft by $\dfrac{1 \text{ yd}}{3 \text{ ft}}$.

The common factor, ft, divides out.

$$\frac{29 \text{ ft}}{1} \cdot \frac{1 \text{ yd}}{3 \text{ ft}} = \frac{29 \text{ yd}}{3}$$

$$= 9\tfrac{2}{3} \text{ yd}$$

To convert 42 yd to feet, multiply 42 yd by $\dfrac{3 \text{ ft}}{1 \text{ yd}}$.

The common factor, yd, divides out.

$$\frac{42 \text{ yd}}{1} \cdot \frac{3 \text{ ft}}{1 \text{ yd}} = 42 \cdot 3 \text{ ft}$$

$$= 126 \text{ ft}$$

Some measures, such as speed, involve two types of measurements. Speed involves distance and time. In science, measurements of speed often need to be converted into different units.

EXAMPLE 1	Convert 1,100 feet per second (ft/s) into feet per minute (ft/min).
Plan	Write 1,100 ft/s as $\dfrac{1{,}100 \text{ ft}}{1 \text{ s}}$. Since 60 s = 1 min, multiply by $\dfrac{60 \text{ s}}{1 \text{ min}}$.
Solution	$\dfrac{1{,}100 \text{ ft}}{1 \text{ s}} \cdot \dfrac{60 \text{ s}}{1 \text{ min}} = \dfrac{1{,}100 \text{ ft} \cdot 60}{1 \text{ min}} = \dfrac{66{,}000 \text{ ft}}{1 \text{ min}}$, or 66,000 ft/min
	Thus, 1,100 ft/s is equivalent to 66,000 ft/min

EXAMPLE 2   Convert 60 miles per hour (mi/h) to feet per second (ft/s).

Plan   Write 60 mi/h as $\dfrac{60 \text{ mi}}{1 \text{ h}}$. Then use conversion fractions based on these equivalent measures: 5,280 ft = 1 mi, 1 h = 60 min, and 1 min = 60 s

Solution $\dfrac{60 \text{ mi}}{1 \text{ h}} \cdot \dfrac{5{,}280 \text{ ft}}{1 \text{ mi}} \cdot \dfrac{1 \text{ h}}{60 \text{ min}} \cdot \dfrac{1 \text{ min}}{60 \text{ s}} = \dfrac{60 \cdot 5{,}280 \text{ ft}}{60 \cdot 60 \text{ s}}$

$= \dfrac{88 \text{ ft}}{1 \text{ s}}$, or 88 ft/s

Thus, 60 mi/h is equivalent to 88 ft/s.

TRY THIS   1. Convert 10 miles per hour (mi/h) to inches per second (in./s).

Conversion fractions can be used with square units. Refer to the figure of 1 yard square. Since 3 ft = 1 yd, you can square each side of the equation to show that 9 ft² = 1 yd².

Then, $\dfrac{9 \text{ ft}^2}{1 \text{ yd}^2} = 1$ and $\dfrac{1 \text{ yd}^2}{9 \text{ ft}^2} = 1$

Similarly, 12 in. = 1 ft, so 144 in² = 1 ft².

Then, $\dfrac{144 \text{ in}^2}{1 \text{ ft}^2} = 1$ and $\dfrac{1 \text{ ft}^2}{144 \text{ in}^2} = 1.$

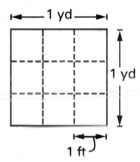

EXAMPLE 3   A rectangular rug measures 14.5 ft by 12 ft. What is its area in square yards? Give your answer to the nearest integer.

Plan   Use $A = lw$ to find the area in square feet. Then multiply by $\dfrac{1 \text{ yd}^2}{9 \text{ ft}^2}$.

Solution   The area of the rug is 14.5 ft × 12 ft = 174 ft².

$\dfrac{174 \text{ ft}^2}{1} \cdot \dfrac{1 \text{ yd}^2}{9 \text{ ft}^2} = \dfrac{174}{9} \text{ yd}^2$, or $\approx 19 \text{ yd}^2$

Thus, the area is 19 yd² to the nearest square yard.

TRY THIS   2. A rectangular patio measures 84 in. by 65 in. What is its area to the nearest square foot?

Classroom Exercises

Determine the conversion fraction or fractions that can be used for the conversion indicated. Use the Table of Equivalent Measures if necessary.

1. 20 yd to feet
2. 81 in. to feet
3. 36 oz to pounds
4. 300 g to milligrams
5. 250 cm to meters
6. 750 g to kilograms
7. 3 mi/h to miles per minute
8. 40 mi/h to feet per minute
9. 30 yd^2 to square feet

Written Exercises

1–9. Convert each measure in Classroom Exercises 1–9 as indicated.

Use dimensional analysis to convert each measure.

10. 75 mi/h to feet per second
11. 24 tons/h to pounds per minute
12. 352 ft/s to miles per hour
13. 12 gallons/min to quarts per second
14. 6.5 ft/min to inches per second
15. 4.5 lb/min to tons per hour

16. A satellite is traveling around the earth at an average speed of about 4.1 mi/s. How many miles per hour is this?

17. A rectangular rug measures 16 ft by 11.5 ft. What is its area in square yards?

18. The figure at the right shows a cube with a volume of 1 m^3. What is its volume in cubic decimeters? In cubic centimeters?

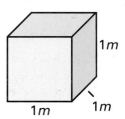

Mixed Review

Evaluate.   *1.1, 1.3*

1. $10 - 5a$ for $a = \frac{1}{5}$
2. $64x^4$ for $x = \frac{2}{3}$

Solve.   *3.3, 3.5*

3. $\frac{x}{4} - 3 = 8$
4. $8x - \frac{2}{3}(15 - 9x) = 12$

Add or subtract.   *8.5*

5. $\frac{2n^2}{n - 1} + \frac{3}{1 - n}$
6. $\frac{y}{y + 4} - \frac{3}{4 + y}$

Solve.   *4.3, 4.7*

7. Find two consecutive integers whose sum is 137.
8. If 40% of a number is 78, what is the number?

Mixed Problem Solving

If you find that you often make careless errors as you write the equation that models a problem, pay more attention to the step where you *define the variables*. Remember that the equation is often easier to write if you let x represent the smaller quantity.

For example, in Exercise 13, let x represent the amount of this month's electric bill. Then $x + 18.70$ represents the amount of last month's electric bill.

1. Find two consecutive odd integers whose sum is -84.

2. One number is 12 times another number. Their sum is 117. Find the numbers.

3. One number is 2 more than 4 times a second. The sum of the numbers is 22. Find the numbers.

4. Find three consecutive even integers such that the sum, decreased by 52, is equal to the second integer.

5. Kristin's age is 6 less than $\frac{1}{2}$ of Slim's age. The sum of their ages is 108 years. Find their ages.

6. A triangle has an area of 36 in^2 and a height of 12 in. Find the length of the base.

7. Each base angle of an isosceles triangle has degree measure 8 less than half that of the vertex angle. Find all three angle measures.

8. Membership fees at the health club are $80 less than twice the original cost. The fees this year are $460. What was the original cost?

9. One side of a triangle is 7 in. longer than a second side. The remaining side is 4 in. shorter than the second side. The perimeter is 78 in. Find the length of each side.

10. Sam Ferris lost 25% of the value of his stock portfolio when the stock market collapsed. His portfolio is now worth $86,125. How much money did he lose?

11. The regular price of a ski suit is $210. It is on sale for $140. Find the rate of discount.

12. The selling price of a compact disc player is $243. The profit is 35% of the cost. Find the cost.

13. Last month's electric bill was $18.70 more than this month's bill. The bill for the two months totaled $73.98. What was this month's bill?

14. Mary lives 2 mi from the store. She walks at a rate of 6 mi/h. How long must she walk to get from home to the store?

15. Separate 87 people into two groups so that the first group has 9 fewer than 3 times the number of people in the second group.

16. The product of the first and third of three consecutive integers is 37 less than 20 times the second. Find the three integers.

Chapter 9 Review

Key Terms

conversion fractions   (p. 364)
dimensional analysis   (p. 364)
direct variation   (p. 348)
extraneous solution   (p. 338)
extremes   (p. 343)
literal equation   (p. 349)

means   (p. 343)
proportion   (p. 343)
Proportion Property   (p. 343)
ratio   (p. 343)
rational equation   (p. 337)
supplementary angles   (p. 346)

Key Ideas and Review Exercises

9.1   To solve an equation containing rational expressions, multiply each side by the LCM of all the denominators.

Solve. Check for extraneous solutions.

1. $\dfrac{3}{a - 6} - \dfrac{4}{a + 2} = \dfrac{5}{a^2 - 4a - 12}$

2. $\dfrac{-2}{x^2 - 9} + \dfrac{3}{x + 3} = \dfrac{5}{x - 3}$

9.2   To solve a proportion, set the product of the extremes equal to the product of the means.

Solve.

3. $\dfrac{4}{a + 1} = \dfrac{5}{2a - 4}$

4. $\dfrac{n - 3}{5} = \dfrac{2n + 3}{6}$

5. $\dfrac{2x - 1}{-3} = \dfrac{1}{x + 2}$

6. $\dfrac{y}{5} = \dfrac{y}{y - 1}$

9.3   To solve a literal equation or formula for one of its variables, follow the same steps you use in solving a nonliteral equation.

Solve for x.

7. $7x + b = c$

8. $3x - b = cd$

9. $ax + bx = 6c$

10. $-7x + b = 3x - 10b$

9.4   To solve problems about motion, begin with a sketch and a table. Represent the distance, the rate, and the time traveled by each person or moving object. Write an equation and solve it. Determine whether the answer is reasonable. Check it in the original problem.

Solve.

11. Two cars traveled in opposite directions from the same starting point. The rate of one car was 30 km/h faster than the rate of the second car. After 3 h, the cars were 300 km apart. Find the rate of each car.

12. Mike jogged 15 km in the same time that it took Jan to jog 20 km. Jan's rate was 3 km/h faster than Mike's. How fast did each travel?

9.5 To solve problems about work, complete a table such as the one below. For each person, rate of work × time worked = part of job completed.

	Part of job done in 1 h	Number of hours working together	Part of job completed
First name	?	?	?
Second name	?	?	?

If the job is completed, then the parts of the job completed by each person must have a sum of 1.

Solve.

13. Working alone, it takes Milt 8 h and Ellen 10 h to paint a garage. How long will it take them to do the job if they work together?

14. Together, Howard and Willie can assemble a TV kit in 6 h. If it takes Howard 9 h to do the job alone, how long would it take Willie to do the job alone?

9.6 To convert from one unit of measurement to another using dimensional analysis, multiply by conversion fractions such as the following.

$$\frac{60 \text{ s}}{1 \text{ min}} = 1, \frac{1 \text{ mi}}{5{,}280 \text{ ft}} = 1, \text{ and } \frac{1 \text{ yd}^2}{9 \text{ ft}^2} = 1$$

For example, $660 \text{ ft} = \frac{660 \text{ ft}}{1} \cdot \frac{1 \text{ mi}}{5{,}280 \text{ ft}} = \frac{660}{5{,}280} \text{ mi} = \frac{1}{8} \text{ mi}$

Convert each measure as indicated.

15. 180 in. to feet

16. 27 ft² to square yards

17. 75 cm to meters

18. 15 lb/in² to pounds per square foot

19. 66 ft/s to miles per hour

20. 3 km/h to meters per minute

21. Explain how to convert 4.5 gallons per day to quarts per hour.

Solve. Check for extraneous solutions.

1. $\dfrac{1}{x} + \dfrac{1}{4x} = 5$

2. $\dfrac{1}{x + 2} = \dfrac{1}{2x + 4} + \dfrac{1}{2}$

3. $\dfrac{x + 1}{x - 4} = \dfrac{4x + 4}{x^2 - 4x}$

4. $\dfrac{n + 2}{n - 4} - n = \dfrac{12}{4 - n}$

Solve.

5. $\dfrac{m}{9} = \dfrac{5}{3}$

6. $\dfrac{4}{7} = \dfrac{x}{5}$

7. $\dfrac{3x - 5}{6} = \dfrac{2x + 1}{4}$

8. $\dfrac{b - 3}{4} = \dfrac{9}{b + 6}$

Solve for x.

9. $ax + 9 = -6$

10. $ax = b - c$

11. $px + qx = 3$

12. $kx - bc = 5d + fx$

Convert each measure as indicated.

13. 180 in² to square feet

14. 1,320 ft/s to miles per minute

Solve.

15. If 8 out of 9 people buy an AM/FM radio, how many buy this type of radio in a city with a population of 81,000?

16. Sarah started out on her bike traveling at 9 mi/h. One hour later, Carlos left from the same point on his bike and pedaled along the same route at 12 mi/h. How many hours had he pedaled before he caught up with Sarah?

17. The Saltzmans drove 65 km/h to visit their daughter. They returned later at the rate of 80 km/h. It took them 8 h less time to return home than it did to go. How long did it take to return?

18. It takes Edith 4 h to paint her room. Her brother, Fred, can do it in 5 h. How long will it take to do the job if they work together?

19. It takes Rico twice as long as Woody to build a bridge over a stream. How long would it take each of them to do it alone if they can build the bridge together in 9 h?

20. The perimeter of a triangle is 45 cm. Find the length of the shortest side if the lengths of the sides are in the ratio 2:3:4.

21. Solve $\dfrac{xy}{a} - \dfrac{tx}{b} = \dfrac{4}{ab}$ for x.

College Prep Test

Choose the *one* best answer to each question or problem.

1. In 1986 a moving company transported 32,000 tons of cargo. In 1990 the same company handled 48,800 tons of cargo. The average annual increase in tons handled was __?__.
   (A) 4,200   (B) 5,600
   (C) 8,000   (D) 12,200
   (E) 16,800

2. The product of 798 and 694 is __?__.
   (A) 553,813   (B) 553,814
   (C) 553,812   (D) 553,815
   (E) 553,817

3. Find the value closest to the sum.
   $$70 + 60 + 30 + \frac{3}{4} + \frac{4}{3}$$
   (A) 161.55   (B) 167.80
   (C) 240.75   (D) 235.80
   (E) 315

4. The sum of three consecutive odd integers is 21. The smallest of these integers is __?__.
   (A) 3   (B) 5
   (C) 7   (D) 9
   (E) 11

5. The perimeter of a rectangle is 54 in. Its length is 15 in.

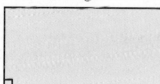

   15 in.

   The area of the rectangle is __?__.
   (A) 27 in²   (B) 39 in²
   (C) 144 in²   (D) 180 in²
   (E) 225 in²

6. Which of the following is not a multiple of 11?
   (A) 5,555   (B) 968
   (C) 1,111   (D) 11,111
   (E) 2,805

7. How many numbers are there between 1 and 101 that are divisible by either 2 or 7, but not both?
   (A) 50   (B) 58
   (C) 63   (D) 69
   (E) 7

8. Let $A \cdot B$ be defined by the equation $A \cdot B = (7 - B)(8 - A)$. Find the numerical value of $3 \cdot 5$.
   (A) 18   (B) 20
   (C) 15   (D) 12
   (E) 10

9. The average of 20 students' test scores is 84. If the two highest and the two lowest scores are eliminated, the average of the remaining scores is 88. What was the average of the test scores eliminated?
   (A) 86   (B) 68   (C) 77
   (D) 93   (E) 34

10. How many centimeters are there in p meters?
    (A) $10p$ (B) $100p$
    (C) $1,000p$ (D) $0.10p$
    (E) $0.100p$

11. If $n > \frac{n^2}{10}$, then n may take on which of the following values?
    (A) -40 (B) 40
    (C) 0   (D) 10
    (E) 0.5

12. Find the sum of all the distinct whole number factors of 80.
    (A) 66   (B) 87
    (C) 105   (D) 186
    (E) 204

Divers that explore the inner world of the oceans can avoid the painful and dangerous "bends" by carefully calculating the amount of oxygen in the diving tank, the duration of the dive, and the speed of rise to the surface.

10.1 Coordinates of Points in a Plane

Objectives

To give the coordinates of a point in a plane
To identify the quadrant in which a given point is located
To graph a point, given its coordinates

You already know that only one number is needed to locate a point on a number line. To locate a point in a plane, two numbers, called **coordinates,** are needed.

The figure at the right shows a coordinate plane. It has two number lines, called **axes,** that intersect in a point called the **origin.**

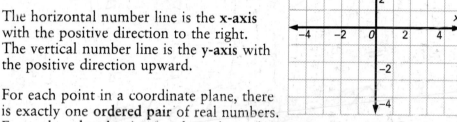

The horizontal number line is the **x-axis** with the positive direction to the right. The vertical number line is the **y-axis** with the positive direction upward.

For each point in a coordinate plane, there is exactly one **ordered pair** of real numbers. For each ordered pair of real numbers, there is exactly one point that is its graph. The figure shows point A, the graph of $(4, 2)$, and point B, the graph of $(2, 4)$.

To graph or **plot** a point given its coordinates, follow these steps: Start at the origin and move to the right if the first coordinate is positive or to the left if it is negative. Then move up if the second coordinate is positive or down if it is negative.

Examples 1 and 2 show how to graph ordered pairs of numbers.

EXAMPLE 1

Point P has coordinates $(5, -3)$.
Graph the point.

Solution

Start at the origin. Move 5 units to the right. Then move 3 units down.

Label the point as $P(5, -3)$.

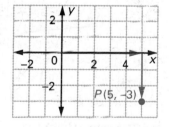

TRY THIS

1. Plot each point on the same graph. Write the ordered pair next to each point.

   $A(-3, 1)$ $B(-2, -3)$ $C(4, 1)$ $D(1, -2)$

Sometimes, a point such as *P* is shown but its coordinates are not given. To determine its coordinates, find the number on the *x*-axis that is directly above *P* and the number on the *y*-axis that is directly to the left of *P*.

In the figure, the number 3 is on the *x*-axis directly above *P*. It is called the **x-coordinate** of the point. The number -2 is on the *y*-axis directly to the left of *P*. It is called the **y-coordinate** of the point. Thus, $(3, -2)$ are the coordinates of point *P*.

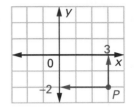

The *x*-coordinate of a point is also called the *abscissa*. The *y*-coordinate is also called the *ordinate*.

EXAMPLE 2 Find the coordinates of point *A*.

Solution Point *A* is 2 units to the left of the *y*-axis and 1 unit above the *x*-axis.

Therefore, the coordinates of point *A* are $(-2, 1)$.

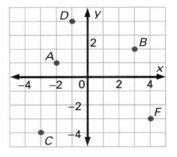

TRY THIS 2. Find the coordinates of points *B*, *C*, *D*, and *F* on the graph above.

The axes divide a coordinate plane into four **quadrants**, as shown. Notice that the quadrants are numbered in a counterclockwise direction, beginning at the upper right. Each point is located in one of the quadrants or on one of the axes. The origin has the coordinates $(0, 0)$ and is located on both axes.

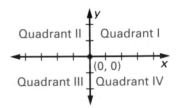

EXAMPLE 3 Give the quadrant for each point.

    a. $P(3, 2)$ **b.** $Q(-2, 4)$ **c.** $R(-1, -4)$ **d.** $S(4, -4)$

Solution   Plot each point.

    a. $P(3, 2)$ is in Quadrant I.

    b. $Q(-2, 4)$ is in Quadrant II.

    c. $R(-1, -4)$ is in Quadrant III.

    d. $S(4, -4)$ is in Quadrant IV.

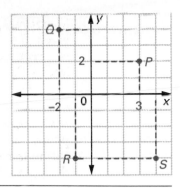

TRY THIS   Give the quadrants for each point.
3. $W(-3, 4)$ 4. $X(4, -1)$ 5. $Y(2, 5)$ 6. $Z(-1, 1)$

The next example illustrates how to determine the fourth vertex of a rectangle if the other three are known. Recall that the opposite sides of a rectangle are equal in length, and its adjacent sides are perpendicular.

EXAMPLE 4   Three vertices of rectangle $ABCD$ are $A(1, 1)$, $B(6, 1)$, and $C(6, 4)$. Find the coordinates of the fourth vertex D.

Solution   Graph the points A, B, and C. Point D must be directly above A and directly to the left of C. D has the same x-coordinate as A and the same y-coordinate as C.

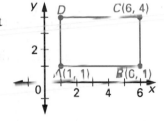

Thus, the coordinates of the fourth vertex are $D(1, 4)$.

TRY THIS   7. $A(1, -3)$, $B(1, 2)$, and $C(4, 2)$ are the vertices of a rectangle. Find the coordinates of the fourth vertex.

Focus on Reading

Determine whether each statement is true or false. If false, give a reason for your answer.

1. There is exactly one ordered pair of numbers that locates a given point in the coordinate plane.
2. Every point is in one of four quadrants.
3. The abscissa of an ordered pair is always positive.
4. The horizontal axis is the x-axis.
5. The ordinate of every point on the x-axis is zero.

Classroom Exercises

Tell what point has the given coordinates.

1. $(3, 1)$ **2.** $(-5, 1)$ **3.** $(0, 3)$

4. $(-4, 0)$ **5.** $(3, -4)$ **6.** $(-4, -2)$

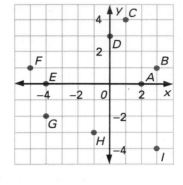

For each point, tell which number is the abscissa and which is the ordinate.

7. A **8.** C **9.** H

Graph each point in the same coordinate plane.

10. $P(7, -2)$ **11.** $Q(-2, 7)$ **12.** $R(0, 5)$

13. $S(-1, 0)$ **14.** $T(1, 1)$ **15.** $U(-5, -5)$

Written Exercises

Give the coordinates of each point.

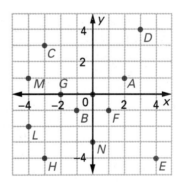

1. A **2.** B

3. C **4.** D

5. E **6.** F

7. G **8.** H

9. L **10.** M

11. N **12.** O

Which points in the diagram above are in the given quadrant?

13. Quadrant I   **14.** Quadrant II

15. Quadrant III   **16.** Quadrant IV

Graph each point in the same coordinate plane.

17. $A(5, -2)$ **18.** $B(-2, 3)$

19. $C(-3, -1)$ **20.** $D(4, 0)$

21. $E(-3, 0)$ **22.** $F(2, -5)$

23. $G(-1, -2)$ **24.** $H(0, -4)$

Graph the three points in the same coordinate plane.

25. $A(-3, 2)$, $B(-2, -1)$, $C(2, 0)$ **26.** $P(2, -1)$, $Q(0, -3)$, $R(-2, 3)$

27. $M(5, -1)$, $N(-4, -2)$, $P(-4, 3)$ **28.** $R(0, 2)$, $S(-4, -5)$, $T(3, -4)$

29. $D(-3, -2)$, $E(1, 4)$, $F(5, 0)$ **30.** $A(-2, -3)$, $B(5, -2)$, $C(0, 0)$

A, B, and **C** are three vertices of a rectangle. Find the
coordinates of the fourth vertex of the rectangle.

31. $A(-1, 2)$, $B(4, 2)$, $C(4, 4)$

32. $A(3, -1)$, $B(7, -1)$, $C(7, 3)$

33. $A(3, 0)$, $B(5, 0)$, $C(5, 5)$

34. $A(-4, -3)$, $B(3, -3)$, $C(3, 3)$

Using the graph at the right, find the point(s) whose
coordinates satisfy the given condition.

35. The abscissa is -2.   **36.** The ordinate is 1.

37. The abscissa is positive.   **38.** The ordinate is negative.

39. The sum of the abscissa and the ordinate is 5.

40. Write a short paragraph to explain the construction
of a coordinate system. Mention how the axes are
located, how they are labeled, how direction is
determined, and the relation between ordered pairs
of real numbers and points. Give examples.

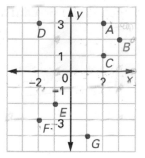

A, B, and **C** are three vertices of parallelogram **ABCD.**
Find the coordinates of the fourth vertex of the parallelogram.

41. $A(1, 1)$, $B(5, 1)$, $C(7, 3)$

42. $A(2, -1)$, $B(7, -1)$, $C(8, 1)$

43. $A(-1, 1)$, $B(4, 1)$, $C(6, 4)$

44. $A(-1, -3)$, $B(4, -3)$, $C(5, -1)$

45–48. In Exercises 41–44, suppose that the order of the vertices
(clockwise or counterclockwise) is not in the alphabetical order
"ABCD." Find all possible positions for vertex D.

49. Find two ordered pairs (x, y) such that $2|x - 6| - 4 = 8$
and $\dfrac{10}{y^2 + 2y} = \dfrac{5}{y + 2}$.

Mixed Review

Solve and check.   *3.3, 3.5, 4.6*

1. $4x - 9 = 39$

2. $\frac{2}{3}x + 15 = -5$

3. $10a + 2(1 - a) = 6a - 4$

4. $1.8 - 3.1n = 48.6 + 7.3n$

Graph the solution set on a number line.   *5.4*

5. $5x - 7 \geq 8$

6. $2x - 18 \leq 34$

7. The square of a number is 6 less than 5 times the number. Find the
number.   *7.9*

10.2 Relations and Functions

Objectives   To graph relations and functions
To determine the domain and the range of a relation
To determine whether a relation is a function

Anne worked as a lifeguard for $7 per hour. In 1 hour she earned $7, in 2 hours she earned $14, in 3 hours she earned $21, and in 4 hours she earned $28. The number of hours she worked and the amount she earned can be described by a set of ordered pairs.

$$S = \{(1, 7), (2, 14), (3, 21), (4, 28)\}$$

A set of ordered pairs is called a **relation**. The set S is a relation. The set of all first coordinates is called the **domain** of a relation. For S, the domain is $\{1, 2, 3, 4\}$. The set of all second coordinates is called the **range** of a relation. For S, the range is $\{7, 14, 21, 28\}$. For the relation $N = \{(\text{James}, 19), (\text{Kris}, 23), (\text{Scott}, 19)\}$, the domain is $\{\text{James}, \text{Kris}, \text{Scott}\}$, and the range is $\{19, 23\}$. Notice that 19 is listed only once.

EXAMPLE 1   Graph the relation $B = \{(3, 0), (-1, 2), (4, 1), (-2, -1), (1, -2)\}$. Then give the domain and range of B.

Solution   The domain is the set of all first coordinates.

The range is the set of all second coordinates.

The domain of B is $\{-2, -1, 1, 3, 4\}$.

The range of B is $\{-2, -1, 0, 1, 2\}$.

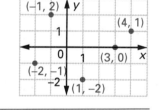

TRY THIS   1. Give the domain and range of the relation
$M = \{(2, 1), (0, 0), (-1, -2), (3, 6)\}$.

Notice that for the relation $B = \{(3, 0), (-1, 2), (4, 1), (-2, -1), (1, -2)\}$, no first coordinates are the same. This kind of relation is called a *function*. In a function some of the second coordinates may be the same, but all the first coordinates must be different.

Definition   A **function** is a relation in which no two ordered pairs have the same first coordinate.

EXAMPLE 2   Given the relation $A = \{(1, -3), (-1, 3), (2, 5), (-2, -3), (3, -1)\}$, determine the domain and range. Is A a function?

Plan   Determine whether any two first coordinates are the same.

Solution   The domain of A is $\{-2, -1, 1, 2, 3\}$.
The range of A is $\{-3, -1, 3, 5\}$.
Since no ordered pairs have the same first coordinate, A is a function.

EXAMPLE 3   List the set of ordered pairs in relation G.
Is G a function?

Plan   List the set of ordered pairs. Then determine whether any two first coordinates are the same.

Solution $G = \{(-2, 1), (3, 2), (-2, 3), (-1, -3)\}$.
Since the ordered pairs $(-2, 1)$ and $(-2, 3)$ have the same x-coordinate, G is not a function.

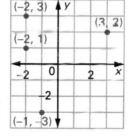

TRY THIS   2. Is $D = \{(-2, 4), (-1, 1), (0, 0), (1, 1), (1, 2)\}$ a function?

Classroom Exercises

Determine which relations are functions and which are not functions.

1. $\{(1, 2), (-3, 2), (4, -1), (2, 1), (2, 3)\}$ 2. $\{(-3, 1), (4, 2), (3, -1), (2, -4)\}$
3. $\{(4, 2), (4, -1), (3, -2), (1, 4), (-2, 4)\}$ 4. $\{(3, -2), (-3, 2), (5, -2), (-1, -1)\}$

State the domain and the range of each relation.

5. $\{(2, 1), (-3, 2), (-1, 4)\}$ 6. $\{(-4, 0), (3, -1), (2, 3)\}$
7. $\{(0, -3), (-2, 5), (1, -6)\}$ 8. $\{(5, 6), (7, 0), (-8, 1)\}$
9. $\{(35, \text{John}), (43, \text{Hilda}), (10, \text{Dawn})\}$ 10. $\{(\text{red}, 1), (\text{blue}, 10), (\text{red}, 3)\}$

Written Exercises

Graph. Give the domain and range of the relation.

1. $\{(3, 1), (0, -2), (5, -3), (-3, -1)\}$ 2. $\{(4, 0), (-3, -2), (-2, 1), (2, -1)\}$
3. $\{(-1, 2), (4, 3), (-1, 4), (2, -3)\}$ 4. $\{(3, -2), (3, -4), (0, 2), (2, -2)\}$

State the domain and the range of each relation. Is it a function?

5. $\{(-6, -3), (7, -3), (-4, 7), (5, 10)\}$ **6.** $\{(0, 1), (3, 0), (0, 0), (-5, 0)\}$

7. $\{(-3, -4), (3, -2), (2, -3), (-3, 5)\}$ **8.** $\{(9, 6), (6, 9), (5, 4), (4, 5)\}$

List the set of ordered pairs of each relation. Is the relation a function?

9.

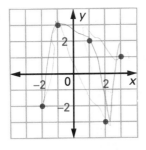

10.

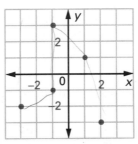

Determine whether or not the relation is a function.

11. $\{(-3, 1), (4, 0), (2, -3), (5, -1), (3, -3)\}$

12. $\{(4, 1), (5, 0), (-2, 3), (4, -2), (3, 2)\}$

13. $\{(0, -3), (-1, 2), (-1, -3), (5, 0), (2, 1)\}$

14. $\{(3, -4), (-4, 2), (5, 1), (-2, 3), (0, 3)\}$

15. $\{(-5, -1), (4, 3), (3, -1), (-5, 5), (0, 2)\}$

16. $\{(-3, -2), (-1, 4), (3, -1), (-5, 2), (4, -1)\}$

17. The life expectancy of a monkey is 15 years, an African elephant 35 years, a beaver 5 years, and a grizzly bear 25 years. Write a relation that describes this information. Determine the domain and the range.

18. An elephant can run 25 mi/h, a reindeer 32 mi/h, a greyhound 39 mi/h, and an elk 45 mi/h. Write a relation that describes this information. Determine the domain and the range.

19. For what value of k will the relation $R = \{(2k + 1, 3), (3k - 2, -6)\}$ *not* be a function?
(HINT: R will not be a function if $2k + 1 = 3k - 2$.)

20. For what value of k will the relation $S = \{(2k + 3, 1), (3k - 1, -2)\}$ *not* be a function?

21. Write a paragraph explaining what is meant by a relation and a function. Be sure to include these features: examples of functions, examples of relations that are not functions, and examples of functions that show a specific relationship between domain and range.

For what value(s) of k will the relation *not* be a function?

22. $A = \{(k^2, 16), (4k, 32)\}$

23. $B = \{(k^2 - 5k, 10), (k + 7, 4)\}$

24. $R = \{(k^3 - 5k^2 + 3k, -5), (-k, 4)\}$

25. $S = \{(|k + 1| + 2, 4), (8, 7)\}$

Graph the function described below. The domain of each function is $\{-2, -1, 0, 1, 2\}$.

26. In each ordered pair, the second number is equal to twice the absolute value of the first number.

27. In each ordered pair, the second number is the opposite of the absolute value of the first number.

28. In each ordered pair, the second number is the square of the first number.

29. In each ordered pair, the second number is either 2 or -2. If the first number is nonnegative, then the second number is 2. If the first number is negative, then the second number is -2.

Mixed Review

Evaluate. *1.1, 2.6*

1. $x + 9$ for $x = 12$

2. $4y - 3$ for $y = 5$

3. $5m^2$ for $m = -4$

4. x^2y for $x = -3$ and for $y = -4$

Solve. *7.7, 9.1*

5. $\dfrac{3x}{2} + 1 = \dfrac{6x}{5} - \dfrac{14}{10}$

6. $3x^2 + 8x - 3 = 0$

◢/Using the Calculator

Scientific calculators are often compared by the number of "functions" they can perform. Select several function keys and test one at a time. Form an ordered pair by first listing the entry, and then the result displayed. You may try making the same entry several times. For example,

$\boxed{x^2}$ key:	$\boxed{\sqrt{x}}$ key:
(19, 361)	(361, 19)
(27, 729)	(729, 27)
(−27, 729)	(729, 27)

1. Examine the set of relations obtained by using the $\boxed{x^2}$ key. Is this relation a function?

2. Is the set of relations displayed by the $\boxed{\sqrt{x}}$ key a function?

3. Do the function keys on a calculator give sets of values that are functions?

10.3 Values of a Function

Objectives

To find values of a function using the notation $f(x)$
To determine the range of a function for a given domain

A **function** is a relation in which no two ordered pairs have the same first coordinate. Consider the set of ordered pairs below.

$$\{(2, 5), (6, 9), (-1, 2), (-3, 0)\}$$

Since no two of the ordered pairs have the same first coordinate, the relation is a function. You know that you can graph this function in a coordinate plane. Another way to picture this function is in a **mapping** as illustrated below.

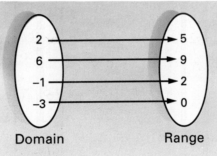

You can see that the domain is $\{-3, -1, 2, 6\}$. The range is $\{0, 2, 5, 9\}$. From the mapping, note that for each number in the domain, there is just one number in the range.

EXAMPLE 1 Which relations are functions?

a.
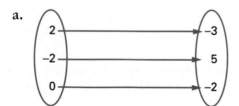

b.
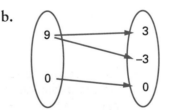

Solutions

a. For each number in the domain, there is exactly one number in the range. So the relation *is* a function.

b. For the number 9 in the domain, there are two numbers in the range. So the relation *is not* a function.

Which relations are functions?

1. $S = \{(-1, 1), (2, 1), (3, 2)\}$ 2. $T = \{(1, 3), (-1, -3), (0, 0)\}$

This mapping shows the function
$f = \{(-2, -8), (1, 4), (3, 12)\}$.
The -2 in the domain corresponds to
-8 in the range. Similarly, the 1 in the
domain corresponds to 4 in the range.

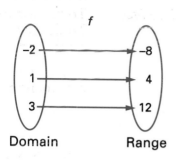

Each number in the *range* of a function f
is called a **value of the function.**
Thus, when x is -2, the value of the
function shown is -8. This can be
represented as

$$f(-2) = -8$$

which is read "the value of f at -2 is -8." (Here, f is *not* a variable
and $f(-2)$ does *not* mean "f times negative 2.")

Similarly, the values of f at 1 and 3 are represented as

$$f(1) = 4 \text{ and } f(3) = 12.$$

EXAMPLE 2 | Find the indicated value of the function.
a. $f(\ \ 1)$ **b.** $f(-3)$

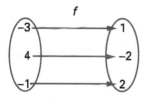

Solutions | **a.** The value of f **b.** The value of f
at -1 is 2.   at -3 is 1.

$f(-1) = 2$ $f(-3) = 1$

Find the indicated value of the function
for each of the following.

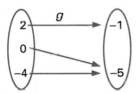

3. $g(2)$ 4. $g(-4)$

Sometimes a function can be defined by an algebraic expression or rule.
Consider the function with domain $D = \{-12, -5, -2, 0, 2, 5, 12\}$,
where $f(x) = x + 2$.

This indicates that for each number x in the domain, the value of the
function is $x + 2$. Thus, when x is 5 or 12 or any other number in the
domain, the value of the function can be computed as shown.

$f(5) = 5 + 2 = 7$ $f(12) = 12 + 2 = 14$

Thus, $f(5) = 7$.   Thus, $f(12) = 14$.

EXAMPLE 3   Given $f(x) = 4x^2 - 1$ and the domain $D = \{-2, 1, 3\}$, find the indicated values of the function and the range.

          a. $f(3)$ **b.** $f(1)$ **c.** $f(-2)$

Solutions

a. $f(x) = 4x^2 - 1$
$f(3) = 4(3^2) - 1$
$= 4(9) - 1$
$= 36 - 1$
$= 35$

b. $f(x) = 4x^2 - 1$
$f(1) = 4(1^2) - 1$
$= 4(1) - 1$
$= 4 - 1$
$= 3$

c. $f(x) = 4x^2 - 1$
$f(-2) = 4(-2)^2 - 1$
$= 4(4) - 1$
$= 16 - 1$
$= 15$

Thus, the range of f is $\{3, 15, 35\}$.

TRY THIS   **5.** Given $g(x) = -3x^2 + 6$ and the domain $D = \{-3, 0, 3\}$, find the range of g.

Classroom Exercises

Find the indicated value of the function shown.

1. $f(-1)$ **2.** $f(7)$ **3.** $f(3)$ **4.** $f(-2)$

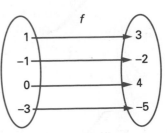

Given a function $g(x) = 3x + 6$, find the indicated value of the function.

5. $g(8)$ **6.** $g(-2)$ **7.** $g(0)$ **8.** $g(-5)$

Written Exercises

Which relations are functions?

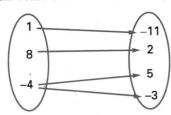   **2.**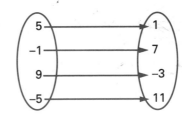

Find the indicated value of the function shown at the right.

3. $f(0)$ **4.** $f(-1)$ **5.** $f(1)$ **6.** $f(-3)$

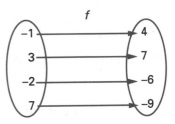

Given $f(x) = 2x - 6$, find the indicated value.

7. $f(5)$ **8.** $f(3)$ **9.** $f(1)$ **10.** $f(-5)$

Given $g(x) = -4x + 5$, find the indicated value.

11. $g(0)$ **12.** $g(3)$ **13.** $g(-3)$ **14.** $g(7)$

Given $f(x) = x^2 - 9$, find the indicated values.

15. $f(2)$ **16.** $f(5)$ **17.** $f(-1)$ **18.** $f(-4)$

Given $g(x) = -2x^2 + 1$, find the indicated values.

19. $g(0)$ **20.** $g(-3)$ **21.** $g(2)$ **22.** $g(-4)$

Use the given domain D to find the range of each function.

23. $f(x) = 3x - 5$, $D = \{-1, 0, 3\}$ **24.** $g(x) = -3x + 1$, $D = \{-2, 1, 4\}$

25. $f(x) = 2x + 6$, $D = \{-5, -1, 4\}$ **26.** $g(x) = 5x - 3$, $D = \{-3, -2, -1\}$

27. $f(x) = x - 4$,   **28.** $g(x) = -3x^2 - 4$,
      $D = \{-2, -1, 3\}$ $D = \{-1, 2, 3\}$

29. $f(x) = x^2 - 4$,   **30** $g(x) = -4x + 9$,
      $D = \{-14.1, 0.04, 21.06\}$ $D = \{-2.01, 3.65, 5.98\}$

If a machine produces 280 appliances per hour, the total number of appliances produced in x hours can be represented as a function $f(x) = 280x$.

31. How many appliances can be produced in 3.5 h?   **32.** How many more appliances can be produced in 7 h than in $4\frac{1}{4}$ h?

Use the given domain to find the range of the function.

33. $f(x) = -x^3 + x^2 + 5$,   **34.** $g(x) = 2x^3 - 3x + 1$,
      $D = \{-2, -1, 2\}$ $D = \{-3, -1, 4\}$

35. $f(x) = |x|$, $D = \{-4, 0, -3\}$ **36.** $g(x) = (x - 3)^2$, $D = \{-3, 2, 3\}$

37. $f(x) = (2x - 1)^2$, $D = \{-5, 3, 4\}$ **38.** $g(x) = |x - 3|^2$, $D = \{-3, 2, 3\}$

Write an equation with $f(x)$ to show how the numbers in the domain and the range are related.

39. $\{(1, 2), (-2, -4), (3, 6), (0, 0)\}$ **40.** $\{(1, 5), (3, 17), (-2, -13), (-4, -25)\}$

Mixed Review

Simplify.   *2.2, 2.8*

1. $|7| + |-7|$ **2.** $|-1.7| + |1.8|$ **3.** $|8| \cdot |0|$ **4.** $|-2| \cdot |-4|$

5. $-3 \cdot 5 + 4(-2) - 9(-5)$ **6.** $8(-1) + (-2)^2 - 4 \cdot 3$

Factor.   *7.3, 7.4*

7. $x^2 - 4x + 3$ **8.** $x^2 + 2x - 8$ **9.** $2x^2 + 3x - 2$ **10.** $3x^2 - x - 2$

11. Find two consecutive integers whose product is 342.   *7.9*

10.4 Equations with Two Variables

Objective	To solve an equation with two variables for a given replacement set

The perimeter of each rectangle below can be represented by an equation. In each case, begin with the perimeter formula, $p = 2l + 2w$.

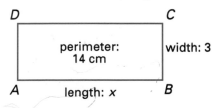

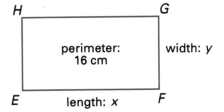

Equation: $14 = 2x + 2 \cdot 3$
Solution: *one* solution
$\qquad x = 4$
(Verify that 4 *is* a solution by substituting it into the equation.)

Equation: $16 = 2x + 2y$
Solutions: *many* solutions
$\qquad x = 2$ when $y = 6$,
$\qquad x = 5$ when $y = 3$,
$\qquad x = 7$ when $y = 1$,
$\qquad$ and so on
(Use substitution to verify that these numbers *are* solutions.

EXAMPLE 1	Find two solutions of the equation $5x - y = 9$.
Plan	Choose any value for x and solve for y.
Solution	Let $x = -1$. $\qquad\qquad$ Let $x = \frac{1}{5}$.

$$5(-1) - y = 9 \qquad\qquad 5(\tfrac{1}{5}) - y = 9$$
$$-5 - y = 9 \qquad\qquad\quad\; 1 - y = 9$$
$$-y = 14 \qquad\qquad\qquad -y = 8$$
$$y = -14 \qquad\qquad\qquad\;\; y = -8$$

Thus, two solutions are $(-1, -14)$ and $(\frac{1}{5}, -8)$.

TRY THIS	1. Find two solutions of the equation $2x - 3y = 5$.

The solution set for an equation with two variables is a set of ordered pairs. To find the solution set for an equation such as $2x + 3y = 15$:
1. Solve the equation for y.
2. Then substitute numbers for x.

EXAMPLE 2 Find the solution set for $2x + 3y = 15$ if the replacement set for each variable is $\{0, 3, 5\}$.

Plan Solve the equation for y in terms of x. Substitute values from $\{0, 3, 5\}$ for x. Accept only numbers from $\{0, 3, 5\}$ for y.

Solution
$$2x + 3y = 15$$
$$3y = 15 - 2x$$
$$y = 5 - \frac{2}{3}x$$

Let $x = 0$.
$y = 5 - \frac{2}{3}(0)$
$y = 5$
So, $(0, 5)$ *is* a solution.

Let $x = 3$.
$y = 5 - \frac{2}{3}(3)$
$= 5 - 2$
$= 3$
So, $(3, 3)$ *is* a solution.

Let $x = 5$.
$y = 5 - \frac{2}{3}(5)$
$= 5 - \frac{10}{3}$
$= 1\frac{2}{3}$ ← Not in the replacement set
$(2, 1\frac{2}{3})$ is *not* a solution.

The solution set is $\{(0, 5), (3, 3)\}$.

EXAMPLE 3 The area of a rectangle is 20 cm². Find all possible whole-number values of l and w.

Solution
$$A = lw$$
$$20 = lw$$
$$l = \frac{20}{w}$$

Both w and l must be whole numbers. So, use values for w that are factors of 20.

Check each ordered pair (w, l) in $20 = lw$.

The solution set is $\{(1, 20), (2, 10), (4, 5), (5, 4), (10, 2), (20, 1)\}$.

w	$\dfrac{20}{w}$	l	ordered pair (w,l)
1	$\frac{20}{1}$	20	(1, 20)
2	$\frac{20}{2}$	10	(2, 10)
4	$\frac{20}{4}$	5	(4, 5)
5	$\frac{20}{5}$	4	(5, 4)
10	$\frac{20}{10}$	2	(10, 2)
20	$\frac{20}{20}$	1	(20, 1)

TRY THIS 2. The perimeter of a rectangle is 24 in. Find all the possible whole number values of its sides.

Note that if the replacement set in Example 3 were the set of rational numbers or the set of real numbers, the solution set would consist of an unlimited number of ordered pairs. For example, if $w = \frac{1}{2}$, then $l = 40$; if $w = \frac{1}{3}$, $l = 60$, and so on.

Classroom Exercises

Solve for y in the ordered pair so that it shows a solution for $3x + y = 5$.

1. $(0, y)$ **2.** $(4, y)$ **3.** $(-2, y)$

Find the solution set if the replacement set for each variable is $\{1, 2, 3, 4, 5\}$.

4. $-x + 3y = 6$ **5.** $3x - 2y = 8$ **6.** $2x - y = 4$
7. $2x + y = 3$ **8.** $5x - 3y = 1$ **9.** $-7x + y = 2$

Written Exercises

Find two solutions for each given equation. Use $\{0, 1, \cancel{2, 3, 4, 5, 6}\}$ as the replacement set for each variable. ~~only~~ only due 0+1

1. $4x - y = 2$ **2.** $2x + y = 16$ **3.** $5x - 2y = 10$
4. $x - 3y = 3$ **5.** $2x + 4y = 12$ **6.** $3x - 2y = -6$

Find the solution set if the replacement set is the set of whole numbers. If there are many solutions, find two.

7. $-3x + 2y = 6$ **8.** $5x - 3y = -8$ **9.** $6x - 3y = 12$
10. $5x - y = -3$ **11.** $-2x + 3y = 9$ **12.** $-x - y = -4$
13. $x + 3y = 5$ **14.** $-x + 4y = -3$ **15.** $-2x - 3y = -9$

Find the solution set if the replacement set is the set of whole numbers.

16. $xy = 10$ **17.** $ab = 12$ **18.** $mn = 18$
19. $3xy = 48$ **20.** $2pq = 72$ **21.** $5ab = 125$
22. $x^2 + y^2 = 13$ **23.** $x^2 + y^2 = 16$ **24.** $3x^2 + y^2 = 7$

For Exercises 25–28, write an equation in two variables. Then find the solution set if the replacement set is the set of whole numbers.

25. The area of a rectangle is 32 cm².

26. The area of a triangle is 24 in².
   (HINT: Area $= \frac{1}{2}bh$)

27. The sum of two even numbers is 10.

28. The sum of two odd numbers is 12.

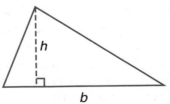

29. If m and n are positive single-digit numbers, find all the possible solutions of $3m + 6n = 33$.

30. If p and q are positive two-digit numbers, find all possible solutions of $2p - 3q = 11$.

31. If p and q are two-digit numbers and $q > 0$, find all possible solutions of $3p + 2q = -36$.

32. If a and b are integers, how many solutions of $-3ab = 30$ are there?

Midchapter Review

Give the coordinates of each point. *10.1*

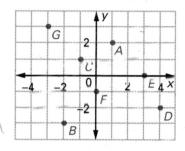

1. A **2.** B

3. C **4.** D

5. E **6.** F

7. G

Graph each point in the same coordinate plane. *10.1*

8. $P(-1, 2)$ **9.** $Q(5, 0)$ **10.** $R(-3, -1)$ **11.** $S(4, -4)$

Give the domain and the range of each relation. Is it a function? *10.2*

12. $\{(-2, 3), (6, 3), (-1, -2), (5, -1)\}$ **13.** $\{(1, 3), (-1, 6), (1, -2), (3, -2)\}$

Given $f(x) = -5x + 1$, find each indicated value. *10.3*

14. $f(-3)$ **15.** $f(0)$ **16.** $f(2)$ **17.** $f(-1)$

Use the given domain D to find the values of each function. *10.3*

18. $g(x) = 3x - 4, D = \{-3, 0, 2\}$ **19.** $f(x) = 3x^2 - x + 2, D = \{-2, 0, 3\}$

Find the solution set if the replacement set for each variable is $\{0, 1, 2, 3, 4, 5\}$. *10.4*

20. $x + 3y = 10$ **21.** $2x - 3y = 1$

22. The area of a rectangle is 36 cm². Find all possible values of l and w if they must be whole numbers. *10.4*

23. For the possible pairs of whole numbers for the length and the width of a rectangle when the area is 36 cm², predict which pair results in a rectangle with the least perimeter. Check your prediction.

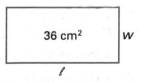

Making a Graph

Many problems can be solved by using graphs. One type is the motion problem, which is related to the distance formula, $d = rt$. If the rate traveled is constant, then the distance traveled increases as the time increases. The graph is a straight line.

Mrs. Zemora left her office at 9:00 A.M. and drove 50 mi/h to attend a business meeting in a town 400 mi away. One hour later her assistant left the same office with a package that Mrs. Zemora needed and drove 60 mi/h. At what time did he catch up to her? Write the equations and make a graph. Find where the lines intersect.

	Mrs. Zemora		Assistant	
	t	$d = (50t)$	t	$d = 60t$
9 A.M.	0	0	t	$(60t)$
10 A.M.	1	50	0	0
11 A.M.	2	100	1	60
12 NOON	3	150	2	120
1 P.M.	4	200	3	180
2 P.M.	5	250	4	240
3 P.M.	6	300	5	300
4 P.M.	7	350	6	360

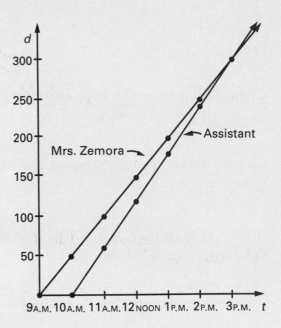

The graphs of $d = 50t$ and $d = 60t$ intersect at 3:00 P.M.

Therefore, Mrs. Zemora's assistant caught up to her at 3:00 P.M.

Exercises

1. How many hours did the assistant drive to catch Mrs. Zemora?

2. How far did each drive?

3. If Mrs. Zemora had driven 60 mi/h, how fast would the assistant have to drive to catch up to her by 3:00 P.M.? Make a graph.

Application: Fixed and Variable Costs

In order to make a profit, Pete's Pizza Parlor prices each pizza higher than the costs of making and delivering the pizzas. Certain costs for making a pizza remain fixed for pizzas of all sizes. These fixed costs include amounts paid for rent, taxes, electricity and other utilities, equipment, and personnel. On the other hand, the cost of the ingredients changes with the size of each pizza.

Pete uses this formula to estimate the cost of the ingredients for his SuperDuper Special pizza.

$$I = 0.045d^2$$

In the formula, I represents the cost in dollars of the ingredients, and d represents the diameter of a pizza in inches. Note that the size of a pizza is expressed in terms of its diameter.

Exercises

Solve each problem. Assume that all problems refer to Pete's SuperDuper Special pizza.

1. Find the cost of the ingredients for a 10-inch pizza and for a 12-inch pizza.

2. The fixed costs for each pizza amount to $5.00. Find the total cost of producing a 10-inch pizza and for producing a 12-inch pizza.

3. If Pete wants to make a 10% profit on each pizza, what should be the selling price of a 10-inch pizza? Of a 12-inch pizza?

4. Pete wants to make a new SuperSize pizza that will sell for $18.20. What size should the pizza be? Round your answer to the nearest inch.

10.5 Graphing Linear Equations

Objectives

To graph linear equations

To determine whether a relation is a function, by the vertical-line test

The solution set of $x + y = 3$ is a set of ordered pairs. Some of the solutions are $(0, 3)$, $(2, 1)$, and $(4, -1)$. None of the ordered pairs in the solution set has the same first coordinate. Thus, the equation $x + y = 3$ defines a function which is called a **linear function.** Such a function can be described by a *linear equation in two variables.* The equations $x + y = 3$ and $4x - 5y = 6$ are examples of such equations.

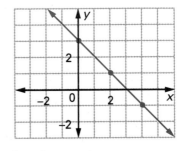

Definition

An equation of the form $Ax + By = C$, with A and B not both 0, is called the **standard form** of a linear equation in two variables.

EXAMPLE 1   Graph $-2x + y = 1$.

Plan   Solve for y in terms of x. Then find three ordered pairs that are solutions for the equation. You can draw the graph through two points. The third point is used as a check.

Solution

$$-2x + y = 1$$
$$y = 2x + 1$$

Make a table of values. Choose -1, 0, and 1 as values for x, find the corresponding values for y, and draw the graph through the points.

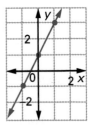

x	$2x + 1$	y	(x, y)
-1	$2 \cdot (-1) + 1$	-1	$(-1, -1)$
0	$2 \cdot 0 + 1$	1	$(0, 1)$
1	$2 \cdot 1 + 1$	3	$(1, 3)$

TRY THIS   1. Graph $x - y = 3$.   2. Graph $x = 2y + 1$.

Sometimes you are asked to graph a linear function given in $f(x)$ notation. $f(x) = 3x$ indicates that for each number x, the value of the function is $3x$. The same relationship can be represented as $y = 3x$.

EXAMPLE 2   Graph the linear function $f(x) = 3x$.

Solution   Make a table of values that shows three ordered pairs, $(x, f(x))$.

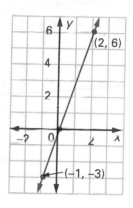

x	3x	f(x)	(x, f(x))
−1	3 · (−1)	−3	(−1, −3)
0	3 · 0	0	(0, 0)
2	3 · 2	6	(2, 6)

Plot the points and draw the graph.

TRY THIS   3. Graph $f(x) = x − 1$.   4. Graph $f(x) = −2x + 1$.

These equations are special cases of the standard form, $Ax + By = C$.

$y = 3$ This equation is equivalent to $0 \cdot x + 1 \cdot y = 3$.

$x = −2$ This equation is equivalent to $1 \cdot x + 0 \cdot y = −2$.

EXAMPLE 3   Graph the equation $y = 3$.

Solution   Any ordered pair that has 3 as its ordinate is a solution of $y = 3$. Three such ordered pairs are listed below.

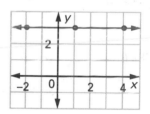

$(−2, 3)$ $(1, 3)$ $(4, 3)$

The graph is a horizontal line three units above the x-axis.

TRY THIS   5. Graph $y = −4$.   6. Graph $y = 0$.

The graph of a linear equation of the form $y = c$ is a *horizontal line*. A function whose graph is a horizontal line is a **constant linear function**.

EXAMPLE 4   Graph the equation $x = −2$. Is the line the graph of a function?

Solution   Any ordered pair that has −2 as its abscissa is a solution of $x = −2$. Three such ordered pairs are listed below:

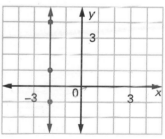

$(−2, −1)$ $(−2, 1)$ $(−2, 4)$

The graph is a vertical line two units to the left of the y-axis.

Since each ordered pair has the same first coordinate, the line is not the graph of a function

The graph of a linear equation of the form $x = c$ is a *vertical line*. On a vertical line, all the points have the same first coordinate. This suggests that a vertical line can be used to determine whether a graph is the graph of a function.

The Vertical Line Test
If no vertical line can be found that intersects a graph more than once, then the relation is a function. If there is a vertical line that intersects the graph more than once, then the relation is not a function.

EXAMPLE 5 Determine whether each of the following is the graph of a function.

a. 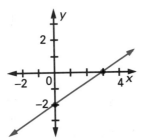 b. 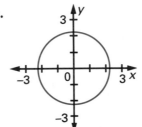 c.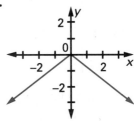

Plan Draw vertical lines. Check to see whether any vertical line intersects the graph in more than one point.

Solutions a. 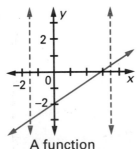 b. 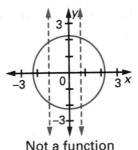 c.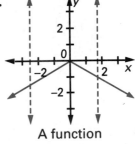

A function   Not a function   A function

TRY THIS Which of the following is the graph of a function?

7. 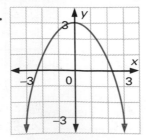 8. 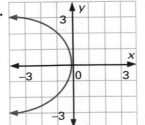 9.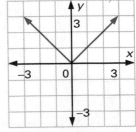

Focus on Reading

Match each phrase at the left with one or more graphs at the right. Justify your answer.

1. linear function
2. horizontal line
3. vertical line
4. constant linear function
5. not a function

a.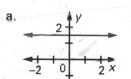

b.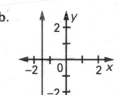

c.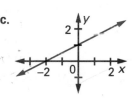

Classroom Exercises

Graph each equation.

1. $x + y = 7$ 2. $y = 5$ 3. $x = -4$ 4. $8x + 3y = 12$

Use your graphs in Exercises 1–4 to answer these questions.

5. Which graphs represent relations?
6. Which graphs represent functions?
7. Which graphs represent constant linear functions?
8. Which graphs do not represent functions?

Written Exercises

Graph each equation.

1. $x + y = 9$ 2. $x - y = 3$ 3. $x + y = -5$ 4. $x - y = -1$
5. $x = 6$ 6. $y = 2$ 7. $x + 4 = 0$ 8. $y = -5$

Solve for y in terms of x. Then graph the equation.

9. $-2x + y = 0$ 10. $3x + y = 9$ 11. $4x = 4y$ 12. $6x + 3y = 12$
13. $4x - 2y = 6$ 14. $6x - 3y = 6$ 15. $-4x + y = -1$ 16. $-6x + 2y = 10$

Graph each equation. Which relations are linear functions? Which functions are constant linear functions?

17. $2x - y = 3$ 18. $y = -3$ 19. $x = 2$ 20. $-x = 4$
21. $4x + 2y = 10$ 22. $x - 6 = 0$ 23. $y = -4$ 24. $0 \cdot x + 1 \cdot y = 7$

Use the vertical line test to determine which relations are functions.

25.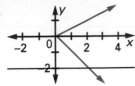

26.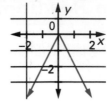

27.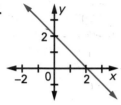

28.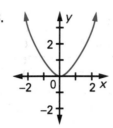

Graph each function.

29. $f(x) = 4x$ **30.** $f(x) = 3x - 5$ **31.** $f(x) = -x$ **32.** $f(x) = -3x - 2$

Write an equation. Then draw the graph.

33. The sum of $2x$ and y is 10.

34. y is 5 less than x.

35. The opposite of $3x$ equals $\frac{1}{2}y$.

36. y equals twice the absolute value of x.

37. $\frac{2}{3}x$ is 1 more than $\frac{1}{6}y$.

38. No matter what x is, twice y equals 9.

Graph each function.

39. $f(x) = \frac{x}{4}$

40. $f(x) = 2 - \frac{1}{3}x$

41. $\frac{f(x) - 4}{2} = x - 2$

42. $3x - 2f(x) = 4$

43. $3x - [2x - f(x)] = 4$

44. $4 - [6 - (f(x)] = 8$

Mixed Review

Add, subtract, multiply, or divide.   *6.7, 6.8, 6.9, 8.4, 8.7*

1. $(2x^2 + 3x + 4) + (x^2 - 7x - 6)$

2. $(5y^2 - 3y + 7) - (6y^2 - 4y + 7)$

3. $-8n^2(2n^2 - 4n + 5)$

4. $(x - 7)(x + 8)$

5. $(2y + 4)(y - 6)$

6. $(y + 3)(y - 3)$

7. $\dfrac{x^2 - x - 6}{x^2 - 36} \div \dfrac{2x^2 - 7x + 3}{x^2 + 8x + 12}$

8. $\dfrac{2}{x + 3} - \dfrac{15}{x^2 - 9} + \dfrac{2}{x - 3}$

9. The selling price of a turntable is $156. The profit is 30% of the cost. Find the cost.   *4.8*

10.6 Direct Variation

To determine whether a relation is a direct variation
To determine the constant of variation
To find missing values in direct variations

Peter earns $20 per hour playing in a band. If he works 1 h, he earns $20; if he works 2 h, he earns $40, and so on. The amount of money he earns is directly related to the number of hours he works. The relationship can be expressed by the equation $e = 20n$, where e represents the total earnings, 20 is the number of dollars earned per hour, and n represents the number of hours worked. The equation $e = 20n$ is an example of *direct variation*.

Definitions

A **direct variation** is a linear function defined by an equation of the form $y = kx$, where k is a nonzero real number.

The constant k is called the **constant of variation**.

The equation $y = kx$ is read "y varies directly as x."

EXAMPLE 1 y varies directly as x. y is 45 when x is 9. Find the constant of variation. Then find y when x is 7.

Solution Write an equation for direct variation.

$$y = kx$$

Substitute 45 for y and 9 for x.

$$45 = k \cdot 9$$
$$9k = 45$$
$$k = 5$$

Thus, the constant of variation is 5.

Replace k with 5 in $y = kx$.

$$y = 5x$$

Substitute 7 for x.

$$y = 5 \cdot 7$$
$$y = 35$$

Thus, y is 35 when $x = 7$.

TRY THIS
1. y varies directly as x and y is 18 when x is 27.
   Find x when y is 8.

Sometimes a table of ordered pairs (x, y) is given, and you need to determine whether the relationship is a direct variation.

EXAMPLE 2   From the table, determine whether y varies directly as x. If so, find the constant of variation.

x	y
2	-12
5	-30
-2	12

Plan   Use $\frac{y}{x} = k$. See whether $\frac{y}{x} = k$ for all pairs (x, y) such that $x \neq 0$ and $y \neq 0$.

Solution $\dfrac{-12}{2} = -6$ $\dfrac{-30}{5} = -6$ $\dfrac{12}{-2} = -6$

Thus, y varies directly as x, and the constant of variation is -6

TRY THIS   2. From the set of ordered pairs, determine the constant of variation.
$$\{(-3, 5), (6, -10), (-15, 25)\}$$

In Example 2, the ratios $\frac{-12}{2}$, $\frac{-30}{5}$, and $\frac{12}{-2}$ have the same value, -6. Therefore, the following *proportions* are true.

$$\frac{-12}{2} = \frac{-30}{5} \qquad\qquad \frac{-30}{5} = \frac{12}{-2} \qquad\qquad \frac{-12}{2} = \frac{12}{-2}$$

In general, if two ratios, $\frac{y_1}{x_1}$ and $\frac{y_2}{x_2}$, have the same value, k, then the *direct variation* $y = kx$ can be written as the proportion $\frac{y_1}{x_1} = \frac{y_2}{x_2}$.

EXAMPLE 3   The distance d that a plane travels varies directly as the time t that it travels if the rate of travel is constant. If a plane travels 2,600 mi in 4 h, how far does it travel in 6 h?

Plan   Write the direct variation as a proportion.

Solution   Since $\frac{d}{t}$ is constant, write: $\dfrac{d_1}{t_1} = \dfrac{d_2}{t_2}$

Substitute 2,600 for d_1, $\dfrac{2,600}{4} = \dfrac{d_2}{6}$
4 for t_1, and 6 for t_2.

Solve for d_2. $2{,}600(6) = 4d_2$

$$d_2 = \frac{2{,}600(6)}{4}, \text{ or } 3{,}900$$

Thus, the distance traveled in 6 h is 3,900 mi

TRY THIS   3. The number of widgets a machine can make varies directly as the time it operates. The machine can make 1,275 widgets in 2 hours. How many can it make in 7 hours?

Which statements do not apply to $\frac{d}{t} = \frac{7}{5}$? Explain.

1. d varies directly as t.
2. d is directly proportional to t.
3. The constant of variation is 7.
4. t varies directly as d.
5. d is directly proportional to $\frac{7}{5}$.
6. $d = \frac{7}{5}t$.

Classroom Exercises

Find the constant of variation, if y varies directly as x.

1. $y = -3x$
2. $\frac{y}{x} = \frac{4}{3}$
3. $7s = t$
4. $c = 2\pi r$

For Exercises 5–8, y varies directly as x.

5. y is 27 when x is 6.
Find y when x is 12.

6. y is 100 when x is 40.
Find y when x is 16.

7. y is 6 when x is 9.
When y is 32, what is x?

8. y is 25 when x is 20.
When y is 35, what is x?

Determine whether y varies directly as x. If so, find the constant of variation.

9.	x	y
	8	4
	18	9
	20	10

10.	x	y
	30	2
	90	6
	40	3

11.	x	y
	-1	-7
	-2	-14
	-3	-21

12.	x	y
	-10	5
	10	-5
	20	-10

Written Exercises

In each of the following, y varies directly as x.

1. y is 54 when x is 9.
Find y when x is 3.

2. y is -36 when x is -4.
Find y when x is 7.

3. y is 27 when x is -3.
Find y when x is 18.

4. y is -10 when x is -4.
Find y when x is -6.

5. y is 100 when x is 60.
When y is 80, what is x?

6. y is 9 when x is 12.
When y is 48, what is x?

Determine whether y varies directly as x. If so, find the constant of variation.

7.	x	y
	5	20
	6	24
	-3	-12

8.	x	y
	-75	-15
	-60	-12
	50	10

9.	x	y
	7	15
	10	18
	15	23

10.	x	y
	-30	3
	-20	2
	50	-5

Solve each problem.

11. The cost of chocolates varies directly as the number of pounds. If 2 lb of chocolates cost $4.60, find the cost of 5 lb of chocolates.

12. The weight of a metal rod varies directly as its length. If a 12-ft rod weighs 18 lb, how much does a 20-ft rod weigh?

13. The distance a car travels varies directly as the time traveled, but only if the rate of travel is constant. If a car travels 330 mi in 6 h, how far does it travel in 8 h? (Assume rate is constant.)

14. The property tax on a house varies directly as the assessed value of the house. The tax on a house assessed at $20,000 is $4,000. Find the taxes on a house assessed at $35,000.

15. At a given time and place, the height of a vertical pole varies directly as the length of its shadow. A 6-m pole casts a 9-m shadow. Find the height of a building that casts a 60-m shadow.

16. The number of kilograms of water in a person's body varies directly as a person's mass. A person with a mass of 100 kg contains 75 kg of water. How many kilograms of water are in a person with a mass of 96 kg?

17. Gas consumption of a car is approximately proportional to the distance traveled. A car uses 40 liters of gas to travel 240 km. About how much gas will the car use to travel 300 km?

18. The weight of an object on the moon varies directly as its weight on earth. On earth, an object weighs 125 lb. But on the moon it weighs 20 lb. What would an 80-pound crate weigh on the moon?

19. y varies directly as x^2. If y is 64 when x is 7, find y when x is 3.

20. y varies directly as x^2. If y is 49 when x is 12, find y when x is 9.

21. The distance that a falling object travels varies directly as the square of the time it falls. A ball falls 320 m in 8 s. How far will it fall in 18 s?

22. The distance needed to stop a car varies directly as the square of its speed. It requires 173 m to stop a car traveling at 82 km/h. What distance is required to stop a car traveling 88 km/h?

Mixed Review

Solve. *3.2, 3.3, 4.6*

1. $5y = -80$ =

2. $-6x = 72$

3. $-\frac{2}{3}x = 16$

4. $-\frac{3}{5}y = -45$ =

5. $4n + 15 = 7$

6. $3.2x = 0.75 - 0.7x$

7. Two cars traveled in opposite directions from the same starting point. The rate of one car was 15 km/h faster than the other car. After 2 h, the cars were 240 km apart. Find the rate of each car. *9.4*

10.7 Inverse Variation

Objectives
To determine whether a relation is an inverse variation
To determine the constant of variation in an inverse variation
To find missing values in inverse variations

A train is traveling to a city 240 mi away. The faster it goes, the less time it will take. In the table, notice that rate × time is a constant, 240.

Rate in miles per hour (r)	20	30	40	60	80	120
Time in hours (t)	12	8	6	4	3	2

The equation, $r \cdot t = 240$, or $t = \dfrac{240}{r}$, is an example of *inverse variation*. We say that the time, t, varies inversely as the rate, r.

Definition

> An **inverse variation** is a function defined by an equation of the form $xy = k$, or $y = \dfrac{k}{x}$ where k is a nonzero real number. The constant k is called the **constant of variation**.

EXAMPLE 1 Given that y varies inversely as x and $y = 12$ when $x = 5$, find the constant of variation. Then find y when x is 20.

Solution

Write an equation for inverse variation. $xy = k$

Substitute 5 for x and 12 for y. $5 \cdot 12 = k$

$$k = 60$$

So, k is 60.

Replace k by 60 in $xy = k$. $xy = 60$

Substitute 20 for x. $20y = 60$

$$y = \frac{60}{20}$$

$$y = 3$$

Thus, y is 3 when x is 20.

TRY THIS

1. Given that y varies inversely as x, and $y = 6$ when $x = 3$, find y when $x = -36$.

For a table of ordered pairs (x, y) such as the one at the right, you can tell whether y varies inversely as x by finding the product $x \cdot y$ for each pair.

x	y
3	16
12	4
−6	−8

$$3 \cdot 16 = 48 \qquad 12 \cdot 4 = 48 \qquad (-6) \cdot (-8) = 48$$

The product $x \cdot y$ is 48 for each pair. Therefore, y varies inversely as x, and the constant of variation is 48.

The graph of an inverse variation is *not* a straight line. One part of the graph of $xy = 48$, or $y = \dfrac{48}{x}$, is shown below. This figure shows the graph when both x and y are positive. Another part of the graph is located in Quadrant III (where both x and y are negative).

x	$\dfrac{48}{x}$	y	(x, y)
3	$\dfrac{48}{3}$	16	(3, 16)
4	$\dfrac{48}{4}$	12	(4, 12)
6	$\dfrac{48}{6}$	8	(6, 8)
8	$\dfrac{48}{8}$	6	(8, 6)
12	$\dfrac{48}{12}$	4	(12, 4)
16	$\dfrac{48}{16}$	3	(16, 3)

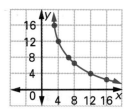

The inverse variation $xy = k$ can be expressed using subscripts, as shown below.

$$x_1 y_1 = k \text{ and } x_2 y_2 = k, \text{ so } x_1 y_1 = x_2 y_2$$

EXAMPLE 2 In a closed container, the volume V of a gas varies inversely as the pressure p that is applied to the gas. If the volume is 100 m³ under 5 atmospheres of pressure, find the volume under 8 atmospheres of pressure.

Plan Since V varies inversely as p, use $p_1 V_1 = p_2 V_2$.

Solution

Substitute 100 for V_1, 5 for p_1, and 8 for p_2.

Solve for V_2.

$$p_1 V_1 = p_2 V_2$$
$$5 \cdot 100 = 8 \cdot V_2$$
$$V_2 = \frac{5 \cdot 100}{8}$$
$$= 62.5$$

Thus, the volume is 62.5 m³ when the pressure is 8 atmospheres.

Classroom Exercises

Find the constant of variation for each inverse variation.

1. $xy = 30$ **2.** $lw = 16$ **3.** $rt = 400$ **4.** $y = \dfrac{-48}{x}$

For Exercises 5–8, **y** varies inversely as **x.**

5. y is 3 when x is 8. Find y when x is 2.

6. y is 12 when x is 9. Find y when x is 36.

7. y is 8 when x is 6. When y is 24, what is x?

8. y is 32 when x is 3. When y is 16, what is x?

For Exercises 9 and 10, let $y = \dfrac{36}{x}$.

9. If x increases, what happens to y?

10. If x decreases, what happens to y?

Written Exercises

In each of the following, **y** varies inversely as **x.**

1. y is 13 when x is 4. Find y when x is 26.

2. y is 18 when x is 6. Find y when x is 9.

3. y is 3 when x is 8. Find y when x is 6.

4. y is 4 when x is -16. Find y when x is -8.

5. y is 20 when x is 4. When y is 80, what is x?

6. y is -60 when x is $\frac{3}{5}$. When y is 2, what is x?

7. y is 3 when x is -8. When y is -6, what is x?

8. y is 12 when x is $\frac{3}{4}$. When y is 27, what is x?

Determine whether y varies inversely as x. If so, find the constant of variation.

9.

x	y
3	4
2	6
-4	-3
12	2

10.

x	y
6	4
-8	-3
-12	2
3	-8

11.

x	y
3.2	20
6.4	10
12.8	5
21.9	3

12.

x	y
3.2	15.0
6.4	7.5
10.0	4.8
19.2	2.5

Solve each problem.

13. The current in an electric circuit varies inversely as the resistance. When the current is 40 amps, the resistance is 25 ohms. Find the current when the resistance is 15 ohms.

14. The time to travel a fixed distance varies inversely as the rate of travel. When the time traveled is 6 h, the rate of travel is 90 km/h. Find the time when the rate of travel is 80 km/h.

15. The number of vibrations a string makes under constant tension is inversely proportional to its length. If a 32-cm string vibrates 420 times per second, what length string vibrates 640 times per second?

16. When two meshed gears revolve, their speeds are inversely proportional to the number of teeth they have. If a gear with 60 teeth revolves at a speed of 2,500 rev/min, at what speed should a gear with 90 teeth revolve?

17. The length of a rectangle with a constant area varies inversely as the width. When the length is 24 in., the width is 8 in. Find the length when the width is 12 in.

18. The volume of gas varies inversely as the pressure. If the volume is 60 m³ under 6 atmospheres of pressure, find the volume under 4 atmospheres of pressure.

19. The base of a triangle with constant area varies inversely as the height. When the base is 22 cm, the height is 6 cm. Find the length of the base when the height is 12 cm.

20. The frequency of a radio wave is inversely proportional to its wave-length. If a 300-m wave has a frequency of 2,000 kilocycles, what length wave has a frequency of 1,000 kilocycles?

21. The height of a cylinder of constant volume varies inversely as the square of the radius of the base. The height of a cylinder is 12 m and the radius of the base is 5 m. Find the height of the cylinder of the same volume with a base radius of 6 m.

22. The brightness of the illumination of an object varies inversely as the square of the distance of the object from the source of illumination. If a light meter reads 45 luxes at a distance of 3 m from a light source, find the reading at 5 m from the source.

23. The weight of a body at, or above, the earth's surface varies inversely as the square of the body's distance from the earth's center. An object has a weight of 350 lb when it is at the earth's surface. What is its weight when it is 250 mi above the earth's surface? (Use 4,000 mi as the earth's radius.)

24. How far above the earth's surface would the object in Exercise 23 have to be for its weight to be 290 lb?

Mixed Review

Simplify.   *6.1, 6.3*

1. $-3y(-2y^3)$

2. $-a^2 \cdot (-a)^2$

3. $-ab(-2ab)$

4. $\dfrac{25ab}{5a^3b}$

5. $\dfrac{36a^3bc^4}{-6ab^4c^5}$

6. $\dfrac{(3a^3b^2)^3}{9ab^7}$

Solve.   *7.7*

7. $x^2 - 8x + 15 = 0$

8. $x^2 - 3x - 4 = 0$

9. $y^2 + 5y = 0$

10. $y^2 - 16 = 0$

11. $2y^2 = 2 - 3y$

12. $-y = 6y^2 - 1$

13. Five is what percent of 8?   *4.7*

14. Eighty is 125% of what number?   *4.7*

Problem Solving Strategies

Restating the Problem

When you are asked to show that a general statement is true, it sometimes helps to restate the problem first.

Example Show that there is no smallest positive rational number.

Restating the problem may give you an idea of how to solve it. In this case, restate the problem as shown below.

> Show that for any positive rational number, you can always find another positive rational number that is smaller.

Represent any rational number as $\dfrac{p}{q}$, where p and q are positive integers.

Then you can always find a positive rational number smaller than $\dfrac{p}{q}$ by adding 1 to the denominator:

Original Rational Number   **Smaller Rational Number**

$$\dfrac{p}{q} \qquad\qquad\qquad \dfrac{p}{q + 1}$$

To help see that $\dfrac{p}{q + 1} < \dfrac{p}{q}$, think of some examples.

$$\frac{1}{4} < \frac{1}{3} \qquad \frac{1}{11} < \frac{1}{10} \qquad \frac{1}{1,001} < \frac{1}{1,000}$$

You can see that for any positive rational number, no matter how small, you can always find a smaller one. In other words, there is no *smallest* positive rational number.

Show that each statement is true.

1. There is no largest integer. (Restate. Show that for any integer, you can always find a larger integer.)
2. There is no largest rational number.
3. There is no smallest rational number.
4. There is no pair of integers whose sum is 10 and whose difference is 5.
5. There is no smallest element of the set of rational numbers greater than 3 and less than 4.
6. There is an infinite number of rational numbers between any two rational numbers.

Chapter 10 Review

Key Terms

constant linear function   (p. 393)
constant of variation   (p. 397, 401)
coordinate plane   (p. 373)
direct variation   (p. 397)
domain   (p. 378)
function   (p. 378)
inverse variation   (p. 401)
linear function   (p. 392)

mapping   (p. 382)
ordered pair   (p. 373)
origin   (p. 373)
range   (p. 378)
relation   (p. 378)
value of a function   (p. 383)
x- and y-axis   (p. 373)
x- and y-coordinates   (p. 374)

Key Ideas and Review Exercises

10.1   To graph a point given its coordinates, start at the origin and move right if the abscissa is positive, or left if it is negative. Then move up if the ordinate is positive, or down if it is negative.

Graph each point in the same coordinate plane.

1. $(3, -1)$ **2.** $(-2, 4)$ **3.** $(-1, -3)$ **4.** $(3, 2)$

5. $(0, 5)$ **6.** $(5, 4)$ **7.** $(-1, 0)$ **8.** $(-2, 1)$

10.2   To determine the domain of a relation, find the set of first coordinates. To determine the range of a function, find the set of second coordinates.

To show that a relation is a function, show that no two ordered pairs have the same first coordinate.

Given the relation $G = \{(-1, 3), (1, 5), (-6, -3), (7, 3), (-3, 1)\}$.

9. Determine the domain of G.   **10.** Determine the range of G.

11. Is G a function? Explain your answer.

10.3   To find the value of a function $f(x)$, substitute a given value for x in the expression that defines the function.

To determine the range of a function, find the set of function values for all elements in the domain.

Given $f(x) = x^2 - 8$, **find the indicated value.**

12. $f(1)$ **13.** $f(-2)$ **14.** $f(5)$ **15.** $f(-6)$

16. Use the domain $D = \{-1, 0, 5\}$ to find the range of $g(x) = 3x - 5$.

10.4   To solve an equation with two variables x and y, substitute values of x from the replacement set and solve for y. If the value of y is in the replacement set, then (x, y) is a solution of the equation.

17. Find two solutions of the equation $2x - 3y = 0$. Use $\{0, 1, 2, 3\}$ as the replacement set.

10.5   To graph a function described by a linear equation, find three ordered pairs that are solutions of the equation. If the function is given in $f(x)$ form, find three ordered pairs $(x, f(x))$. Then plot the ordered pairs and draw the graph.

The vertical line test can be used to determine whether a relation is a function. If no vertical line can be found that intersects the graph of the relation in more than one point, then the relation is a function.

Graph each equation or function.

18. $y = 3x + 4$ 19. $4x - 2y = 4$ 20. $x = 3$ 21. $y = -2$
22. $-2x - y = 3$ 23. $f(x) = 2x + 3$ 24. $f(x) = -3x - 1$ 25. $f(x) = -x + 2$

Use the vertical line test to determine which relations are functions

26. 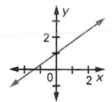   27. 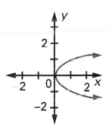   28. 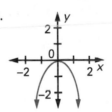   29.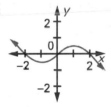

10.6, 10.7   To solve problems with constant variation:

1. Use $y = kx$ or $\dfrac{y}{x} = k$ for direct variation;

   use $xy = k$ or $y = \dfrac{k}{x}$ for inverse variation.

2. Substitute for x and y to find the constant of variation, k.

3. Using the value of k, substitute for one variable to find the other.

30. y varies directly as x, and y is 48 when x is 6. Find y when x is 8.

31. y varies inversely as x, and y is 15 when x is 3. Find y when x is 9.

32. Given the set of ordered pairs $\{(8, 6), (-12, -4), (-16, -3)\}$, write in your own words how to determine whether y varies directly as x, or whether y varies inversely as x, or neither.

Chapter 10 Test

1. Graph the points $A(-1, 4)$, $B(0, -1)$, and $C(-4, 4)$ in the same coordinate plane.

Give the domain and range of the relation. Is it a function?

2. $\{(4, -3), (3, 0), (-1, 5), (4, 2)\}$

3. $\{(3, -3), (1, -3), (0, 4), (-1, 2)\}$

4. For what value of k will the relation $R = \{(-2k+3, 4),$ $(5k-4, -3)\}$ *not* be a function?

Given $g(x) = 5x^2 - 4$, find the indicated value.

5. $g(-2)$

6. $g(3)$

7. $g(0)$

8. $g(-3)$

9. Use the domain $D = \{-3, 0, 3\}$ to find the range of $f(x) = (x - 3)^2$.

10. Find two solutions for $4x - y = 3$. Use $\{0, 1, 2, 3, 4, 5\}$ as the replacement set for each variable.

Graph each equation.

11. $y = -3$

12. $x = 4$

13. $2x - 3y = 6$

14. $x = 2y$

Use the vertical line test to determine which relations are functions.

15.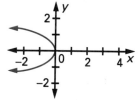

16.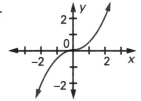

17. Determine whether y varies directly as x, or whether y varies inversely as x, or neither. If there is a variation, find the constant of variation.

x	y
-3	12
2	-8
5	-20

18. y varies directly as x, and y is 30 when x is -6. Find y when x is 8.

19. y varies inversely as x, and y is -4 when x is 4. Find x when y is 8.

20. The width of a rectangle of constant area varies inversely as the length. If the width is 4 ft when the length is 16 ft, find the width when the length is 32 ft.

21. If y varies directly as the square of x, and y is 50 when x is 5, find y when x is 6.

22. If $f(x) = 3x - 1$ and $g(x) = x^2$, find $f(g(-2))$.

Choose the one best answer to each question or problem.

1. A train traveling at 40 mi/h is stopped $3\frac{1}{3}$ mi from its destination at 7:00 A.M. At what time would the train have arrived if it had not been delayed?
   (A) 7:10 A.M.   (B) 6:55 A.M.
   (C) 7:03 A.M.   (D) 7:05 A.M.
   (E) 7:53 A.M.

2. Connect points $P(2, 0)$, $Q(6, 0)$, and $R(4, 5)$ with line segments. Which of the following is true?
   (A) $RQ < PQ$ (B) $RQ < RP$
   (C) $RP = RQ$ (D) $RQ = PQ$
   (E) $RP = PQ$

3. Inside the square, the area of each circle is 16π. What is the area of the shaded region?

   (A) $256 - 64\pi$ (B) $256 - 16\pi$
   (C) $64\pi - 256$ (D) $64 - 64\pi$
   (E) $64\pi - 64$

4. For what value of k will $x^2 + 8x + k = 0$ have one solution?
   (A) 4   (B) -4 (C) 8
   (D) -16 (E) 16

5. If the operation $*$ for positive numbers is defined as $x * y = x^2 + xy$, then $3 * (3 * 3)$ is __?__.
   (A) 63   (B) 18   (C) 27
   (D) 36   (E) 21

6. The vertices of triangle ABC are $A(3, 1)$, $B(3, 5)$, $C(5, 1)$. The area of triangle ABC is __?__.
   (A) 2   (B) 4   (C) 8
   (D) 12   (E) 16

7. Six consecutive odd integers are given. The sum of the first three is 33. What is the sum of the last 3?
   (A) 24   (B) 39   (C) 42
   (D) 45   (E) 51

8. Mary Alice drove 300 km at 50 km/h. If she had driven 10 km/h faster, how many hours would be saved?
   (A) 11   (B) 10   (C) 6
   (D) 5   (E) 1

9. If the operation $*$ for positive numbers is defined as $m * n = \dfrac{mn}{m + n}$, then $(3 * 3) * 3$ is __?__.
   (A) 3   (B) 1   (C) $\dfrac{3}{2}$
   (D) $\dfrac{9}{4}$ (E) $\dfrac{9}{2}$

10. If $\dfrac{2}{3} \cdot \dfrac{3}{4} \cdot \dfrac{4}{5} \cdot \dfrac{5}{6} \cdot \dfrac{6}{7} \cdot n = 5$, then what is the value of n?
    (A) $\dfrac{2}{35}$ (B) 1   (C) $\dfrac{35}{7}$
    (D) $\dfrac{35}{2}$ (E) 35

11. If $\dfrac{3}{4}$ of a number is 54, then $\dfrac{1}{3}$ of the number is __?__.
    (A) $13\frac{1}{2}$ (B) 18   (C) 24
    (D) 32   (E) $40\frac{1}{2}$

12. If $4x - 4y = 1$, what is the value of $\sqrt{x - y}$?
    (A) $\dfrac{1}{16}$ (B) $\dfrac{1}{4}$ (C) $\dfrac{1}{2}$
    (D) 2   (E) 4

Cumulative Review *(Chapters 1–10)*

Add or subtract.

1. $\dfrac{2x}{14} + \dfrac{x}{7} + \dfrac{5x}{6}$ *8.6*

2. $\dfrac{p - 4}{10} - \dfrac{2p - 3}{15}$

3. $\dfrac{-a - 3}{a^2 + a - 6} + \dfrac{6}{2 - a}$ *8.7*

Simplify. Then give the degree of the polynomial.

4. $8a^3 - 4a^2 - a - 4a^3 + a^2$ *6.6*

5. $-6 + 3y^4 - 2y^2 + 8y - y^4 - y^2$

6. $-5x + 3 - 4x^2 - x + x^2 + 3x$

Divide and simplify.

7. $24y^5 \div (-6y^2)$ *6.3*

8. $(-18a^4 + 24a^3 + 9a) \div 3a$ *8.8*

9. $\dfrac{64m^9 - 32m^6 + 48m^5}{-4m^2}$

10. $\dfrac{3a^2 + 13a - 10}{3a - 2}$ *8.1*

11. $(x^3 - 12x^2 - 6) \div (x - 2)$ *8.8*

Multiply and simplify.

12. $-3x^5 \cdot (6x^4)$ *6.1*

13. $-2a^4b \cdot (-3ab^4)$

14. $\dfrac{8x^3y^2}{5xy^4} \cdot \dfrac{-3xy^5}{4x^2y}$ *8.3*

15. $2x^{-3}y^2 \cdot 5x^5y^0$ *6.4*

Solve.

16. $|3m - 2| = 13$ *5.6*

17. $\dfrac{x - 3}{2} + \dfrac{x}{4} = 6$ *4.5*

18. $9a - (6 - a) = 18 - 2a$ *3.5*

19. $5m - 3 = -2m^2$ *7.7*

20. $y^2 - 8y = 0$

21. $x^3 - x^2 - 6x = 0$

22. $6x^2 + x - 1 = 0$

23. $25 - m^2 = 0$

For each of Exercises 24–27, choose the one best answer.

24. The value of x for which   *8.1*
    $\dfrac{2x - 6}{5x + 10}$ is undefined is $\underline{\ ?\ }$.
    (A) 2   (B) -2 (C) 3
    (D) -3 (E) none of these

25. Solve $-5x - 3 \le 12$.   *5.2*
    (A) $x \ge -3$ (B) $x > -3$
    (C) $x \le -3$ (D) $x < -3$
    (E) None of these

26. Evaluate $-3x - 4y^2$ for   *2.8*
    $x = -1$ and $y = -2$.
    (A) 19   (B) -19
    (C) -13 (D) 13
    (E) None of these

27. Subtract $-3a^2 + 4a$ from   *6.7*
    $a^3 + 5a^2 - 3a - 10$.
    (A) $a^3 + 8a^2 - 7a - 10$
    (B) $a^3 + 2a^2 + a - 10$
    (C) $-a^3 - 8a^2 + 7a + 10$
    (D) $a^3 + 8a^2 + 4a - 10$
    (E) None of these

Which property is illustrated?

28. $-5(2x - 3) = -5 \cdot 2x +$ *1.6*
    $(-5)(-3)$

29. $a + b = b + a$ *1.5*

30. $x \cdot 1 = x$ *1.7*

31. $a + 0 = a$ *2.3*

32. $a + (b + c) = (b + c) + a$ *1.5*

33. $x \cdot y = y \cdot x$

Factor completely.

34. $6a^2 + a - 1$ 7.4

35. $25x^2 - 1$ 7.5

36. $3m^3 + 12m^2 - 15m$ 7.6

37. $-9a^2 + 9$

38. $6x^2 - 54$

Simplify.

39. $(x^4 - x) - (6x + 10 - 4x^3)$ 6.7

40. $-(8a^3 + 6 - 7a^2) - (a^2 + 5)$

41. $(-3x^2y^3)^2$ 6.2

42. $\dfrac{18a^4b^6}{-6ab^7}$ 6.3

43. $(8x^4y^5)(-4xy^7)$ 6.1

Write an algebraic expression for each word expression.

44. y more than the product of 12 and x 4.1

45. Six more than $\frac{1}{5}$ of n

46. t more than triple the cost of d dollars

47. Seven less than twice a number, increased by 3 more than 4 times the number

Solve each word problem.

48. If 3 times Dan's age is decreased by 10 more than twice his age, the result is 22. How old is he?   3.3

49. Marina leases a car for $45 plus $.28/mi. How far can she travel, to the nearest mile, on a budget of $310?

50. The second of three numbers is 6 times the first. The third is 5 more than the second. If the second is decreased by twice the third, the result is -40. Find the three numbers.   4.2

51. Forty-two percent of 80 is what number?   4.7

52. Twelve percent of what number is 10.8?

53. Twenty-seven is what percent of 90?

54. The first side of a triangle is 4 cm longer than the second side. The third side is 3 times the second side. The perimeter is 44 cm. How long is each side?   4.4

55. Eight more than 4 times a number is at most 32. Find the numbers.   5.2

56. The selling price of a video player is $420. The profit is 25% of the cost. Find the cost.   4.8

57. If the square of a number is increased by 12, the result is the same as 8 times the number. Find the number.   7.8

58. Find two consecutive even integers such that the sum of the squares is 244.   7.9

59. The size of next year's graduating class will be 98% of this year's. There are 320 in this year's class. How many students will be in the graduating class?   4.8

60. Alex averages 625 mi per week on his car. His car averages 26 mi/gal. If gasoline sells for $1.40/gallon, how much does he spend on gasoline per week?   9.6

61. The sum of three consecutive odd integers is -129. Find the integers.   4.3

The work of Dr. Selma Burke may be in your pocket right now! She is the sculptor who carved the profile of President Franklin D. Roosevelt that appears on every dime.

11.1 Slope of a Line

Objective

To find the slope of a line

When walking or pedaling a bike up a hill, you can notice the steepness of the hill. The steepness, or *slope*, is defined as the ratio of the vertical *rise* of the hill to the horizontal *run* of the hill. The steeper the hill, the greater the slope.

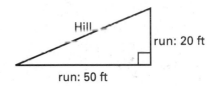

The slope of the hill at the right above is $\frac{20}{50}$, or $\frac{2}{5}$. This means that the hill rises 2 ft vertically for every 5 ft of horizontal distance.

In mathematics, you find slopes of lines in a coordinate plane. The slope of a line is found by forming the ratio $\frac{\text{rise}}{\text{run}}$. The *rise* represents *vertical* change from one point to another. The *run* represents *horizontal* change between the same two points. If a line *slants upward* as you move from left to right, the line has a *positive* slope. If a line *slants downward* as you move from left to right, its slope is *negative*.

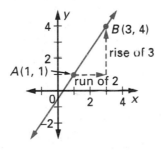

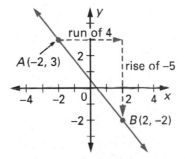

Line *AB* slants upward.

$$\text{slope} = \frac{\text{rise}}{\text{run}} = \frac{3}{2}$$

Line *AB* slants downward.

$$\text{slope} = \frac{\text{rise}}{\text{run}} = \frac{-5}{4} = -\frac{5}{4}$$

For two points such as $A(2, 1)$ and $B(3, 5)$, the run is the difference in the *x*-coordinates and the rise is the *corresponding* difference in the *y*-coordinates.

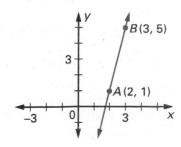

change in *x*-coordinates: $3 - 2 = 1$

change in *y*-coordinates: $5 - 1 = 4$

Therefore, the slope is $\frac{4}{1}$, or 4.

ÉXAMPLE 1   Graph the line passing through each pair of points. Then find the slope
of each line.

   a. $A(2, 3)$ and $B(7, 6)$ **b.** $R(2, 5)$ and $S(6, 3)$

Solutions   **a.**

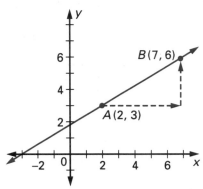

b.

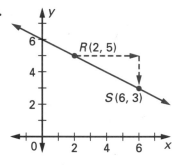

slope $= \dfrac{\textit{change in y-coordinates}}{\textit{change in x-coordinates}}$ slope $= \dfrac{\textit{change in y-coordinates}}{\textit{change in x-coordinates}}$

$= \dfrac{6-3}{7-2} = \dfrac{3}{5}$ $= \dfrac{3-5}{6-2} = \dfrac{-2}{4} = -\dfrac{1}{2}$

TRY THIS   Graph the line passing through each pair of points. Then find the slope
of each line.

   1. $C(2, -1)$ and $D(5, -3)$
   2. $E(-4, 3)$ and $F(1, -3)$

In the figure at the right, $A(x_1, y_1)$ and
$B(x_2, y_2)$ represent any two points. The subscripts are used to distinguish between the
coordinates of the two points. Note that
the coordinates are subtracted in the same
order,
$y_2 - y_1$ and $x_2 - x_1$.

Slope is usually represented by the letter m,
as shown in the definition below.

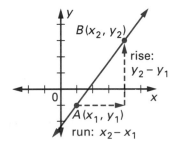

Definition

> For any two points $A(x_1, y_1)$ and $B(x_2, y_2)$, on a nonvertical line, the
> **slope** m of the line is defined as follows:
>
> $$m = \dfrac{\textit{change in y-coordinates}}{\textit{change in x-coordinates}}, \text{ or } m = \dfrac{y_2 - y_1}{x_2 - x_1}, \text{ where } x_1 \neq x_2$$

EXAMPLE 2   Find the slope of the line determined by $P(0, 4)$ and $Q(3, 1)$.

Solution   Slope of $\overleftrightarrow{PQ} = \dfrac{y_2 - y_1}{x_2 - x_1}$

$= \dfrac{4 - 1}{0 - 3}$

$= \dfrac{3}{-3}$, or -1

Thus, the slope of $\overleftrightarrow{PQ}$ is -1.

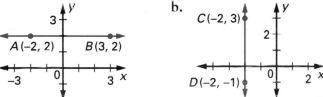

EXAMPLE 3   Find the slope of each line.

a.

b.

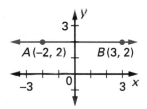

Solutions

a. slope of $\overleftrightarrow{AB} = \dfrac{y_2 - y_1}{x_2 - x_1}$

$= \dfrac{2 - 2}{3 - (-2)}$

$= \dfrac{0}{5}$

$= 0$

The slope is zero.

b. slope of $\overleftrightarrow{CD} = \dfrac{y_2 - y_1}{x_2 - x_1}$

$= \dfrac{3 - (-1)}{-2 - (-2)}$

$= \dfrac{4}{0}$, undefined.

The slope is undefined.

TRY THIS   Find the slope of the line determined by each pair of points.

3. $A(-3, 5)$ and $B(2, 8)$ 4. $H(-1, 4)$ and $K(-1, 5)$
5. $S(4, -2)$ and $T(-4, 2)$

As Example 3 illustrates, the slope of a horizontal line is 0, since $\dfrac{y_2 - y_1}{x_2 - x_1} = \dfrac{0}{x_2 - x_1} = 0$. The slope of a vertical line is undefined, since $\dfrac{y_2 - y_1}{x_2 - x_1} = \dfrac{y_2 - y_1}{0}$ (with a zero denominator) is undefined.

Information about the slope of a line can be determined by the direction in which it slants.

Slope: positive
Slant: up to the right

Slope: negative
Slant: down to the right

Slope: 0
Slant: horizontal

Slope: undefined
Slant: vertical

Classroom Exercises

Use this diagram for Exercises 1–3.

1. What is the rise?   2. What is the run?
3. What is the slope of the line?

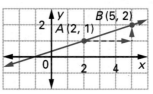

For points A and B, is the slope of $\overleftrightarrow{AB}$ positive, negative, zero, or undefined?

4. $A(2, 3), B(6, 8)$ 5. $A(1, 4), B(10, 6)$ 6. $A(0, 1), B(4, 5)$
7. $A(6, 4), B(-8, 4)$ 8. $A(5, -3), B(5, 7)$ 9. $A(-3, 2), B(6, -4)$

Find the slope of $\overleftrightarrow{PQ}$ for the given points, and describe the slant of the line.

10. $P(-2, 1), Q(3, 4)$ 11. $P(-1, 6), Q(1, -4)$ 12. $P(4, 1), Q(4, -6)$

Written Exercises

Find the slope of each line.

1.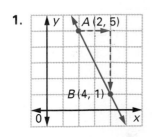

2.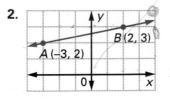

3.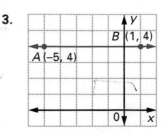

Find the slope of the line determined by the given points M and N.

4. $M(2, 5), N(4, 6)$ 5. $M(6, 5), N(4, 3)$ 6. $M(1, 0), N(2, 8)$
7. $M(4, 8), N(0, 8)$ 8. $M(-1, 3), N(-3, 9)$ 9. $M(-2, 3), N(-2, -4)$

Find the slope of $\overleftrightarrow{MN}$ for the given points, and describe the slant of the line.

10. $M(3, -4)$, $N(7, -2)$ **11.** $M(4, 7)$, $N(-3, 7)$ **12.** $M(7, -6)$, $N(4, -3)$

13. $M(-3, -2)$, $N(-7, -1)$ **14.** $M(4, -2)$, $N(3, -3)$ **15.** $M(7, -3)$, $N(-2, -3)$

16. $M(0, -6)$, $N(-7, 0)$ **17.** $M(-9, -3)$, $N(-9, 6)$ **18.** $M(0, -4)$, $N(5, -4)$

19. The vertices of a triangle are at $A(1, 3)$, $B(3, 5)$ and $C(4, 1)$. Find the slope of each side of the triangle.

20. The vertices of a rectangle are at $R(-2, 4)$, $V(-2, -4)$, $S(3, -4)$, and $T(3, 4)$. Find the slope of each side of the rectangle.

21. Find the slope of a line passing through $A(a, 0)$ and $B(0, a)$.

Use the given expressions to find the slope of $\overleftrightarrow{AB}$.

22. $A(4n, 3r)$, $B(6n, 2r)$ **23.** $A(-8n, -2r)$, $B(-n, -r)$

24. $A(2n - 1, 3r - 2)$ **25.** $A(-3n + 4, 2r - 1)$
$B(4n + 3, 5r - 1)$ $B(8n, 5r + 2)$

26. Plot the four points $A(2, 3)$, $B(6, 3)$, $C(6, -1)$, and $D(2, -1)$. Which lines determined by pairs of these points have a slope of 0?

27. In Exercise 26, which of the lines determined by pairs of the points have an undefined slope?

28. In Exercise 26, which of the lines determined by pairs of the points have a negative slope?

Determine the value(s) of the variable so that $\overleftrightarrow{XY}$ has the given slope.

29. $X(4, -3)$, $Y(a, 9)$; slope $= 1$ **30.** $X(-3, 2)$, $Y(7, a)$; slope $= \frac{2}{3}$

31. $X(-4, 5a)$, $Y(-1, a^2)$; slope $= 0$ **32.** $X(6, a^2 - 5a)$, $Y(-3, 2a^2 - a)$; slope $= 0$

33. $X(5, -8a)$, $Y(10, a^2)$; slope $= -3$ **34.** $X(-2, a)$, $Y(3, 6a^2)$; slope $= \frac{2}{5}$

Mixed Review

Graph the solution set on a number line. *5.7*

  1. $|x| \leq 3$ **2.** $|x| > 2$ **3.** $|-x| \geq 4$ **4.** $|x - 3| < 5$

Multiply. *6.9, 6.10*

  5. $(3a - 1)(2a + 3)$ **6.** $(7x + 5)(2x - 1)$ **7.** $(2m - n)(2m + n)$ **8.** $(2x - 3)^2$

9. Keith started out in his car at the rate of 58 km/h. One hour later Shirley left from the same point driving along the same road at 70 km/h. How long did it take her to catch up to Keith? *9.4*

10. The square of a number is 11 more than 10 times the number. Find the number(s). *7.8*

11.2 Equation of a Line: Point-Slope Form

To write an equation of a line, given a point on the line and its slope
To write an equation of a line, given two points on the line
To write an equation of a line, given a table or graph

This figure shows a line, $\overleftrightarrow{HG}$, through $H(2,-4)$. The slope of the line is -2. Let $G(x,y)$ be any other point on the line. The slope m of a line is

$$\frac{y_2 - y_1}{x_2 - x_1}.$$

So, for the line through H and G,

$$\frac{y - (-4)}{x - 2} = -2$$
$$y + 4 = -2(x - 2)$$

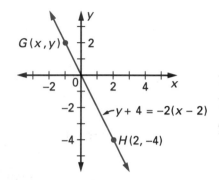

Thus, $y + 4 = -2(x - 2)$ is an equation of $\overleftrightarrow{HG}$.

This derivation suggests the following *point-slope* form of an equation.

Equation of a Line: Point-Slope Form
The **point-slope form** of the equation of a line with slope m and containing point $P(x_1, y_1)$ is $y - y_1 = m(x - x_1)$.

EXAMPLE 1   Find an equation of the line passing through point $P(2,-3)$ with slope $\frac{4}{3}$. Write your answer in the form $Ax + By = C$.

Solution   Use $y - y_1 = m(x - x_1)$. $y - (-3) = \frac{4}{3}(x - 2)$

Multiply each side by 3. $3(y + 3) = 4(x - 2)$
$$3y + 9 = 4x - 8$$

Rewrite the equation in
the form $Ax + By = C$. $-4x + 3y = -17$, or $4x - 3y = 17$

Thus, $4x - 3y = 17$ is an equation of the line passing through $P(2,-3)$ with slope $\frac{4}{3}$.

TRY THIS   1. Find the equation of the line passing through $R(-1, 4)$ and with slope $-\frac{2}{3}$. Write your answer in the form $Ax + By = C$.

You can also use slope to write an equation of a line that passes through two given points.

EXAMPLE 2   Write an equation of $\overleftrightarrow{PQ}$ passing through points $P(4, -1)$ and $Q(2, 1)$.

Solution $m = \dfrac{y_2 - y_1}{x_2 - x_1} = \dfrac{1 - (-1)}{2 - 4} = \dfrac{2}{-2} = -1$

Substitute in $y - y_1 = m(x - x_1)$, using -1 for m and either of the given points for (x_1, y_1).

$$y - (-1) = -1(x - 4)$$
$$y + 1 = -x + 4$$
$$x + y = 3$$

Thus, $x + y = 3$ is an equation, in standard form, of $\overleftrightarrow{PQ}$ passing through points $P(4, -1)$ and $Q(2, 1)$.

EXAMPLE 3   Write an equation in the form $Ax + By = C$.

a.

x	y
1	2
3	1
5	0

b.

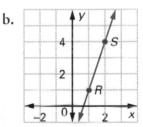

Solutions

a. Choose any two ordered pairs in the table. For example, use $(1, 2)$ and $(5, 0)$.

$$m = \dfrac{0 - 2}{5 - 1} = \dfrac{-2}{4} = -\dfrac{1}{2}$$

Next, use $y - y_1 = m(x - x_1)$.

$$y - 2 = -\tfrac{1}{2}(x - 1)$$

$$2(y - 2) = -1(x - 1)$$

$$2y - 4 = -x + 1$$

$$x + 2y = 5$$

b. Choose any two convenient points on the graph: R and S. Determine the ordered pairs and use them.

$R(1, 1)$ and $S(2, 4)$

$$m = \dfrac{4 - 1}{2 - 1} = \dfrac{3}{1} = 3$$

Next, use $y - y_1 = m(x - x_1)$.

$$y - 1 = 3(x - 1)$$

$$-3x + y = -2$$

$$3x - y = 2$$

TRY THIS   2. Write an equation of the line passing through the points $A(-3, 3)$ and $B(-1, -1)$. Write the equation in the form $Ax + By = C$.

EXAMPLE 4 When a weight of 2 oz is attached to a spring, the length of the spring is 3 in. When a weight of 4 oz is attached, the length of the spring is 4 in. Assume that the relation between the attached weight and the spring length is linear for ($0 \leq$ weight ≤ 8). Write an equation for the relation in the form $Ax + By = C$, and draw its graph.

Solution Let x represent the weight attached to the spring: $0 \leq x \leq 8$.

Let y represent the resulting length of the spring.

Use the ordered pairs (2, 3) and (4, 4) to find m.

$$m = \frac{4 - 3}{4 - 2} = \frac{1}{2}$$

Now substitute in $y - y_1 = m(x - x_1)$, using either ordered pair.

$$y - 3 = \frac{1}{2}(x - 2)$$

$$2(y - 3) = 1(x - 2)$$

$$2y - 6 = x - 2$$

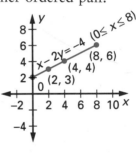

Thus, $-x + 2y = 4$, or $x - 2y = -4$.

The graph is shown at the right.

Since the values of x are restricted to $0 \leq x \leq 8$, the graph is a line segment, not a line.

TRY THIS 3. Use the graph in Example 4 to determine the length of the spring when a weight of 6 oz is attached.

Classroom Exercises

Find an equation for the line passing through the given point with the given slope. Give the equation in the form $y - y_1 = m(x - x_1)$.

1. $P(2, 3)$; slope $= 3$
2. $P(3, 1)$; slope $= -2$
3. $P(5, 4)$; slope $= \frac{2}{3}$
4. $P(-1, 2)$; slope $= \frac{1}{2}$

Find an equation, in the form $Ax + By = C$, of the line passing through the given point and having the given slope.

5. $P(-1, -2)$; slope $= -3$
6. $P(5, -4)$; slope $= \frac{2}{3}$

Find an equation, in the form $Ax + By = C$, of the line passing through the given points.

7. $P(4, 0)$, $Q(3, -4)$ **8.** $P(-3, -1)$, $Q(1, 5)$ **9.**

x	y
1	2
2	0
4	-4

Written Exercises

Write an equation, in the form $Ax + By = C$, of the line passing through the given point and having the given slope.

1. $P(-3, 4)$; slope $= -\frac{1}{3}$ **2.** $P(4, 1)$; slope $= 4$

3. $P(-2, 8)$; slope $= -\frac{1}{4}$ **4.** $P(3, -4)$; slope $= 3$

5. $P(0, 0)$; slope $= -5$ **6.** $P(-1, -5)$; slope $= 0$

7. $P(-9, -3)$; slope $= \frac{3}{4}$ **8.** $P(8, 0)$; slope $= -\frac{5}{6}$

Write an equation, in the form $Ax + By = C$, of the line passing through the given points.

9. $P(3, 1)$, $Q(2, 4)$ **10.** $P(-1, -5)$, $Q(3, -6)$

11. $P(2, 0)$, $Q(-1, 4)$ **12.** $P(-1, -6)$, $Q(3, -7)$

13. $P(-1, 6)$, $Q(-3, -4)$ **14.** $P(5, 4)$, $Q(-5, -3)$

15. $P(0, -3)$, $Q(5, 0)$ **16.** $P(-3, -4)$, $Q(-1, -4)$

Write an equation, in the form $Ax + By = C$, for each graph or table.

17. 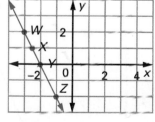   **18.**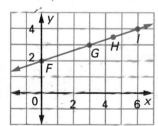

19.

x	y
2	4
3	6
4	8

20.

x	y
2	0
6	2
12	5

21.

x	y
0	2
2	-4
4	-10

22.

x	y
0	3
6	-1
9	-3

Write an equation, in the form $Ax + By = C$, of the line passing through the given point and having the given slope.

23. $P(\frac{1}{2}, \frac{1}{4})$; slope $= 3$

24. $P(\frac{3}{4}, \frac{2}{3})$; slope $= -2$

25. $P(\frac{5}{4}, -\frac{5}{6})$; slope $= \frac{1}{2}$

26. $P(-\frac{1}{2}, -\frac{3}{5})$; slope $= \frac{3}{4}$

27. When a weight of 3 oz is attached to a spring, the length of the spring is 5 in. When a weight of 8 oz is attached, the length of the spring is 7.5 in. Assume that the relationship between weight and length is linear for $0 \le$ weight ≤ 10. Write an equation for the relation in the form $Ax + By = C$, and draw its graph.

28. From the graph drawn in Exercise 27, determine the length of the spring when a weight of 9 oz is attached.

Write an equation, in the form $Ax + By = C$, of the line passing through the given point and having the given slope.

29. $P(0, d)$; slope $= 4$

30. $P(\frac{2}{3}, 0)$; slope $= 6k$

31. $P(\frac{1}{3}, 0)$; slope $= -4g$

32. $P(-s, t)$; slope $= 5s$

Write an equation of the line passing through the given points.

33. $P(r, 2)$, $Q(3, -2r)$

34. $P(s, t)$, $Q(5s, -6t)$

35. Write three equations, each in the form $Ax + By = C$, of lines that meet these conditions:

Line l passes through $(3, 4)$ and $(4.5, 6)$.
Line m passes through $(-6, 4)$ and $(-7.5, 5)$.
Line n passes through $(8, -10)$ and $(4, -5)$.

What do you notice about the value of C in each equation? Graph all the lines in the same plane. Do the three lines intersect in the same point? If so, give the coordinates of the point.

Mixed Review

Evaluate for $x = -2$ and $y = 3$.   *1.1, 2.6*

1. $y + 15$

2. $3x - 2y$

3. $xy - 3y$

4. $-4xy + 5y - x$

5. $x^3 - 3y^2 + 2xy$

6. $x^2 - y - 3xy + y^2$

7. The length of a rectangle is 6 more than 3 times the width. The perimeter is 44 cm. Find the length and the width.   *4.4*

8. The retail price of a camera is $399. The profit is 40% of the cost. Find the cost.   *4.8*

Application: Temperature and Altitude

When flying at certain altitudes, pilots of small planes must be concerned with the possible icing of moisture on their planes' wings.

As the altitude of the plane increases, the outside air temperature cools about one degree Fahrenheit for each 273 feet.

Exercises

Refer to these additional facts to solve each problem.

- Water freezes at 32°F.
- One mile equals 5,280 feet.

1. If the ground temperature is 70°F, what will the air temperature be at an altitude of one mile? Round your answer to the nearest degree.

2. If the outside temperature at the altitude at which the plane is flying is 24°F below the ground temperature, what is the altitude of the plane? Round your answer to the nearest tenth of a mile.

3. A pilot notices ice on the wings of his plane, and decides to descend to an altitude with a temperature of 37°F. How many feet does the pilot descend?

4. If the ground temperature is 68°F, how high in feet can a small plane fly before the outside temperature is at the freezing point?

5. Write a formula that a pilot could use to compute the temperature, t, in degrees Fahrenheit at a height of h feet above the ground when the ground temperature is G° Fahrenheit.

6. Test your formula to see whether it produces the same data as shown in the table at the right. If it does not, rewrite your formula.

t	G	h (in feet)
58	80	6,000
30	56	7,000

7. A pilot knows that she can fly without ice forming on the plane's wings if the outside temperature is 37°F or higher. If she wishes to fly at 10,000 feet, what is the minimum ground temperature needed?

11.3 Equation of a Line: Slope-Intercept Form

Objectives

To write an equation of a line, given its slope and y-intercept
To find the slope and y-intercept of a line, given its equation
To graph a line using its slope and y-intercept or both of its intercepts
To write the slope-intercept form of an equation of a line, given its graph

The line $\overleftrightarrow{MN}$ at the right intersects the x-axis at $(-3, 0)$ and the y-axis at $(0, 4)$. The number -3 is the x-*intercept* of the line. The number 4 is the y-*intercept* of the line.

In general, the **x-intercept** of a line is the abscissa of the point where the line intersects the x-axis. The **y-intercept** is the ordinate of the point where the line intersects the y-axis.

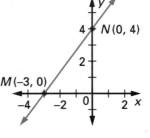

The slope of the line above is $\frac{4}{3}$. To write an equation of the line, you can use $m = \frac{4}{3}$ and the point $(0, 4)$ in $y - y_1 = m(x - x_1)$.

$$y - 4 = \tfrac{4}{3}(x - 0), \text{ or } y - 4 = \tfrac{4}{3}x, \text{ or } y = \tfrac{4}{3}x + 4$$

slope y-intercept

Now consider any line that has slope m and passes through $(0, b)$. The y-intercept of the line is b.

To write an equation of the line, substitute 0 for x_1 and b for y_1 in $y - y_1 = m(x - x_1)$.

$$y - b = m(x - 0)$$
$$y - b = mx$$
$$y = mx + b$$

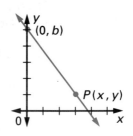

Since the slope of the line is m and the y-intercept is b, $y = mx + b$ is called the *slope-intercept form* of the equation.

> **Equation of a Line: Slope-Intercept Form**
>
> If a line has slope m and y-intercept b, the **slope-intercept form** of the equation of the line is $y = mx + b$.

EXAMPLE 1   Write an equation of a line with slope $\frac{1}{2}$ and y intercept -5.

Plan   Substitute $\frac{1}{2}$ for m and -5 for b in $y = mx + b$.

Solution

$y = mx + b$

$y = \frac{1}{2}x + (-5)$

$y = \frac{1}{2}x - 5$, or $x - 2y = 10$ ⟵ Standard form: $Ax + By = C$

EXAMPLE 2   Write each equation in slope-intercept form. Identify the slope and y-intercept.

a. $2x + 3y = 9$ 　　　　　　　　　 b. $y + 3x = 0$

Plan   Solve each equation for y. The coefficient of x is the slope, and the y-intercept is the constant term.

Solutions

a. $3y = -2x + 9$ 　　　　　　　 b. $y = -3x + 0$

$\quad y = -\frac{2}{3}x + 3$ 　　　　　　　　 The slope is -3
　　　　　　　　　　　　　　　　　The y-intercept is 0.

The slope is $-\frac{2}{3}$

The y-intercept is 3

TRY THIS   **1.** Write an equation of a line with slope $-\frac{2}{3}$ and y-intercept 3.

2. Write the equation $3x - 2y = 12$ in slope-intercept form.

To graph a line given its y-intercept and its slope, plot the point $(0, b)$. Then use the slope to plot a second point. (A third point can be plotted as a check.)

EXAMPLE 3   Write the slope m and the y-intercept b of the line with equation $y = \frac{3}{4}x + 2$. Then graph the equation.

Solution   The slope is $\frac{3}{4}$. The y-intercept is 2.

Plot $(0, 2)$, the point of intersection of the line and the y-axis. Using the slope $\frac{3}{4}$, go right 4 and up 3. Plot $(4, 5)$. Draw the line through P and Q.

TRY THIS   **3.** Graph the equation $y = -\frac{1}{2}x - 4$.

EXAMPLE 4   Find the slope-intercept form of $2x + 3y = -3$. Graph the equation.

Solution

$$2x + 3y = -3$$
$$3y = -2x - 3$$
$$y = -\frac{2}{3}x - 1 \quad \longleftarrow y = mx + b$$

Plot $P(0, -1)$, the point of intersection of the line and the y-axis. Using the slope $-\frac{2}{3}$, or $\frac{-2}{3}$, go right 3 and down 2. Plot $Q(3, -3)$. Draw the line through P and Q.

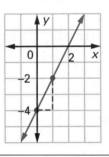

EXAMPLE 5   Write an equation, in slope-intercept form, of the line shown.

Plan   Determine the y-intercept and the slope.

Solution   The y-intercept is -4. Using $(0, -4)$ and another convenient point such as $(1, -2)$, find the slope. Go right 1, up 2. The slope is $\frac{2}{1}$, or 2. So, in slope-intercept form, an equation of the line is $y = 2x - 4$.

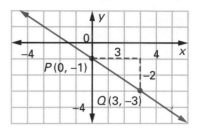

TRY THIS   4. Write $2x - 5y = -10$ in slope-intercept form. Then graph the equation.

Equations such as $3x + 6y = 12$ can also be graphed by using intercepts.

To find the x-intercept, let $y = 0$. Then $x = 4$. To find the y-intercept, let $x = 0$. Then $y = 2$. The graph is the line through $(4, 0)$ and $(0, 2)$.

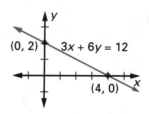

Classroom Exercises

State the slope and the y-intercept of the line with the given equation.

1. $y = 3x + 4$ **2.** $y = -2x + \frac{1}{3}$ **3.** $y = -6x$

4. $y = 5$ **5.** $3x - y = 4$ **6.** $2x - 5y = -10$

Write an equation of the line with the given slope m and y-intercept b.

7. $m = -\frac{2}{3}, b = 1$ **8.** $m = 3, b = \frac{1}{2}$ **9.** $m = \frac{1}{2}, b = -2$

Written Exercises

Write an equation of the line with the given slope m and y-intercept b.

1. $m = 5, b = 2$

2. $m = -3, b = 4$

3. $m = \frac{1}{2}, b = -4$

4. $m = -\frac{1}{3}, b = -\frac{1}{5}$

5. $m = -\frac{1}{9}, b = -7$

6. $m = \frac{1}{5}, b = -\frac{1}{4}$

7. $m = -4, b = \frac{4}{3}$

8. $m = -\frac{6}{5}, b = -\frac{1}{3}$

9. $m = 0, b = \frac{1}{3}$

Find the slope m and the y-intercept b.

10. $3x - 2y = 8$

11. $-5x - 3y = 12$

12. $x + 4y = 12$

13. $-3y + 4x = 15$

14. $2x + 5y = -15$

15. $-x + y = -9$

16. $y - 3x = -10$

17. $3x - 5y = 20$

18. $7x - 8y = 16$

Write the slope and y-intercept. Then graph the equation.

19. $y = 2x - 3$

20. $y = -4x + 5$

21. $y = -3x + 1$

22. $y = \frac{2}{3}x + 2$

23. $y = -\frac{4}{3}x - 2$

24. $y = \frac{3}{5}x - 4$

25. $y = 3x$

26. $y = -\frac{2}{3}x$

27. $y = -4x$

Graph by using the x-intercept and the y-intercept.

28. $2x - 3y = 6$

29. $5x + 2y = 10$

30. $3y + 4x = -12$

31. $y + x = -2$

32. $3y - x = -6$

33. $3x - 5y = 15$

Write the equation in slope-intercept form. Then graph the line.

34. $3x - y = 0$

35. $2y + 5x = 0$

36. $-x + y = 0$

37. $4x - 3y = 2$

38. $3x + 2y = -3$

39. $y + 3x = 0$

For the line shown, write its equation in slope-intercept form.

40.

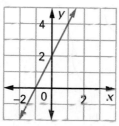

41.

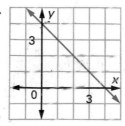

42.

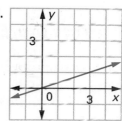

43. The Ace Tool Company rents out a floor waxer for $2 per hour plus $4 for the wax. Suppose you rent a floor waxer for x hours. Write an equation that shows what the total cost y will be.

44. Graph the equation for Exercise 43. Assume that $1 \leq x \leq 6$. Use the graph to determine what the cost for 5 h will be.

Write an equation of the line described.

45. The line has a y-intercept of -5 and the same slope as the line with equation $y = -3x + 2$.

46. The line has a y-intercept of 3 and the same slope as the line with equation $4x + 6y = -12$.

Write the equation in slope-intercept form. Then graph the line. *11.3*

47. $2x - (3 - 2y) = 8$

48. $6 - (4 - 2y) = 5x + 1$

49. $4x - 2(3 - 3x) = 3y - 6$

50. $8(-y + 2) + 6(y + 3) = 2(x - \frac{1}{2})$

51. The equation $F = \frac{9}{5}C + 32$ shows the relationship between Fahrenheit temperature F and Celsius temperature C. Draw a graph of the relation. Let Celsius readings be indicated along the horizontal axis, and Fahrenheit readings along the vertical axis.

Midchapter Review

Find the slope of $\overleftrightarrow{PQ}$ for the given points, and describe the slant of the line. *11.1*

1. $P(-2, 3)$, $Q(8, -1)$

2. $P(2, -1)$, $Q(-3, 9)$

3. $P(6, 1)$, $Q(3, -4)$

4. $P(-4, -2)$, $Q(-5, 3)$

Find the slope of the line $\overleftrightarrow{MN}$ for the given points. *11.1*

5. $M\left(\frac{1}{4}, \frac{1}{5}\right)$, $N\left(\frac{5}{4}, \frac{4}{5}\right)$

6. $M\left(\frac{2}{3}, \frac{1}{4}\right)$, $N\left(\frac{5}{6}, -\frac{3}{4}\right)$

Write an equation, in the form $Ax + By = C$, of the line passing through the given point and having the given slope. *11.2*

7. $P(-1, 6)$; slope $= -\frac{2}{3}$

8. $P(2, 0)$; slope $= -3$

Write an equation, in the form $Ax + By = C$, of the line passing through the given points. *11.2*

9. $P(0, -5)$, $Q(6, 7)$

10. $P(1, 3)$, $Q(7, 1)$

Write an equation, in slope-intercept form, of the line with the given slope m and y-intercept b. *11.3*

11. $m = -5$, $b = \frac{4}{3}$

12. $m = 0$, $b = \frac{4}{5}$

Write the equation in slope-intercept form. Then graph the line. *11.3*

13. $4x - 5y = 8$

14. $9x + 3y = 12$

11.4 Line Relationships

This photograph shows a painting by the famous artist Piet Mondrian. Notice how Mondrian used geometric shapes formed by parallel and perpendicular lines to create his art. In this lesson, you will explore relationships of lines in a coordinate plane.

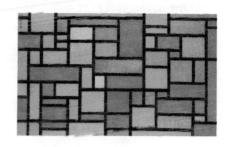

EXAMPLE 1   Graph $y - 5 = 2x$ and $y - 2x = -1$ in the same coordinate plane. Will the two graphs intersect?

Solution   Write the equations in slope-intercept form. Then graph the equations using the slope and y-intercept.

$$y - 5 = 2x \qquad y - 2x = -1$$
$$y = 2x + 5 \qquad\quad y = 2x - 1$$

The graphs are shown at the right.

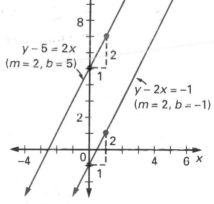

$y - 5 = 2x$ $(m = 2, b = 5)$

$y - 2x = -1$ $(m = 2, b = -1)$

Since the lines have the same slope ($m = 2$) but different y-intercepts, the lines do not intersect. The two lines are parallel.

TRY THIS

1. Graph $4x + 2y = 6$ and $2x + y = 1$ in the same coordinate plane. Describe the graphs.

Parallel Lines and Equal Slopes

If two lines have equal slopes, then the two lines are parallel.

Vertical lines are parallel also, as the figure at the right illustrates. Recall that the slope of a vertical line is undefined (see page 415).

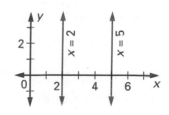

EXAMPLE 2   Graph $y = -\frac{3}{2}x + 4$ and $y = \frac{2}{3}x - 6$ in the same coordinate plane.

Do the two graphs intersect? What is the relationship of the two lines?

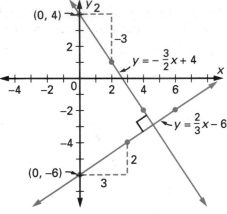

Solution   To graph $y = -\frac{3}{2}x + 4$, use the slope $-\frac{3}{2}$ and the y-intercept 4.

To graph $y = \frac{2}{3}x - 6$, use the slope $\frac{2}{3}$ and the y-intercept -6.

The graphs are shown at the right. The two lines intersect. They seem to be perpendicular.

TRY THIS   2. Graph $x + 2y = 1$ and $2x - y = 4$ in the same coordinate plane. Describe the graphs.

In Example 2, the lines appear to be perpendicular, and the product of their slopes is -1: $-\frac{3}{2} \cdot \frac{2}{3} = -1$. This suggests the following generalization.

Perpendicular lines

If two lines have slopes whose product is -1, then the two lines are perpendicular.

One other case of perpendicular lines occurs when one line is horizontal ($m = 0$) and the other line is vertical (m undefined).

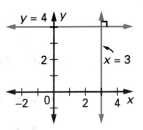

Some lines are neither parallel nor perpendicular. Lines with equations $y = -x + 1$ and $y = -\frac{1}{5}x + 1$ intersect but are not perpendicular. The product of their slopes is not -1.

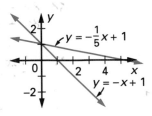

Classroom Exercises

Graph the pair of equations in the same coordinate plane. Tell whether the lines are parallel, perpendicular, or neither.

1. $y = -3x + 5$
$y = \frac{1}{3}x$

2. $y = 2x - 1$
$y = -2x + 2$

3. $y = \frac{2}{5}x + 4$
$y = \frac{2}{5}x + 1$

4. $y = 4$
$x = -2$

Without drawing the graphs, tell whether the lines are parallel, perpendicular, or neither.

5. $y = -\frac{5}{3}x + 3$
$y = \frac{3}{5}x$

6. $y = 9$
$y = 5$

7. $x = 4$
$y = 1$

8. $y = \frac{1}{2}x - 1$
$y = \frac{1}{2}x + 3$

Written Exercises

Graph the pair of lines in the same coordinate plane. Tell whether the lines are parallel, perpendicular, or neither parallel nor perpendicular.

1. $y = \frac{1}{2}x$
$y = -2x$

2. $y = 3x - 2$
$y = -3x + 4$

3. $y = \frac{2}{3}x - 1$
$y = \frac{2}{3}x + 5$

4. $y = \frac{5}{4}x - 3$
$y = \frac{4}{5}x + 2$

5. $y = -\frac{5}{6}x + 1$
$y = -\frac{5}{6}x + 4$

6. $y = -\frac{3}{4}x + 2$
$y = \frac{4}{3}x - 2$

7. $y - x = 2$
$y + x = 2$

8. $x - y = 5$
$x - y = 7$

9. $x - 3y = 4$
$3x + y = 1$

Without drawing the graphs, tell whether the lines are parallel, perpendicular, or neither.

10. $y = 4x$
$y = \frac{1}{4}x$

11. $y = -\frac{1}{3}x + 2$
$y = 3x - 4$

12. $y = \frac{1}{5}x + 1$
$y = \frac{1}{5}x - 2$

13. $x + 2y = 5$
$x + 3y = 5$

14. $8x - 4y = 12$
$8x + 4y = 8$

15. $y = 7$
$y + 2 = 0$

16. $\frac{y}{10} - \frac{x}{4} = 2$
$\frac{x}{2} - \frac{y}{5} = 1$

17. $0.02x - 0.03y = 4$
$1.5x + y = 2$

18. $x - (3y + 2) = 4$
$6x + 2(y - 1) = 1$

19. Write an explanation in your own words of how to tell whether two lines in a coordinate plane are parallel, perpendicular, or neither.

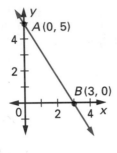

20. Write three equations of lines that are parallel to $\overleftrightarrow{AB}$.

21. Write three equations of lines that have the same y-intercept as $\overleftrightarrow{AB}$.

22. Consider the equation $-2x + ry = 10$, where r is a positive number. Choose a value such as 5 for r and write the equation. Then let the value of r decrease and write several other equations. What happens to the slopes of the graphs as r decreases? Draw several graphs to check your answer.

23. Consider the equation $4x + 3y = k$, where k is any real number. Choose a value such as -3 for k and write the equation. Then let the value of k increase and write several other equations. What happens to the slopes of the graphs as k increases? What happens to the y-intercepts? Draw several graphs to check your answers.

24. If two or more points are points of the same line, then the points are called **collinear points.** Explain why the points A, B, and C of a coordinate plane must be collinear if $\overleftrightarrow{AB}$ and $\overleftrightarrow{BC}$ have the same slope. (HINT: If $\overleftrightarrow{AB}$ and $\overleftrightarrow{BC}$ have the same slope, then either they are parallel or they are the same line. Show that one of these cases cannot be true. Then the other case must be true.)

Use the results of Exercise 24 to determine whether or not the given points are collinear.

25. $P(0, -1)$, $Q(5, -3)$, $R(-5, 1)$ 26. $P(-1, -1)$, $Q(1, 0)$, $R(3, 1)$

27. $P(7, 1)$, $Q(10, -1)$, $R(-7, -1)$ 28. $P(0, 0)$, $Q(1, 2)$, $R(2, 4)$

29. $P(-6, 1)$, $Q(-3, 1)$, $R(0, 1)$ 30. $P(8, 2)$, $Q(8, 7)$, $R(8, -1)$

Mixed Review

Solve. **3.1, 3.3, 9.2**

1. $3x - 9 = 3$ 2. $a + 4 = 1$

3. $5y + 2 = -8$ 4. $-\frac{1}{2}x - 4 = 6$

5. $\frac{x}{8} = \frac{5}{2}$ 6. $\frac{x - 3}{2} = \frac{x + 4}{-3}$

7. A track team won 8 out of 12 meets. What percent of its meets did the team win? **4.7**

8. The regular price of a T-shirt is $12. It is on sale for 30% off. What is the sale price? **4.7**

11.5 Graphing Linear Inequalities

Objectives

To graph linear inequalities in two variables
To write inequalities for given graphs

You have been graphing linear equations such as $y = \frac{2}{3}x - 2$. The graph of every linear equation separates a coordinate plane into two regions called **half-planes**. Every point in the plane is either on the line or in one of the half-planes. This figure shows the graph of $y = \frac{2}{3}x - 2$ and the half-planes related to it.

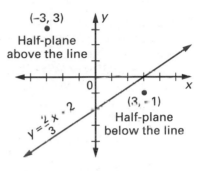

For any point with coordinates (x, y), one of these relationships must be true.

$$y = \frac{2}{3}x - 2 \qquad y > \frac{2}{3}x - 2 \qquad y < \frac{2}{3}x - 2$$

For example, for $(-3, 3)$, $y > \frac{2}{3}x - 2$ is true.

$$3 > \frac{2}{3}(-3) - 2$$
$$3 > -2 - 2$$
$$3 > -4 \quad \text{True}$$

For $(3, -1)$, $y < \frac{2}{3}x - 2$ is true.

$$-1 < \frac{2}{3}(3) - 2$$
$$-1 < 2 - 2$$
$$-1 < 0 \quad \text{True}$$

The set of all points for which $y > \frac{2}{3}x - 2$ is true is called the **open half-plane** above the line. The set of all points for which $y < \frac{2}{3}x - 2$ is true is called the open half-plane below the line. The set of all points for which $y = \frac{2}{3}x - 2$ is true is the **boundary line**.

A half-plane that includes the boundary line is called a **closed half-plane**. In the graph of an inequality, a solid boundary line indicates that the boundary is part of the graph. A dashed line is used to indicate that the boundary is *not* part of the graph.

Summary

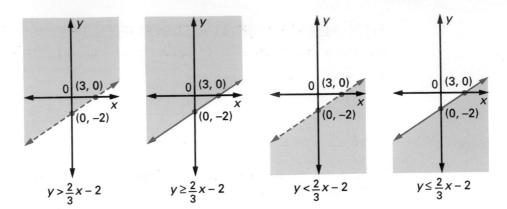

$$y > \tfrac{2}{3}x - 2 \qquad y \geq \tfrac{2}{3}x - 2 \qquad y < \tfrac{2}{3}x - 2 \qquad y \leq \tfrac{2}{3}x - 2$$

EXAMPLE 1 Graph $y < \tfrac{1}{2}x + 3$.

Plan Use the slope-intercept method to graph the boundary line whose equation is $y = \tfrac{1}{2}x + 3$. Then shade the appropriate half-plane, and check.

Solution The boundary line has the equation

$y = \tfrac{1}{2}x + 3$. Using the point $(0, 3)$ and the

slope $\tfrac{1}{2}$, draw the boundary as a dashed line

since it is not part of the graph. Shade the half-plane below the boundary line.

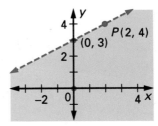

Check To check that the correct half-plane is shaded, test two points, one above the line and one below it. Choose each point so that the coordinates are easily checked.

Check $P(-2, 4)$: $\quad y < \tfrac{1}{2}x + 3$ $\qquad$ Check $O(0, 0)$: $\quad y < \tfrac{1}{2}x + 3$

$\qquad\qquad\qquad 4 \overset{?}{<} \tfrac{1}{2}(-2) + 3$ $\qquad\qquad\qquad\qquad 0 \overset{?}{<} (0) + 3$

$\qquad\qquad\qquad\qquad\qquad\qquad\qquad\qquad\qquad\qquad 0 \overset{?}{<} 0 + 3$

$\qquad\qquad\qquad 4 \overset{?}{<} -1 + 3$ $\qquad\qquad\qquad\qquad 0 \overset{?}{<} 3$

$\qquad\qquad\qquad 4 \overset{?}{<} 2$ $\qquad\qquad\qquad\qquad\qquad 0 < 3 \quad$ True

$\qquad\qquad\qquad 4 < 2 \quad$ False

So, the graph of $y < \tfrac{1}{2}x + 3$ is the half-plane below the boundary line.

TRY THIS **1.** Graph $y < -2x + 1$. $\qquad$ **2.** Graph $y > \tfrac{2}{3}x - 1$.

Note that when you graph an inequality such as $y < \tfrac{1}{2}x + 3$, you are graphing the *solution set* of the inequality. The ordered pair $(0, 0)$ is one solution of $y = \frac{1}{2}x + 3$. For every point in the half-plane below the dashed line, there is an ordered pair of numbers that is a solution of $y < \frac{1}{2}x + 3$.

EXAMPLE 2   Graph $2x - y \le 3$.

Plan   Rewrite the inequality so that y is alone on one side. Then the equation for the boundary line will be in slope-intercept form.

Solution   Multiply each side by -1 and simplify.

$$2x - y \le 3$$
$$-y \le -2x + 3$$
$$-1(-y) \ge -1(-2x + 3) \quad \longleftarrow \text{Reverse the order of the inequality.}$$
$$y \ge 2x - 3$$

Graph $y = 2x - 3$. Since $y \ge 2x - 3$ means $y > 2x - 3$ or $y = 2x - 3$, the boundary line is part of the graph. So, use a solid line for the boundary. Shade the half-plane above the line.

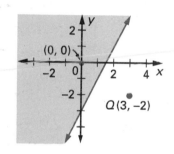

Check   Check the coordinates of two test points in the *original inequality*.

Check $O(0, 0)$.

$$2x - y \le 3$$
$$2(0) - 0 \overset{?}{\le} 3$$
$$0 - 0 \overset{?}{\le} 3$$
$$0 \overset{?}{\le} 3$$
$$0 < 3 \quad \text{True}$$

Check $Q(3, -2)$.

$$2x - y \le 3$$
$$2(3) - (-2) \overset{?}{\le} 3$$
$$6 + 2 \overset{?}{\le} 3$$
$$8 \overset{?}{\le} 3$$
$$8 \le 3 \quad \text{False}$$

So, the graph of $2x - y \le 3$ is the boundary line and the half-plane above the line.

TRY THIS   3. Graph $x + y \ge -2$.   4. Graph $2y - x \ge 4$.

In the next example, you will consider a horizontal line and a vertical line, and the half-planes associated with each line. Observe that in the case of a vertical line, the half-planes are to the right and left of the line, not above and below it.

EXAMPLE 3   Graph each inequality.

       a. $y \geq -2$ **b.** $x < 3$

Solutions   **a.** Graph $y = -2$. Since the in-
                equality symbol is $\geq$, the
                boundary line is part of the
                graph. So, use a solid line for
                the boundary. Shade the half-
                plane above the line.

b. Graph $x = 3$ with a dashed
line. Since the x-coordinate of
every point to the left of the
line satisfies $x < 3$, shade the
half-plane to the left of the
line.

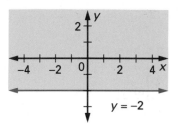

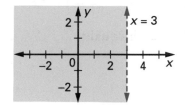

So, the graph of $y \geq -2$ is
the line and the half-plane
above the line.

So, the graph of $x < 3$ is the
half-plane to the left of the
boundary line.

EXAMPLE 4   Write an inequality of the graph shown
            at the right.

Solution   The boundary line passes through $(0, 4)$ and
has slope 1. So, an equation for the line is
$y = x + 4$. Since the boundary line is solid,
it is part of the graph. The region above the
line is shaded. Thus, $y \geq x + 4$ is an inequality for the graph.

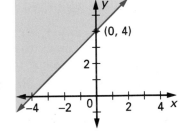

TRY THIS   **5.** Graph $y \leq 4$.   **6.** Graph $x \geq -1$.

Classroom Exercises

State whether the shaded half-plane will be above, below, to the left, or
to the right of the boundary line. State whether the boundary line will
be solid or dashed.

  1. $y \geq 2x - 1$ **2.** $y < 3x - 4$ **3.** $x < -3$ **4.** $y < 2$

  5. $y > 4$ **6.** $x \geq -2$ **7.** $y \leq 8x - 7$ **8.** $y < -x + 3$

Graph each inequality.

  9. $y \geq -2x + 1$ **10.** $y > -3x - 2$ **11.** $x \leq 1$ **12.** $y \geq -1$

Written Exercises

Graph each inequality.

1. $y > x + 3$	**2.** $y < x + 2$	**3.** $y \geq x + 1$	**4.** $y \leq x - 3$
5. $y \geq 2x - 1$	**6.** $y \leq 2x + 3$	**7.** $y < 4$	**8.** $y > 5$
9. $y \leq -3$	**10.** $x > 1$	**11.** $x \geq -2$	**12.** $x \leq 3$
13. $y < -\frac{3}{2}x$	**14.** $y > \frac{1}{2}x - 3$	**15.** $y \geq -\frac{1}{5}x - 1$	**16.** $y < -\frac{2}{5}x + 2$
17. $2x + 3y < 9$	**18.** $3x - 2y \leq 8$	**19.** $-3x - 5y \leq 5$	**20.** $-2x + 4y > 8$
21. $-6x - y \leq -1$	**22.** $8x - 3y < -4$	**23.** $-x - y \geq -3$	**24.** $2x - 4y > 10$

Write an inequality for the graph.

25.

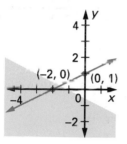

26.

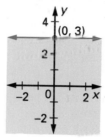

27.

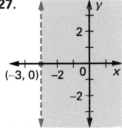

For each sentence, write an inequality. Use x and y as the variables. Tell what each variable represents.

28. The majority of American families save less than $\frac{1}{10}$ of their income.

29. The perimeter of a quadrilateral is greater than or equal to 4 times the length of its shortest side.

Graph the inequality in a coordinate plane.

30. $|x| > 2$	**31.** $|y| > 3$	**32.** $|x| < 1$	**33.** $|y| \leq 1$	**34.** $|y - 2| > 0$

Mixed Review

Simplify. *6.2, 6.3*

1. $(-3x^2y)^4$ **2.** $-5a^3(-2a^4b^2)^3$ **3.** $\dfrac{-18a^3b^2c^6}{9a^5bc^2}$

Factor completely. *7.5, 7.6*

4. $a^2 - 36$ **5.** $81x^2 - 16$ **6.** $x^3 + x^2 - 2x$

Solve for x. *9.3*

7. $-5x + b - x - 4b$ **8.** $\dfrac{1}{b} - \dfrac{1}{a} = \dfrac{1}{x}$

Problem Solving Strategies

Using Logical Reasoning

Ronald mows lawns for three families. The three families live in houses at points A, B, and C as shown on the street grid at the right. Ronald plans to move into a house that is as close as possible to all three houses.

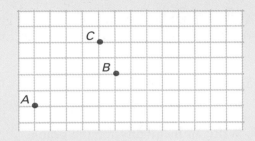

Notice that Ronald doesn't necessarily want to be at an equal distance from each of the three houses. Rather, he wants the shortest possible total distance for the three trips he makes from his house to the lawns he mows. The route to the houses must be along horizontal or vertical streets. No diagonal shortcuts are allowed! That is, if Ronald's house is at R, he wants T, the total distance, to be as small as possible.

T = (dist. from R to A) + (dist. from R to B) + (dist. from R to C)

To help Ronald decide where to live, you might use the strategy of *Guessing and Checking* or you might try this strategy.

Place R at some point. Then find T. Next consider moving one block north. Will this shorten the distance from R to A? From R to B? From R to C? Whenever you get more *yes* answers than *no* answers, make the move. From the new position of R, consider the same questions. If there are two *yes* answers to the one *no* answer, make the move. Eventually, when there are only *yes* answers, you will find the best possible location for R.

Problems such as this have many practical applications, such as finding locations for schools, airports, and telephone lines.

Exercises

1. Copy the grid and find the best location for Ronald's house. Call the lower left corner the origin, $(0, 0)$ and give the ordered pair that names the position of R.

2. After Ronald moves to his new house, his customer at point B moves 7 blocks away. Ronald thought that he might have to move again, but he checked the map and decided that it wasn't necessary. Give the ordered pair that names B's new location.

3. This new strategy will not work if you are trying to find the shortest possible distance to an even number of points. Explain why.

Making a table is an effective strategy to use in solving some problems. Making a table helps to organize the given information and also helps you to identify the relationships that can be expressed as an equation.

Solve each problem.

1. How fast must a bus travel to cover a distance of 150 mi in $2\frac{1}{2}$ h?

2. Flying at 420 mi/h, how long does it take a plane to travel 1,420 mi?

3. The width of a rectangle is 10 cm less than the length. The perimeter is 52 cm. Find the length and width.

4. Juan worked 12 h longer than Jeanine. Together they worked 42 h. How long did each work?

5. In a basketball game, Kyle's score was 6 less than 3 times Craig's score. Together they scored 42 points. Find their scores.

6. A television repair person charges $30 to make a house call plus $42 an hour for each hour she works. Her bill for a job was $198. How many hours did she work?

7. The sum of two consecutive odd integers is 144. Find the integers.

8. Find three consecutive even integers whose sum is 90.

9. If $10,000 is invested at a simple interest rate of 7.4% per year for 4 years, how much interest is earned?

10. Lincoln Memorial High School has 2,750 students. If 6% are absent, how many students are absent?

11. Mary's wage was increased by 0.12 of last year's wage, which was $12.50 per hour. What does she earn now?

12. The sum of a number and 0.6 of the number is 38.88. Find the number.

13. Six less than 7 times a number is the same as the square of the number. Find the number.

14. The length of a rectangle is 2 cm more than 3 times its width. The area is 33 cm². Find its dimensions.

15. Find two consecutive even integers whose product is 168.

16. Find two consecutive odd integers whose product is 255.

17. Jim walked along a path at 4 mi/h. Rachel left from the same point as Jim $\frac{1}{2}$ h later, and ran along the same path at 9 mi/h. How long did she run before catching up with Jim?

18. It would take Steve 14 h to build some stairs. Helen would take 18 h to build the same stairs. How long would it take them to build the stairs if they worked together?

19. The cost of gasoline varies directly as the number of gallons. If 3 gallons cost $3.66, find the cost of 14 gallons of gasoline.

20. The volume of a gas varies inversely as the pressure. If the volume is 55 in³ under 25 lb/in² of pressure, find the volume under 6 lb/in² of pressure.

Key Terms

boundary line   (p. 433)
closed half-plane   (p. 433)
half-plane   (p. 433)
open half-plane   (p. 433)
parallel lines   (p. 429)
perpendicular lines   (p. 430)
point-slope form   (p. 418)

rise   (p. 413)
run   (p. 413)
slope   (p. 414)
slope-intercept form   (p. 424)
x-intercept   (p. 424)
y-intercept   (p. 424)

Key Ideas and Review Exercises

11.1   To find the slope of a line, use

$$\text{slope} = \frac{\text{change in } y\text{-coordinates}}{\text{change in } x\text{-coordinates}}, \text{ or } m = \frac{y_2 - y_1}{x_2 - x_1}, \text{ where } x_1 \neq x_2.$$

If the slope is positive, the line slants up to the right.
If the slope is negative, the line slants down to the right.
If the slope is zero, the line is horizontal.
If the slope is undefined, the line is vertical.

Find the slope of the line determined by the given points A and B.

1. $A(3, 4)$, $B(-7, 6)$ **2.** $A(-2, -3)$, $B(8, -5)$ **3.** $A(5, -1)$, $B(5, 4)$

Find the slope of $\overleftrightarrow{MN}$ for the given points, and describe the slant of the line.

4. $M(4, -2)$, $N(-5, 3)$ **5.** $M(7, 4)$, $N(6, 5)$ **6.** $M(-6, -5)$, $N(7, -5)$

11.2   To write an equation of a line, given one of its points and its slope, use $y - y_1 = m(x - x_1)$, where the given point is (x_1, y_1) and the given slope is m.

To write an equation of a line, given two of its points, find the slope m. Then use $y - y_1 = m(x - x_1)$, where (x_1, y_1) is either of the two given points.

Write an equation, in the form $Ax + By = C$, of the line passing through the given point and having the given slope.

7. $P(4, 3)$; slope $= \frac{2}{5}$ **8.** $P(5, -3)$; slope $= -3$ **9.** $P(1, 6)$; slope $= 0$

Write an equation, in the form $Ax + By = C$, of the line passing through the given points.

10. $P(7, 1)$, $Q(8, -6)$ **11.** $P(-5, 6)$, $Q(-2, 7)$ **12.** $P(4, 1)$, $Q(-5, -2)$

11.3 To write an equation of a line, given its slope and y-intercept, use the form $y = mx + b$, where m is the slope and b is the y-intercept.

To find the slope m and the y-intercept b, given the equation of a line, write it in the form $y = mx + b$. Then identify m and b.

To graph an equation using its intercepts, let $y = 0$ and solve for x, and let $x = 0$ and solve for y. Then draw a line through the two points.

To graph a line using its slope and y-intercept, write the equation in slope-intercept form, $y = mx + b$. Plot the point $(0, b)$. Use the slope to plot a second point. Then draw a line through the two points.

13. Write an equation of the line with slope $-\frac{3}{4}$ and y-intercept 6.

Find the slope m and the y-intercept b.

14. Graph the equation $3x + y = -6$ using the x-intercept and the y-intercept.

15. Graph the equation $-2x + y = -2$ using the slope and y-intercept.

11.4 Two lines are parallel if their slopes are the same and their y-intercepts differ, or if both lines are vertical (slope undefined).

Two lines are perpendicular if their slopes have a product of -1, or if one line is vertical (slope undefined) and the other is horizontal (slope = 0).

Tell whether the lines are parallel, perpendicular, or neither.

16. $y = \frac{1}{4}x + 6$
$y = -4x + 1$

17. $y = \frac{1}{2}x + 3$
$y = \frac{1}{2}x$

18. $y = x - 3$
$y = -x + 5$

19. $y + 3x = -3$
$y - 3x = 0$

20. $2x + 3y = 4$
$3x - 2y = 6$

21. $y - 3 = 0$
$y = 8$

11.5 To graph a linear inequality in two variables, first graph the related equation as a boundary line. Draw this as a dashed line if it is not part of the graph. Then shade the half-plane to the left or right, or above or below the boundary line.

Graph the inequality.

22. $y > -x + 1$

23. $3x - 4y \geq 12$

24. $y < -1$

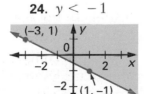

25. Write an explanation in your own words of how to write an inequality for the graph at the right. Refer to the equation of the boundary line and to the shaded half-plane.

Find the slope of the line determined by the given points M and N.

1. $M(-1, 8)$, $N(7, -9)$

2. $M(10, -2)$, $N(1, -4)$

3. $M(4, 1)$, $N(-6, 1)$

4. $M(3, 5)$, $N(3, -2)$

5. Find the slope of $\overleftrightarrow{AB}$ for $A(-1, 4)$ and $B(5, 6)$.

Write an equation, in the form $Ax + By = C$, for the line passing through the given point and having the given slope.

6. $P(-4, -3)$; slope $= -\frac{5}{4}$

7. $P(1, -1)$; slope $= \frac{4}{3}$

Write an equation, in the form $Ax + By = C$, of the line passing through the given points.

8. $P(-3, 4)$, $Q(-1, 8)$

9. $P(-2, -3)$, $Q(9, -4)$

10. Write the slope and the y-intercept of the line with equation $y = -\frac{2}{3}x + 1$. Then graph the equation.

11. Graph $4x - 3y = -12$ using the x-intercept and the y-intercept.

12. Write the equation $2y + 5x = -6$ in slope-intercept form, and graph.

Tell whether the lines are parallel, perpendicular, or neither.

13. $y = 6x - 12$
$y = 6x - 3$

14. $y - 2x = 8$
$y = -2x - 2$

15. $y = \frac{1}{5}x$
$y = -5x + 2$

16. $5y = 3x - 5$
$3y + 5x = 2$

Graph the inequality.

17. $y \geq -2x + 3$

18. $3x - 2y > 8$

19. Write an inequality for the graph at the right.

20. Write an equation, in the form $Ax + By = C$, of the line with y-intercept 3 and slope the same as that of the line with equation $2x - 3y = 6$.

21. Use slopes to determine whether points $P(-1, 6)$, $Q(8, -9)$, and $R(5, -4)$ are collinear.

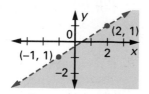

College Prep Test

In each Exercise, you are to compare a quantity in Column 1 with a quantity in Column 2. Write the letter of the correct answer from these choices.

A—The quantity in Column 1 is greater than the quantity in Column 2.
B—The quantity in Column 2 is greater than the quantity in Column 1.
C—The quantity in Column is equal to the quantity in Column 2.
D—The relationship cannot be determined from the given information.

Note: Information centered over both columns refers to one or both of the quantities to be compared.

Column 1	Column 2	Column 1	Column 2
1. $a \neq 0$, $b \neq 0$		**4.** Triangle ABC is a right triangle.	
$\dfrac{a}{b} - 1$	$\dfrac{b}{a} - 1$		

Column 1	Column 2	Column 1	Column 2
2. $x < 0$		x	30
$x^3 + x$	0	**5.**	
		$x(y + x)$	$xy + z$
3. $\dfrac{10^n}{10^5} > 1$		**6.** $a > 0$, $b < 0$	
n	5	$b - a$	$|b| + a$

For Exercises 7–11, choose the letter of the correct answer.

7. If $y = x + 3$, what is the value of $(x - y)^3$?
(A) -27 (B) 27   (C) 9
(D) -9 (E) 6

8. If $x = 3$, which of the following is not an odd integer?
(A) $3x + 4$ (B) $x - 4$ (C) $-x$
(D) $x^2 + 2$ (E) $6x - 10$

9. If $2 - 3y = -13$ and $x + y = 3$, what is the value of x^3?
(A) 125   (B) -125 (C) 8
(D) -8 (E) 3

10. Solve $\dfrac{1 - \dfrac{y}{x}}{8} = 3$ for x.
(A) $-y - 24$ (B) $y + 24$
(C) $-\dfrac{y}{23}$ (D) $23y$ (E) None of these

11. If a wheel rotates 180 times each minute, how many degrees does it rotate in 10 s? (HINT: There are 360 degrees in one rotation.)
(A) 30   (B) 360   (C) 1,080
(D) 5,400   (E) 10,800

Navaho Indians, famous for handwoven blankets and beautifully crafted silver and turquoise jewelry, originally learned to weave from the neighboring Pueblo Indians. Today, however, they create their own unique geometric designs.

12.1 Systems of Equations—Graphing

Objectives

To solve systems of two linear equations by graphing

To determine the number of solutions of a system of two linear equations

A storekeeper has $120 to give as bonus money to his two workers, Jean and Karl. If Jean gets j dollars and Karl gets k dollars, then

$$j + k = 120.$$

That year, Jean worked 3 times as many hours as Karl, so Jean will get 3 times as much bonus money as Karl. Thus,

$$j = 3k.$$

These two linear equations in two variables form a **system of linear equations**.

$$j + k = 120$$
$$j = 3k$$

Each equation has a solution set of ordered pairs. For example, (20, 100) is a solution of $j + k = 120$, since $20 + 100 = 120$, and (30, 10) is a solution of $j = 3k$, since $30 = 3 \cdot 10$.

The ordered pair that makes *both* equations true is the **solution of the system**.

The solution can be found by graphing both equations in the same coordinate plane. The graphs of $j + k = 120$ and $j = 3k$ meet at a point with coordinates that appear to be (90,30). If this ordered pair satisfies both equations, then it is a solution of the system.

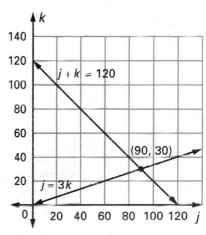

$$j + k = 120$$
$$j = 3k$$

Check:

$$
\begin{aligned}
j + k &= 120 \\
90 + 30 &\overset{?}{=} 120 \\
120 &= 120 \quad \text{True}
\end{aligned}
$$

$$
\begin{aligned}
j &= 3k \\
90 &\overset{?}{=} 3(30) \\
90 &= 90 \quad \text{True}
\end{aligned}
$$

Thus, Jean gets $90 and Karl gets $30.

EXAMPLE 1 Solve the system $\begin{aligned} y &= x - 1 \\ y &= -x + 3 \end{aligned}$ by graphing.

Plan Use the slope–intercept method to graph each equation.

Solution

$y = x - 1$
slope: 1
y-intercept: -1

$y = -x + 3$
slope: -1
y-intercept: 3

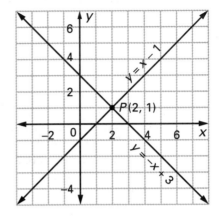

The graphs intersect at $P(2, 1)$.
Check to see whether $(2, 1)$
satisfies both equations.

Check

$y = x - 1$
$1 \overset{?}{=} 2 - 1$
$1 = 1$ True

$y = -x + 3$
$1 \overset{?}{=} -2 + 3$
$1 = 1$ True

Thus, the solution is $(2, 1)$

TRY THIS 1. Solve the system $\begin{aligned} y &= 2x - 1 \\ y &= -3x + 4 \end{aligned}$ by graphing.

When two lines have the *same* slope and *different* y-intercepts, the lines will not intersect.

EXAMPLE 2 Solve the system $\begin{aligned} y &= 2x + 4 \\ y &= 2x - 3 \end{aligned}$ by graphing.

Solution Graph each equation.

$y = 2x + 4$
slope: 2
y-intercept: 4

$y = 2x - 3$
slope: 2
y-intercept: -3

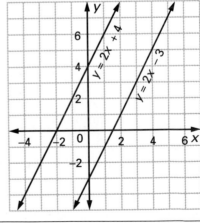

The graphs of the equations have the same slope but different y-intercepts. They are *parallel* lines.

Because there is no point of intersection, there is no ordered pair that satisfies both equations.
Thus, the system has *no solution*.

When two lines have the same slope and the same y-intercepts, their graphs coincide.

EXAMPLE 3   Solve the system $\begin{array}{l} y = 3x + 2 \\ -6x + 2y = 4 \end{array}$ by graphing.

Solution   Write $-6x + 2y = 4$ in slope-intercept form and compare the two
equations.

$$-6x + 2y = 4$$
$$2y = 6x + 4$$
$$y = 3x + 2$$

Note that $-6x + 2y = 4$ is *equivalent*
to $y = 3x + 2$. Their graphs are the
same line, with slope 3 and y-intercept
2. Since the coordinates of every point
on the line satisfy both equations, the
system has *infinitely many* solutions.

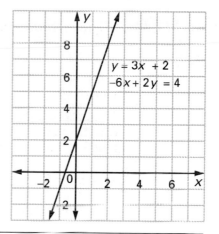

TRY THIS   Solve each system by graphing.

2. $2x + y = -1$
   $2x + y = 4$

3. $x - y = 3$
   $2y - 2x = -6$

The number of solutions of a system of two linear equations can be
determined by comparing the slopes and y-intercepts of the equations.

EXAMPLE 4   Determine the number of solutions of the system: $\begin{array}{l} y = -\frac{1}{2}x + 3 \\ x + 2y = 5 \end{array}$

Plan   Write the second equation in slope-intercept form. Then compare the
slopes and the y-intercepts.

Solution $x + 2y = 5$
   $2y = -x + 5$
   $y = -\frac{1}{2}x + \frac{5}{2}$

Equation	Slope	y-intercept
(1) $y = -\frac{1}{2}x + 3$	$-\frac{1}{2}$	3
(2) $y = -\frac{1}{2}x + \frac{5}{2}$	$-\frac{1}{2}$	$\frac{5}{2}$

Since the slopes are the same and the y-intercepts are different, the
system has no solution.

TRY THIS   Determine the number of solutions for each system.

4. $2x - y = 4$
   $2y = 4x - 3$

5. $y = 7$
   $y = 3x + 1$

The chart below summarizes how to determine the number of solutions of a system of two linear equations.

Slopes	y-intercepts	Graph	Number of solutions
different ⟶	same or different ⟶	two intersecting lines ⟶	1
same ⟨	different ⟶	two parallel lines ⟶	0
	same ⟶	same line ⟶	infinitely many

Classroom Exercises

Tell the number of solutions for each system graphed below.

1.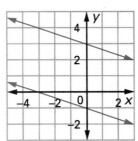

2.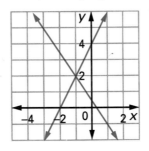

3.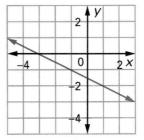

Give the solution of each system graphed below.

4.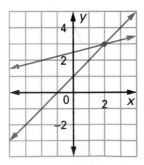

5.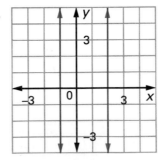

6.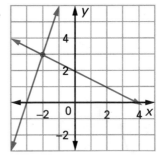

Is the given ordered pair a solution of the given system?

7. $(2, 1)$; $y = -3x + 7$
$y = 2x - 3$

8. $(-1, -7)$; $y = x - 6$
$y = 3x + 5$

9. $(5, 1)$; $x - y = 4$
$x + 2y = 7$

Solve each system by graphing.

10. $y = 2x - 3$
$y = -1$

11. $y = -\frac{1}{3}x - 2$
$x - 3y = -12$

12. $x - 2y = -6$
$y = -\frac{3}{2}x - 1$

Written Exercises

Use the graph to find the solution of each system of equations.

1. $y = x - 4$
$\quad y = -x - 2$

2. $y = 2x + 4$
$\quad y = -\frac{1}{3}x + 4$

3. $y = -x - 2$
$\quad y = x + 8$

4. $y = x - 4$
$\quad y = -\frac{1}{3}x + 4$

5. $y = x + 8$
$\quad y = x - 4$

6. $y = 2x + 4$
$\quad y = -x - 2$

7. $y = x + 8$
$\quad y = -\frac{1}{3}x + 4$

8. $y = x - 4$
$\quad y = 0$

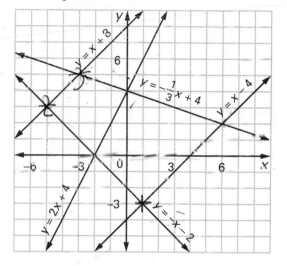

Solve each system by graphing.

9. $y = x + 6$
$\quad y = -2x$

10. $y = -x + 4$
$\quad y = 2x - 2$

11. $y = \frac{1}{3}x + 1$
$\quad y = -x + 3$

12. $x = -3$
$\quad y = 2x + 1$

13. $x - y = 6$
$\quad y = -2$

14. $y = 2x + 3$
$\quad y = -5x - 4$

15. $y = -2x + 9$
$\quad y = 4x - 3$

16. $y = 3x - 9$
$\quad y = -4x + 5$

For each system, determine the number of solutions.

17. $y = \frac{1}{3}x + 2$
$\quad y = \frac{1}{3}x - 7$

18. $y = 6x + 1$
$\quad y = -x + 1$

19. $y = 3x - 4$
$\quad y = -\frac{1}{3}x + 6$

20. $y = \frac{1}{2}x - 4$
$\quad 2y = x - 8$

21. $x - 2y = 6$
$\quad 2x - 4y = 12$

22. $x = 3$
$\quad y = -2$

23. $x + y = 4$
$\quad x = 4$

24. $x - 3y = 1$
$\quad x - 3y = -9$

Solve by graphing. If necessary, estimate answers to the nearest half-unit.

25. $x - y = 2$
$\quad 3x - 2y = 6$

26. $x + 3y = 6$
$\quad x - 3y = 6$

27. $y = -2x + 5$
$\quad 3x - 2y = 4$

28. $2x + y = -4$
$\quad 5x + 3y = -6$

29. $2x - 2y = 1$
$\quad x + 2y = 8$

30. $3x + 2y = 10$
$\quad -x + 6y = 0$

31. $2x + 3y = 9$
$\quad 2x - 3y = -3$

32. $3x + 5y = -5$
$\quad 2y + 5 = 0$

33. Explain why a system whose solution is $\left(-\frac{7}{8}, \frac{5}{3}\right)$, cannot be solved accurately by graphing.

34. If two equations in a system have the same slope, how many solutions could the system have?

35. If two equations in a system have the same y-intercept, how many solutions could the system have?

36. If two equations in a system have different slopes, how many solutions could the system have?

37. If two equations in a system have different y-intercepts, how many solutions could the system have?

38. A triangular region is enclosed by the x-axis and the lines whose equations are $-3x + y = 0$ and $y = -3x + 6$. Give the coordinates of the three vertices of the triangle.

39. A quadrangular region is enclosed by the x-axis, the y-axis, and the lines whose equations are $y = x + 3$ and $y = -2x + 6$. Give the coordinates of the four vertices of the region.

40. If $(3, -1)$ is a solution of the system $\begin{matrix} Ax + 2y = 10 \\ x - By = 8 \end{matrix}$, find A and B.

41. Write in your own words how to determine the number of solutions of a system of two linear equations in two variables.

Mixed Review

Solve for x.   *3.5, 9.2, 9.3*

1. $-15 = 3(x + 7)$

2. $\dfrac{x + 3}{7} = \dfrac{4}{6}$

3. $2x + a = c$

Simplify.   *2.10, 6.1, 6.4*

4. $5(3x - y) - 2(x + y)$

5. $5ab^2(-2a^3b)$

6. $2x(4x^2y)^{-1}$

Factor completely.   *7.3, 7.5, 7.6*

7. $x^2 - 7x + 12$

8. $a^2 + 24a + 144$

9. $2y^3 - 32y$

Solve.   *7.8, 7.9*

10. Ten times a number is 24 less than the square of the number. Find the number.

11. The area of a rectangular parking lot is 1056 m². The length of the lot is 20 meters greater than its width. Find the dimensions (length and width) of the lot.

Problem Solving Strategies

Working Backwards

One Saturday morning, Peter and Jerry leave their homes at the same time and bicycle to meet each other. Peter bicycles at 15 miles per hour and Jerry travels at 17 miles per hour. They meet at 11:00 A.M. If they live 50 miles apart, how far apart are they at 10:30 A.M.?

You could begin to solve this problem by making a table based on the distance formula, $d = rt$. However, you can also arrive at the answer by applying the strategy of *Working Backwards*. Start from the moment the two boys meet. Think about what happens as the hands of a clock move backwards from the moment of meeting.

Time	Miles Left to Travel
10 A.M. (1 h before meeting)	Peter: 15 mi Jerry: 17 mi
10:30 A.M. $\left(\frac{1}{2}\text{ h before meeting}\right)$	Peter: 7.5 mi Jerry: 8.5 mi

Since $7.5 + 8.5 = 16$, Peter and Jerry are 16 miles apart at 10:30 A.M.

Exercises

Use the Working Backwards strategy to solve these problems.

1. Two trains start toward each other at the same time on the same track. At 8 P.M., they are 400 miles apart. One is traveling at 50 miles per hour, and the other is traveling at 36 miles per hour. Fifteen minutes before they might crash, the engineer on one train sees the light of the second train. How far apart are the trains?

2. What information in Exercise 1 was not needed to solve the problem?

3. The dough from a batch of raisin bread doubles in bulk every 90 minutes. If the bowl is competely filled at 4 o'clock, at what time was the bowl half full?

12.2 The Substitution Method

Objective	To solve systems of equations using the substitution method

In the previous lesson, the following system of equations was solved by graphing.

$$j + k = 120$$
$$j = 3k$$

For some systems, the graphing method will give only approximate solutions, while the *substitution method* will always give an exact solution. The **substitution method** is based on the property: If $a = b$, then a can be replaced by b and b can be replaced by a.

Since $j = 3k$ in the system above, you can replace j by $3k$ in the first equation, $j + k = 120$, as shown at the right.

$$3k + k = 120$$
$$4k = 120$$
$$k = 30$$

Then, since $j = 3k$,
$$j = 3 \cdot 30 = 90.$$

EXAMPLE 1 Solve the system $\begin{array}{l} y = -3x + 5 \\ -6x + y = -1 \end{array}$ using the substitution method.

Solution The first equation gives the value of y in terms of x.

$$y = -3x + 5 \qquad (1)$$
$$-6x + y = -1 \qquad (2)$$

Substitute $-3x + 5$ for y in Equation (2) and solve for x.

$$-6x - 3x + 5 = -1$$
$$-9x = -6$$
$$x = \frac{2}{3}$$

To find the value of y, substitute $\frac{2}{3}$ for x in either equation. Equation (1) is used here.

$$y = -3x + 5$$
$$y = -3 \cdot \frac{2}{3} + 5$$
$$y = -2 + 5$$
$$y = 3$$

Thus, the solution is $\left(\frac{2}{3}, 3\right)$. The check is left for you.

TRY THIS Solve each system by substitution.

1. $y = 2x + 1$
   $3x + y = -4$

2. $2x - y = 5$
   $y = -x + 4$

If neither original equation is solved for one variable, look for a variable whose coefficient is 1 or -1. Then solve the equation for that variable. If no variable has a coefficient of 1 or -1, you can still use the substitution method to solve the system.

EXAMPLE 2 Solve the system $\begin{array}{l} x - 4y = 17 \\ 2x + y = -2 \end{array}$ by the substitution method.

Plan The coefficient of x is 1 in the first equation. So, solve the first equation for x in terms of y. Then substitute in the second equation.

Solution

$$x - 4y = 17 \qquad (1)$$
$$x = 4y + 17$$

Substitute $4y + 17$ for x in Equation (2) and solve for y.

$$2x + y = -2 \qquad (2)$$
$$2(4y + 17) + y = -2$$
$$8y + 34 + y = -2$$
$$9y + 34 = -2$$
$$9y = -36$$
$$y = -4$$

Substitute -4 for y in $x = 4y + 17$. (This equation is used since it is already solved for x.)

$$x = 4y + 17$$
$$x = 4(-4) + 17$$
$$x = -16 + 17$$
$$x = 1$$

Thus, the solution is $(1, -4)$. The check is left for you.

EXAMPLE 3 Solve using the substitution method: $\begin{array}{l} 3x + 2y = 5 \quad (1) \\ 5x + 3y = 9 \quad (2) \end{array}$

Plan Solve Equation (1) for y. Then substitute for y in Equation (2).

Solution

$$3x + 2y = 5 \qquad (1)$$
$$2y = -3x + 5$$
$$y = -\tfrac{3}{2}x + \tfrac{5}{2}$$

Now substitute $-\tfrac{3}{2}x + \tfrac{5}{2}$ for y in Equation (2).

$$5x + 3y = 9 \qquad (2)$$
$$5x + 3\left(-\tfrac{3}{2}x + \tfrac{5}{2}\right) = 9$$
$$5x - \tfrac{9}{2}x + \tfrac{15}{2} = 9$$
$$10x - 9x + 15 = 18$$
$$x = 3$$

Now substitute 3 for x in either equation and solve for y: $y = -2$

Thus, the solution is $(3, -2)$. The check is left for you.

TRY THIS Solve each equation by substitution.

3. $\begin{array}{l} x + 2y = 3 \\ 3x - y = -1 \end{array}$

4. $\begin{array}{l} 5x + 2y = 1 \\ 3x - 2y = 7 \end{array}$

To solve a system of equations using substitution:

1. Solve one of the equations for one of its variables (if neither equation is already solved for one of the variables).
2. Substitute for that variable in the other equation.
3. Solve the resulting equation.
4. Find the value of the second variable by substituting the result from Step (3) in either of the equations.
5. Check the solution in *both* of the original equations.

Classroom Exercises

For each system, solve one of the equations for one of the variables.

1. $x + 8 = 5y$
$3x = 7y - 8$

2. $2x + y = 14$
$3x + 2y = -1$

3. $2x + 5y = 7$
$x + 3y = 0$

4. $2x - 3y = 4$
$13 + .y = \frac{1}{4}x$

Solve using the substitution method.

5. $x - 3y = 9$
$y = 2$

6. $3a + b = 7$
$b = a - 1$

7. $5c + 3d = -1$
$c + d = 3$

8. $x + y = 3$
$x - y = 9$

Written Exercises

Solve using the substitution method.

1. $y = x$
$3x - y = -4$

2. $x + y = 8$
$y = x - 2$

3. $x + y = 12$
$y = 2x$

4. $y = 2x - 6$
$x - y = 4$

5. $x = y - 8$
$-3x = -y + 16$

6. $x - y = -1$
$-2x + 3y = 5$

7. $y = 3x - 14$
$y = -5x + 2$

8. $y = 5x + 4$
$y = -2x - 3$

9. $3x - 5y = -9$
$4x + y = -12$

10. $5x + 4y = 0$
$x - y = 9$

11. $y + x = -1$
$3x - 4y = 4$

12. $4x + 3y = 3$
$x + 2y = 2$

13. $3x + y = 2$
$x - y = 0$

14. $5x - y = 1$
$y = -3x + 1$

15. $2x - y = -1$
$x - 2y = -11$

16. $x - y = 6$
$x + y = 3$

17. $3x = y + 12$
$-5y = -4x + 16$

18. $2x + y = 1$
$10x - 4y = 2$

19. $3y - 2 + x = 0$
$-2x = 4y + 2$

20. $y = \frac{1}{2}x - 9$
$y = \frac{3}{2}x + 1$

21. $3x - 2y = 8$
$2x + 3y = 14$

22. $3y = 5 - 2x$
$1 = 4x + 3y$

23. $-3x + 6y = 8$
$-2x + 6y = 12$

24. $2c - d = -6$
$c + d = 8$

25. $3(x + y) = -9$
$5x - 9y = -1$

26. $\frac{x + y}{4} = 6$
$x - \frac{3}{2}y = -6$

27. $\frac{y}{2} = \frac{12 - 3x}{3}$
$3x - y = 7$

28. $3x = 4 - y$
$\frac{x}{3} + \frac{y}{5} = \frac{8}{15}$

29. $3g = \frac{1}{2}h + 3$
$h - 2 = -g$

30. $x + 12 = -5y$
$\frac{y}{2} = \frac{x}{4}$

31. $p - q = \frac{1}{2}$
$\frac{1}{7}p = q - \frac{3}{7}$

32. $2a + b = 1$
$\frac{a}{5} - 1 = \frac{b}{2}$

33. $\frac{x + y}{2} - 10$
$3y = 2x$

34. $4a + b - 8 = 0$
$5a + 3b - 3 = 0$

35. $2u - r + 2 = 0$
$6u + 12r = 1$

36. $4s + 3t - 1 = 0$
$2 = 8s + 6t$

Try to solve each system using the substitution method. Explain the results.

37. $y = -\frac{1}{3}x + 5$
$3y = -x - 9$

38. $y = \frac{1}{2}x + 3$
$-x + 2y = 6$

Solve each system of three equations for x, y, and z. Use the substitution method.

39. $3x + 2y + z = 7$
$4y + 5z = -1$
$x = y + 1$

40. $-5x - 2y + z = 7$
$3x + 2y = -9$
$z - x = 3$

Mixed Review

1. 35 is 5% of what number? *4.7*

Factor. *7.3, 7.5*

2. $y^2 - 2y - 35$

3. $x^2 + 10x + 25$

4. $x^2 - 16$

Solve. *3.5, 5.2, 7.7*

5. $9 - (7 - x) = 5x - 6$

6. $4x - 9 \leq 1 + 3x$

7. $3a^2 + 7a - 6 = 0$

8. Subtract $\frac{3y + 2}{y - 8}$ from 2. Simplify, if possible. *8.7*

Solve. *10.6, 10.7*

9. The cost, c, of cleaning a carpet varies directly as its area, A. The cost of cleaning a 9-ft by 12-ft carpet is $21.60. At the same rate per square foot, how much will it cost to clean a carpet 18 ft long by 10 ft wide?

10. The amount of time it takes Jenny to travel to the seashore varies inversely as the rate of travel. At 30 mph, it takes Jenny 4 hours to make the trip from her home to the shore. How long will it take if she travels at a rate of 60 mph?

12.3 Problem Solving: Using Two Variables

Objective   To solve word problems using systems of equations

The problems in this chapter will be solved by writing two equations in two variables and solving the resulting system. Although some of the problems can be solved using one equation and one variable, it is often easier to use two variables.

EXAMPLE 1   A pencil and 3 erasers cost 50¢. Two pencils and 4 erasers cost 86¢. Find the cost of 1 pencil and the cost of 1 eraser.

Solution   Let p = cost of 1 pencil, in cents.
Let e = cost of 1 eraser, in cents.

One pencil and 3 erasers cost 50¢.	$p + 3e = 50$ (1)
Two pencils and 4 erasers cost 86¢.	$2p + 4e = 86$ (2)
Solve Equation (1) for p.	$p = 50 - 3e$
Substitute $50 - 3e$ for p in (2)	$2(50 - 3e) + 4e = 86$
and solve for e.	$100 - 6e + 4e = 86$
	$-2e = -14$
	$e = 7$
Substitute 7 for e in $p = 50 - 3e$.	$p = 50 - 3 \cdot 7$
Solve for p.	$= 50 - 21$, or 29

Check   One pencil and 3 erasers cost 50¢: $1 \cdot 29 + 3 \cdot 7 = 29 + 21 = 50$

Two pencils and 4 erasers cost 86¢: $2 \cdot 29 + 4 \cdot 7 = 58 + 28 = 86$

Thus, one pencil costs 29¢ and one eraser costs 7¢.

EXAMPLE 2   The perimeter of a rectangle is 54 cm. The length is 1 cm shorter than 3 times the width. Find the length and the width.

Solution   What are you to find?   length and width of a rectangle

Draw and label a figure.

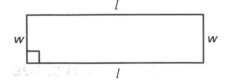

What is given?   perimeter = 54 cm
length = 1 cm less than 3 times the width

(THINK: $\frac{1}{2}$ the perimeter is 27 cm.)

$l + w = 27$

Choose two variables. What do they represent?	Let l = the length. Let w = the width.
Write two equations.	$2l + 2w = 54$ (1) $l = 3w - 1$ (2)
Solve the system. Substitute $3w - 1$ for l in Equation (1).	$2(3w - 1) + 2w = 54$ $6w - 2 + 2w = 54$ $8w - 2 = 54$ $8w = 56$ $w = 7$
Now substitute in Equation (2).	$l = 3w - 1$ (2) $= 3(7) - 1$ $= 21 - 1$ $l = 20$

The answers are reasonable.

$\frac{1}{2}$ the perimeter is 27,

and $20 + 7 = 27$.

Check Check in the original problem.

Is the perimeter 54 cm? Yes, because
$2 \cdot 20 + 2 \cdot 7$
$= 40 + 14 = 54$.

Is the length 1 cm shorter than 3 times the width? Yes, because
$3 \cdot 7 - 1 = 21 - 1 = 20$

State the answer. The length is 20 cm and the width is 7 cm.

TRY THIS

1. The sum of two numbers is 53. One number is 3 less than the other. Find the numbers.

2. The perimeter of a rectangle is 80 ft. One side is $\frac{2}{3}$ the length of the other. Find the dimensions of the rectangle.

Classroom Exercises

For each problem, use the given information to write two equations in two variables. State what each variable represents.

1. Mary is 3 times as old as Jean. The difference in their ages is 18 years. Find each girl's age.

2. A 73-ft length of wire is cut into two pieces. How long is each piece if one is 9 ft longer than the other.

3. The sum of two numbers is 121. The first number is 11 less than the second number. Find the two numbers.

4. One notebook and 3 packs of paper cost $6.20. Two notebooks and 1 pack of paper cost $8.65. Find the cost of a notebook and of a pack of paper.

Written Exercises

Solve each problem by using two equations and two variables.

1. Bob is 11 years older than Hank. The sum of their ages is 27 years. Find the age of each.

2. Marcia is 3 times as old as Kate. The difference between their ages is 12 years. Find the age of each.

3. The perimeter of a rectangle is 46 m. The length is 8 m more than 4 times the width. Find the length and the width.

4. The difference of two numbers is 5. Three times the larger, decreased by 5 times the smaller, is 7. Find the numbers.

5. Separate $74 into two parts so that one amount is $7 less than twice the other amount.

6. Paul drove 5 times as far as Tim. The sum of their distances was 48 mi. How far did each drive?

7. Mr. Hernandez weighs 3 times as much as his son, Carlos. Together, they weigh 280 lb. How much does each weigh?

8. Two hamburgers and 1 salad cost $2.95. Five hamburgers and 3 salads cost $8.00. Find the cost of a hamburger and the cost of a salad.

9. Jane is 4 times as old as Karen. Jane's age decreased by Karen's age is 21 years. Find the age of each.

10. A piece of ribbon 52 cm long is cut into two pieces. The first piece is 7 cm longer than twice the length of the second. How long is each piece?

11. Jack scored 6 more points than twice the number of points Igor scored. Their combined score was 27 points. How many points did each score?

12. Sun Lee has a total of 33 tapes and records. The number of tapes is 3 less than twice the number of records. How many of each does he have?

13. The length of a rectangle is 5 in. more than twice the width. The perimeter is 52 in. Find the length and the width of the rectangle.

14. The perimeter of a rectangle is 68 cm. The length is 2 cm less than 3 times the width. Find the length and width.

15. The sum of two numbers is 20. The first number decreased by the second number is 2. Find the numbers.

16. The product of 4 and the sum of two numbers is 140. The difference of the two numbers is 13. Find the numbers.

17. There are twice as many students on Mr. Sneed's team as on Mr. Johnson's team. Together, they want to raise $360 to buy uniforms. According to the size of the teams, how much money should each team raise?

18. A hotel charges less for weekend nights than for weekday nights. Three weekday nights and 1 weekend night cost $286. Four weekend nights and 2 weekday nights cost $414. Find the cost of a weekend night and the cost of a weekday night.

19. The formula $F = \frac{9}{5}C + 32$ is used to change from degrees Celsius to degrees Fahrenheit. At what temperature do both scales show the same number?

20. One number is 4 less than 3 times a second number. If 3 more than twice the first number is decreased by twice the second number, the result is 11. Find the numbers.

21. Two angles are *complementary*; that is, the sum of their degree measures is 90. The measure of one angle is 6 less than twice the measure of the other. Find the measure of each angle.

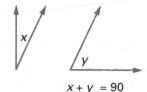

$$x + y = 90$$

22. Two angles are *supplementary*; that is, the sum of their degree measures is 180. The measure of one angle is 12 more than 3 times the measure of the other. Find the measure of each angle.

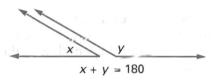

$$x + y = 180$$

23. A number and twice another number are added. Twice this sum is 346. The sum of the original two numbers is 118. Find the numbers.

24. Half the sum of two numbers is equal to 91. Twice the larger number subtracted from 3 times the smaller number is 51. Find the numbers.

25. Half the sum of the distances traveled by Nicole and Melissa is 640 km. If $\frac{1}{4}$ of the distance Nicole traveled is 5 km more than $\frac{1}{6}$ of the distance Melissa traveled, how far did each travel?

26. During the holiday weekend, the number of campers admitted to a park was 5 less than $\frac{1}{2}$ the number of trailers admitted. If 4 more trailers had been admitted, there would have been a total of 89 trailers and campers. How many trailers and how many campers were admitted?

Mixed Review

Solve. If there is no solution, so indicate. (Exercises 1–6)   *4.5, 4.6, 5.6, 7.7, 9.2*

1. $\frac{2}{5}x + 4 = 3 + \frac{1}{2}x$

2. $0.04x = 0.1$

3. $-8 - 2|4x - 2| = 16$

4. $x^2 - x - 30 = 0$

5. $6y^2 + 28y = -32$

6. $\frac{a - 6}{4} = \frac{2}{a - 4}$

7. Multiply $(2c + 7)(c - 9)$. *6.9*

8. Add $\frac{2}{x - 2} + \frac{3}{x - 5} + \frac{7}{x^2 - 7x + 10}$. *8.7*

12.4 The Addition Method

Objectives	To solve systems of equations using the addition method
	To explain why a given system cannot be solved using a given method

You have solved systems of equations using graphs and using the substitution method. In this lesson, you will use the **addition method.** It is based on the following form of the Addition Property of Equality.

$$\begin{array}{ll} \text{If} & a = b \\ \text{and} & \underline{c = d} \\ \text{then} & a + c = b + d \end{array}$$

Adding the left sides and the right sides of two equations is often referred to as "adding the equations."

EXAMPLE 1   Use the addition method to solve $\begin{array}{l} x + y = 4 \\ -x + y = -2 \end{array}$.

Plan   Since x and $-x$ are opposites, eliminate the x terms by adding the equations. Then solve for y.

Solution
$$\begin{array}{ll} x + y = 4 & (1) \\ \underline{-x + y = -2} & (2) \\ \quad\; 2y = 2 & \\ \quad\;\; y = 1 & \end{array}$$

Substitute 1 for y in either equation; then solve for x.
$$\begin{array}{l} x + y = 4 \\ x + 1 = 4 \\ \quad\;\; x = 3 \end{array}$$

Check
$$\begin{array}{ll} x + y = 4 & -x + y = -2 \\ 3 + 1 \overset{?}{=} 4 & -3 + 1 \overset{?}{=} -2 \\ \quad 4 = 4 \;\text{True} & \quad -2 = -2 \;\text{True} \end{array}$$

Thus, the solution is $(3, 1)$.

TRY THIS   Use the addition method to solve each system.

1. $\begin{array}{l} x - 2y = 2 \\ 2x + 2y = 1 \end{array}$

2. $\begin{array}{l} \frac{1}{2}r + \frac{2}{5}s = 15 \\ -\frac{1}{2}r + \frac{4}{5}s = 45 \end{array}$

Sometimes a system is easier to solve if you write the equations in standard form first,

EXAMPLE 2 Use the addition method to solve $\begin{matrix} 2x = 3y - 5 \\ 3y = 4x + 1 \end{matrix}$

Solution

1. Write in standard form and solve for one variable.

$$2x - 3y = -5$$
$$\underline{-4x + 3y = 1}$$
$$-2x = -4$$
$$x = 2$$

2. Substitute for x and solve.

$$3y = 4(2) + 1$$
$$3y = 8 + 1$$
$$3y = 9$$
$$y = 3$$

Check $(2, 3)$ in both original equations.
Thus, the solution is $(2, 3)$.

EXAMPLE 3 Two packages have a total weight of 39 lb. One package weighs 7 lb more than the other package. Find the weight of each package.

What are you to find?	The weights of two packages
What is given?	The total weight of two packages is 39 lb. One package weighs 7 lb more than the other package.
Choose two variables. What do they represent?	Let $x =$ weight of heavier package. Let $y =$ weight of lighter package.
Write two equations.	$x + y = 39$ (1) $x = y + 7$ (2)
Solve the system using the addition method.	$\begin{aligned} x - y &= 7 \quad (2) \\ \underline{x + y} &= \underline{39} \quad (1) \\ 2x &= 46 \\ x &= 23 \\ 23 + y &= 39 \\ y &= 16 \end{aligned}$
Check in the original problem.	Is the total weight 39 lb? Yes, since $23 + 16 = 39$.
	Does one package weigh 7 lb more than the other? Yes, since $23 = 16 + 7$.
State the answer.	The packages weigh 23 lb and 16 lb.

TRY THIS 3. Lupe has $9 less than Juanita. Together they have $53. How much does each person have?

Classroom Exercises

Add each pair of equations. State the resulting equation. Then solve the system.

1. $x + y = 15$
$-x + 3y = -7$

2. $2x - 5y = 1$
$-x + 5y = -3$

3. $4m + n = -9$
$-4m - 3n = 3$

4. $2x + y = 3$
$-x - y = 3$

5. $\frac{1}{2}p - q = 9$
$-\frac{1}{2}p + 2q = -3$

6. $\frac{1}{4}x + 2y = 10$
$\frac{1}{4}x - 2y = -2$

7. $x - 0.5y = 10$
$x + 0.5y = 8$

8. $0.4x + y = 5$
$0.6x - y = 0$

9. $3x + 5y = 4$
$-3x + 4y = 14$

Written Exercises

Solve using the addition method.

1. $x - 3y = -3$
$x + 3y = 9$

2. $-2x + 3y = 2$
$2x + 7y = 18$

3. $3x + 7y = 3$
$x - 7y = 1$

4. $-7c - d = 19$
$3c + d = -7$

5. $-2x + 8y = 14$
$2x + 7y = 16$

6. $5p - 4q = 1$
$7p + 4q = 11$

7. $2x + 9y = 4$
$-5x - 9y = 17$

8. $5x - y = 13$
$y + x = -1$

9. $-3x + 5y = 14$
$3x + 8y = 12$

10. $5x - 3y = -5$
$-5x + 2y = 1$

11. $3r - 7s = 24$
$3r + 7s = 6$

12. $s + 2t = 10$
$-2t = 3s + 8$

13. $4x - 3y = 3$
$7x = 19 - 3y$

14. $y = -2x + 3$
$-2x + y = -4$

15. $0.2x + y = 6$
$0.7x - y = 3$

Solve each problem using a system of two equations and the addition method.

16. The sum of two numbers is 40. Their difference is 16. Find the two numbers.

17. Jane weighs 8 lb less than Pat. Their total weight is 202 lb. How much does each weigh?

18. If Jean and Joe combined their weekly allowances, they would have $12. Jean's allowance is $2 more than Joe's. Find the weekly allowances for Jean and Joe.

19. Together, a house and a lot cost $78,500. The difference between the cost of the house and the cost of the lot is $35,900. Find the cost of the house and the cost of the lot.

20. Mary's salary is $50 more than Sue's salary. If 3 times Mary's salary is added to Sue's salary, the result is $1,550. Find Mary's salary and Sue's salary.

21. The total cost of two books is $32.90. One book costs $3 more than the other book. Find the cost of each book.

Solve each system using the addition method.

22. $-\frac{1}{3}p + \frac{3}{5}q = 1$
$\frac{4}{3}p - \frac{3}{5}q = 5$

23. $\frac{2}{3}r + \frac{4}{5}s = 4$
$-\frac{2}{3}r + \frac{3}{5}s = 10$

24. $2(x + y) = 3x$
$x + 6y = 0$

25. $-3(x + 5y) = 0$
$15y - 4x = 35$

26. $4x - y = 7$
$3x - (6 - y) = 1$

27. $0.18x - 0.13y = -3.6$
$-0.18x + 0.25y = 7.2$

28. Write an explanation of why the system shown below cannot be solved using the addition method. What can you do to the second equation so that you can use the addition method?

$$3x - 4y = 13$$
$$-2x + y = -2$$

What values of r and s will eliminate the y-term?

29. $r(-2x + y - 5) + s(x + 3y - 1) = 0$ **30.** $r(2x + 3y - 3) + s(3x - 5y + 2) = 0$

Write each equation of the system in the form $Ax + By = C$. Then solve using the addition method.

31. $\frac{x + y}{3} = 2$
$\frac{x - y}{2} = -1$

32. $\frac{2c + d}{5} = c + d$
$\frac{4d + 3c}{7} = d + 3$

33. $\frac{x + 2y}{3} = 2$
$1 = \frac{5x - 2y}{6}$

34. $\frac{x + 3}{2} = x + 4y$
$x = 5y$

35. $16x - 6y = -1 + 6y$
$\frac{2}{3}x = 4y + 3$

36. $2(5x - 3y) = 2x + 1$
$6y + \frac{9}{2} = x$

37. Solve the system $\begin{array}{l} Ax + By = C \\ -Ax + Dy = E \end{array}$ for y, where $B + D \neq 0$.

Mixed Review

Solve.   *3.5, 5.2, 5.7, 7.7*

1. $6 = 7 - (4 - x)$ **2.** $5x - 3 < 9 + 3x$ **3.** $|x| < 2$ **4.** $25 = y^2$

Divide.   *8.4, 8.8*

5. $7x\overline{)49x^3 - 21x^2 + 14x}$

6. $\frac{15a^4b}{9a^2 - 18b} \div \frac{5a^3b^3}{6a - 12}$

7. Find three consecutive integers whose sum is -54.   *4.3*

8. It takes James 10 h and Bob 15 h to plow a field. How long will it take them if they work together?   *9.5*

12.5 The Multiplication with Addition Method

Objective

To solve systems of equations using multiplication with addition

In the system at the right, adding the two equations does not eliminate either variable. In such a case, you can use the Multiplication Property of Equality, as shown in Example 1.

$$-x + y = -3$$
$$\underline{4x + y = 2}$$
$$3x + 2y = -1$$

EXAMPLE 1 Solve the system $\begin{array}{l} -x + y = -3 \\ 4x + y = 2 \end{array}$ using multiplication with addition.

Plan Multiply each side of the first equation by -1 to make the y terms opposites. Then solve the system using the addition method.

Solution

$$-1(-x + y) = -1(-3)$$

$$x - y = 3 \quad (1)$$
$$\underline{4x + y = 2} \quad (2)$$

Add (1) and (2). $\quad 5x \quad\quad = 5$

$$x = 1$$

Substitute 1 for x in (1).
$$-x + y = -3$$
$$-1 + y = -3$$
$$y = -2$$

Thus, the solution is $(1, -2)$. The check is left for you.

EXAMPLE 2 Solve the system. $\begin{array}{l} -y = 7 - 4x \quad (1) \\ 5x + 3y = 13 \quad (2) \end{array}$

Plan First add $4x$ to each side of (1) to get the x and y terms on one side. Then multiply each side by 3 to make the y terms opposites.

Solution

$$(1) \quad\quad -y = 7 - 4x$$
$$(3) \quad\quad 4x - y = 7$$
$$3(4x - y) = 3 \cdot 7$$
$$(4) \quad 12x - 3y = 21$$
$$(2) \quad \underline{5x + 3y = 13}$$

Add (4) and (2). $\quad 17x \quad\quad = 34$

$$x = 2$$

Substitute 2 for x in (2).
$$5x + 3y = 13$$
$$5 \cdot 2 + 3y = 13$$
$$10 + 3y = 13$$
$$3y = 3$$
$$y = 1$$

Thus, the solution is $(2, 1)$. The check is left for you.

TRY THIS Solve each system.

1. $x - 3y = 18$
   $x + 5y = 2$

2. $-4y = x - 3$
   $2x + 3y = -9$

This method of using addition with multiplication, if necessary, is sometimes called the *linear-combination* method of solving a system. You may need to use the Multiplication Property with both equations.

EXAMPLE 3   Solve the system $\begin{array}{ll} 5x + 6y = 14 & (1) \\ 3x - 4y = 16 & (2) \end{array}$

Solution   Multiply Equation (1) by 3 and Equation (2) by -5.

$$3(5x + 6y) = 3 \cdot 14 \qquad \text{Substitute } -1 \text{ for } y \text{ in (1).}$$
$$-5(3x - 4y) = -5 \cdot 16 \qquad 5x + 6y = 14$$
$$15x + 18y = 42 \quad (3) \qquad 5x + 6(-1) = 14$$
$$-15x + 20y = -80 \quad (4) \qquad 5x - 6 = 14$$

Add (3) and (4).
$$38y = -38 \qquad\qquad 5x = 20$$
$$y = -1 \qquad\qquad x - 4$$

Thus, the solution is $(4, -1)$. The check is left for you.

EXAMPLE 4   At a fruit-packing plant, fruit of uniform size is shipped in gift baskets. For a large basket, 8 grapefruit and 14 oranges weigh 15 lb. For a small basket, 4 grapefruit and 10 oranges weight 9 lb. Find the approximate weight of a grapefruit and of an orange.

Solution   Let g = the weight of a grapefruit, in pounds.
Let r = the weight of an orange, in pounds.

Solve the system: $\begin{array}{l} 8g + 14r = 15 \\ 4g + 10r = 9 \end{array}$. You will find that $r = \frac{1}{2}$ and $g = 1$.

Thus, a grapefruit weighs about 1 lb and an orange weighs about $\frac{1}{2}$ lb.

The solution and check are left for you.

TRY THIS   3. Two baseballs and a bat cost $41. Five baseballs and two bats cost $94. Find the cost of one baseball.

◢◢◢ *Focus on Reading*

List five steps, in order, to solve the system: $\begin{array}{l} (1) \ 7x + 2y = 11 \\ (2) \ -2x + 5y = 8 \end{array}$

a. Solve for x.
b. Multiply each side of Equation (1) by 2.
c. Add Equations (1) and (2) and solve for y.
d. Substitute the value for y in (1) or (2).
e. Multiply each side of Equation (2) by 7.

Classroom Exercises

Find a number by which you would multiply one equation before eliminating variables using addition.

1. $2x - 3y = 8$
$-5x + y = 3$

2. $x + 2y = -1$
$x - 3y = 2$

3. $7x - 6y = 8$
$-2x - 2y = 1$

4. $3x - 2y = 5$
$2x + 4y = 14$

Solve each system using multiplication with addition.

5. $x + 2y = 7$
$x + 3y = 10$

6. $2x - y = -8$
$3x + 6y = -12$

7. $6p - 2q = -8$
$3p + 7q = 4$

8. $2x - 3y = 2$
$3x - 4y = -1$

Written Exercises

Solve each system using multiplication with addition.

1. $x + y = 4$
$2x + 3y = 9$

2. $5x + 2y = 7$
$x + 4y = 5$

3. $x + 4y = 14$
$6x - 2y = 6$

4. $3x + 5y = 11$
$2x - 3y = 1$

5. $3x + 2y = 12$
$2x + 5y = 8$

6. $2s - 5t = 22$
$2s - 3t = 6$

7. $2x - 7y = 3$
$5x - 4y = -6$

8. $3x + 9y = 0$
$11x - 2y = 35$

9. $3x - 7y = 8$
$2x - 5y = 7$

10. $7p + 3q = 13$
$3p - 2q = -1$

11. $3x - 2y = 6$
$5x + 7y = 41$

12. $5x + 2y = 7$
$3x + 7y = 10$

13. $5x - 2y = 8$
$3x = 5y + 1$

14. $3c = 2d + 5$
$2c + 5d = 16$

15. $4x - 3y = 1$
$y = -2x + 3$

16. $2x + 7y = -4$
$6x = 24 - 3y$

17. $10x = 3y + 2$
$5x = 2y + 3$

18. $2x = 4y + 1$
$x = y$

19. $9x + 2y = 2$
$21x + 6y = 4$

20. $3x - 4y = -1$
$6x + 8y = 10$

21. $7y - \frac{1}{2}x = 2$
$-2y = x + 4$

22. $r + \frac{3}{2}s = 0$
$s - 2 = -r$

23. $2.5c - d = 5$
$4d = 3c - 6$

24. $x - 1.5y = 4$
$0.8x = -0.4y$

Solve each problem.

25. Three pairs of sneakers and 2 pairs of socks cost $78. Two pairs of sneakers and 4 pairs of socks cost $60. Find the cost of a pair of sneakers and a pair of socks.

26. Harry bought 2 mints and 5 apples for $2.36. Craig bought 4 mints and 3 apples for $1.78. Find the cost of a mint and the cost of an apple.

27. When buying string for a kite, Jay found that 3 small spools of string and 1 large spool would give him a total of 115 yd of string. Two small spools and 2 large spools would give him a total of 130 yd. How many yards of string are in the small spool and in the large spool?

28. When Jane babysat for 8 h and did odd jobs for 3 h, she made a total of $39. When she babysat for 2 h and did odd jobs for 5 h, she made a total of $31. How much does she charge per hour for babysitting and for doing odd jobs?

29. A jacket with 1 pair of trousers costs $114. A jacket with 2 pairs of trousers costs $153. Find the cost of a jacket and the cost of a pair of trousers.

Solve each system using multiplication with addition.

30. $\dfrac{2(x + 6y)}{3} = 2$

$x + 10y = -1$

31. $\dfrac{x - 2y}{8} = \dfrac{1}{2}$

$3x + 2y = 4$

32. $x - \dfrac{3}{4}y = \dfrac{1}{4}$

$\dfrac{1}{2}x + \dfrac{1}{4}y = \dfrac{3}{4}$

33. $\dfrac{6}{7}x - y = \dfrac{3}{7}$

$\dfrac{9}{7}x + 2y = \dfrac{1}{7}$

34. $\dfrac{c}{6} + \dfrac{d}{4} = \dfrac{3}{2}$

$\dfrac{2}{3}c - \dfrac{d}{2} = 0$

35. $6x - 3(y - 2x) = 3x + 15$

$y - (4y - x) = 7x - 15$

36. Solve the system $\begin{array}{l} Ax + By = C \\ Dx + Ey = F \end{array}$ for x and y, where $AE \neq BD$.

37. Use your answer to Exercise 36 and a calculator to solve the system $\begin{array}{l} 4x + 5y = 24.05. \\ 2x + 3y = 13.15 \end{array}$

Midchapter Review

Solve each system of equations. Use the most convenient method.

1. $y = 6x + 8$
$y = -4x - 2$

2. $3x + y = 7$
$x - y = 5$

3. $x = y$
$3x + 4y = 7$

4. $5x - 4y = 13$
$-3x + 2y = 1$

5. $x = 4y - 3$
$3x + 5y = -1$

6. $\dfrac{1}{3}x - \dfrac{3}{4}y = 5$
$\dfrac{2}{3}x - \dfrac{3}{4}y = 4$

7. $-5c + d = -13$
$c + d = -1$

8. $-2x + 8y = -1$
$4x - 6y = 7$

Solve each problem using a system of two equations with two variables.

9. The sum of two numbers is 15. Five times the first number minus 2 times the second number is 12. Find the two numbers.

10. At a resort, 1 round of golf and 2 tennis lessons cost $55. Three rounds of golf and 5 tennis lessons cost $150. At this rate, what is the cost of 1 round of golf and 1 tennis lesson?

11. At an arcade game, you get 5 points each time you hit the target, but you lose 2 points each time you miss. After 26 tries, Jason's score was -3. How many hits and misses did he have?

12. One egg and 2 slices of bacon cost $1.40. Two eggs and 3 slices of bacon cost $2.55. At this rate, what is the cost of 1 egg and the cost of 1 slice of bacon?

13. Mary worked 2 h more than 3 times the number of hours that Victor worked. If they worked a total of 86 h, how long did each work?

12.6 Problem Solving: Digit Problems

Objective

To solve two-digit number problems using systems of equations

Any two-digit number can be written in expanded form as

$$\begin{array}{ccc} \text{tens digit} & \text{units digit} \\ \downarrow & \\ 36 = 10 \cdot 3 & + 6 \end{array}$$

The chart below introduces vocabulary that will be used in the examples and exercises.

Tens digits	Units digit	The two-digit number	Sum of the digits	Number with digits reversed
4	7	$10 \cdot 4 + 7$, or 47	$4 + 7$, or 11	$10 \cdot 7 + 4$, or 74
t	u	$10t + u$	$t + u$	$10u + t$

EXAMPLE 1

The sum of the digits of a two-digit number is 11. The number is 13 times the units digit. Find the number.

Solution

What are you to find?   a two-digit number

What is given?   The sum of the digits is 11.
                      The number is 13 times the units digit.

Choose two variables.   Let $t = $ the tens digit.
What do they represent?   Let $u = $ the units digit.
                             Then $10t + u = $ the two-digit number.

Write two equations.   (1) $t + u = 11$
                             (2) $10t + u = 13u$, or $10t - 12u = 0$

Solve the system.   Multiply (1) by -10.   Replace u by 5 in (1).

$$\begin{array}{ll} -10(t + u) = -10 \cdot 11 & t + u = 11 \\ -10t - 10u = -110 \quad (3) & t + 5 = 11 \\ \underline{10t - 12u = 0 \qquad (2)} & t = 6 \\ -22u = -110 & \\ u = 5 & \text{So, } 10t + u = 65. \end{array}$$

Check

Check in the original problem.   Is the sum of the digits 11?
                                      Yes, $6 + 5 = 11$

                                      Is the number 13 times the units digit?
                                      Yes, $65 = 13 \cdot 5$

State the answer.   The number is 65.

EXAMPLE 2   Three times the tens digit of a two-digit number, increased by the units digit, is 16. If the digits are reversed, the new number is 1 less than twice the original number. Find the original number.

Solution   What are you to find?   a two-digit number

What is given?

$3 \cdot$ tens digit $+$ units digit $= 16$
number with digits reversed $=$
    $2 \cdot$ original number $- 1$

Choose two variables.
What do they represent?

Let $t =$ the tens digit.
Let $u =$ the units digit.
$10t + u =$ original two-digit number
$10u + t =$ new number (digits reversed)

Write two equations.

(1) $3t + u = 16$
(2) $10u + t = 2(10t + u) - 1$

Solve the system.

Solve Equation (1)
  for u.

$3t + u = 16$
$u = 16 - 3t$

Write Equation (2)
  with variables on
  one side.

$10u + t = 2(10t + u) - 1$
$10u + t = 20t + 2u - 1$
(3) $8u - 19t = -1$

Replace u by $16 - 3t$
  in Equation (3) and
  solve for t.

$8(16 - 3t) - 19t = -1$
$128 - 24t - 19t = -1$
$-43t = -129$
$t = 3$

To find u, replace t by
  3 in $u = 16 - 3t$.

$u = 16 - 3 \cdot 3$
$u = 7$

So, $10t + u = 10(3) + 7$, or 37.

Thus, the number is 37.

The check is left for you.

TRY THIS   1. The units digit of a two-digit number is 4 less than 6 times the tens digit. If the digits are reversed, the new number is 2 less than 3 times the original number. Find the original number.

Classroom Exercises

1. What is the sum of the digits of 48?

2. In 80, what is the units digit?

3. In the number 63, what is the tens digit?

4. What new number is formed when the digits of 25 are reversed?

5. Does reversing the digits of a two-digit number affect the sum of the digits?

Solve each problem.

6. The sum of the digits of a two-digit number is 11. The tens digit is 7 more than the units digit. Find the number.

7. The sum of the digits of a two-digit number is 9. The number is 6 times the units digit. Find the number.

8. The units digit of a two-digit number is 5 times the tens digit. If the digits are reversed, the new number is 36 more than the original number. Find the original number.

Written Exercises

Solve each problem.

1. The tens digit of a two-digit number is 3 times the units digit. The difference between the digits is 6. Find the number.

2. The tens digit of a two-digit number is 4 more than the units digit. The number is 7 less than 8 times the sum of the digits. Find the number.

3. The sum of the digits of a two-digit number is 7. If the digits are reversed, the new number is 27 more than the original number. Find the original number.

4. The sum of the digits of a two-digit number is 10. If the digits are reversed, the new number is 18 less than the original number. Find the original number.

5. The units digit of a two-digit number is 4 times the tens digit. If the digits are reversed, the new number is 54 more than the original number. Find the original number.

6. The tens digit of a two-digit number is 3 times the units digit. If the digits are reversed, the new number is 36 less than the original number. Find the original number.

7. The tens digit of a two-digit number is 3 more than twice the units digit. If the digits are reversed, the new number is 54 less than the original number. Find the original number.

8. Four times the units digit of a two-digit number is 1 less than the tens digit. If the digits are reversed, the new number is 63 less than the original number. Find the original number.

9. The units digit of a two-digit number is 12 less than twice the tens digit. If the digits are reversed, the new number is 3 less than 8 times the tens digit of the original number. Find the original number.

10. The units digit of a two-digit number is 1 more than 4 times the tens digit. If the digits are reversed, the new number is 5 more than 3 times the original number. Find the original number.

11. Use h, t, and u to represent a three-digit number. Then represent the number with its digits reversed.

12. When the digits of a three-digit number are reversed, what is true of the tens digit?

13. In a three-digit number, the tens digit is twice the units digit, and the hundreds digit is 1 more than the units digit. The sum of the digits is 17. Find the number.

14. In a three-digit number, the hundreds digit is 6 less than the units digit. The tens digit is 1 more than the hundreds digit. The sum of the digits is 13. Find the number.

15. Show that if a two-digit number is added to the number with its digits reversed, the result is divisible by 11.

16. Show that if a two-digit number is subtracted from the number with its digits reversed, the result is divisible by 9.

17. Find all possible two-digit numbers such that twice the tens digit increased by the units digit is 19.

18. In a three-digit number, the hundreds digit and the tens digit are the same. The sum of the digits is 18. If the digits are reversed, the number is decreased by 297. Find the number.

Mixed Review

Factor completely.   *7.4, 7.5, 7.6*

1. $5a^2 - 19a - 4$

2. $36x - 4x^3$

3. $-9x^2 + 15x + 3x^3$

Simplify if possible.   *8.5, 8.6, 8.7*

4. $\dfrac{6}{5x} + \dfrac{9}{5x}$

5. $\dfrac{6}{y + 5} - \dfrac{4}{y - 5} + \dfrac{8}{y^2 - 25}$

6. $\dfrac{2}{3a^2} + \dfrac{4}{5a} - \dfrac{1}{9a^3}$

7. Find the slope of $\overleftrightarrow{AB}$ determined by points $A(-4, -2)$ and $B(2, 3)$.   *11.1*

8. Write an equation for $\overleftrightarrow{CD}$ determined by points $C(-1, 5)$ and $D(0, 2)$.   *11.2*

9. Write an equation, in the form $Ax + By = C$, of a line with a slope of $-\dfrac{2}{5}$ and a y-intercept of -3.   *11.2, 11.3*

12.7 Problem Solving: Age Problems

Objective   To solve problems about ages using systems of equations

Problems about ages may involve ages in the past or in the future as well as in the present time. It is customary to let a variable represent the present age of a person. For example,

$$\text{Let } t = \text{Tim's age now.}$$
$$\text{Then } t + 6 = \text{Tim's age 6 years from now,}$$
$$t - 1 = \text{Tim's age last year,}$$

and so on.

EXAMPLE 1   Paul is 3 times as old as Cathy. In 8 years, he will be twice as old as she will be. How old is each now?

Solution

What are you to find?	Paul's and Cathy's ages now
What is given?	Paul's age now = 3 · Cathy's age now Paul's age in 8 years = 2 · Cathy's age in 8 years
Choose two variables. What do they represent?	Let c = Cathy's age now. Then $c + 8$ = her age in 8 years. Let p = Paul's age now. Then $p + 8$ = his age in 8 years.
Write two equations.	$p = 3c \qquad\qquad (1)$ $p + 8 = 2(c + 8) \quad (2)$

Solve the system.

Substitute $3c$ for p in (2). Solve for c.

$$3c + 8 = 2(c + 8)$$
$$3c + 8 = 2c + 16$$
$$c + 8 = 16$$
$$c = 8$$

Substitute 8 for c in (1). Solve for p.

$$p = 3 \cdot 8$$
$$p = 24$$

Check   Check in the original problem.

Is Paul 3 times as old as Cathy? Yes, $24 = 3 \cdot 8$. In 8 years, will Paul be twice as old as Cathy will be? Yes, since Paul will be 32 years old, Cathy will be 16 years old, and $32 = 2 \cdot 16$.

State the answer.

Cathy is 8 years old.
Paul is 24 years old.

EXAMPLE 2   Elaine is 15 years younger than Al. Ten years ago, Al was 4 times as old as Elaine was then. How old is each now?

Solution   Let e = Elaine's age now.
Let a = Al's age now.

Al's age now:	$a = e + 15$	(1)
Al's age 10 years ago:	$a - 10 = 4(e - 10)$	(2)
Substitute $e + 15$	$e + 15 - 10 = 4e - 40$	
for a in (2) and	$e + 5 = 4e - 40$	
solve for e.	$45 = 3e$	
	$e = 15$	
Substitute 15 for e in (1).	$a = 15 + 15$, or 30	

Thus, Elaine is 15 years old now, and Al is 30 years old. The check is left for you.

TRY THIS   1. David is 4 years younger than Joan. Six years ago, Joan was 3 times as old as David was then. How old is each now?

Classroom Exercises

Give an expression for each age if j — Janet's present age.

1. Janet's age 5 years from now

2. twice Janet's age 4 years ago

Refer to the problem below for Exercises 3–6.

Darlene is 4 times as old as Kara. In 10 years, she will be twice as old as Kara will be then. How old is each now?

3. What are you to find?

4. What is given?

5. Write two equations. Let k = Kara's age now. Let d = Darlene's age now.

6. Solve the system of equations and answer the question.

Solve each problem.

7. Leah is 8 years younger than Walt. Twelve years ago Walt was twice as old as Leah was then. How old is each now?

8. Roberto is 30 years younger than Kate. In 12 years, Kate will be 3 times as old as Roberto will be. Find the present ages of Roberto and Kate.

Written Exercises

For each problem, find the age of each person now.

1. Mrs. O'Malley is 28 years older than her son Sean. She was 5 times as old as her son 14 years ago.

2. In 4 years, Mike will be 3 times as old as Chris will be. The sum of their ages now is 56.

3. Four years ago, Shirley's age was 2 years more than 4 times Kim's age. Four years from now, she will be 3 times as old as Kim will be.

4. A grandfather is 5 times as old as his granddaughter. In 6 years, he will be 4 times as old as his granddaughter will be.

5. The sum of Mary's and Al's ages is 48. Twelve years ago, Mary was twice as old as Al.

6. Kathy's father is 6 times as old as Kathy. Two years ago, he was 8 times as old as Kathy was.

7. Denise is 14 years older than Jack. In 10 years, the sum of their ages will be 60.

8. Wilma is 8 years younger than Josh. In 6 years, the sum of their ages will be 46.

9. Regina is $\frac{3}{5}$ as old as Mort. Ten years from now, she will be $\frac{4}{5}$ as old as he will be.

10. Four years ago, Rich was $\frac{2}{3}$ as old as Marie. Six years from now, he will be $\frac{4}{5}$ as old as she will be.

11. In 16 years, Ian's age will be 4 years less than $\frac{1}{2}$ Judy's age then. The sum of their ages now is 36.

12. Elias is $2\frac{1}{2}$ times as old as his daughter. In $8\frac{1}{2}$ years, he will be twice as old as his daughter will be.

13. Penelope is $\frac{1}{2}$ as old as William. In $6\frac{1}{2}$ years, she will be $\frac{2}{3}$ as old as William will be.

14. Carl is $1\frac{2}{3}$ times as old as his friend. In $\frac{1}{2}$ year, Carl will be $1\frac{3}{5}$ as old as his friend.

15. Clint is 8 years older than Fern. Fern is $1\frac{1}{2}$ times as old as Geri. Clint's age will be twice Geri's age 4 years from now.

16. Enid is 9 years older than Alice. Cathy was $\frac{3}{4}$ as old as Alice was 2 years ago. Next year, Enid will be twice as old as Cathy will be.

Mixed Review

Use the given formulas and values to find the perimeter.   *1.4*

1. $p = a + b + c$
   $a = 6$ m, $b = 9$ m, $c = 6$ m

2. $p = 4s$
   $s = 12$ cm

3. Find the perimeter of a rectangle if the length is 6.2 cm and the width is 4.7 cm. Use the formula $p = 2l + 2w$.   *1.4*

4. What is 15% of 42?   *4.7*

5. Six is what percent of 30?   *4.7*

6. Write an equation for a line with slope $\frac{2}{3}$ and y-intercept -5.   *11.3*

12.8 Problem Solving: Coin and Mixture Problems

Objective To solve coin and mixture problems using systems of equations

When solving problems about coins, you often need to express the value of the coins in cents, as shown in the chart below.

Coins	Number of coins	Value of coins in cents
7 nickels	7	$5 \cdot 7 = 35$
4 dimes	4	$10 \cdot 4 = 40$
3 dimes and 5 quarters	8	$10 \cdot 3 + 25 \cdot 5 = 155$
n nickels and q quarters	$n + q$	$5n + 25q$

Cents are used rather than dollars in order to avoid decimals.

EXAMPLE 1 Jane has a collection of nickels and quarters worth $3.05. She has 7 more nickels than quarters. How many coins of each type does she have?

Solution

What are you to find? the number of nickels and the number of quarters

What is given? value of nickels + value of quarters = 305¢
number of nickels = number of quarters + 7

Choose two variables. What do they represent? Let n = the number of nickels.
Let q = the number of quarters.

Write two equations. (1) $5n + 25q = 305$
(2) $n = q + 7$

Solve the system.
Substitute $q + 7$ for n in (1). Solve for q.
$5(q + 7) + 25q = 305$
$5q + 35 + 25q = 305$
$30q = 270$
$q = 9$

Substitute 9 for q in (2). Solve for n.
$n = 9 + 7$
$n = 16$

Check

Check in the original problem.
Are 9 quarters and 16 nickels worth $3.05?
Yes, because
$9 \cdot 25 + 16 \cdot 5 = 225 + 80 = 305$ cents.

Are there 7 more nickels than quarters?
Yes, because $16 = 9 + 7$.

State the answer. Jane has 16 nickels and 9 quarters.

1. John has a collection of dimes and quarters worth $4.50. He has 4 more quarters than dimes. How many coins of each type does he have?

The same method that is used for solving coin problems can be used to solve other problems about mixtures.

EXAMPLE 2   A coffee wholesaler mixes Colombian beans selling at $1.20/lb with Venezuelan beans selling at $1.60/lb. He wants a mixture of 90 pounds to sell at $1.24/lb. How many pounds of each should he use?

Solution

What are you to find?	The number of pounds of each kind of coffee bean needed for a 90-lb mixture worth $1.24/lb.
What is given?	Colombian beans sell at $1.20/lb. Venezuelan beans sell at $1.60/lb. 90 lb are wanted in all.
Choose two variables. What do they represent?	Let c = the number of pounds of Colombian beans. Let v = the number of pounds of Venezuelan beans.

Write two equations.

$$c + v = 90 \qquad \qquad (1)$$
$$120c + 160v = 124 \cdot 90 \quad (2)$$

Solve the system.
   Solve (1) for c.
   Substitute in (2).
   Solve for v.

$$c = 90 - v$$
$$120(90 - v) + 160v = 124 \cdot 90$$
$$10{,}800 - 120v + 160v = 11{,}160$$
$$v = 9$$

Substitute in (1).

$$c + 9 = 90$$
$$c = 81$$

Check in the original problem.

Does the mixture weigh 90 lb? Yes, $9 + 81 = 90$.

Does the value of 81 lb of Colombian beans plus the value of 9 lb of Venezuelan beans equal the value of the mixture? Yes, since $81 \times \$1.20 + 9 \times \$1.60 = \$97.20 + \$14.40$ and $90 \times \$1.24 = \$111.60$.

State the answer.

The wholesaler should use 81 lb of Colombian beans and 9 lb of Venezuelan beans.

EXAMPLE 3   A 20% alcohol solution is mixed with a 30% alcohol solution to obtain 25 gal of a 24% solution. How many gal of each are needed?

Solution
Let l = the number of gal of the 20% solution.
Let h = the number of gal of the 30% solution.

$$\underset{l}{\underset{\text{of 20\% solution}}{\text{no. of gal}}} + \underset{h}{\underset{\text{of 30\% solution}}{\text{no. of gal}}} = 25$$

$$l + h = 25$$

$$\underset{0.20\,l}{\underset{\text{20\% solution}}{\text{alcohol in}}} + \underset{0.30h}{\underset{\text{30\% solution}}{\text{alcohol in}}} = \underset{0.24(25)}{\underset{\text{24\% solution}}{\text{alcohol in}}}$$

Solve the system.

$$l + h = 25 \qquad (1)$$
$$0.20l + 0.30h = 0.24(25) \qquad (2)$$

Multiply (2) by 100.
$$20l + 30h = 600 \qquad (3)$$
Multiply (1) by -20.
$$-20l - 20h = -500 \qquad (4)$$

Add equations (3) and (4).
$$10h = 100$$
$$h = 10$$

Substitute 10 for h in (1).
$$l + 10 = 25$$
$$l = 15$$

Thus, 15 gal of the 20% solution and 10 gal of the 30% solution are needed. The check is left for you.

TRY THIS
2. A 36% salt solution is mixed with a 42% salt solution to obtain 21 gallons of a 40% solution. How many gallons of each are needed?

Classroom Exercises

Express the total value in cents. (Exercises 1–6)

1. q quarters and d dimes
2. n nickels and q quarters
3. b dollars and d dimes
4. n nickels and k dollars
5. c tickets at $1.75 each and r tickets at $3.00 each
6. r lb of oranges at 45¢/lb and q lb of grapefruit at 49¢/lb
7. Sarah has $2.30 in quarters and dimes. She has 5 fewer dimes than quarters. How many coins of each type does she have?
8. A cash register contains 15 coins in dimes and nickels. The total value is $1.25. How many coins of each type are there?

Written Exercises

Solve.

1. José has 6 more dimes than quarters. He has $1.65 total. How many coins of each type does he have?
2. If 24 coins in half-dollars and dimes are worth $3.60, how many coins of each type are there?

3. A box of walnuts mixed with pecans costs $15.75. Walnuts cost $3.75/lb and pecans cost $4.50/lb. The number of pounds of walnuts is 3 times the number of pounds of pecans. How many pounds of each type are there?

4. Heidi sold 56 tickets to a play and collected $215.00. Adult tickets cost $4.50 each and student tickets cost $3.50 each. How many tickets of each kind did she sell?

5. A 10% salt solution is mixed with an 18% salt solution to obtain 32 oz of a 15% solution. How many ounces of each are needed?

6. A 15% acid solution is mixed with a 25% acid solution to obtain 20 gallons of a 21% acid solution. How many gallons of each are needed?

7. Ed has 95¢ in dimes and nickels. The total number of coins is 1 more than twice the number of dimes. How many coins of each type are there?

8. Angelo has $1.90 in dimes and nickels. If he has 4 fewer nickels than 5 times the number of dimes, how many dimes does he have?

9. Milk that is 2% butterfat is mixed with milk that is 4% butterfat to make 10 gallons that is 3.25% butterfat. How many gallons of each type are needed?

10. Thirty quarts of a 24% iodine solution were mixed with a 52% solution to make a 40% iodine solution. How many quarts of the 52% solution were needed?

11. Ms. Garcia wants to sell a box of fruit that contains cherries and plums for $19.20. The cherries sell for $2.40/kg. The plums sell for $3.60/kg. The total number of kilograms of fruit is 3 kg more than twice the number of kilograms of plums. How many kilograms of each type of fruit are in the box?

12. A pharmacist wants to add water to a solution that contains 80% medicine. She wants to obtain 12 oz of a solution that is 20% medicine. How much water and how much of the 80% solution should she use?

13. Brine is a solution of salt and water. If a tub contains 50 lb of a 5% salt solution of brine, how much water must evaporate to change it to an 8% solution?

14. How many liters of water must be evaporated from 60 liters of a 12% acid solution to make it a 36% acid solution?

15. How many liters of a 72% alcohol solution must be added to 15 liters of an 18% solution to obtain a 25% alcohol solution?

Mixed Review

Solve for x.   *3.4, 5.6, 5.7, 9.1, 9.3*

1. $-14 + 3x = 6 + 2x - 5$

2. $4x + 2a = b$

3. $3|x + 2| = 12$

4. $|x - 5| < -4$

5. $\dfrac{14}{x^2 + 7x - 18} = \dfrac{x + 5}{x + 9} + \dfrac{4}{x - 2}$

Give the slope and the *y*-intercept of the line with the given equation.   *11.3*

6. $y = 4x - 2$

7. $y = x$

8. $2x - 4y = 7$

12.9 Problem Solving: Motion Problems

| Objective | To solve motion problems using systems of equations |

Problems related to distance, rate, and time are based on the formula $d = rt$. It is often helpful to draw a diagram and organize the data in a chart before writing the equations.

EXAMPLE 1 A freight train left Pennsylvania Station traveling at 35 mi/h. Two hours later, a high-speed train left Pennsylvania Station on parallel tracks traveling 55 mi/h. In how many hours after the slow train starts will the two trains meet?

Solution Let t = time (hours) for the slow train and
$t - 2$ = time for the fast train.
Let d = distance (miles) each train travels before they meet.

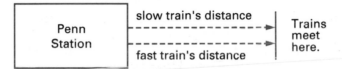

distance	= rate	× time
Slow train	d	35	t
Fast train	d	55	$t - 2$

$$d = 35t \qquad (1)$$
$$d = 55(t - 2) \qquad (2)$$

Substitute $35t$ for d in (2).

$$35t = 55(t - 2)$$
$$35t = 55t - 110$$
$$-20t = -110$$
$$t = 5\tfrac{1}{2}$$
$$\text{and } t - 2 = 3\tfrac{1}{2}$$

Check Is the distance traveled at 35 mi/h for $5\tfrac{1}{2}$ h the same as the distance traveled at 55 mi/h for $3\tfrac{1}{2}$ h? Yes, since
$$35\left(\tfrac{11}{2}\right) = 55\left(\tfrac{7}{2}\right) = \tfrac{385}{2}, \text{ or } 192\tfrac{1}{2} \text{ mi.}$$

Thus, the trains will meet $5\tfrac{1}{2}$ h after the slow train starts.

EXAMPLE 2   The distance between Chicago and New York is 735 mi. A plane left Chicago flying with the wind and landed in New York in 1 h 45 min. Then the plane left New York flying against the same wind, and landed in Chicago after 2 h. Find the rate of the plane in calm air and the rate of the wind.

Solution   Let w = rate of wind.   Let r = rate of plane in calm air.
Then $r + w$ = rate of the plane with the wind and
       $r - w$ = rate of the plane against the wind.

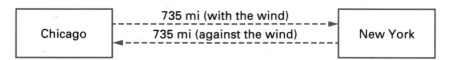

	distance =	rate	×	time	
with wind	735	$r + w$		$1\frac{3}{4}$	⟵ 1 h 45 min
against wind	735	$r - w$		2	

Solve the system.

$$735 = (r + w) \cdot \frac{7}{4} \quad (1)$$
$$735 = (r - w) \cdot 2 \quad (2)$$

Multiply each side of (1) by $\frac{4}{7}$.

$$\frac{4}{7} \cdot 735 = r + w$$
$$420 = r + w \quad (3)$$

Multiply each side of (3) by 2.
Then add Equation (2).

$$840 = 2r + 2w$$
$$\underline{735 = 2r - 2w \quad (2)}$$
$$1{,}575 = 4r$$
$$393\frac{3}{4} = r$$

Substitute $393\frac{3}{4}$ for r in (3).

$$420 = 393\frac{3}{4} + w$$
$$26\frac{1}{4} = w$$

Thus, the rate of the plane in calm air is $393\frac{3}{4}$ mi/h and the rate of the wind is $26\frac{1}{4}$ mi/h. The check is left for you.

TRY THIS   A car left Dodge City traveling at 50 mi/h. One hour 30 min later, another car left Dodge City using the same highway traveling at 60 mi/h. In how many hours after the slow car starts will the two cars meet?

Classroom Exercises

Complete the table. All rates are in miles per hour.

	Rate of boat in still water	Rate of current	Rate of boat upstream	Rate of boat downstream
1.	10	2		
2.	25	3		
3.	14		13	
4.		5	14	
5.		6		24
6.			25	35
7.	r	c		

8. On a bike hike, Jim rode his bike at a rate of 5 mi/h. Barry followed Jim, leaving from the same place 1 hour later. He rode at a rate of 8 mi/h. In how many hours did Barry catch up with Jim?

Written Exercises

Solve each problem.

1. A freight train left Columbus traveling 40 mi/h. Two hours later a passenger train left the same station traveling 50 mi/h on a parallel track. How many hours after the freight train left will the trains meet?

2. A car left Detroit traveling 45 mi/h. A second car left from the same place $1\frac{1}{2}$ h later. It traveled on the same road and met the first car after driving $4\frac{1}{2}$ h. Find the rate of the second car.

3. A motorboat went 12 mi upstream in 40 min. It made the return trip downstream with the same current in 15 min. Find the rate of the boat in still water.

4. A rowing team rowed their boat 12 mi upstream in $1\frac{3}{4}$ h. They made the return trip downstream with the same current in 1 h. Find the rate of the current.

5. A pilot flew a distance of 960 mi in 8 h against the wind. On the return trip he made the flight in 6 h with the same wind behind him. What was the rate of the plane in still air?

6. A carrier pigeon flew against the wind for 1 h to deliver a message. It made the return trip with the same wind in 45 min. The trip was 6 mi each way. Find the rate of the pigeon in still air and the rate of the wind.

7. Jean and José started bicycling from the same spot in the same direction. Jean rode at a rate of 12 mi/h. José rode at a rate of 10 mi/h. After how many hours will they be 10 mi apart?

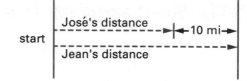

8. Mr. Shan drove from his home to Springfield at 45 mi/h. On the return trip, he averaged 55 mi/h. He traveled a total of 6 h. How far is his home from Springfield?

9. At what rate did a car travel to catch up with a motorcycle in 6 h if the motorcycle traveled at 30 mi/h and left 3 h before the car?

10. The current of the Wahakee River runs 2 mi/h. It took Marcia and Jessie 45 min to paddle upstream and 30 min to come back with the current. What was their rate of paddling in still water?

11. A fish swam upstream for 1 h and then returned downstream with the current. It took only 40 min to return to its starting point. The rate of the current is 2 mi/h. How far did the fish travel each way?

12. The rate of a boat in still water is 12 mi/h. The boat can travel 18 mi upstream in the same time that it can travel 24 mi downstream. Find the rate of the current.

13. A plane flew 900 mi. If it had flown 75 mi/h faster, the plane could have traveled 1,350 mi in the same time. Find the speed of the plane during the 900-mile trip.

14. A bus traveled 180 mi. If weather conditions had been better, it could have driven 5 mi/h faster and completed the trip in 30 min less time. How fast did the bus travel?

15. Let r be the rate of a boat in still water and c be the rate of the current. Show that the rate of the boat going downstream is equal to the rate of the boat going upstream plus twice the rate of the current.

Mixed Review

Graph the solution set.   *5.2, 5.3, 5.7*

1. $2y - 15 > -9$

2. $x > -3$ *and* $x \leq 1$

3. $|y - 4| \geq 3$

Multiply.   *6.8, 6.9, 6.10*

4. $3a(2a^2 + 6a + 5)$

5. $(x + 5)(x - 9)$

6. $(y + 11)^2$

7. Use the formula $A = 4s^2$ to find A for $s = 7$.   *1.4*

8. Jack's hourly wage jumped from $5 to $7. What was the percent increase in his wage?   *4.7*

9. Separate 80 people into two groups such that one group is 4 times as large as the other.   *4.2*

12.10 Systems of Inequalities

Objective	To solve systems of inequalities by graphing

In Chapter 11 you graphed linear inequalities such as $y > x - 1$. In this lesson you will graph *systems* of linear inequalities.

The solution set of $y > x - 1$ consists of the coordinates of every point in the shaded region above the line $y = x - 1$.

To solve a system of inequalities such as

$$y > x - 1$$
$$3x + 2y < 6$$

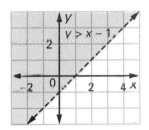

by graphing, locate all points whose coordinates satisfy *both* inequalities. Graph both inequalities in the same coordinate plane. The intersection of the two regions will contain all points whose coordinates are solutions of the system.

EXAMPLE 1 Solve the system $\begin{array}{l} y > x - 1 \\ 3x + 2y \le 6 \end{array}$ by graphing.

Solution Graph the boundary for each half-plane by the slope-intercept method.

Graph $y = x - 1$ with a dashed line since the boundary is not included. Shade the open half-plane above the line.

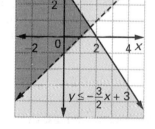

$3x + 2y \le 6$, or $y \le -\frac{3}{2}x + 3$

Graph $y = -\frac{3}{2}x + 3$ with a solid line since the boundary is included. Shade the closed half-plane *below* the line.

To check, choose a point inside the double-shaded region. Try $(0, 0)$.

$y > x - 1$	$3x + 2y \le 6$
$0 \overset{?}{>} 0 - 1$	$3 \cdot 0 + 2 \cdot 0 \overset{?}{\le} 6$
$0 \overset{?}{>} -1$	$0 + 0 \overset{?}{\le} 6$
$0 > -1$ True	$0 \le 6$ True

Thus, the double-shaded region contains all points whose coordinates are the solutions of the system. There are infinitely many solutions.

EXAMPLE 2   Solve the system $\begin{array}{l} 2x > 4 - y \\ y < -2x - 1 \end{array}$ by graphing.

Solution   Find the equation of the boundary line of
$2x > 4 - y$ in slope-intercept form. Solve for y.

$$2x > 4 - y$$
$$2x + y > 4$$
$$y > -2x + 4 \quad \longleftarrow \text{boundary: } y = -2x + 4$$

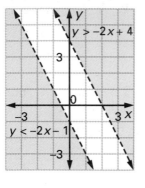

The equations of the boundaries of the half-
planes are $y = -2x - 1$ and $y = -2x + 4$.
Use dashed lines for both boundaries. The regions do not intersect.
Thus, the system has no solution.

TRY THIS   Solve each system by graphing.

1. $y \leq x + 4$
   $3y - 2x > 6$

2. $3y + 9x \leq 6$
   $y + 3 \geq \frac{1}{3}x$

In Example 2, note that if the inequality signs were reversed, the resulting system would have infinitely many solutions. They would be the
coordinates of points lying between the two parallel lines.

EXAMPLE 3
$$\begin{array}{l} x > -3 \end{array}$$
Solve the system $y \leq 2$ by graphing.
$$y \geq 2x - 1$$

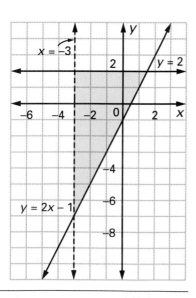

Plan   Graph each inequality. Locate the region
that is the intersection of all three graphs.

Solution   When each inequality is graphed, the
intersection of the three graphs is the triangular region shown at the right.

To check, show that the coordinates of a
point in the triangular region satisfy all
three inequalities. The check is left for
you. Try $(0, 0)$.

TRY THIS   3.   Solve the system consisting of these three inequalities.

   a. $x + y \geq 2$ b. $2x - y \leq 3$ c. $y > 0$

Classroom Exercises

To graph each inequality, would you use a dashed line or a solid line?
Would you shade the region above or below the line?

1. $y > x - 6$

2. $y \leq -2x + 7$

3. $y \geq -x + 5$

4. $2x + y < -8$

5. $3x - y > -2$

6. $4x + 3y \leq 1$

Tell whether or not the given coordinates are a solution of the system
of inequalities.

7. $(4,3)$
$y < x + 1$
$y > -x + 5$

8. $(-1,-6)$
$y \leq 2x - 4$
$y > -x + 2$

9. $(2,-3)$
$3x - 2y \geq 12$
$4x + 2y \leq 2$

Written Exercises

Solve by graphing.

1. $y \geq -5$
$x > 2$

2. $y < 4$
$x \geq -3$

3. $y > 3$
$y \leq -2$

4. $x \leq 4$
$x \geq -1$

5. $y < x + 2$
$x \geq -1$

6. $y > 3x + 2$
$y \leq 3x - 1$

7. $y > -2x - 3$
$y < -2x + 4$

8. $2x + y < 3$
$3y > -6x - 3$

9. $3x - 2y < 2$
$3x + 2y > -2$

10. $y - 2x > -3$
$x - 3y < 9$

11. $y - x < 0$
$y \geq 2x - 3$

12. $x > y + 1$
$2x + y \geq -4$

Solve by graphing.

13. $y \leq 2$
$x < 2$
$y > -1$

14. $x \geq -2$
$y \geq 3$
$x < 1$

15. $x \geq 1$
$y < -2$
$x - 2y \leq 8$

16. $y < 4$
$x \geq 0$
$x + y > 2$

17. $y \geq 0$
$x + 4y < 8$
$3x - 2y > -4$

18. $y - 2x > 1$
$x + y - 6 < 0$
$y > -2$

19. $x \geq -3$
$x < 4$
$y < -1$
$y \geq -5$

20. $x \leq 3$
$x < -2$
$y \leq 7$
$y > -1$

21. $x > -1$
$x \leq 2$
$y > 4$
$y \leq -3$

22. $|x| > 3$
$|x| \leq 5$

23. $|y| \geq 2$
$|y| < 6$

24. $|x| \leq 4$
$|y| \leq 2$

Mixed Review

1. Evaluate $3x^4$ for $x = -2$. *2.6*

2. Add $-7x^2yz + 10x^2yz$. *6.6*

3. Simplify $(2a^2b^3)^4$. *6.2*

4. Multiply $(3y - 8)(y + 1)$. *6.9*

5. Factor $2x^2 - 3x - 5$. *7.4*

6. Solve $x^2 - 11x + 28 = 0$. *7.7*

A technique called *linear programming* is used to solve a variety of problems in business, industry, and government. The problems involve decisions that will maximize or minimize certain quantities, such as profit. Linear inequalities are used to represent given conditions, or *constraints*.

Example

A company produces two kinds of special handmade bolts: zero-bolts and one-bolts. Boltmaker *A* takes 2 min to make a zero-bolt and 4 min to make a one-bolt. Boltmaker *B* takes 3 min to make a zero-bolt and 1 min to make a one-bolt. Working a maximum of 3 h per day, each boltmaker makes the same number of zero-bolts and the same number of one-bolts. The profit is \$3 on each zero-bolt and \$4 on each one-bolt. How many of each type should be made for a maximum daily profit?

Solution

1. Use two variables to represent the data.

Let x = the total number of zero-bolts produced each day.
Let y = the total number of one-bolts produced each day.

Then the daily profit in dollars is $3x + 4y$.

2. Write a system of inequalities to represent the constraints.

THINK: Each boltmaker makes $\frac{1}{2}$ of the zero-bolts and
$\frac{1}{2}$ of the one-bolts produced each day. $\longrightarrow \frac{1}{2}x + \frac{1}{2}y$

Each boltmaker works a maximum of 3 hours, or 180 minutes per day.

Time Boltmaker *A* works $\longrightarrow$ $2 \cdot \frac{1}{2}x + 4 \cdot \frac{1}{2}y \leq 180$, or $x + 2y \leq 180$

Time Boltmaker *B* works $\longrightarrow$ $3 \cdot \frac{1}{2}x + 1 \cdot \frac{1}{2}y \leq 180$, or $3x + y \leq 360$

The number of bolts made cannot be negative. $\longrightarrow$ $x \geq 0, y \geq 0$

3. Graph the system of inequalities. The shaded region is the graph of the solution set. Each vertex is found by solving a system of equations.

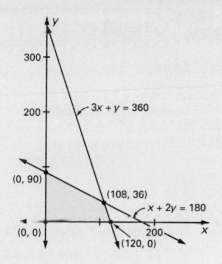

System	Solution (vertex)
$x = 0$ $y = 0$	$(0,0)$
$x + 2y = 180$ $x = 0$	$(0,90)$
$3x + y = 360$ $y = 0$	$(120,0)$
$x + 2y = 180$ $3x + y = 360$	$(108,36)$

4. Since $3x + 4y$ represents the profit, find the ordered pair for which $3x + 4y$ has a maximum value. It can be proved that a maximum or minimum value of such an expression occurs at a vertex.

Vertex	$(0,0)$	$(0,90)$	$(120,0)$	$(108,36)$
$3x + 4y$	$3 \cdot 0 + 4 \cdot 0$	$3 \cdot 0 + 4 \cdot 90$	$3 \cdot 120 + 4 \cdot 0$	$3 \cdot 108 + 4 \cdot 36$
Value	0	360	360	468 (maximum)

Thus, each day the bolt company should make 108 zero-bolts and 36 one-bolts. The maximum profit is $468 a day.

EXERCISES

Use the following system of inequalities for Exercises 1–3.
$$x \geq 0, \ y \geq 0, \ x \leq 5, \ 5y + 3x \leq 30$$

1. Graph the system of inequalities and shade the solution set.

2. Find the maximum and the minimum value of $x + 5y$.

3. Find the maximum and the minimum value of $x - y$.

4. The Econo-Company manufactures two sizes of TV screens, size A and size B. The screens are made by two machines. The old machine makes a size-A in 4 min and size-B in 1 min. The new machine makes a size-A in 2 min and a size-B in 8 min. Each machine makes the same number of size-A screens and the same number of size-B screens and operates, at most, 2 h per day. If the profit is $2 on a size-A and $3 on a size-B, how many of each size should be made per day to make the maximum profit?

Chapter 12 Review

Key Terms

addition method   (p. 460)
linear combination method   (p. 465)
multiplication with addition method   (p. 464)
substitution method   (p. 452)
system of linear equations   (p. 445)
tens digit   (p. 468)
units digit   (p. 468)

Key Ideas and Review Exercises

12.1   To solve a system of two linear equations by graphing, graph both equations in the same coordinate plane. If the lines intersect in a point, the coordinates of the point are the solution.

Solve by graphing.

1. $2x - y = -5$
  $y = -x + 2$

2. $y = 2x - 1$
  $x - 3y = -7$

3. $2x + 3y = 5$
  $x - 2y = 6$

12.2   To solve a system of linear equations using the substitution method, solve one equation for one of the variables. Substitute the value for that variable in the other equation. Solve the equation. Find the value of the second variable by substituting the value of the first variable in either equation of the system and then solve the equation.

Solve by using the substitution method.

4. $y = 2x + 1$
  $3x - y = 7$

5. $3x - 4y = 19$
  $x + y = 4$

6. $5x - 3y = 1$
  $x + y = 1$

12.3   To solve word problems using systems of equations:

  1. Choose two variables to represent two unknowns.

  2. Use two facts from the problem to write two equations with the two variables.

  3. Solve the resulting system. Check in the original problem.

Solve each problem using two equations and two variables.

7. The length of a rectangle is 6 m more than 3 times the width. The perimeter is 44 m. Find the length and the width.

8. Barbara's age is 5 years less than her brother's age. If her age is increased by 3 times her brother's age, the result is 51 years. Find each of their ages.

To solve a system of linear equations using addition, the equations must contain opposite terms in one variable. If necessary, multiply one or both equations by a number to obtain this result. Add the equations to eliminate the variable. Then proceed as in the substitution method.

Solve using the addition method. Use multiplication first, if necessary.

9. $3x + 4y = 11$
$-3x + y = -16$

10. $x - 3y = 1$
$2x + 6y = 14$

11. $5x - 3y = 8$
$2x = 7y + 9$

12. Write a description of two algebraic methods of solving the system: $\dfrac{2x + 3y = 16}{x - y = 3}$.

12.6,
12.7,
12.8,
12.9 To solve special types of word problems, choose variables as follows:

- For two-digit numbers, let t = the tens digit, u = the units digit, and $10t + u$ = the number. ($10u + t$ = the number with the digits reversed)

- For age problems, choose variables to represent the present ages.

- For coin problems, represent both the number and value of each coin. For example, if q = the number of quarters and d = the number of dimes, then $25q$ and $10d$ are the values of the quarters and dimes.

- For mixture problems, represent the total amount of each solution and the amount of a particular ingredient in each solution.

- For motion problems, draw a diagram to represent distance, rate, and time in a chart. Use the equation $d = rt$.

13. Jim is 6 years older than Pete. Two years ago, Jim was twice as old as Pete. How old is each now?

14. Tad has 6 more quarters than dimes. He has $3.25 total. How many coins of each type does he have?

15. The sum of the digits of a two-digit number is 9. If the digits are reversed, the new number is 27 less than the original number. Find the original number.

16. Mr. and Mrs. Lee drove home from Canton, he at 40 mi/h and she at 50 mi/h. If she left 1 h after he did, and they reached home at the same time, how far did they drive?

17. A butterfly flew 4 mi with the wind in 1 h. It returned against the same wind in 1 h 15 min. Find the rate of the wind.

18. Milk that is 5% butterfat is mixed with milk that is 2% butterfat. How much of each is needed to obtain 60 gallons that is 3% butterfat?

12.10 To solve a system of inequalities by graphing, graph the inequalities in the same coordinate plane. The intersection of the graphs is the set of points whose coordinates are the solution.

19. Solve the system $\dfrac{y > x + 1}{y < -x - 7}$ by graphing.

1. Solve the system $\begin{array}{l} 2x + y = 5 \\ y = 4x - 1 \end{array}$ by graphing.

Solve using the substitution method.

2. $y = 3x + 1$
$-2x + 3y = 10$

3. $2(y - 8) + 3x = 0$
$7x = 19 - y$

Solve using the addition method. Use multiplication first if necessary.

4. $3x - 2y = 17$
$5x + 2y = 23$

5. $-7c + 2d = -5$
$-9c + 4d = -7$

Solve by graphing.

6. $y < x + 4$
$2x + y \geq -2$

7. $x \geq 2$
$y < 2$
$x - 2y \leq 6$

Solve each problem using two equations and two variables.

8. The sum of the digits of a two-digit number is 15. If the digits are reversed, the new number is 27 less than the original number. Find the original number.

9. A parking meter contains \$3.20 in nickels and quarters. There are 3 times as many nickels as quarters. How many coins of each type are in the parking meter?

10. Paul is three times as old as Kate. Fourteen years from now, Paul will be twice as old as Kate. How old is each now?

11. A robin flew 3 mi against the wind in 40 min. It returned the same distance, flying with the same wind in 30 min. Find the rate of the wind.

12. A freight train left Paddington Station traveling 35 mi/h. A passenger train left 2 h later on parallel tracks at 40 mi/h. How far from the station will the passenger train meet the freight train?

13. A science teacher wants to obtain 6.25 qt of a 35% acid solution by mixing a 25% acid solution with a 75% acid solution. How much of each type of solution should be in the mixture?

Solve using the most convenient method.

14. $\dfrac{x}{3} - \dfrac{y}{2} = \dfrac{4}{3}$
$3x - 7y = 7$

15. $\dfrac{4}{3}x - y = \dfrac{5}{3}$
$\dfrac{-2x + 9y + 1}{6} = 0$

College Prep Test

In each item, you are to compare the quantity in Column 1 with the quantity in Column 2. Write the letter of the correct answer from the following choices.

    A—The quantity in Column 1 is greater than the quantity in Column 2.
    B—The quantity in Column 2 is greater than the quantity in Column 1.
    C—The quantity in Column 1 is equal to the quantity in Column 2.
    D—The relationship cannot be determined from the given information.

NOTE: Information centered over both columns refers to one or both of the quantities to be compared.

Column 1	Column 2
1. $x - 5$ and $y = 7$	
$2x - y$	$2y - x$
2. $x < 0$	
$x^3 - 3$	1
3. $a^2 - b^2$	$(a + b)(a - b)$
4. $\lvert x \rvert$	$\lvert x - 2 \rvert$
5. $y = -x$	
x	y
6. area of circle A	half the area of circle B

Column 1	Column 2
7. $x > 0$ and $y > 0$	
$2x + 3y$	$2x - 3y$

Column 1	Column 2
8. x	y
$2x - y = 4$	
$3x + y = 6$	
9. slope of line $y = -x + 1$	slope of line $y = -2x - 2$
10. $3(4x - y)$	$-3(y - 4x)$
11. x	y
$0 < x < 7$	
$0 < y < 5$	
12. $3y - x$	$3x - y$
$2x + 9y = 24$	
$5y = 2x + 4$	
13. $y \neq 0$	
$\dfrac{x + y}{y}$	$\dfrac{x}{y} + 1$

1. Evaluate $2y^2 - 4y - 1$ for $y = 3$. **1.3**

2. Simplify $\dfrac{3 + 5}{7 - 2}$. **1.2**

3. Which property is illustrated? **1.6**
   $7(4x + 1) = 7 \cdot 4x + 7 \cdot 1$

4. Simplify $8 + 2(4x - 3) + x$. **1.7**

5. Evaluate $4c^3 - 7c$ for $c = -2$. **2.8**

6. Simplify: **2.9**
   $-3y + 2x - 7y + 4 - x$

7. Simplify: **2.10**
   $7(8 - x) - 2(3x + 4)$

Solve.

8. $8 = r + 17$ **3.1**

9. $-4 = \frac{2}{3}c$ **3.2**

10. $7x + 4 - 2x = 19$ **3.3**

11. $-2(7y + 9) = 4(3 - y)$ **3.5**

12. $\frac{1}{2}y - 2 = \frac{3}{5}y$ **4.5**

13. $0.5x + 7.2 = -0.7x$ **4.6**

14. $-3x + 2 \le -13$ **5.2**

15. $|x - 3| = 9$ **5.6**

Graph the solution set.

16. $|x - 2| < 2$ **5.7**

17. $x < 6 \text{ and } x \ge -2$ **5.4**

Simplify. (Exercises 18–21)

18. $-\frac{2}{3}ab^2(3ab^3)$ **6.1**

19. $(-2x^2yz^3)^3$ **6.2**

20. $\dfrac{-6a^2b^3c}{3abc^4}$ **6.3**

21. $x^2 - 8x^3 + 3 - x - x^2 + 2x^3 - 4$ **6.6**

22. Subtract $a^2 - a + 2$ from $3a^2 - a - 5$. **6.7**

23. Multiply $(x + 5)(x^2 + 2x + 1)$. **6.9**

24. Multiply $(3b + 4c)(3b - 4c)$. **6.10**

Factor completely. (Exercises 25–27)

25. $y^2 - 4y - 21$ **7.3**

26. $4x^2 - 20x + 25$ **7.5**

27. $4x^3 - 12x^2 + 8x$ **7.6**

28. Solve $y^2 + 6y - 16 = 0$. **7.7**

Simplify. (Exercises 29–31)

29. $\dfrac{9 - y^2}{y^2 - 5y - 24}$ **8.2**

30. $\dfrac{x - 7}{x} \div \dfrac{x^2 - 3x - 28}{x^2 + 4x}$ **8.4**

31. $3x - 3 + \dfrac{2}{x + 1}$ **8.7**

32. Divide $(8m^3 - 4m + 12)$ by $(2m - 1)$. **8.8**

Solve for x. (Exercises 33–35)

33. $\frac{1}{3} - \frac{2}{x} = \frac{5}{2x}$ **9.1**

34. $\dfrac{x - 1}{5} = \dfrac{x + 2}{3}$ **9.2**

35. $px - 7 = 5a$ **9.3**

36. Give the domain and the range of the relation: $\{(2, -1), (2, 1), (3, -2), (1, 3)\}$. Is the relation a function? **10.2**

37. If $f(x) = 4x^2 - x$, find $f(-1)$. **10.3**

38. Graph $x - 2y = 6$. **10.5**

39. Find the slope of the line determined by $C(4, -3)$ and $D(2, 1)$. **11.1**

40. Write an equation for the line passing through $R(1, -3)$ and having a slope of -2. **11.2**

41. Solve: $2x - 4y = 8$
    $y = 2x + 1$ **12.2**

42. Solve: $x - y = 7$
    $3x + 2y = 11$.   **12.5**

43. The perimeter of a rectangle is 56 m. The width is 2 m less than the length. Find the length and width.   **4.4**

44. One number is 8 more than 3 times the other. If the larger is decreased by twice the smaller, the result is 10. Find the numbers.   **4.2**

45. The formula $l_1w_1 = l_2w_2$ can be used to balance two weights, w_1 and w_2, on a seesaw. Their distances from the fulcrum are l_1 and l_2, respectively. If a 120-lb boy sits on a seesaw 5 ft from the fulcrum, how far from the fulcrum must a 100-lb boy sit to balance the seesaw?   **3.6**

46. The first side of a triangle is 4 ft shorter than twice the second side. The third side is 3 times as long as the first side. Represent the three lengths in terms of one variable.   **4.1**

47. 18 is what percent of 24?   **4.7**

48. What is 42% of 76?

49. The price of a tape increased from $8 to $9. What was the percent increase in the price?

50. How much simple interest is earned when $1,500 is invested at 6.5% for 3 years?

51. The selling price of a microwave oven is $162. The profit is 80% of the cost. Find the cost.   **4.8**

52. A freight elevator can carry 2,500 lb safely. A shipping crate weighs 80 lb. At most, how many crates can be safely carried on the elevator?   **5.5**

53. The area of a rectangle is 65 ft². The length is 2 ft less than 3 times the width. Find the length and the width.   **7.9**

54. A computer can execute an instruction in an average of 2 microseconds (1 microsecond = 1 millionth of a second). A certain program requires 6,372 instructions. How many seconds will it take the program to run? Round your answer to two digits. Then give your answer in scientific notation.   **6.5**

55. The degree measures of the two smaller angles of a right triangle are in a ratio of 2:3. Find the measure of each angle of the triangle.   **9.2**

56. It took Jane the same time to drive 270 mi as it took Jake to drive 300 mi. Jane's speed was 5 mi/h slower than Jake's speed. How fast did each drive?   **9.4**

57. Working together, Mrs. Kalb and her daughter can paint a room in 4 h. It takes Mrs. Kalb twice as long as it takes her daughter to do it alone. How long would it take each to do it alone?   **9.5**

58. The current in an electrical circuit varies inversely as the resistance. When the current is 50 amps, the resistance is 32 ohms. Find the current when the resistance is 20 ohms.   **10.7**

13 RADICALS

Studio photographers may work in areas such as the fashion, publishing, and advertising industries. They make precise adjustments to camera lenses and measure the light carefully with a meter to produce imaginative and dramatic effects.

13.1 Rational Numbers and Irrational Numbers

Objectives

To express rational numbers as decimals
To write repeating or terminating decimals in fractional form
To determine whether a decimal is a rational or an irrational number
To explain how to write a repeating decimal in fractional form

On a number line, each point corresponds to some *real* number. Some of these numbers are *rational* numbers.

Numbers such as -2, $-1\frac{3}{4}$, -1, 0, $\frac{1}{2}$, $\frac{7}{8}$, and 1 are rational numbers.

Definition

A **rational number** is a real number that can be expressed in the form $\frac{a}{b}$, where a and b are integers and $b \neq 0$.

Note that every integer a is a rational number because $a = \frac{a}{1}$.

EXAMPLE 1   Show that each number is a rational number.

a. 3   b. 0   c. $-6\frac{5}{8}$ d. -5 e. 1.67

Solutions   a. $3 = \frac{3}{1}$ b. $0 = \frac{0}{1}$ c. $-6\frac{5}{8} = \frac{-53}{8}$ d. $-5 = \frac{-5}{1}$ e. $1.67 = \frac{167}{100}$

TRY THIS   Show that each number is a rational number.

1. 2.4   2. -1 3. $2\frac{1}{5}$ 4. $-1\frac{1}{4}$ 5. 4

Rational numbers can be expressed as decimals. Some rational numbers can be expressed as *terminating decimals*. For example, $\frac{1}{2} = 0.5$ and $\frac{5}{8} = 0.625$. Others can be expressed as *repeating decimals*. For example, $\frac{2}{3} = 0.666 \cdots = 0.\overline{6}$ and $\frac{5}{11} = 0.4545 \cdots = 0.\overline{45}$. The bars mean that 6 and 45 repeat indefinitely.

EXAMPLE 2   Express each rational number as a decimal. Then classify the decimal as either terminating or repeating.

    a. $\frac{3}{4}$ **b.** $-\frac{5}{8}$ **c.** $\frac{7}{9}$ **d.** $-1\frac{5}{11}$

Plan   Divide the numerator of each fraction by the denominator.

Solutions   **a.** $\frac{3}{4}$ **b.** $-\frac{5}{8}$ **c.** $\frac{7}{9}$ **d.** $-1\frac{5}{11}$

$$\begin{array}{c} 0.75 \\ 4\overline{)3.00} \end{array} \qquad \begin{array}{c} 0.625 \\ 8\overline{)5.000} \end{array} \qquad \begin{array}{c} 0.777\ldots \\ 9\overline{)7.000} \end{array} \qquad \begin{array}{c} 0.4545\ldots \\ 11\overline{)5.0000} \end{array}$$

$$\frac{3}{4} = 0.75 \qquad -\frac{5}{8} = -0.625 \qquad \frac{7}{9} = 0.\overline{7} \qquad -1\frac{5}{11} = -1.\overline{45}$$

     terminating   terminating   repeating   repeating

EXAMPLE 3   For each repeating decimal, write a fraction $\frac{a}{b}$, where a and b are integers.

    a. $0.\overline{5}$ **b.** $3.7\overline{2}$

Plan   Let $n =$ the decimal. Multiply each side of the equation by 10^1, or 10, since exactly one digit repeats. Subtract the first equation from the second.

Solutions   **a.**   Let $n = 0.555\ldots$ **b.**   Let $n = 3.7222\ldots$

$$\begin{array}{rl} 10n &= 5.555\ldots \\ -\quad n &= 0.555\ldots \\ \hline 9n &= 5.000\ldots \\ n &= \frac{5}{9} \end{array} \qquad\text{Multiply by 10}\longrightarrow \qquad \begin{array}{rl} 10n &= 37.222\ \ldots \\ -\quad n &= 3.722\ \ldots \\ \hline 9n &= 33.5 \\ 90n &= 335 \\ n &= \frac{335}{90},\text{ or } \frac{67}{18} \end{array}$$

to eliminate the decimal.

Thus, $0.\overline{5} = \frac{5}{9}$.   Thus, $3.7\overline{2} = \frac{67}{18}$.

TRY THIS   **6.** Write $\frac{3}{7}$ and $-2\frac{1}{5}$ as decimals.

                 7. Write $0.0\overline{9}$ and $-2.\overline{3}$ as fractions.

When a repeating decimal contains a block of two or more repeating digits, the process for finding the corresponding fraction is similar. However, if a is the number of repeating digits, multiply by 10^a in order to obtain a terminating decimal after the subtraction.

EXAMPLE 4   Write a fraction $\frac{a}{b}$, where a and b are integers, for the repeating decimal $12.\overline{47}$.

Solution   Multiply each side of $n = 12.47\overline{47}$ by 10^2, or 100, since two digits repeat.

$$\begin{array}{r} 100n = 1{,}247.47\overline{47} \\ -\quad n = \phantom{1{,}24}12.47\overline{47} \\ \hline 99n = 1{,}235 \\ n = \dfrac{1{,}235}{99} \end{array}$$

Thus, $12.\overline{47} = \frac{1{,}235}{99}$.

TRY THIS   8. Write $-0.\overline{45}$ and $4.\overline{15}$ as fractions.

There are some points on the number line that do not correspond to rational numbers. These points correspond to **irrational numbers**.

The decimals for irrational numbers are *nonterminating* and *nonrepeating*. In 2.525525552 . . . , each string of 5s has one more 5 than the preceding string. Therefore, no block of digits repeats indefinitely.

Other irrational numbers have no pattern. One such irrational number is π. To the nearest millionth, π is 3.141593. The table below shows examples of rational and irrational numbers.

Number	Rational or Irrational	Expressed as $\frac{a}{b}$ (a and b integers, b ≠ 0)
0.373373337 . . .	Irrational	Not possible
0.88888 . . .	Rational	$\frac{8}{9}$
-0.423	Rational	$-\frac{423}{1{,}000}$
0.28293031 . . .	Irrational	Not possible

If you combine the set of rational numbers and the set of irrational numbers, the result is the set of *real numbers*. In other words, a number is a real number if it is a rational number or an irrational number.

You have previously worked with the following sets of numbers.

Set of natural or counting $N = \{1, 2, 3, \cdots\}$
   numbers, N
Set of whole numbers, W $W = \{0, 1, 2, 3, \cdots\}$
Set of integers, I $I = \{\cdots,\ 3, -2, -1, 0, 1, 2, 3, \cdots\}$

If all members of a set X are also members of a set Y, then X is said to be a **subset** of Y. The diagram below shows how subsets of real numbers are related. Notice that N is a subset of W. Also, W is a subset of I.

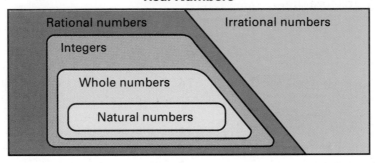

Real Numbers

Classroom Exercises

Identify each set of numbers as natural numbers, whole numbers, integers, rational numbers, irrational numbers, or real numbers.

1. the set of numbers that can be expressed as terminating or repeating decimals

2. the set of numbers that are expressed as nonterminating, nonrepeating decimals

3. the set of real numbers that are not rational

4. the set of whole numbers together with the set of negative integers

5. $\{0, 1, 2, 3, \ldots\}$

6. $\{1, 2, 3, 4, \ldots\}$

Written Exercises

Show that each number is rational by expressing it in the form $\frac{a}{b}$, where a and b are integers.

1. 1   **2.** $13\frac{2}{5}$ **3.** $-2\frac{7}{8}$ **4.** 0.7   **5.** -7 **6.** -4.53

Express each number as a decimal. Then classify the decimal as either terminating or repeating.

7. $\frac{2}{3}$ **8.** $\frac{4}{5}$ **9.** $-\frac{1}{6}$ **10.** $\frac{3}{7}$ **11.** $-2\frac{7}{9}$ **12.** $-1\frac{1}{4}$

Write a fraction $\frac{a}{b}$, where a and b are integers, for each repeating decimal.

13. $5.\overline{6}$ **14.** $15.5\overline{6}$ **15.** $4.\overline{3}$ **16.** $8.1414\ldots$

17. $0.\overline{62}$ **18.** $3.\overline{9}$ **19.** $0.7\overline{5}$ **20.** $5.8181\ldots$

21. $0.\overline{182}$ **22.** $10.\overline{351}$ **23.** $2.\overline{8642}$ **24.** $5.139139\ldots$
25. $52.\overline{2735}$ **26.** $476.\overline{438}$ **27.** $5.\overline{257}$ **28.** $15.3\overline{534}$

Express each rational number as a decimal. Then classify the decimal as either terminating or repeating.

29. $\frac{435}{333}$ **30.** $\frac{159}{99}$ **31.** $\frac{231}{1,232}$ **32.** $\frac{492}{450}$

True or false? Justify your answer. (Exercises 33–42)

33. The set of integers is a subset of the set of rational numbers.
34. Every nonterminating, nonrepeating decimal is a rational number.
35. Every irrational number is real.
36. A rational number cannot be negative.
37. Zero is a real number.
38. 0.3 is an irrational number.
39. Zero is a natural number.
40. Every real number is rational.
41. Every rational number is real.
42. Some integers are irrational.

43. Write an explanation of why every integer is a rational number.

44. Explain how to write a repeating decimal in fractional form.

45. When two repeating decimals are added, the sum is the decimal for the sum of the corresponding fractions. Give an illustration to show this. (HINT: Use $0.\overline{3}$ and $0.\overline{6}$.)

46. Describe the pattern found in the decimals for $\frac{1}{7}$, $\frac{2}{7}$, $\frac{3}{7}$, $\frac{4}{7}$, $\frac{5}{7}$, and $\frac{6}{7}$.

47. Form a decimal by using the following procedure. First, write the decimal point. Toss a coin. If "heads" comes up, write 2 at the right of the decimal point in the tenths place. Otherwise, write a different digit. Use the coin-tossing procedure to select either 2 or another digit for the hundredths place, the thousandths place, and so on, indefinitely. Is the constructed number rational or irrational? Explain your reasoning.

48. Explain how to construct an irrational number by using a pair of dice. Why would the number be irrational?

Mixed Review

Evaluate. *1.1, 1.3*

1. $x + 7.2$ for $x = 5.9$ **2.** $5.3w$ for $w = 4$
3. $x - y$ for $x = 8.1$ and $y = 4.7$ **4.** $6x^2 - x$ for $x = 5$

Simplify, if possible. If not possible, so indicate. *1.2, 6.2, 8.1, 8.2*

5. $39 - 3 \cdot 6 - 6 \cdot 2$ **6.** $\frac{2}{3}\left(\frac{3}{5} - \frac{1}{5}\right)$ **7.** $4 + (7 - 3)6$

8. $(3x^4y^2)^3$ **9.** $\frac{3x - 15}{x - 5}$ **10.** $\frac{x - 9}{9 - x^3}$

13.2 Square Roots

Objective	To find square roots of positive numbers

The inverse of squaring a number is finding its *square root*, that is, finding one of two equal factors of the number.

Since $49 = 7^2$ and $49 = (-7)^2$, the number 49 has two square roots, 7 and -7. The *principal square root* is the positive square root, which is written as $\sqrt{49}$. Therefore, $\sqrt{49} = 7$.

In general, for any real number a, a^2 is positive, and $\sqrt{a^2} = |a|$.

Definition

> The **principal square root** of a positive real number is the positive square root of the number.

The symbol $\sqrt{49}$ is called a **radical**, $\sqrt{}$ is called a **radical sign**, and the number under the radical sign is called the **radicand**. So, 49 is the radicand of $\sqrt{49}$.

Notice that $-\sqrt{49} = -7$, but $\sqrt{-49}$ is not a real number, since there is no real number whose square is -49.

EXAMPLE 1 Simplify.

a. $\sqrt{36}$ b. $\sqrt{81}$ c. $-\sqrt{81}$

Solutions

a. $36 = 6^2$ b. $81 = 9^2$ c. $81 = 9^2$
Thus, $\sqrt{36} = 6$. Thus, $\sqrt{81} = 9$. Thus, $-\sqrt{81} = -9$.

TRY THIS Simplify: 1. $\sqrt{121}$ 2. $-\sqrt{64}$

An important property used in multiplying and simplifying square roots is illustrated below.

$$\sqrt{4} \cdot \sqrt{100} = 2 \cdot 10 = 20 \text{ and } \sqrt{4 \cdot 100} = \sqrt{400} = 20$$
$$\text{So, } \sqrt{4} \cdot \sqrt{100} = \sqrt{4 \cdot 100}.$$

> **Product Property for Square Roots**
> For all real numbers a and b, where $a \geq 0$ and $b \geq 0$,
> $\sqrt{a} \cdot \sqrt{b} = \sqrt{a \cdot b}$ and $\sqrt{a \cdot b} = \sqrt{a} \cdot \sqrt{b}$.

| **EXAMPLE 2** | Simplify. |
| | a. $\sqrt{5} \cdot \sqrt{7}$ |

b. $\sqrt{8} \cdot \sqrt{8}$

Plan Use the Product Property for Square Roots.

Solutions

a. $\sqrt{5} \cdot \sqrt{7} = \sqrt{5 \cdot 7}$
   $= \sqrt{35}$

b. $\sqrt{8} \cdot \sqrt{8} = \sqrt{8^2}$
   $= 8$

TRY THIS Simplify: 3. $\sqrt{3} \cdot \sqrt{5}$ 4. $-\sqrt{4} \cdot -\sqrt{4}$

Part **b** of Example 2 shows that $\sqrt{8} \cdot \sqrt{8} = \sqrt{8^2} = 8$, or $(\sqrt{8})^2 = 8$.

In general, for $a \geq 0$, $(\sqrt{a})^2 = \sqrt{a} \cdot \sqrt{a} = \sqrt{a \cdot a} = \sqrt{a^2} = a$.

The numbers 4, 9, 16, and $\frac{1}{25}$ are *perfect squares* since $\sqrt{4} = \sqrt{2^2} = 2$, $\sqrt{9} = \sqrt{3^2} = 3$, $\sqrt{16} = \sqrt{4^2} = 4$, and $\sqrt{\frac{1}{25}} = \sqrt{\left(\frac{1}{5}\right)^2} = \frac{1}{5}$.

Definition

A **perfect square** is a positive rational number whose principal square root is a rational number.

If the radicand is not a perfect square, the square root is an *irrational number*. To simplify such a radical, find the greatest perfect square factor of the radicand. Then use $\sqrt{a \cdot b} = \sqrt{a} \cdot \sqrt{b}$.

EXAMPLE 3 Simplify.

a. $\sqrt{18}$

b. $\sqrt{72}$

Solutions

a. $\sqrt{18} = \sqrt{9 \cdot 2}$
   $= \sqrt{9} \cdot \sqrt{2}$
   $= 3\sqrt{2}$

b. $\sqrt{72} = \sqrt{36 \cdot 2}$
   $= \sqrt{36} \cdot \sqrt{2}$
   $= 6\sqrt{2}$

Calculator check: (Compare the approximations in the displays.)

a. 18 $\boxed{\sqrt{}}$ 4.2426407 and 2 $\boxed{\sqrt{}}$ $\boxed{\times}$ 3 $\boxed{=}$ 4.2426407

b. 72 $\boxed{\sqrt{}}$ 8.4852814 and 2 $\boxed{\sqrt{}}$ $\boxed{\times}$ 6 $\boxed{=}$ 8.4852814

TRY THIS Simplify: 5. $\sqrt{27}$ 6. $-\sqrt{50}$

Sometimes it is difficult to recognize the greatest perfect square factor. In that case, factor the radicand into its prime factors.

EXAMPLE 4   Simplify.
    a. $6\sqrt{84}$ **b.** $-3\sqrt{990}$

Plan   First, factor into primes to find the greatest perfect square factor.

Solutions
    a. $6\sqrt{84} = 6\sqrt{2 \cdot 2 \cdot 3 \cdot 7}$ **b.** $-3\sqrt{990} = -3\sqrt{3 \cdot 3 \cdot 2 \cdot 5 \cdot 11}$
                     $= 6\sqrt{4} \cdot \sqrt{21}$ $= -3\sqrt{9} \cdot \sqrt{110}$
                     $= 6 \cdot 2 \cdot \sqrt{21}$ $= -3 \cdot 3 \cdot \sqrt{110}$
                         $= 12\sqrt{21}$ $= -9\sqrt{110}$

EXAMPLE 5   The area of a circular garden is 100π ft². Find its diameter.

Solution
$$A = \pi r^2$$
$$100\pi = \pi r^2$$
$$r^2 = 100$$
$$r = \sqrt{100}, \text{ or } 10 \text{ ft} \qquad \text{So, the diameter is } 20 \text{ ft.}$$

TRY THIS   Simplify: **7.** $5\sqrt{60}$ **8.** $-2\sqrt{125}$
                    9. The area of a square is 169 cm². Find the length of each side.

Focus on Reading

Tell whether the statement is true or false. If false, explain why.
  1. $\sqrt{36} = 6$ **2.** $-\sqrt{25} = -5$ **3.** $\sqrt{-1} = -1$ **4.** $\sqrt{10} \cdot \sqrt{10} = 10^2$

Classroom Exercises

State each radicand as its greatest perfect square factor times another factor.
  1. $\sqrt{8}$ **2.** $\sqrt{50}$ **3.** $\sqrt{27}$ **4.** $\sqrt{48}$ **5.** $\sqrt{300}$

Simplify.
  6. $\sqrt{9}$ **7.** $-\sqrt{81}$ **8.** $\sqrt{3,600}$ **9.** $\sqrt{500}$ **10.** $\sqrt{28}$

Written Exercises

Simplify.
  1. $\sqrt{4}$ **2.** $\sqrt{100}$ **3.** $\sqrt{16}$ **4.** $\sqrt{25}$ **5.** $-\sqrt{18}$
  6. $\sqrt{121}$ **7.** $\sqrt{144}$ **8.** $-\sqrt{49}$ **9.** $\sqrt{64}$ **10.** $\sqrt{169}$
11. $\sqrt{27}$ **12.** $\sqrt{20}$ **13.** $\sqrt{32}$ **14.** $\sqrt{75}$ **15.** $\sqrt{108}$
16. $\sqrt{24}$ **17.** $-\sqrt{8}$ **18.** $\sqrt{50}$ **19.** $-\sqrt{72}$ **20.** $\sqrt{98}$

21. $\sqrt{3} \cdot \sqrt{7}$ **22.** $\sqrt{7} \cdot \sqrt{6}$ **23.** $\sqrt{11} \cdot \sqrt{7}$ **24.** $\sqrt{15} \cdot \sqrt{2}$

25. $\sqrt{15} \cdot \sqrt{15}$ **26.** $\sqrt{10} \cdot \sqrt{10}$ **27.** $\sqrt{7} \cdot \sqrt{7}$ **28.** $\sqrt{35} \cdot \sqrt{35}$

29. $-4\sqrt{180}$ **30.** $9\sqrt{243}$ **31.** $-6\sqrt{600}$ **32.** $15\sqrt{343}$

33. $10\sqrt{224}$ **34.** $-7\sqrt{275}$ **35.** $12\sqrt{252}$ **36.** $-20\sqrt{363}$

37. $\sqrt{18} \cdot \sqrt{14}$ **38.** $-\sqrt{30} \cdot \sqrt{40}$ **39.** $\sqrt{72} \cdot \sqrt{\frac{4}{9}}$ **40.** $\sqrt{\frac{9}{25}} \cdot \sqrt{50}$

Solve each problem.

41. The area of a square garden plot is 256 ft². What is the length of each side?

42. The area of a circle is 121π cm². What is the radius of the circle?

43. The length of a rectangle is 3 times its width. The area of the rectangle is 192 cm². What is the length and the width of the rectangle?

Simplify.

44. $\sqrt{686}$ **45.** $-\sqrt{2,016}$ **46.** $-2\sqrt{3,179}$ **47.** $3\sqrt{675}$

The time T (in seconds) it takes for a pendulum to swing back and forth is given by the formula

$$T = 2\pi\sqrt{\frac{l}{g}}$$

where l is the length of the pendulum in meters and g is the acceleration due to gravity, which is 9.8 meters per second per second (m/s²).

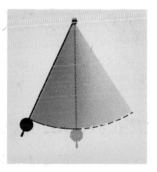

Find the time T for each value of l. Give answers in terms of π and in simplest radical form.

48. $l = 0.8$ **49.** $l = 1.8$ **50.** $l = 5.0$ **51.** $l = 9.8$

Mixed Review

Factor completely.   *7.3, 7.6*

1. $x^2 + 8x + 12$ **2.** $x^2 - x - 6$ **3.** $y^2 - 9y + 18$

4. $2y^3 - 2y$ **5.** $3x^3 - 27x$ **6.** $2x^3 + 16x^2 + 30x$

Find the slope of $\overline{PQ}$ determined by the given points.   *11.1*

7. $P(9, 1), Q(-6, 3)$ **8.** $P(0, -8), Q(7, -2)$ **9.** $P(-1, -3), Q(8, -4)$

13.3 Approximating Square Roots

Objectives	To approximate square roots by using a square root table
	To approximate square roots after simplifying radicals
	To approximate square roots by the divide-and-average method

The value of the square root of a whole number that is not a perfect square can be approximated in different ways. One way is to use a calculator. Another way is to use a Table of Roots and Powers.

EXAMPLE 1   Find an approximation of $\sqrt{15}$ by using a square root table. A portion of the table is shown below.

Table of Roots and Powers		
Number	**Square**	**Square Root**
1	1	1.000
2	2	1.414
⋮	⋮	⋮
14	196	3.742
15	225	3.873

Solution   Read down to the number in the number column. Then read across to the square root column.

So, $\sqrt{15} \approx 3.873$. (Recall that the symbol $\approx$ means "is approximately equal to.")

TRY THIS   1. Find an approximation of $\sqrt{2}$ using a square root table.

When possible, simplify a radical before using the square root table.

EXAMPLE 2   Approximate $\sqrt{500}$ to the nearest tenth.

Solution $\sqrt{500} = \sqrt{100 \cdot 5} = \sqrt{100} \cdot \sqrt{5} = 10\sqrt{5} \approx 10(2.236) \approx 22.36$
Thus, $\sqrt{500} \approx 22.4$.

TRY THIS   2. Approximate $\sqrt{108}$ to the nearest tenth.

The *divide-and-average* method can help you find square roots.

$$\overset{6 \leftarrow \text{quotient}}{\text{divisor} \longrightarrow 6\overline{)36}}$$

When 36 is divided by 6, the quotient is also 6, since $\sqrt{36} = 6$.

$$\overset{5 \leftarrow \text{quotient}}{\text{divisor} \longrightarrow 3\overline{)15}}$$

When 15 is divided by 3, the quotient is 5, so $\sqrt{15}$ is *between* 3 and 5. (From the table you know that $\sqrt{15} \approx 3.873$.)

EXAMPLE 3 Approximate $\sqrt{32}$ to the nearest tenth by using the divide-and-average method.

Solution

1. Locate 32 between two perfect squares.

    $25 < 32 < 36$
    $5^2 < 32 < 6^2$
    So, $5 < \sqrt{32} < 6$.

2. Divide 32 by any number in the interval from 5 through 6. (Use 5.5.)

    $$\overset{5.8\ 1 \leftarrow \text{two decimal places}}{5.5\ \overline{)3\ 2.0\ 0\ 0}}$$

3. Average 5.5 and 5.81 to find a new divisor.

    one decimal place

    $$\frac{5.5 + 5.81}{2} = \frac{11.31}{2} = 5.65$$

4. Divide 32 by 5.65. The divisor and quotient agree to the nearest tenth.

    $$\overset{5.6\ 6\ 3}{5.65\ \overline{)3\ 2.0\ 0\ 0\ 0\ 0}}$$

    divisor ≈ 5.7; quotient ≈ 5.7

Thus, $\sqrt{32} \approx 5.7$. This is closer to 6 than to 5. This is reasonable since 32 is closer to 6^2 than to 5^2.

(This procedure can be continued to find more accurate values for $\sqrt{32}$.)

EXAMPLE 4 The area of a square field is 53 m². Find the length of a side of the field correct to the nearest tenth of a meter.

$A = s^2 \ |\ s$

Solution

$A = s^2$
$53 = s^2$
$s = \sqrt{53} \leftarrow$ (THINK: $7^2 = 49$ and $8^2 = 64$, so $\sqrt{53}$ is between 7 and 8.)
$s \approx 7.280 \longleftarrow$ From the table of square roots

Thus, the length of a side of the field is approximately 7.3 m.

TRY THIS 3. The area of a circle is 71π cm². Find the length of the radius to the nearest tenth. Use $A = \pi r^2$.

Classroom Exercises

Between what two consecutive whole numbers is the square root?

1. $\sqrt{74}$ **2.** $\sqrt{38}$ **3.** $\sqrt{43}$ **4.** $\sqrt{111}$ **5.** $\sqrt{52}$ **6.** $\sqrt{12}$

Approximate to the nearest tenth. Use a square root table.

7. $\sqrt{22}$ **8.** $\sqrt{86}$ **9.** $\sqrt{43}$ **10.** $\sqrt{93}$ **11.** $\sqrt{12}$ **12.** $\sqrt{71}$

Written Exercises

Approximate to the nearest tenth. Use a square root table.

1. $\sqrt{19}$ **2.** $\sqrt{97}$ **3.** $\sqrt{48}$ **4.** $\sqrt{51}$ **5.** $\sqrt{62}$ **6.** $\sqrt{90}$

7. $\sqrt{72}$ **8.** $\sqrt{33}$ **9.** $\sqrt{84}$ **10.** $\sqrt{21}$ **11.** $\sqrt{13}$ **12.** $\sqrt{35}$

Approximate to the nearest tenth. Use the divide-and-average method.

13. $\sqrt{38}$ **14.** $\sqrt{27}$ **15.** $\sqrt{65}$ **16.** $\sqrt{44}$ **17.** $\sqrt{98}$ **18.** $\sqrt{71}$

Approximate to the nearest tenth. Use either a square root table or the divide-and-average method.

19. $\sqrt{245}$ **20.** $\sqrt{124}$ **21.** $\sqrt{248}$ **22.** $\sqrt{775}$ **23.** $\sqrt{550}$ **24.** $\sqrt{463}$

25. Find all the integers between 1 and 100 whose square roots are integers.

26. Find all the integers between 120 and 250 whose square roots are integers.

Solve each problem. Round answers to the nearest tenth.

27. The area of a square is 18 cm². Find the length of a side.

28. The area of a square is 47 cm². Find the length of a side.

29. The area of a circle is 31π. Find the length of the radius. Use $A = \pi r^2$.

30. The area of a circle is 134π. Find the length of the radius. Use $A = \pi r^2$.

31. The length of a rectangle is 4 times the width. The area is 440 m². Find the length and the width of the rectangle.

32. The area of a rectangle is 90 cm². The length is 3 times the width. Find the length and the width of the rectangle.

33. Approximate $\sqrt{0.40}$ to the nearest tenth without using a calculator.

34. Write an explanation of why $\sqrt{57}$ is a number between 7 and 8.

A centripetal force keeps an object moving in a circular path at a constant velocity. The formula used to calculate centripetal force F is $F = \dfrac{mv^2}{r}$, where r is the radius, m is the mass, and v is the velocity.

35. A discus thrower swings a discus, then lets it fly. Before it flies off, what is its velocity in meters per second if its mass is 4 kg, the radius of its path is 0.8 m, and the force on the arm of the thrower is 80 newtons?

36. A centripetal force of 78 newtons keeps a ball swinging on a chain 3 m in length. If the mass of the ball is 2 kg, find the velocity of the ball in meters per second. Give the answer to one decimal place.

Mixed Review

Simplify.   2.2, 2.10, 6.1, 6.3

1. $-|-3| \cdot |-4|$

2. $-1(-24)$

3. $-7(3^2)$

4. $-(3a - 2b) - 2a$

5. $x^5 \cdot x^2$

6. $a \cdot a^4$

7. $(-3a^5)(4a^3)$

8. $\dfrac{-4x^3y^2}{16xy^5}$

Application: Electricity

Appliances that produce high amounts of heat (hairdryers, heaters, toasters) cost more to run than other kinds of appliances. Wires in these appliances oppose, or resist, the flow of electrons so the wires turn red and become hot. More power is required to push electrons through a wire that has high resistance. This formula gives the electrical current, I, in amperes, A, for an appliance that uses W watts of power and has a resistance of R ohms.

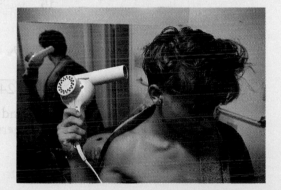

$$I = \sqrt{\dfrac{W}{R}}$$

Use the formula to find the amps for each of these appliances. Round your answers to the nearest tenth.

1. A toaster that uses 575 watts of power and has a resistance of 20 ohms

2. An electric heater that uses 790 watts of power and has a resistance of 16 ohms

3. An iron that uses 632.5 watts of power and has a resistance of 20.9 ohms

13.4 The Pythagorean Theorem

Objectives

To find the length of one side of a right triangle, given the lengths of the other two sides

To determine whether a triangle is a right triangle, given the lengths of its three sides

A surveyor walked 8 m east, then 6 m north. How far was she from the starting point?

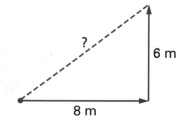

This problem can be solved by using a relationship between the sides of a **right triangle**, that is, a triangle with one right angle. A right angle has a degree measure of 90 and is indicated in diagrams by the symbol ⌐, as in the figure below.

In the sixth century B.C., Pythagoras, a Greek philosopher and mathematician, discovered a relationship between the hypotenuse and the two legs of a right triangle. It is known as the *Pythagorean Theorem*.

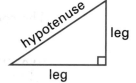

Pythagorean Theorem
If triangle ABC is a right triangle with c the length of the hypotenuse and a and b the lengths of the legs, then $c^2 = a^2 + b^2$.

In this lesson, c will represent the length of the hypotenuse of a right triangle and a and b the lengths of the legs.

For the problem about the surveyor, it is necessary to find the length of the hypotenuse, given legs of lengths 6 m and 8 m.

Use the Pythagorean Theorem.

$$c^2 = a^2 + b^2$$
$$= 6^2 + 8^2$$
$$= 36 + 64$$
$$= 100$$
$$c = \sqrt{100}, \text{ or } 10$$

So, the surveyor was 10 m from her starting point.

EXAMPLE 1   For each right triangle, find the missing length. If the answer is not a rational number, give it in simplest radical form.

       a. $a = 2, b = 6$ **b.** $a = 8, c = 17$

Plan   Use the Pythagorean Theorem, $c^2 = a^2 + b^2$.

Solutions   **a.** 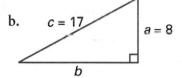   **b.**

a.
$$c^2 = a^2 + b^2$$
$$= 2^2 + 6^2$$
$$= 4 + 36$$
$$= 40$$
$$c = \sqrt{40}, \text{ or } c = 2\sqrt{10}$$

b.
$$c^2 = a^2 + b^2$$
$$17^2 = 8^2 + b^2$$
$$289 - 64 = b^2$$
$$225 = b^2$$
$$b = \sqrt{225} = 15$$

TRY THIS   1. The lengths of the legs of a right triangle are 5 and 12. Find the length of the hypotenuse.

The *converse of the Pythagorean Theorem* is also true.

Converse of the Pythagorean Theorem
If $c^2 = a^2 + b^2$, where a, b, and c are the lengths of the sides of a triangle, then the triangle is a right triangle.

EXAMPLE 2   Given the lengths of three sides of a triangle, determine whether the triangle is a right triangle.

       a. $3, 3, 3\sqrt{2}$ **b.** $4, 9, 7$

Plan   Let $c =$ the length of the longest side. Determine if $c^2 = a^2 + b^2$.

Solutions   **a.**
$$c^2 \overset{?}{=} a^2 + b^2$$
$$(3\sqrt{2})^2 \overset{?}{=} 3^2 + 3^2$$
$$9(2) \overset{?}{=} 9 + 9$$
$$18 = 18$$
So, $c^2 = a^2 + b^2$.

The triangle *is* a right triangle.

b.
$$c^2 \overset{?}{=} a^2 + b^2$$
$$9^2 \overset{?}{=} 4^2 + 7^2$$
$$81 \overset{?}{=} 16 + 49$$
$$81 \neq 65$$
So, $c^2 \neq a^2 + b^2$.

The triangle *is not* a right triangle.

EXAMPLE 3 A 10-ft ladder is leaning against a building. Its base is 3 ft from the base of the building. How high up the building will the ladder reach? Round the answer to the nearest tenth of a foot.

Solution Draw a diagram and label the parts.

$$c^2 = a^2 + b^2$$
$$10^2 = 3^2 + b^2$$
$$100 = 9 + b^2$$
$$91 = b^2$$
$$b = \sqrt{91}$$
$$b \approx 9.539, \text{ or } 9.5 \text{ to the nearest tenth}$$

Thus, the ladder will reach approximately 9.5 ft up the wall.

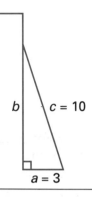

TRY THIS 2. A rectangle is 3 m long and 8 m wide. Find the length of a diagonal to the nearest tenth.

Classroom Exercises

For each right triangle, find the missing length. If the answer is not a rational number, write it in simplest radical form. Use $c^2 = a^2 + b^2$.

1. $a = 3, b = 4$
2. $a = 1, b = 3$
3. $a = 6, c = 9$
4. $b = 7, c = 7\sqrt{2}$
5. $b = 40, c = 50$
6. $a = 5, b = 5\sqrt{3}$

Given the lengths of three sides of a triangle, determine whether the triangle is a right triangle.

7. 10, 15, 20
8. $\sqrt{6}, \sqrt{15}, 3$
9. $3, 3\sqrt{3}, 6$

Written Exercises

Solve each problem.

1. Find the length of the hypotenuse if the lengths of the legs of a right triangle are 3 m and 4 m.

2. Find the length of the hypotenuse if the lengths of the legs of a right triangle are 5 cm and 12 cm.

3. The length of the hypotenuse of a right triangle is 4 m. The length of one leg is 2 m. Find the length of the other leg. Give the answer in simplest radical form.

4. The length of the hypotenuse of a right triangle is 6 cm. The length of one leg is 4 cm. Find the length of the other leg. Give the answer in simplest radical form.

For each right triangle, find the length of the hypotenuse. If the answer is not a rational number, write it in simplest radical form.

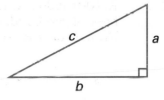

5. $a = 2, b = 4$

6. $a = 7, b = 9$

7. $a = 12, b = 14$

8. $a = 24, b = 10$

9. $a = 3, b = 5$

10. $a = 9, b = 13$

11. $a = 5, b = 7$

12. $a = \sqrt{3}, b = \sqrt{6}$

13. $a = \sqrt{5}, b = 10$

For each right triangle, find the missing length. If the answer is not a rational number, write it in simplest radical form.

14. $a = 3, b = 7$

15. $a = 5, c = 8$

16. $b = 9, c = 23$

17. $a = 9, c = 41$

18. $b = 10, c = 12$

19. $a = 5, c = 13$

20. $a = 7, b = 11$

21. $a = 3, c = 9$

22. $b = 4, c = 7$

23. $b = 9, c = 15$

24. $b = 5, c = 11$

25. $a = 7, b = 10$

Given the lengths of three sides of a triangle, determine whether it is a right triangle.

26. 9, 12, 15

27. 4, 5, 3

28. 2, 3, 4

29. 20, 21, 29

30. 14, 48, 50

31. 15, 39, 36

32. 21, 72, 75

33. 20, 30, 40

34. $\sqrt{3}, \sqrt{4}, \sqrt{5}$

35. 7, 9, $\sqrt{130}$

36. $\sqrt{7}, 8, \sqrt{71}$

37. 5, 12, $\sqrt{119}$

38. $\sqrt{5}, 12, 13$

39. $\sqrt{3}, 4, \sqrt{19}$

40. 10, 12, $\sqrt{22}$

For each right triangle, find the missing length. If the answer is not a rational number, write it in simplest radical form.

41. $a = 3\sqrt{3}, c = 7$

42. $b = 4\sqrt{2}, c = 10$

43. $a = \sqrt{5}, b = 5\sqrt{7}$

44. $a = 4\sqrt{7}, b = 3\sqrt{5}$

45. $a = 5\sqrt{6}, c = 14$

46. $b = 8\sqrt{2}, c = 6\sqrt{8}$

47. $b = 3\sqrt{7}, c = 4\sqrt{7}$

48. $a = 3\sqrt{11}, b = 4\sqrt{10}$

49. $a = 11\sqrt{3}, b = 4\sqrt{5}$

Solve each problem. If an answer is not rational, round it to the nearest tenth of the unit.

50. A 6-m ladder is leaning against a building. Its base is 1 m from the base of the building. How high up the building will the ladder reach?

51. Find the length of the diagonal across a television screen that is 18 cm wide and 18 cm long.

52. A carpenter wants to build a brace for a gate that is 4 ft wide and 5 ft high. Find the length of the brace.

53. A rectangular field is 50 yd wide and 120 yd long. How long is the diagonal path connecting two opposite corners of the field?

54. A 15-m loading ramp is connected to a dock 3 m high. How far is the foot of the ramp from the loading dock?

55. A surveyor walked 9 km east, then 6 km north. How far was the surveyor from his starting point?

56. A baseball diamond is a square with sides 90 ft in length. How far is it from second base to home plate?

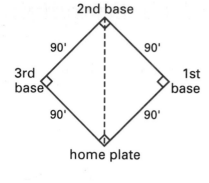

57. A mover must try to fit a thin circular mirror, 2 m in diameter, through a doorway measuring 1 m by 1.8 m. Will the mirror fit through the doorway?

Use the diagram at the right for Exercises 58 and 59. The diagram shows a square with sides of length $a + b$. The four-sided figure inside the square is a square with sides of length c.

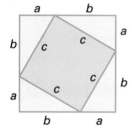

58. Use the concept of area to explain why the following equation is true: $(a + b)^2 = 4(\frac{1}{2}ab) + c^2$

59. Use the Equation in Exercise 58 to verify the Pythagorean Theorem.

60. Find the greatest possible length of a ski to be placed flat in a box that is 4 ft by 5 ft. Give the answer to the nearest inch.

61. Derive a formula for finding the altitude h of an equilateral triangle in terms of s, the length of a side.

Mixed Review

Simplify. *6.1*

1. $x^5 \cdot x^4$
2. $(5a^2)(-6a^3)$
3. $(-3x^4)(2x)$
4. $(-a^3b^2)(-3a^4b^5)$
5. $(-3b^3c^4)(-b^4c^4)$
6. $(4a^6b^7)(-2a^7b^{10})$
7. The price of a bus ticket was $80. The price was increased by 12%. What is the new price? *4.7*
8. A baseball team won 16 games and lost 4 games. What percent of its games did the team win? *4.7*
9. A rectangle is 8 cm long and 6 cm wide. If the length and the width are increased by the same amount, the area is increased by 32 cm². Find the amount by which each side must be increased. *7.9*

13.5 Simplifying Radicals

Objective

To simplify square roots in which the radicands contain variables raised to even or odd powers

Square roots such as $\sqrt{2^6}$ and $\sqrt{10^4}$ can be simplified using the Product of Powers Property $b^{m+n} = b^m \cdot b^n$, as shown below.

$$\sqrt{2^6} = \sqrt{2^3 \cdot 2^3} = 2^3 \qquad\qquad \sqrt{10^4} = \sqrt{10^2 \cdot 10^2} = 10^2$$

These examples illustrate a property of square roots of the form $\sqrt{a^{2n}}$, where $2n$ is an even number and a is positive. For the examples and exercises of this lesson, assume that each base is a positive number.

Square Root Property of Even Powers
For every even number $2n$, $\sqrt{a^{2n}} = \sqrt{a^{n+n}} = \sqrt{a^n \cdot a^n} = a^n$, where $a > 0$.

EXAMPLE 1 Simplify $4\sqrt{25a^8b^{18}}$.

Solution
$$\begin{aligned}
4\sqrt{25a^8b^{18}} &= 4 \cdot \sqrt{25} \cdot \sqrt{a^8} \cdot \sqrt{b^{18}} \\
&= 4 \cdot 5 \cdot a^4 \cdot b^9 \\
&= 20a^4b^9
\end{aligned}$$

Square Root Property of Odd Powers
For every odd number $2n + 1$, $\sqrt{a^{2n+1}} = \sqrt{a^{2n} \cdot a^1} = a^n\sqrt{a}$, where $a > 0$.

EXAMPLE 2 Simplify $-3\sqrt{28x^3y^7}$.

Solution
$$\begin{aligned}
-3\sqrt{28x^3y^7} &= -3\sqrt{4 \cdot 7 \cdot x^2 \cdot x^1 \cdot y^6 \cdot y^1} \\
&= -3\sqrt{4 \cdot 7} \cdot \sqrt{x^2 \cdot x} \cdot \sqrt{y^6 \cdot y} \\
&= -6\sqrt{7} \cdot x\sqrt{x} \cdot y^3\sqrt{y} \\
&= -6xy^3 \cdot \sqrt{7} \cdot \sqrt{x} \cdot \sqrt{y} \\
&= -6xy^3\sqrt{7xy}
\end{aligned}$$

TRY THIS Simplify: **1.** $4\sqrt{27x^5y^3}$ **2.** $-2\sqrt{32x^7y^4}$

EXAMPLE 3   Simplify $-7x^5y\sqrt{12x^9y^6z^{11}}$.

Plan   Use $\sqrt{a^{2n}} = a$ and $\sqrt{a^{2n+1}} = a^n\sqrt{a}$.

Solution
$$-7x^5y\sqrt{12x^9y^6z^{11}} = -7x^5y\sqrt{4 \cdot 3 \cdot x^8 \cdot x \cdot y^6 \cdot z^{10} \cdot z}$$
$$= -7x^5y \cdot 2x^4y^3z^5\sqrt{3xz}$$
$$= -14x^9y^4z^5\sqrt{3xz}$$

TRY THIS   Simplify: **3.** $-6x^3y^2z\sqrt{9x^5y^9z^3}$

4. $4x^3z^4\sqrt{8y^9z^8}$

Classroom Exercises

Simplify.

1. $\sqrt{a^8}$ **2.** $\sqrt{x^9}$ **3.** $\sqrt{a^5}$ **4.** $\sqrt{b^{12}}$

5. $\sqrt{y^{15}}$ **6.** $\sqrt{m^{36}}$ **7.** $\sqrt{y^{21}}$ **8.** $\sqrt{a^{19}}$

9. $\sqrt{y^{14}}$ **10.** $\sqrt{m^7}$ **11.** $\sqrt{a^2}$ **12.** $\sqrt{b^{11}}$

13. $\sqrt{16x^{14}}$ **14.** $\sqrt{81b^{17}}$ **15.** $-2\sqrt{18m^5n^6}$ **16.** $5\sqrt{50a^{24}b^{25}}$

Written Exercises

Simplify.

1. $\sqrt{4x^{24}}$ **2.** $-\sqrt{9a^{14}}$ **3.** $-\sqrt{16y^{16}}$ **4.** $-\sqrt{16a^{20}}$

5. $14\sqrt{25y^{28}}$ **6.** $-9\sqrt{36x^{32}}$ **7.** $5\sqrt{81b^{30}}$ **8.** $-10\sqrt{49y^{44}}$

9. $\sqrt{9a^7}$ **10.** $-3\sqrt{x^5}$ **11.** $2\sqrt{4y^3}$ **12.** $5\sqrt{15x^{15}}$

13. $-2\sqrt{36c^5}$ **14.** $10\sqrt{3x^5}$ **15.** $-2\sqrt{12a^9}$ **16.** $5\sqrt{24x^{13}}$

17. $\sqrt{x^9y^7}$ **18.** $-2\sqrt{20a^5b^{11}}$ **19.** $-\sqrt{45m^7n^5}$ **20.** $8\sqrt{18x^{15}y^9}$

21. $-\sqrt{40xy^5}$ **22.** $-4\sqrt{50x^3y^7}$ **23.** $4\sqrt{18a^{17}b^{15}}$ **24.** $-\sqrt{32a^{11}b}$

25. $\sqrt{4a^{10}b^{12}}$ **26.** $-\sqrt{25x^4y^6}$ **27.** $-\sqrt{49a^{12}b^{10}}$ **28.** $\sqrt{81m^{16}n^{20}}$

29. $8\sqrt{9x^{14}y^{40}}$ **30.** $-12\sqrt{4a^{18}b^{16}}$ **31.** $12\sqrt{36x^{24}y^{36}}$ **32.** $-\sqrt{100m^{10}n^{30}}$

33. $9\sqrt{27a^{15}b^9}$ **34.** $5\sqrt{12a^{11}b^{13}}$ **35.** $10\sqrt{24x^{21}y^{33}}$ **36.** $-4\sqrt{18x^{15}y^9}$

37. $-3a^3b\sqrt{75a^4b^8}$ **38.** $4xy^6\sqrt{12x^4y^{12}}$ **39.** $-5a^3b^4\sqrt{18a^6b^{16}}$

40. $-5x^2y\sqrt{18x^5y^7}$ **41.** $9a^5b^{10}\sqrt{72ab^9}$ **42.** $10xy\sqrt{24x^5y^3}$

43. $7a^4b^{10}\sqrt{36a^{13}b^{11}}$

44. $-10xy^5\sqrt{75x^{22}y^{13}}$

45. $8e^4f^3\sqrt{27e^4f^3}$

46. $-\sqrt{100a^4b^2c^6}$

47. $\sqrt{144x^{10}y^6z^{10}}$

48. $-\sqrt{81a^{24}b^{12}c^8}$

49. $5\sqrt{44x^3yz^4}$

50. $6ab^2c\sqrt{90a^2bc^7}$

51. $-4x^3y^3z\sqrt{60x^7y^9z^6}$

52. $4\sqrt{48x^8y^{14}z^{36}}$

53. $10\sqrt{32a^{41}b^{38}c^{22}}$

54. $4\sqrt{128x^4y^{16}z^{80}}$

55. $-3\sqrt{28a^{30}b^{25}c^{36}}$

56. $9\sqrt{98x^{44}y^{36}z^{18}}$

57. $-3\sqrt{243a^{40}b^{80}c^{100}}$

58. $-6\sqrt{a^{2n+1}}$

59. $-3\sqrt{x^{4n+1}}$

60. $9x\sqrt{y^{16n}z^{5n}}$

Midchapter Review

Express each rational number as a decimal. Then classify the decimal as either terminating or repeating. *13.1*

1. $\frac{1}{5}$

2. $-\frac{5}{6}$

3. $3\frac{2}{3}$

4. $-\frac{3}{11}$

For each repeating decimal, find a fraction $\frac{a}{b}$ where a and b are integers. *13.1*

5. $4.\overline{5}$

6. $13.4\overline{3}$

7. $3.8282\cdots$

8. $0.\overline{153}$

Simplify. *13.2*

9. $\sqrt{81}$

10. $\sqrt{27}$

11. $\sqrt{50}$

12. $-6\sqrt{500}$

Approximate to the nearest tenth. Use a square root table. *13.3*

13. $\sqrt{15}$

14. $\sqrt{43}$

15. $\sqrt{80}$

16. $\sqrt{94}$

17. Approximate $\sqrt{135}$ to the nearest tenth. Use the divide-and-average method. *13.3*

18. The area of a rectangle is 216 cm^2. The length is twice the width. Find the length and the width of the rectangle. *13.3*

For each right triangle, find the missing length. If the answer is not a rational number, give it in simplest radical form. *13.4*

19. $a = 5, b = 5$

20. $a = 3, c = 7$

21. $b = 10, c = 20$

22. $b = 21, c = 29$

Given the lengths of the sides of a triangle, determine if it is a right triangle. *13.4*

23. $18, 24, 30$

24. $2, 3, \sqrt{5}$

25. $10, 11, 15$

26. $20, 48, 52$

Simplify. *13.5*

27. $-4\sqrt{36a^{18}}$

28. $\sqrt{24x^{11}}$

29. $6\sqrt{16x^{12}y^{19}}$

30. $a^2b\sqrt{75a^{21}b^{24}}$

13.6 Adding and Subtracting Radicals

Objective To add and subtract expressions containing radicals

Recall that like terms such as $5a$ and $6a$ can be combined by using the Distributive Property.

$$5a + 6a = (5 + 6)a = 11a$$

Similarly, $5\sqrt{7} + 6\sqrt{7} = (5 + 6)\sqrt{7} = 11\sqrt{7}$

Therefore, you can combine expressions with radicals by adding or subtracting when the radicands are the same.

EXAMPLE 1 Simplify $8\sqrt{2} - 7\sqrt{2} + 4\sqrt{2}$.

Solutions

Method 1
Group the positive terms.
$8\sqrt{2} - 7\sqrt{2} + 4\sqrt{2}$
$\quad = (8\sqrt{2} + 4\sqrt{2}) - 7\sqrt{2}$
$\quad = 12\sqrt{2} - 7\sqrt{2}$
$\quad = 5\sqrt{2}$

Method 2
Combine using the given order.
$8\sqrt{2} - 7\sqrt{2} + 4\sqrt{2}$
$\quad = (8\sqrt{2} - 7\sqrt{2}) + 4\sqrt{2}$
$\quad = 1\sqrt{2} + 4\sqrt{2}$
$\quad = 5\sqrt{2}$

EXAMPLE 2 Simplify $9\sqrt{5} + 3\sqrt{3} - 2\sqrt{5}$.

Solution

$9\sqrt{5} + 3\sqrt{3} - 2\sqrt{5} = (9\sqrt{5} - 2\sqrt{5}) + 3\sqrt{3}$
$\qquad\qquad\qquad\qquad = 7\sqrt{5} + 3\sqrt{3} \quad \longleftarrow$ unlike radicands

TRY THIS Simplify: **1.** $6\sqrt{3} + 4\sqrt{3} - 2\sqrt{3}$ **2.** $5\sqrt{6} - 5\sqrt{2} + 3\sqrt{6}$

You may need to simplify radicals before combining like terms.

EXAMPLE 3 Simplify $5\sqrt{8} - 6\sqrt{2} + 4\sqrt{72}$.

Plan Simplify $\sqrt{8}$ and $\sqrt{72}$ first. Then combine like terms.

Solution

$5\sqrt{8} - 6\sqrt{2} + 4\sqrt{72} = 5\sqrt{4 \cdot 2} - 6\sqrt{2} + 4\sqrt{36 \cdot 2}$
$\qquad\qquad\qquad\qquad = 5 \cdot 2\sqrt{2} - 6\sqrt{2} + 4 \cdot 6\sqrt{2}$
$\qquad\qquad\qquad\qquad = 10\sqrt{2} - 6\sqrt{2} + 24\sqrt{2}$
$\qquad\qquad\qquad\qquad = 28\sqrt{2}$

EXAMPLE 4   Simplify $3b\sqrt{36a^3b} - 14a\sqrt{ab^3} - 4\sqrt{81a^3b^3}$.

Solution
$$3b\sqrt{36a^3b} - 14a\sqrt{ab^3} - 4\sqrt{81a^3b^3}$$
$$= 3b\sqrt{36} \cdot \sqrt{a^2 \cdot ab} - 14a\sqrt{ab \cdot b^2} - 4\sqrt{81} \cdot \sqrt{a^2 \cdot b^2 \cdot ab}$$
$$= 3b \cdot 6 \cdot a\sqrt{ab} - 14a \cdot b\sqrt{ab} - 4 \cdot 9 \cdot a \cdot b\sqrt{ab}$$
$$= 18ab\sqrt{ab} - 14ab\sqrt{ab} - 36ab\sqrt{ab}$$
$$= -32ab\sqrt{ab}$$

EXAMPLE 5   Find the perimeter of a rectangle with a length of $9 - \sqrt{3}$ and a width of $3\sqrt{5}$.

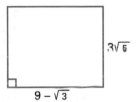
$3\sqrt{5}$

$9 - \sqrt{3}$

Plan   Use $P = l + w + l + w$ or $P = 2l + 2w$.

Solution

$P = l + w + l + w$ $P = 2l + 2w$
$= 9 - \sqrt{3} + 3\sqrt{5} + 9 - \sqrt{3} + 3\sqrt{5}$ $= 2(9 - \sqrt{3}) + 2(3\sqrt{5})$
$= 18 - 2\sqrt{3} + 6\sqrt{5}$ $= 18 - 2\sqrt{3} + 6\sqrt{5}$

Thus, the perimeter of the rectangle is $18 - 2\sqrt{3} + 6\sqrt{5}$.

TRY THIS
3. Simplify $2x\sqrt{25xy^5} + 8y\sqrt{9x^3y^3} - 7xy^2\sqrt{49xy}$.

4. Find the perimeter of a rectangle with a length of $2 + \sqrt{3}$ and a width of $1 + \sqrt{2}$.

Classroom Exercises

Which terms are like terms?
1. $-8\sqrt{2}, \sqrt{2}, \sqrt{7}, \sqrt{14}$
2. $9, 4\sqrt{5}, -\sqrt{5}, \sqrt{3}$
3. $5\sqrt{3}, 4\sqrt{3}, 4\sqrt{2}, -3\sqrt{3}$
4. $-5\sqrt{7}, \sqrt{7}, -3\sqrt{7}, -5$

Simplify.
5. $5\sqrt{3} + 7\sqrt{3}$ 6. $8\sqrt{5} - 2\sqrt{5}$ 7. $14\sqrt{7} + 6\sqrt{7}$ 8. $9\sqrt{2} - 3\sqrt{2}$
9. $35\sqrt{44} - 15\sqrt{99}$ 10. $-15\sqrt{54} - 3\sqrt{150} + 10\sqrt{6}$

Written Exercises

Add or subtract. Simplify.
1. $18\sqrt{2} - 7\sqrt{2} + 12\sqrt{2}$
2. $12\sqrt{3} - 7\sqrt{3} + 2\sqrt{3}$
3. $10\sqrt{5} - 2\sqrt{5} - 9\sqrt{5}$
4. $-4\sqrt{7} + 5\sqrt{7} + 3\sqrt{7}$

5. $7\sqrt{8} - \sqrt{18}$

6. $4\sqrt{75} + 6\sqrt{27}$

7. $-3\sqrt{20} + 2\sqrt{45} - \sqrt{7}$

8. $7\sqrt{18} - 2\sqrt{50} - \sqrt{12}$

9. $6\sqrt{11} + \sqrt{99} + 2\sqrt{44}$

10. $-7\sqrt{98} + 6\sqrt{18} - \sqrt{32}$

11. $8\sqrt{a} - 3\sqrt{a}$

12. $7\sqrt{x} - 3\sqrt{x} + \sqrt{x}$

13. $-16\sqrt{ab} + 5\sqrt{ab} - \sqrt{ab}$

14. $3\sqrt{25xy} + 4\sqrt{36xy} - 2\sqrt{81xy}$

15. $4\sqrt{cd} - 2\sqrt{cd} - \sqrt{cd} + 10\sqrt{cd}$

16. $3x\sqrt{100x^2} - 2x\sqrt{25x^2} + \sqrt{36x^2}$

17. $-2\sqrt{12xy} + 8\sqrt{27xy} - \sqrt{3xy}$

18. $9\sqrt{49ab} + 3\sqrt{81ab} - \sqrt{4ab}$

19. $9\sqrt{32mn} + 2\sqrt{18mn} - 3\sqrt{50mn}$

20. $-10\sqrt{45xy} + 2\sqrt{20xy} + 9\sqrt{80xy}$

21. $\sqrt{4x^3y^2} + xy\sqrt{36x}$

22. $a\sqrt{ab^3} + b\sqrt{a^3b}$

23. $-2\sqrt{a^3b^3} + 3b\sqrt{a^3b} - \sqrt{25ab^3}$

24. $\sqrt{16cd^3} + 3\sqrt{cd^3} - 5d\sqrt{25cd}$

25. $\sqrt{18x^4y} + 3x^2\sqrt{2y}$

26. $4mn\sqrt{49n} + 6\sqrt{m^2n^3}$

27. $5y\sqrt{125x^2} + 8\sqrt{80x^3y^3}$

28. $y\sqrt{12x^3y} - x\sqrt{6xy^3} + \sqrt{54x^3y^3}$

29. $x^2\sqrt{2y} + \sqrt{18x^4y} + 3\sqrt{8x^4y}$

30. $2\sqrt{75x^3y} + x\sqrt{48xy} + 2\sqrt{3x \cdot 3y}$

31. Find the perimeter of a rectangle with a length of $5\sqrt{2}$ and a width of $3 + \sqrt{5}$.

32. The length of a rectangle is $2 + 3\sqrt{5}$ and the width is $1 + 5\sqrt{2}$. Find the perimeter.

Find the perimeter. Write your answer in simplest radical form.

33.

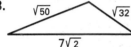

34.

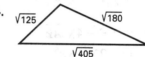

Solve each problem. Give answers in simplest radical form.

35. The area of a square quilt is 104 cm². What is the length? What is its perimeter?

104 cm²

36. The length of a rectangle is $6 + \sqrt{3}$ and the perimeter is $8 + 10\sqrt{3}$. Find the width.

37. Find the perimeter of a right triangle with legs that measure $\sqrt{5}$ and $\sqrt{2}$.

Mixed Review

Solve each equation or system.   *3.4, 3.5, 12.2, 12.5*

1. $3(2x - 5) - 3 = 2x - 8$

2. $0.4x - 3 = 0.1x + 0.09$

3. $y = 2x$
$x + y = 9$

4. $2x - 3y = 8$
$x = 4 - y$

5. $5x + 2y = 12$
$3x - 2y = 4$

6. $2x - 7y = -3$
$9y = 4x + 11$

13.7 Multiplying Radicals

Objective	To multiply and simplify expressions containing radicals

The rectangle at the right is $6\sqrt{3}$ cm long and $2\sqrt{2}$ cm wide. To find the area, use the formula $A = lw$.

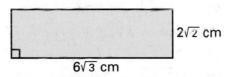
$2\sqrt{2}$ cm

$6\sqrt{3}$ cm

$$A = lw$$

Substitute.
$$A = 6\sqrt{3} \cdot 2\sqrt{2}$$
$$= 6 \cdot 2 \cdot \sqrt{3} \cdot \sqrt{2}$$

Use $\sqrt{a} \cdot \sqrt{b} = \sqrt{ab}$.
$$= 12 \cdot \sqrt{3 \cdot 2} = 12\sqrt{6}$$

The area is $12\sqrt{6}$ cm².

Thus, to multiply two expressions that contain square roots, use the property $\sqrt{a} \cdot \sqrt{b} = \sqrt{ab}$ to multiply the radicals. Then simplify.

EXAMPLE 1 Simplify.

a. $3\sqrt{2x^5} \cdot 4\sqrt{8x}$

b. $-12\sqrt{12a^3} \cdot 4\sqrt{5a^2}$

Solutions

a. $3\sqrt{2x^5} \cdot 4\sqrt{8x}$
$$= 12\sqrt{16x^6}$$
$$= 12 \cdot 4 \cdot x^3$$
$$= 48x^3$$

b. $-12\sqrt{12a^3} \cdot 4\sqrt{5a^2}$
$$= -48\sqrt{60a^5}$$
$$= -48\sqrt{4 \cdot 15 \cdot a^4 \cdot a}$$
$$= -48 \cdot 2 \cdot \sqrt{15} \cdot a^2 \cdot \sqrt{a}$$
$$= -96a^2\sqrt{15a}$$

EXAMPLE 2 Simplify $-3\sqrt{7}(5\sqrt{3} - 2\sqrt{5})$.

Plan Use the Distributive Property, $a(b + c) = ab + ac$.

Solution
$$-3\sqrt{7}(5\sqrt{3} - 2\sqrt{5}) = -3\sqrt{7}(5\sqrt{3}) + (-3\sqrt{7})(-2\sqrt{5})$$
$$= -15\sqrt{21} + 6\sqrt{35}$$

Thus, $-3\sqrt{7}(5\sqrt{3} - 2\sqrt{5}) = -15\sqrt{21} + 6\sqrt{35}$.

TRY THIS Simplify.

1. $2\sqrt{24a^7}(-5\sqrt{9a^3})$

2. $\sqrt{2}(2\sqrt{3} - 3\sqrt{4})$

3. $2\sqrt{3}(-4\sqrt{5} - 6\sqrt{2})$

4. $\sqrt{8x^3} \cdot 2\sqrt{18x^5}$

In Example 3, the FOIL method is used to multiply the two binomials.

$$\begin{array}{ccccccc} & \text{First terms} & \text{Outer terms} & \text{Inner terms} & \text{Last terms} \\ (a + b)(c + d) = & ac & + & ad & + & bc & + & bd \end{array}$$

EXAMPLE 3   Simplify $(4\sqrt{5} + 3\sqrt{2})(2\sqrt{5} - 9\sqrt{2})$.

Solution $(4\sqrt{5} + 3\sqrt{2})(2\sqrt{5} - 9\sqrt{2})$

$$\begin{array}{cccc} \text{First terms} & \text{Outer terms} & \text{Inner terms} & \text{Last terms} \end{array}$$
$$= 4\sqrt{5}(2\sqrt{5}) + 4\sqrt{5}(-9\sqrt{2}) + 3\sqrt{2}(2\sqrt{5}) + 3\sqrt{2}(-9\sqrt{2})$$
$$= \quad 8 \cdot 5 \quad - \quad 36\sqrt{10} \quad + \quad 6\sqrt{10} \quad - \quad 27 \cdot 2$$
$$= 40 - 30\sqrt{10} - 54$$
$$= -14 - 30\sqrt{10}$$

EXAMPLE 4   Simplify $(2\sqrt{7} + 3\sqrt{5})(2\sqrt{7} - 3\sqrt{5})$.

Plan   Use the formula for the special product, $(a + b)(a - b) = a^2 - b^2$.

Solution $(2\sqrt{7} + 3\sqrt{5})(2\sqrt{7} - 3\sqrt{5}) = (2\sqrt{7})^2 - (3\sqrt{5})^2$
$$= 2^2 \cdot (\sqrt{7})^2 - 3^2 \cdot (\sqrt{5})^2$$
$$= 4 \cdot 7 - 9 \cdot 5$$
$$= 28 - 45$$
$$= -17$$

TRY THIS   Simplify.

5. $(6\sqrt{2} - 2\sqrt{3})(3\sqrt{2} - 5\sqrt{3})$

6. $(2\sqrt{3} + 5)^2$

7. $(4\sqrt{11} - 3\sqrt{5})(4\sqrt{11} + 3\sqrt{5})$

Classroom Exercises

Simplify.

1. $\sqrt{5} \cdot \sqrt{5}$

2. $\sqrt{5} \cdot \sqrt{3}$

3. $\sqrt{8} \cdot \sqrt{8}$

4. $2 \cdot 4\sqrt{7}$

5. $\sqrt{3} \cdot 2\sqrt{7}$

6. $\sqrt{2} \cdot 3\sqrt{2}$

7. $5\sqrt{7} \cdot 2\sqrt{7}$

8. $9\sqrt{5a^4} \cdot 3\sqrt{6a^2}$

9. $-3\sqrt{3}(\sqrt{2} - \sqrt{3})$

10. $(\sqrt{7} + \sqrt{6})(\sqrt{7} - \sqrt{6})$

11. $(2\sqrt{3} + 4\sqrt{2})(2\sqrt{3} - 4\sqrt{2})$

12. $(3\sqrt{5} - \sqrt{2})(3\sqrt{5} + \sqrt{2})$

13. $(3\sqrt{2} - 1)(3\sqrt{2} - 1)$

14. $(4\sqrt{7} + 3)(4\sqrt{7} + 3)$

Written Exercises

Simplify.

1. $3\sqrt{4} \cdot 5\sqrt{5}$

2. $9\sqrt{3} \cdot 3\sqrt{5}$

3. $4\sqrt{7} \cdot 4\sqrt{5}$

4. $3\sqrt{2} \cdot 7\sqrt{2}$

5. $10\sqrt{5} \cdot 3\sqrt{2}$

6. $5\sqrt{7} \cdot 2\sqrt{7}$

7. $4\sqrt{x} \cdot 3\sqrt{x}$

8. $7\sqrt{a} \cdot \sqrt{a}$

9. $10\sqrt{2x} \cdot 3\sqrt{2x}$

10. $3\sqrt{7a^3} \cdot 3\sqrt{14a^4}$

11. $4\sqrt{10x^3} \cdot 3\sqrt{5x^4}$

12. $5\sqrt{3y} \cdot 7\sqrt{6y}$

13. $-5\sqrt{6x^5} \cdot 7\sqrt{2x^2}$

14. $-2\sqrt{2a^{10}} \cdot 4\sqrt{12a^6}$

15. $7\sqrt{8y^9} \cdot \sqrt{2y^5}$

16. $4\sqrt{3}(\sqrt{2} + \sqrt{3})$

17. $3\sqrt{7}(3\sqrt{5} - 5\sqrt{2})$

18. $-7\sqrt{2}(5\sqrt{3} - 2\sqrt{6})$

19. $-9\sqrt{6}(\sqrt{5} - 5\sqrt{3})$

20. $6\sqrt{8}(4\sqrt{3} - 2\sqrt{2})$

21. $4\sqrt{2}(5\sqrt{6} - 3\sqrt{2})$

22. $(3\sqrt{6} + \sqrt{5})(2\sqrt{6} - \sqrt{5})$

23. $(3\sqrt{5} + \sqrt{2})(\sqrt{5} - 2\sqrt{2})$

24. $(-2\sqrt{2} + 3\sqrt{3})(4\sqrt{2} - \sqrt{3})$

25. $(-5\sqrt{3} - \sqrt{6})(2\sqrt{3} + \sqrt{6})$

26. $(3\sqrt{7} + \sqrt{5})(3\sqrt{7} - \sqrt{5})$

27. $(4\sqrt{6} + \sqrt{2})(4\sqrt{6} - \sqrt{2})$

28. $(2\sqrt{11} - 3\sqrt{3})(2\sqrt{11} + 3\sqrt{3})$

29. $(6\sqrt{3} - 7\sqrt{2})(6\sqrt{3} + 7\sqrt{2})$

30. $(3\sqrt{2} - 2\sqrt{24})(5\sqrt{2} + \sqrt{24})$

31. $(3\sqrt{12} - 2\sqrt{2})(\sqrt{12} + 5\sqrt{2})$

32. $(7\sqrt{6} - \sqrt{12})(2\sqrt{6} + 2\sqrt{12})$

33. $(\sqrt{3} - 4\sqrt{20})(-3\sqrt{3} + 2\sqrt{20})$

For Exercises 34–39, use $(a + b)^2 = a^2 + 2ab + b^2$.

34. $(2\sqrt{3} + \sqrt{2})^2$

35. $(4\sqrt{2} + 3\sqrt{5})^2$

36. $5(\sqrt{10} - 2\sqrt{2})^2$

37. $(-2\sqrt{3} - \sqrt{5})^2$

38. $(5\sqrt{5} - 2\sqrt{3})^2$

39. $(-7\sqrt{3} - 2\sqrt{5})^2$

Find the area of each rectangle. Give answers in simplest radical form.

40.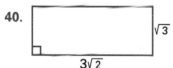

41.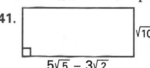

42.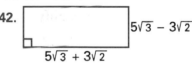

43. Find the area of a triangle with a base of $8\sqrt{5}$ cm and altitude of $2\sqrt{3}$ cm.

44. Find the area of a right triangle if the length of each leg is $\sqrt{5}$ in.

Mixed Review

Factor completely. *7.4, 7.6*

1. $3y^2 - 14y - 24$

2. $8a^2 + 12a - 80$

3. $3a^3 - 5a^2 - 8a$

Solve. *7.7*

4. $3b^2 + 11b + 6 = 0$

5. $2x^2 + 5x + 2 = 0$

6. $6y^2 - y - 1 = 0$

7. Write an equation for the line that passes through points $P(-3, -1)$ and $Q(6, 2)$. *11.2*

13.8 Dividing Radicals

Objectives	To divide and simplify expressions containing radicals
	To simplify radical expressions by rationalizing the denominator

The *Quotient Property* for square roots is similar to the product property, $\sqrt{a} \cdot \sqrt{b} = \sqrt{ab}$. Consider the following illustration.

$$\frac{\sqrt{49}}{\sqrt{100}} = \frac{7}{10} \text{ and } \sqrt{\frac{49}{100}} = \frac{7}{10}, \text{ so } \frac{\sqrt{49}}{\sqrt{100}} = \sqrt{\frac{49}{100}}$$

Quotient Property for Square Roots

For all positive numbers a and b, $\dfrac{\sqrt{a}}{\sqrt{b}} = \sqrt{\dfrac{a}{b}}$.

EXAMPLE 1 Simplify.

a. $\dfrac{\sqrt{45}}{\sqrt{5}}$

b. $\dfrac{\sqrt{100a^7}}{\sqrt{2a^3}}$

Solutions

a. $\dfrac{\sqrt{45}}{\sqrt{5}} = \sqrt{\dfrac{45}{5}} = \sqrt{9} = 3$

b. $\dfrac{\sqrt{100a^7}}{\sqrt{2a^3}} = \sqrt{\dfrac{100a^7}{2a^3}} = \sqrt{50a^4} = \sqrt{25 \cdot 2 \cdot a^4} = 5a^2\sqrt{2}$

TRY THIS Simplify: 1. $\dfrac{\sqrt{108}}{\sqrt{3}}$ 2. $\dfrac{\sqrt{144x^5}}{\sqrt{3x^2}}$

A radical in simplest form contains no radical in the denominator. In Example 1, the radicand in the numerator was exactly divisible by the radicand in the denominator. If this is not the case, it is necessary to *rationalize* the denominator, as shown in Example 2.

EXAMPLE 2 Simplify $\dfrac{-5\sqrt{7}}{\sqrt{12}}$.

Plan Multiply the numerator and the denominator by the least square root needed to make the radicand in the denominator a perfect square.

Solution

$$\frac{-5\sqrt{7}}{\sqrt{12}} = \frac{-5\sqrt{7}}{\sqrt{12}} \cdot \frac{\sqrt{3}}{\sqrt{3}} \qquad \leftarrow \frac{a}{b} = \frac{a \cdot c}{b \cdot c}$$

$$= -\frac{5\sqrt{21}}{\sqrt{36}} = -\frac{5\sqrt{21}}{6}$$

TRY THIS   Simplify: **3.** $\dfrac{-6\sqrt{5}}{\sqrt{8}}$ **4.** $\dfrac{4\sqrt{5}}{\sqrt{27}}$

A radical expression is not simplified if the radicand contains a fraction. To simplify a radical with a fraction in the radicand, use the property $\sqrt{\dfrac{a}{b}} = \dfrac{\sqrt{a}}{\sqrt{b}}$. Then rationalize the denominator.

EXAMPLE 3   Simplify $\sqrt{\dfrac{12}{8a^3}}$.

Solution $\sqrt{\dfrac{12}{8a^3}} = \sqrt{\dfrac{3}{2a^3}} = \dfrac{\sqrt{3} \cdot \sqrt{2a}}{\sqrt{2a^3} \cdot \sqrt{2a}} = \dfrac{\sqrt{6a}}{\sqrt{4a^4}} = \dfrac{\sqrt{6a}}{2a^2}$

TRY THIS   Simplify: **5.** $\sqrt{\dfrac{18}{21x^5}}$ **6.** $\sqrt{\dfrac{10}{6x}}$

Radical expressions such as $-2\sqrt{7} + 3\sqrt{5}$ and $-2\sqrt{7} - 3\sqrt{5}$ that differ only in the sign of one term are called **conjugates**. To simplify an expression such as $\dfrac{3}{2 - \sqrt{3}}$, multiply the numerator and the denominator by $2 + \sqrt{3}$, which is the conjugate of $2 - \sqrt{3}$. Then use $(a + b)(a - b) = a^2 - b^2$. The resulting denominator will be a rational number as shown in Example 4.

EXAMPLE 4   Simplify $\dfrac{3}{2 - \sqrt{3}}$.

Plan   Multiply the numerator and the denominator by $2 + \sqrt{3}$, the conjugate of $2 - \sqrt{3}$.

Solution

$$\frac{3}{2 - \sqrt{3}} = \frac{3 \cdot (2 + \sqrt{3})}{(2 - \sqrt{3}) \cdot (2 + \sqrt{3})} = \frac{3(2 + \sqrt{3})}{2^2 - (\sqrt{3})^2} = \frac{6 + 3\sqrt{3}}{4 - 3}$$
$$= 6 + 3\sqrt{3}$$

So, $\dfrac{3}{2 - \sqrt{3}} = 6 + 3\sqrt{3}$. To check, multiply $(6 + 3\sqrt{3})(2 - \sqrt{3})$.

TRY THIS   Simplify: 7. $\dfrac{4}{2 - \sqrt{5}}$ 8. $\dfrac{8}{2 + \sqrt{6}}$

Classroom Exercises

By what factor should the denominator be multiplied to give a perfect square radicand? Give the least possible square root.

1. $\dfrac{\sqrt{3}}{\sqrt{5}}$
2. $\dfrac{\sqrt{7y}}{\sqrt{5y^3}}$
3. $\dfrac{-3a^4}{\sqrt{6b^5}}$
4. $\dfrac{3\sqrt{7a}}{2\sqrt{8c^7}}$

Simplify.

5. $\dfrac{\sqrt{27x^6}}{\sqrt{3x^2}}$
6. $\dfrac{\sqrt{12}}{\sqrt{18a}}$
7. $\dfrac{9}{\sqrt{27a^5}}$
8. $\dfrac{24xy}{\sqrt{x^6y^3}}$

Written Exercises

Divide and simplify.

1. $\dfrac{\sqrt{35}}{\sqrt{5}}$
2. $\dfrac{\sqrt{48a^5}}{\sqrt{6a^3}}$
3. $\dfrac{\sqrt{50x^3}}{\sqrt{2x}}$
4. $\dfrac{\sqrt{28y^7}}{\sqrt{7y^3}}$

5. $\dfrac{\sqrt{54a^5}}{\sqrt{6a}}$
6. $\dfrac{3}{\sqrt{5}}$
7. $\dfrac{-2}{\sqrt{3}}$
8. $\dfrac{1}{\sqrt{7}}$

9. $\dfrac{14}{\sqrt{2}}$
10. $\dfrac{-10}{\sqrt{5}}$
11. $\dfrac{7\sqrt{2}}{\sqrt{6}}$
12. $\dfrac{-18\sqrt{5}}{\sqrt{9}}$

13. $\dfrac{12\sqrt{4}}{-\sqrt{3}}$
14. $\dfrac{16\sqrt{7}}{\sqrt{8}}$
15. $\dfrac{-36\sqrt{12}}{\sqrt{2}}$
16. $\dfrac{\sqrt{20}}{\sqrt{30x^3}}$

17. $\dfrac{\sqrt{14}}{\sqrt{21a}}$
18. $\dfrac{\sqrt{35}}{\sqrt{15a^5}}$
19. $\dfrac{\sqrt{48}}{\sqrt{16x^3}}$
20. $\dfrac{\sqrt{75}}{\sqrt{50a^7}}$

21. $\dfrac{4}{\sqrt{a^3}}$
22. $\dfrac{-10}{\sqrt{y^5}}$
23. $\dfrac{16}{\sqrt{20a^7}}$
24. $\dfrac{-81}{\sqrt{3a^3}}$

25. $\dfrac{6}{3 - \sqrt{7}}$

26. $\dfrac{4}{1 + \sqrt{2}}$

27. $\dfrac{-12}{\sqrt{7} - 4}$

28. $\dfrac{-7}{5 + \sqrt{2}}$

29. $\dfrac{24ab}{\sqrt{a^4b^3}}$

30. $\dfrac{-16y}{\sqrt{24y}}$

31. $\dfrac{48c^3d^2}{\sqrt{c^2d}}$

32. $\dfrac{30x}{\sqrt{xy^4}}$

33. $\dfrac{18x^4y^3}{\sqrt{xy}}$

34. $\dfrac{-12x^4y^3}{\sqrt{20x^5y^2}}$

35. $\dfrac{3a^4b^5}{\sqrt{6a^2b^3}}$

36. $\dfrac{36c^9d^3}{\sqrt{12cd^3}}$

37. $\dfrac{-15a^4b}{\sqrt{5a^6b^7}}$

38. $\dfrac{100x^7y^4}{\sqrt{xy^2}}$

39. $\dfrac{\sqrt{18b^4c^8}}{\sqrt{3a^3b^6}}$

40. $\dfrac{\sqrt{72x^5y^7}}{\sqrt{8xy^{10}}}$

41. $\dfrac{\sqrt{6\frac{1}{2}}}{\sqrt{4\frac{1}{3}}}$

42. $\dfrac{\sqrt{6\frac{2}{5}}}{\sqrt{5\frac{1}{3}}}$

43. $\dfrac{\sqrt{9\frac{2}{3}}}{\sqrt{5\frac{4}{5}}}$

44. $\dfrac{\sqrt{15\frac{1}{3}}}{\sqrt{9\frac{2}{3}}}$

45. $\dfrac{5}{3\sqrt{5} - 1}$

46. $\dfrac{14}{3 - 2\sqrt{3}}$

47. $\dfrac{12}{5 + 3\sqrt{2}}$

48. $\dfrac{135}{7 + 2\sqrt{7}}$

49. $\dfrac{-15}{3\sqrt{5} - 1}$

50. $\dfrac{100}{5 - \sqrt{2}}$

51. $\dfrac{3}{\sqrt{2} + 2\sqrt{3}}$

52. $\dfrac{-7\sqrt{2}}{-3\sqrt{5} - 2\sqrt{3}}$

Solve.

53. A rectangle has an area of $6\sqrt{10}$ in². If its length is $3\sqrt{5}$ in., what is its width?

54. A rectangle is $2\sqrt{5}$ cm long. If its area is $(6\sqrt{15} - 6\sqrt{10})$ cm², what is its width?

55. The area of a triangle is 72 cm² and its altitude is $6\sqrt{2}$ cm. Find the length of the base.

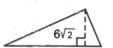

56. The area of a rectangle is $(\sqrt{10} + 3\sqrt{5})$ cm² and its length is $(\sqrt{2} + 3)$ cm. Find its width.

Mixed Review

Evaluate for the given values of the variables.   *1.3, 2.6*

1. x^2 for $x = -\frac{2}{3}$

2. $2a^4$ for $a = -2$

3. $\dfrac{x^2 - 2x}{3x}$ for $x = 3$

4. $5ab^2c^3$ for $a = -1$, $b = 2$, and $c = -2$

Factor.   *7.2, 7.4–7.6*

5. $2m^5n + 16m^4$

6. $6x^2 - x - 2$

7. $m^2 - n^2$

8. $ac + bc + ad + bd$

9. Wanda's age is 12 years more than twice Carlos's age. The sum of their ages is 36. How old is each?   *12.3*

13.9 Radical Equations

Objective	To solve equations containing radicals

An equation with a variable in the radicand, such as $\sqrt{x} = 6$, is called a **radical equation**. To solve $\sqrt{x} = 6$, square each side.

$$\sqrt{x} = 6 \qquad\qquad \text{Check:} \quad \sqrt{x} = 6$$
$$(\sqrt{x})^2 = 6^2 \qquad\qquad\qquad\qquad \sqrt{36} \overset{?}{=} 6$$
$$x = 36 \qquad\qquad\qquad\qquad\qquad 6 = 6 \ \ (\text{True})$$

In this case the original equation ($\sqrt{x} = 6$) is equivalent to the squared equation ($x = 36$), since both have the same solution.

To solve an equation such as $\sqrt{3x - 5} - 4 = 3$, get the radical alone on one side of the equation. Then square each side and solve for x.

EXAMPLE 1 Solve $\sqrt{2x - 5} - 4 = 3$. Check.

Plan Add 4 to each side of the equation to get the radical alone.

Solution

$$\sqrt{2x - 5} - 4 = 3 \qquad \text{Check:} \quad \sqrt{2x - 5} - 4 = 3$$
$$\sqrt{2x - 5} = 7 \qquad\qquad\qquad \sqrt{2(27) - 5} - 4 \overset{?}{=} 3$$
$$2x - 5 = 49 \qquad\qquad\qquad\qquad \sqrt{54 - 5} - 4 \overset{?}{=} 3$$
$$2x = 54 \qquad\qquad\qquad\qquad\qquad \sqrt{49} - 4 \overset{?}{=} 3$$
$$x = 27 \qquad\qquad\qquad\qquad\qquad\quad 7 - 4 \overset{?}{=} 3$$
$$3 = 3 \ \ (\text{True})$$

Thus, the solution is 27.

TRY THIS 1. Solve $\sqrt{4x - 3} - 6 = 3$.

Squaring each side of an equation does not always result in an equivalent equation. Let $x = 9$. Then $x^2 = 81$.

The squared equation has two solutions, 9 and -9, but only 9 checks in the original equation. The root, -9, that was introduced by squaring is called an **extraneous** solution.

When you square both sides of an equation, you must always check *all* solutions in the *original* equation. Eliminate extraneous solutions.

EXAMPLE 2   Solve $\sqrt{x + 2} + 3\sqrt{x - 6} = 0$. Check.

Plan   First, get one radical expression on each side of the equation. Then square each side.

Solution

$$\sqrt{x + 2} + 3\sqrt{x - 6} = 0$$
$$\sqrt{x + 2} = -3\sqrt{x - 6}$$
$$x + 2 = 9(x - 6)$$
$$x + 2 = 9x - 54$$
$$56 = 8x$$
$$7 = x$$

Check $x = 7$.
$$\sqrt{x + 2} + 3\sqrt{x - 6} = 0$$
$$\sqrt{7 + 2} + 3\sqrt{7 - 6} \stackrel{?}{=} 0$$
$$\sqrt{9} + 3\sqrt{1} \stackrel{?}{=} 0$$
$$3 + 3 \stackrel{?}{=} 0$$
$$6 \neq 0$$

There is no solution since 7 is extraneous.

EXAMPLE 3   Solve $\sqrt{y + 1} = y - 5$. Check.

Solution

$$\sqrt{y + 1} = y - 5$$
$$y + 1 = (y - 5)^2$$
$$y + 1 = y^2 - 10y + 25$$
$$0 = y^2 - 11y + 24$$
$$0 = (y - 8)(y - 3)$$
$$y - 8 = 0 \quad or \quad y - 3 = 0$$
$$y = 8 \qquad\qquad y = 3$$

Check $y = 8$.
$$\sqrt{y + 1} = y - 5$$
$$\sqrt{8 + 1} \stackrel{?}{=} 8 - 5$$
$$\sqrt{9} \stackrel{?}{=} 3$$
$$3 = 3 \qquad \text{True}$$

Check $y = 3$.
$$\sqrt{y + 1} = y - 5$$
$$\sqrt{3 + 1} \stackrel{?}{=} 3 - 5$$
$$\sqrt{4} \stackrel{?}{=} -2$$
$$2 \neq -2 \qquad \text{Thus, the solution is } 8.$$

TRY THIS   2. Solve $\sqrt{6y - 8} = y - 4$.

Classroom Exercises

What equation results from squaring each side of the given equation?

1. $\sqrt{y} = 2$ **2.** $\sqrt{2x} = 8$ **3.** $\sqrt{3y - 2} = 7$ **4.** $\sqrt{3x - 1} = \sqrt{2x + 4}$

Solve each equation. Check.

5. $\sqrt{2x - 1} = 7$ **6.** $\sqrt{3y} + 2 = 11$ **7.** $7 + \sqrt{5a} = 9$

8. $2\sqrt{5y} = 10$ **9.** $\sqrt{4x} = 2\sqrt{5}$ **10.** $\sqrt{3x - 1} = \sqrt{5x + 2}$

Written Exercises

Solve each equation. Check.

1. $\sqrt{x} = 5$

2. $8 = \sqrt{y}$

3. $\sqrt{z} = -3$

4. $\sqrt{a} + 2 = 3$

5. $7 = \sqrt{y} - 2$

6. $\sqrt{c} - 4 = 2$

7. $\sqrt{2x + 3} = 7$

8. $13 = \sqrt{3y - 2} + 9$

9. $\sqrt{7x - 2} + 5 = 3$

10. $0 = \sqrt{3x + 4} - 7$

11. $4 - \sqrt{x - 3} = 9$

12. $\sqrt{x} = 3\sqrt{3}$

13. $\sqrt{2y} = 2\sqrt{5}$

14. $\sqrt{44} = 2\sqrt{y}$

15. $2\sqrt{5x - 4} = 12$

16. $4\sqrt{x - 5} = 15$

17. $\sqrt{4x - 2} = \sqrt{3x + 7}$

18. $\sqrt{1 - 7a} = \sqrt{5 - 2a}$

19. $\sqrt{10y + 2} = 2\sqrt{4y - 1}$

20. $\sqrt{3x + 1} + 2\sqrt{x} = 0$

21. $3\sqrt{1 + a} = \sqrt{5a + 1}$

22. $\sqrt{x^2 - 6x} = 4$

23. $\sqrt{x^2 - 12} = -1$

24. $\sqrt{3y + 1} = y - 3$

25. $1 + y = \sqrt{y^2 + 5}$

26. $c - 5 = \sqrt{c + 7}$

27. $\sqrt{x^2 + 2} = x - 2$

28. $\sqrt{2x^2 - 12} = x$

29. $\sqrt{17 - 4y} = y + 1$

30. $\sqrt{4x^2 + 5} = 3x$

31. $a - 2 = \sqrt{2a - 1}$

32. $\sqrt{23 - x} + 3 = x$

33. $6 = \sqrt{2y + 3} + y$

Solve each problem.

34. If the square root of a number is increased by 9, the result is 16. Find the number.

35. The square root of 1 less than 5 times a number is equal to 3. Find the number.

36. Find a number if half the square root of the number is equal to 5.

Solve each equation. Check. (HINT: Square each side two different times.)

37. $\sqrt{x} + 1 = \sqrt{x + 11}$

38. $\sqrt{x} + 4 = \sqrt{x + 40}$

39. $\sqrt{a + 27} = 3 + \sqrt{a}$

40. $\sqrt{y} + 1 = \sqrt{3y - 3}$

41. $\sqrt{x - 7} = 2 + \sqrt{x}$

42. $\sqrt{2x + 4} = 2\sqrt{x + 3}$

Solve each formula for the given variable.

43. $r = \sqrt{\dfrac{A}{\pi}}$ for A

44. $T = 2\pi\sqrt{\dfrac{l}{g}}$ for l

45. $r = \sqrt{\dfrac{3v}{\pi h}}$ for h

Mixed Review

Simplify.   *2.2, 6.2, 6.7, 8.3, 8.7*

1. $-|-14|$

2. $-(7a^2 + 6a^3 - 5) - (a^2 + 3)$

3. $(-3x^5y^3)^2$

4. $\dfrac{8x^4y^2}{5xy^6} \cdot \dfrac{15x^3y^5}{16x^2y^8}$

5. $\dfrac{-4}{n - 3} + \dfrac{2}{n + 4}$

6. $\dfrac{a - 1}{2a + 1} + 3$

7. Four is what percent of 12?   *4.7*

8. Thirty-six percent of what number is 52.2?   *4.7*

9. A sweater sells for $95. If the tax rate is $7\frac{1}{2}\%$, what is the total cost?   *4.8*

Mixed Problem Solving

When solving problems that involve geometric figures, drawing a diagram will help you to visualize the situation and to understand the problem. Remember to label the diagram carefully, and to express given dimensions in terms of one variable, when possible.

Solve each problem.

1. An isosceles triangle has a base angle of 38°. What is the measure of the vertex angle?

2. How fast must a bicycle travel to cover a distance of 105 mi in $3\frac{1}{2}$ h?

3. The length of a rectangle is 8 in. more than 5 times the width. The perimeter is 40 in. Find the length and the width of the rectangle.

4. A plumber charges $50 for a house call plus $48 for each hour she works. Her bill for a job was $194. How many hours did she work?

5. Find the height of a triangle with an area of 240 cm^2 and a base of 13 cm. Use the formula $A = \frac{1}{2}bh$.

6. Use the formula $A = \frac{1}{2}(b + c)h$ to find the area of a trapezoid if the height is 8.7 cm and the bases are 6.4 cm and 12.6 cm long.

7. When a number is decreased by 0.6 of the number, the result is 128. Find the number.

8. A company earned $12,500 more in the second year than in the first. What did it earn each year if the total for the two years was $197,500?

9. A collection of dimes and and quarters is worth $5.00. There are $2\frac{1}{2}$ times as many dimes as quarters. Find the number of coins of each type.

10. Kim has 16 coins, all in nickels and quarters. The total value of the coins is $2.80. How many coins of each type are there?

11. Nine is what percent of 45?

12. Sixteen percent of what number is 36?

13. Find the interest earned on $1,400 invested at a simple interest rate of 8% per year for 9 years.

14. A new car was priced at $16,000. Then the price was increased by 3%. What was the new price?

15. Find two consecutive even integers whose product is 168.

16. Find two consecutive odd integers whose product is 63.

17. Find three consecutive odd integers such that the square of the third minus the square of the second is 9 less than the square of the first.

18. The cost of chocolates varies directly as the weight. If 4 lb of chocolates cost $26, find the cost of 6 lb of chocolates.

19. The volume of a gas varies inversely as the pressure. If the volume of a gas is 48 m^3 at 4.5 atmospheres of pressure, find the volume at 7 atmospheres of pressure.

20. For a triangle of constant area, the height h varies inversely as the length of the base b. If $b = 16$ cm when $h = 36$ cm, find b when $h = 48$ cm.

Chapter 13 Review

Key Terms

conjugates   (p. 523)
irrational number   (p. 497)
perfect square   (p. 501)
principal square root   (p. 500)
Product Property for Square Roots
   (p. 500)
Pythagorean Theorem   (p. 508)
Quotient Property for Square Roots
   (p. 522)
radical   (p. 500)

radical sign   (p. 500)
radicand   (p. 500)
rational number   (p. 495)
rationalize the denominator   (p. 522)
right triangle   (p. 508)
Square Root Property of Even Powers
   (p. 513)
Square Root Property of Odd Powers
   (p. 513)
subset   (p. 498)

Key Ideas and Review Exercises

13.1   To write repeating decimals in fractional form, let $n =$ the decimal. Multiply the equation by 10^a, where a is the number of digits in the block of repeating digits. Subtract the first equation from the second, and solve for n.

For each repeating decimal, write a fraction $\frac{a}{b}$ where a and b are integers.

1. $13.\overline{42}$ **2.** $9.\overline{7}$ **3.** $41.\overline{17}$ **4.** $12.\overline{241}$ **5.** $7.9191\ldots$

13.2   To simplify a square root when the radicand is not a perfect square, find the greatest perfect square factor of the radicand. Then use $\sqrt{a \cdot b} = \sqrt{a} \cdot \sqrt{b}$.

Simplify, if possible. If not possible, so indicate.

6. $\sqrt{18}$ **7.** $\sqrt{79}$ **8.** $\sqrt{99}$ **9.** $4\sqrt{500}$ **10.** $-10\sqrt{180}$

13.3   To approximate the square root of a number, use a square root table or the divide-and-average method.

Approximate to the nearest tenth. Use a square root table.

11. $\sqrt{41}$ **12.** $\sqrt{79}$ **13.** $\sqrt{99}$ **14.** $\sqrt{125}$ **15.** $\sqrt{234}$
16. Approximate $\sqrt{54}$ to the nearest tenth. Use the divide-and-average method.

13.4   To find the length of one side of a right triangle given the lengths of the other two sides, use the Pythagorean Theorem $c^2 = a^2 + b^2$.

To determine whether or not a triangle is a right triangle, use $c^2 = a^2 + b^2$ where c is the length of the longest side.

For each right triangle, find the missing length. Give answers in simplest radical form.

17. $a = 5, b = 7$ **18.** $a = 3, c = 10$ **19.** $b = 8, c = 10\sqrt{3}$

20. Write an explanation of why a triangle with sides 3 cm, 5 cm, and $\sqrt{34}$ cm is a right triangle, but one with sides 8 cm, 10 cm, and 12 cm is not a right triangle.

13.5   To simplify square roots with variables in the radicand, use $\sqrt{a^{2x}} = a^x$ for even powers and $\sqrt{a^{2x+1}} = a^x\sqrt{a}$ for odd powers.

Simplify.

21. $\sqrt{25y^{14}}$ **22.** $-3\sqrt{49a^{22}}$ **23.** $\sqrt{16x^7}$

24. $-\sqrt{36y^{15}}$ **25.** $-\sqrt{18x^5y^{10}}$ **26.** $\sqrt{121xy^8}$

13.6   To add or subtract expressions containing radicals, simplify the radicals, if possible. Then combine like terms.

Add or subtract. Simplify.

27. $9\sqrt{5} - 3\sqrt{5}$ **28.** $-5a\sqrt{4a} + \sqrt{9a^3}$ **29.** $\sqrt{80} - 3\sqrt{45}$

13.7   To multiply and simplify expressions containing radicals, use $\sqrt{a} \cdot \sqrt{b} = \sqrt{ab}$ to multiply the radicals. Then simplify.

Simplify.

30. $5\sqrt{9} \cdot 3\sqrt{3}$ **31.** $9\sqrt{3}(\sqrt{3} + 4\sqrt{6})$ **32.** $(2\sqrt{3} + 3)(3\sqrt{3} - 2)$

13.8   To divide expressions containing radicals, use $\dfrac{\sqrt{a}}{\sqrt{b}} = \sqrt{\dfrac{a}{b}}$ if the radicand in the numerator is divisible by the radicand in the denominator. Otherwise, rationalize the denominator.

Divide and simplify.

33. $\dfrac{\sqrt{95}}{\sqrt{5}}$ **34.** $\sqrt{\dfrac{3}{75x}}$ **35.** $\dfrac{8}{3 + \sqrt{5}}$

13.9   To solve radical equations, get a radical alone on one side of the equation. Then square each side. Check all solutions in the original equation. Eliminate any extraneous solutions.

Solve each equation. Check.

36. $\sqrt{x - 2} + 4 = 9$ **37.** $3 + \sqrt{x + 6} = 0$ **38.** $\sqrt{x^2 + 8x} = 3$

Chapter 13 Test

For each repeating decimal, write a fraction $\frac{a}{b}$ where a and b are integers.

1. $0.\overline{7}$ **2.** $0.\overline{145}$

3. Approximate $\sqrt{13}$ to the nearest tenth. Use a square root table.

4. Approximate $\sqrt{38}$ to the nearest tenth. Use the divide-and-average method.

Simplify.

5. $\sqrt{40}$ **6.** $\sqrt{99}$ **7.** $\sqrt{48} \cdot \sqrt{48}$ **8.** $3\sqrt{64y^{16}}$

9. $\sqrt{4x^5y^7}$ **10.** $-\sqrt{28a^{10}b^{24}}$ **11.** $3c\sqrt{16c^{12}d^9}$ **12.** $5m\sqrt{27m^{15}n^{28}}$

13. $9\sqrt{5} - 4\sqrt{5}$ **14.** $8\sqrt{2} - \sqrt{18} + \sqrt{8}$

15. $3\sqrt{27ab} - 4\sqrt{12ab} + 5\sqrt{ab}$ **16.** $3xy\sqrt{36y} + 7\sqrt{x^2y^3}$

17. $5\sqrt{2} \cdot 3\sqrt{8}$ **18.** $6\sqrt{8x} \cdot \sqrt{5x^5}$

19. $-3\sqrt{2}(\sqrt{7} - 2\sqrt{5})$ **20.** $(3\sqrt{7} - \sqrt{2})(3\sqrt{7} + \sqrt{2})$

21. $(\sqrt{2} - 3\sqrt{5})^2$ **22.** $\dfrac{\sqrt{40}}{\sqrt{8}}$

23. $\dfrac{-5}{\sqrt{3}}$ **24.** $\dfrac{\sqrt{6}}{\sqrt{8y^5}}$ **25.** $\dfrac{3x^2y^3}{\sqrt{6x^4y^5}}$ **26.** $\dfrac{-3}{5 + \sqrt{3}}$

For each right triangle, find the missing length. Give answers in simplest radical form.

27. $a = 6, b = 5$ **28.** $b = 4, c = 9$

Given the lengths of three sides of a triangle, determine whether it is a right triangle.

29. 48, 14, 50   **30.** 5, 10, 15

Solve each equation. Check.

31. $\sqrt{7x} + 1 = 8$ **32.** $x - 3 = \sqrt{2x - 6}$

Solve each problem. Round answers to the nearest tenth.

33. The area of a rectangle is 96 cm². Find the length and the width if the length is 4 times the width.

34. A surveyor walked 10 km north, then 8 km east. How far was the surveyor from his starting point?

Simplify.

35. $-14\sqrt{a^{6m}b^{4m+3}}$ **36.** $(\sqrt{2} - 2\sqrt{3} + \sqrt{5})^2$

College Prep Test

For each Exercise, you are to compare a quantity in Column 1 with a quantity in Column 2. Select the correct answer from the following choices.

A—The quantity in Column 1 is greater than the quantity in Column 2.
B—The quantity in Column 2 is greater than the quantity in Column 1.
C—The quantity in Column 1 is equal to the quantity in Column 2.
D—The relationship cannot be determined from the given information.

NOTE: Information centered over both columns refers to one or both of the quantities to be compared.

Column 1	Column 2
1. $a > 0$	
$\sqrt{a}$	$-\dfrac{a}{\sqrt{a}}$
2. $x \geq 8$	
$\sqrt{x + 8}$	4
3. $4 - \sqrt{6}$	$\sqrt{5} - 4$
4. $\sqrt{\dfrac{1}{4} - \dfrac{1}{36}}$	$\sqrt{\dfrac{1}{4}} - \sqrt{\dfrac{1}{36}}$
5. $x > y > 0$	
$\sqrt{x}$	$\sqrt{xy}$
6. $\sqrt{0.49}$	$(0.7)^2$
7. $\sqrt{\dfrac{1}{0.50}}$	$\sqrt{4}$
8. $a > 0, b < 0, x > 0, y > 0$	
$\dfrac{a}{\sqrt{x}}$	$\dfrac{b}{\sqrt{y}}$

Column 1	Column 2
9.	

$ABCD$ is a square.

Column 1	Column 2
$9x^2$	$4y^2$
10. $a > 0, b > 0$	
$(\sqrt{a + b})^2$	$(\sqrt{a} + \sqrt{b})^2$
11. $\sqrt{7} + \sqrt{13}$	$\sqrt{20}$
12. $3 - \sqrt{x + 12} = 0$	
x	$2x$

Ben Livingston, an artist in neon, is shown here with his Neon Mural #1, a computer-animated cartoon. Two friends of his, a computer programmer and a neon glass bender, helped him turn his ideas into reality.

14.1 The Square Root Property

Objective	To solve quadratic equations by using the Square Root Property

Suppose that a ball falls 80 ft from the roof of a building. How long will it take the ball to reach the ground?

The time t in seconds can be found by using the formula $d = 16t^2$, where d is the distance in feet. Since the ball travels 80 ft, $80 = 16t^2$, or $16t^2 = 80$.

So, $t^2 = 5$ (Only the positive square root
        $t = \sqrt{5} \approx 2.236$ can be the answer.)

Thus, it will take the ball about 2.2 s to reach the ground.

Consider the quadratic equation $x^2 = c$ for different values of c.

$c > 0$ (c is positive)	$c = 0$	$c < 0$ (c is negative)
$x^2 = 36$ There are *two* solutions, 6 and -6, since $6^2 = 36$ and $(-6)^2 = 36$.	$x^2 = 0$ There is *one* solution, 0, since $0^2 = 0$.	$x^2 = -9$ There is *no* real number solution, since there is no real number that has -9 as its square.

The Square Root Property is stated below for $c > 0$.

The Square Root Property
If $x^2 = c$, then $x = \sqrt{c}$ or $x = -\sqrt{c}$, for $c > 0$.

EXAMPLE 1	Find the solution set of $x^2 = 52$.
Plan	Use the Square Root Property.
Solution	$x^2 = 52$ $x = \sqrt{52}$ or $x = -\sqrt{52}$ ⟵ $\sqrt{52} = \sqrt{4} \cdot \sqrt{13} = 2\sqrt{13}$ $x = 2\sqrt{13}$ or $x = -2\sqrt{13}$ ⟵ This can be written as $x = \pm 2\sqrt{13}$.
Check	Since $(2\sqrt{13})^2 = 52$ and $(-2\sqrt{13})^2 = 52$, both solutions check. Thus, the solution set is $\{2\sqrt{13}, -2\sqrt{13}\}$.

TRY THIS   Find the solution set: **1.** $x^2 = 50$ **2.** $x^2 = 27$

Sometimes you may need to use the Addition Property of Equality first. Then apply the Square Root Property.

EXAMPLE 2   Solve $5x^2 - 6 = 3$.

Plan   Write the equation in the form $x^2 = c$. Then solve.

Solution

$$5x^2 - 6 = 3$$
$$5x^2 = 9$$
$$x^2 = \frac{9}{5}$$

$$x = \sqrt{\frac{9}{5}} \quad or \quad x = -\sqrt{\frac{9}{5}}$$

$$x = \frac{3}{\sqrt{5}} \qquad x = -\frac{3}{\sqrt{5}}$$

$$\frac{3 \cdot \sqrt{5}}{\sqrt{5} \cdot \sqrt{5}} = \frac{3\sqrt{5}}{5} \longrightarrow x = \frac{3\sqrt{5}}{5} \qquad x = -\frac{3\sqrt{5}}{5}$$

Thus, the solutions are $\dfrac{3\sqrt{5}}{5}$ and $-\dfrac{3\sqrt{5}}{5}$. The check is left for you.

TRY THIS   Solve.

3. $3x^2 - 2 = 10$ 4. $2x^2 + 1 = 51$

5. $x^2 + 4 = 10$ 6. $3x^2 - 4 = 7$

More complex equations such as $(x + 3)^2 = 49$ can also be solved by using the Square Root Property.

EXAMPLE 3   Find the solution set of $(x + 3)^2 = 49$.

Solution
$$(x + 3)^2 = 49$$
$$x + 3 = \sqrt{49} \quad or \quad x + 3 = -\sqrt{49}$$
$$x + 3 = 7 \qquad\qquad x + 3 = -7$$
$$x = 4 \qquad\qquad\quad x = -10$$

Checks $x = 4$: $(x + 3)^2 = 49$ $x = -10$: $(x + 3)^2 = 49$

$(4 + 3)^2 \overset{?}{=} 49$ $(-10 + 3)^2 \overset{?}{=} 49$

$7^2 \overset{?}{=} 49$ $(-7)^2 \overset{?}{=} 49$

$49 = 49$ True $49 = 49$ True

Thus, the solution set is $\{4, -10\}$.

EXAMPLE 4   Solve $3(2x - 5)^2 - 8 = 10$.

Plan   First add 8 to each side. Then divide each side by 3.

Solution

$$3(2x - 5)^2 - 8 = 10$$
$$3(2x - 5)^2 = 18$$
$$(2x - 5)^2 = 6$$

$$2x - 5 = \sqrt{6} \quad \text{or} \quad 2x - 5 = -\sqrt{6}$$
$$x = \frac{5 + \sqrt{6}}{2} \qquad\qquad x = \frac{5 - \sqrt{6}}{2}$$

Thus, the solutions are $\dfrac{5 + \sqrt{6}}{2}$ and $\dfrac{5 - \sqrt{6}}{2}$, or $\dfrac{5 \pm \sqrt{6}}{2}$.

The check is left for you.

TRY THIS   Solve.

    7. $(x - 2)^2 = 25$ **8.** $2(3x + 4)^2 - 5 = 9$

Classroom Exercises

Solve each equation. Give irrational solutions in simplest radical form.

1. $x^2 = 4$ **2.** $y^2 = 0$ **3.** $c^2 = 15$ **4.** $2x^2 = 32$

5. $y^2 - 21 = 0$ **6.** $(y - 8)^2 = 81$ **7.** $2(a - 5)^2 = 98$ **8.** $(2x + 1)^2 - 4 = 7$

Written Exercises

Solve each equation. Give irrational solutions in simplest radical form.

1. $x^2 = 49$	**2.** $x^2 = 100$	**3.** $a^2 = 0$
4. $x^2 = 11$	**5.** $y^2 = 26$	**6.** $z^2 = 30$
7. $c^2 = 24$	**8.** $x^2 = 72$	**9.** $y^2 = 75$
10. $x^2 = 128$	**11.** $y^2 = 300$	**12.** $x^2 = 250$
13. $x^2 - 64 = 0$	**14.** $y^2 - 15 = 0$	**15.** $z^2 - 32 = 0$
16. $-2x^2 = -50$	**17.** $3x^2 - 75 = 0$	**18.** $-5y^2 = -10$
19. $5a^2 = 3$	**20.** $7y^2 = 1$	**21.** $3x^2 = 16$
22. $-4z^2 = -18$	**23.** $2x^2 = 9$	**24.** $5y^2 - 8 = 1$
25. $7x^2 + 4 = 19$	**26.** $3y^2 - 2 = 1$	**27.** $4a^2 - 2 = 0$
28. $(x + 5)^2 = 36$	**29.** $(c - 4)^2 = 100$	**30.** $(y + 1)^2 = 6$
31. $2(x - 8)^2 = 8$	**32.** $-4(y - 9)^2 = -36$	**33.** $5(c + 1)^2 = 80$

34. $(r - 2)^2 = 19$

35. $(x + 8)^2 = 12$

36. $(z - 4)^2 = 30$

37. $(3x - 4)^2 = 18$

38. $(2y + 1)^2 = 5$

39. $(4c - 3)^2 = 2$

40. $(2y + 3)^2 - 1 = 5$

41. $(6a - 5)^2 + 2 = 8$

42. $(2d + 3)^2 - 4 = -2$

43. $\left(x + \frac{1}{2}\right)^2 = 0$

44. $\left(y + \frac{1}{4}\right)^2 = \frac{1}{16}$

45. $\left(c - \frac{1}{3}\right)^2 = \frac{4}{9}$

In Exercises 46 and 47, use the formula $d = 16t^2$, where d is the distance in feet traveled by a freely falling object dropped from rest, and t is the time of the fall in seconds.

46. Find the time to the nearest tenth of a second for an object to fall 1,500 ft.

47. An object dropped from the top of a tower hit the ground in 4 s. If the tower were twice as tall, how long would it take the object to hit the ground?

48. The area of the floor of a square room is 42 ft². Find the length of each side, to the nearest tenth of a foot.

49. If the area of a square is doubled, the result is 72 m². Find the length of each side of the square.

50. When the length of each side of a square is doubled, the area is 100 cm². Find the length of each side of the square.

Solve. If the equation has no real number solution, write *no solution*.

51. $y^2 + 14y + 49 = 6$

52. $c^2 - 10c + 25 = 2$

53. $m^2 + 16m + 64 = -1$

54. $4x^2 + 12x + 9 = 3$

55. $49y^2 - 42y = -9$

56. $2x^2 + 20x + 50 = 2$

Mixed Review

Multiply. **6.10**

1. $(x + 7)^2$

2. $(y - 4)^2$

3. $(2r + 1)^2$

Factor. **7.5**

4. $x^2 + 16x + 64$

5. $z^2 - 20z + 100$

6. $9y^2 - 30y + 25$

Divide. **8.4**

7. $\dfrac{y}{4x} \div \dfrac{3y^3}{8}$

8. $\dfrac{n + 2}{n} \div \dfrac{-4n - 8}{nm}$

9. $\dfrac{x^2}{x - 1} \div (x + 1)$

Solve. **9.1**

10. The sum of a number and its reciprocal is $-\frac{13}{6}$. Find the numbers.

11. Find two consecutive integers such that the sum of their reciprocals is $\frac{17}{72}$.

14.2 Completing the Square

To solve quadratic equations by completing the square

A square vegetable garden measures $(x + 3)$ meters on each side. It has several sections, as shown in this figure. The areas of most of the sections are given. The sum of the given areas is $x^2 + 3x + 3x$, or $x^2 + 6x$. What is the area, in meters, of the section shown in blue?

You know that the area of the garden can be represented as $(x + 3)^2$, or $x^2 + 6x + 9$. Thus, the area of the section shown in blue is 9 m^2.

In each case below, a binomial of the form $(x + a)$ is squared. The result is a *perfect square trinomial*. In each trinomial, observe the relationship between the coefficient of the x term and the third term.

$$(x + 3)^2 = x^2 + 6x + 9 \qquad (x - 4)^2 = x^2 - 8x + 16$$
$$\left(\tfrac{1}{2} \cdot 6\right)^2 \nearrow \qquad\qquad \left[\tfrac{1}{2} \cdot (-8)\right]^2 \nearrow$$

In both cases, the third term $= \left(\tfrac{1}{2} \cdot \text{coefficient of } x\right)^2$.

To complete the square of a binomial such as $x^2 + 12x$ means to add a third term that will form a perfect square trinomial. To complete the square of a binomial $x^2 + bx$, first take half of b and square it. Then add the square to $x^2 + bx$. The result is a perfect square trinomial.

EXAMPLE 1 Complete the square. Show the result as the square of a binomial.

    a. $x^2 + 12x$ **b.** $y^2 - 5y$

Solutions **a.** $\left(\tfrac{1}{2} \cdot 12\right)^2 = 6^2 = 36$ **b.** $\left[\tfrac{1}{2}(-5)\right]^2 = \left(-\tfrac{5}{2}\right)^2 = \tfrac{25}{4}$

           Add 36.   Add $\tfrac{25}{4}$.

           $x^2 + 12x + 36 = (x + 6)^2$

                                 $y^2 - 5y + \tfrac{25}{4} = \left(y - \tfrac{5}{2}\right)^2$

TRY THIS Complete the square. Write the result as the square of a binomial.

    1. $r^2 - 20r$ **2.** $t^2 + t$

You can use the process of completing the square to solve quadratic equations. Be sure that the quadratic equation is written in the form $ax^2 + bx + c = 0$ before starting this process.

EXAMPLE 2 Find the solution set of $x^2 - 2x - 15 = 0$ by completing the square.

Plan Add 15 to each side. Complete the square for $x^2 - 2x$ and add the result to each side. Then solve by using the Square Root Property.

Solution
$$x^2 - 2x - 15 = 0$$
$$x^2 - 2x = 15$$
$$x^2 - 2x + 1 = 15 + 1 \quad \longleftarrow \quad \text{Add } \left[\tfrac{1}{2}(-2)\right]^2 = (-1)^2 = 1.$$
$$(x - 1)^2 = 16$$
$$x - 1 = \sqrt{16} \quad \text{or} \quad x - 1 = -\sqrt{16}$$
$$x = 1 + 4 \qquad\qquad x = 1 - 4$$
$$x = 5 \qquad\qquad\qquad x = -3$$

Check $x = 5$: $x = -3$:
$$x^2 - 2x - 15 = 0 \qquad\qquad\qquad x^2 - 2x - 15 = 0$$
$$5^2 - 2 \cdot 5 - 15 \overset{?}{=} 0 \qquad\qquad (-3)^2 - 2(-3) - 15 \overset{?}{=} 0$$
$$25 - 10 - 15 \overset{?}{=} 0 \qquad\qquad\qquad 9 + 6 - 15 \overset{?}{=} 0$$
$$0 = 0 \ \text{(True)} \qquad\qquad\qquad\qquad 0 = 0 \ \text{(True)}$$

Thus, the solution set is $\{5, \ -3\}$

EXAMPLE 3 Solve $y^2 + 20y + 17 = 0$ by completing the square.

Solution
$$y^2 + 20y + 17 = 0$$
$$y^2 + 20y = -17$$
$$y^2 + 20y + 100 = -17 + 100 \quad \longleftarrow \text{Add } \left(\tfrac{1}{2} \cdot 20\right)^2 = 10^2 = 100.$$
$$(y + 10)^2 = 83$$
$$y + 10 = \sqrt{83} \qquad \text{or} \quad y + 10 = -\sqrt{83}$$
$$y = -10 + \sqrt{83} \qquad\qquad y = -10 - \sqrt{83}$$

Thus, the solutions are $-10 + \sqrt{83}$ and $-10 - \sqrt{83}$, which can be written as $-10 \pm \sqrt{83}$.

TRY THIS 3. Solve $a^2 - 16a + 13 = 0$ by completing the square.

EXAMPLE 4   Solve $3c^2 = 4c + 1$ by completing the square.

Plan   Subtract $4c$ from each side. Then divide each side by 3 so that the coefficient of c^2 is 1.

Solution

$$3c^2 = 4c + 1$$
$$3c^2 - 4c = 1$$
$$c^2 - \frac{4}{3}c = \frac{1}{3}$$
$$c^2 - \frac{4}{3}c + \frac{4}{9} = \frac{1}{3} + \frac{4}{9} \quad \longleftarrow \text{Add } \left[\frac{1}{2}\left(-\frac{4}{3}\right)\right]^2 = \left(-\frac{2}{3}\right)^2 = \frac{4}{9}.$$
$$\left(c - \frac{2}{3}\right)^2 = \frac{7}{9}$$

$$c - \frac{2}{3} = \sqrt{\frac{7}{9}} \qquad or \qquad c - \frac{2}{3} = -\sqrt{\frac{7}{9}}$$

$$c = \frac{2}{3} + \frac{\sqrt{7}}{3} \qquad\qquad c = \frac{2}{3} - \frac{\sqrt{7}}{3}$$

$$c = \frac{2 + \sqrt{7}}{3} \qquad\qquad c = \frac{2 - \sqrt{7}}{3}$$

Thus, the solutions are $\dfrac{2 \pm \sqrt{7}}{3}$.

TRY THIS
  4. Solve $5x^2 = 2 - 6x$ by completing the square.
  5. Solve $2 = 3a^2 - a$ by completing the square.

Classroom Exercises

What number should be added to make a perfect square trinomial?

1. $x^2 + 2x$ **2.** $y^2 - 10y$ **3.** $z^2 - 4z$ **4.** $a^2 + 12a$

5. $r^2 + 9r$ **6.** $y^2 - y$ **7.** $y^2 - \frac{1}{4}y$ **8.** $n^2 + \frac{3}{4}n$

Simplify, if possible.

9. $1 + \sqrt{25}$ **10.** $-3 - \sqrt{36}$ **11.** $-\frac{2}{5} + \frac{\sqrt{11}}{5}$ **12.** $\frac{3 - \sqrt{49}}{2}$

Solve by completing the square.

13. $x^2 + 12x - 28 = 0$ **14.** $c^2 - 8c - 84 = 0$

15. $x^2 - 7x + 10 = 0$ **16.** $b^2 + 10b + 16 = 0$

17. $a^2 + 6 = -5a$ **18.** $c^2 - c = 30$

Written Exercises

Complete the square. Show the result as the square of a binomial.

1. $x^2 + 14x$ 　　2. $y^2 - 2y$ 　　3. $x^2 + 18x$ 　　4. $x^2 + 11x$

5. $y^2 - 15y$ 　　6. $n^2 - \frac{1}{2}n$ 　　7. $y^2 + \frac{3}{5}y$ 　　8. $x^2 + \frac{2}{3}x$

Solve by completing the square. Give irrational solutions in simplest radical form.

9. $x^2 - 2x - 24 = 0$ 　　10. $c^2 - 4c - 12 = 0$ 　　11. $z^2 - 6z + 5 = 0$

12. $y^2 - 10y + 21 = 0$ 　　13. $a^2 + 2a - 3 = 0$ 　　14. $x^2 - 6x - 27 = 0$

15. $x^2 - 2x - 15 = 0$ 　　16. $y^2 + 4y + 3 = 0$ 　　17. $a^2 - 4a - 21 = 0$

18. $x^2 + 16x + 55 = 0$ 　　19. $r^2 + 6r - 7 = 0$ 　　20. $c^2 + 12c + 32 = 0$

21. $c^2 - 18c + 77 = 0$ 　　22. $x^2 - 24x + 80 = 0$ 　　23. $y^2 - 18y + 72 = 0$

24. $x^2 + 4x + 2 = 0$ 　　25. $y^2 - 8y + 5 = 0$ 　　26. $c^2 + 2c - 5 = 0$

27. $a^2 + 14a + 6 = 0$ 　　28. $x^2 + 2x - 6 = 0$ 　　29. $r^2 - 6r - 4 = 0$

30. $c^2 - 10c + 22 = 0$ 　　31. $y^2 + 6y - 10 = 0$ 　　32. $y^2 - 4y - 7 = 0$

33. $x^2 - 3x + 2 = 0$ 　　34. $y^2 - 7y - 8 = 0$ 　　35. $a^2 + a = 30$

36. $c^2 + 3c = 40$ 　　37. $d^2 - 15d + 56 = 0$ 　　38. $x^2 + 5x = 84$

39. $2y^2 + 7y - 4 = 0$ 　　40. $3x^2 = 3x + 1$ 　　41. $6r^2 = r + 1$

42. $2a^2 + 6a + 5 = 0$ 　　43. $4c^2 + 4 = 17c$ 　　44. $2x + 8 = 3x^2$

45. $2y^2 + 3y = 17$ 　　46. $2x^2 - 2x - 1 = 0$ 　　47. $3a^2 + 2a = 3$

Solve each problem.

48. If 3 times the square of a number is decreased by twice the number, the result is 1. Find the number.

49. Twice the square of a number is equal to the number increased by 3. Find the number.

50. The square of a number is 2 less than 6 times the number. Find the number.

51. The square of a number equals twice the number plus 4. Find the number.

Mixed Review

Solve each open inequality. *5.1, 5.2, 5.7*

1. $x + 5 < 2$ 　　2. $-2n + 10 > 28$ 　　3. $16 - y \le 4$ 　　4. $|x - 2| < 7$

5. Given that $f(x) = -2x^2 + 7$, find $f(-3)$. *10.3*

Solve. *9.2, 9.3*

6. If 3 out of 5 people use Drain-Fix, how many use Drain-Fix in a city of 42,000 people?

7. Solve the formula, $I = prt$, for t. Then find the time t in years for $I = \$200$, $p = \$8,000$, and $r = 5\%$.

14.3 The Quadratic Formula

Objective   To solve quadratic equations by using the quadratic formula

The Parthenon, a building in ancient Greece, has the shape of a rectangle. The width of this rectangle is about six-tenths of the length. Such a rectangle is called a *golden rectangle* because the ratio of the width to the length is considered "most pleasing to the eye." The exact ratio is found by using the quadratic formula (see Written Exercises 36 and 37).

The **quadratic formula** can be used to find the solutions of *any* quadratic equation. Every quadratic equation can be written in the standard form, $ax^2 + bx + c = 0$, where $a > 0$. This form can be solved for x by completing the square. Begin by adding $-c$ to each side.

$$ax^2 + bx + c = 0$$

Add $-c$ to each side.
$$ax^2 + bx = -c$$

Divide each side by a.
$$x^2 + \frac{b}{a}x = -\frac{c}{a}$$

Complete the square.
$$x^2 + \frac{b}{a}x + \frac{b^2}{4a^2} = -\frac{c}{a} + \frac{b^2}{4a^2}$$

Factor the left side.
$$\left(x + \frac{b}{2a}\right)^2 = -\frac{c}{a} + \frac{b^2}{4a^2}$$

$$\left(x + \frac{b}{2a}\right)^2 = -\frac{4ac}{4a^2} + \frac{b^2}{4a^2}$$

Simplify the right side.
$$\left(x + \frac{b}{2a}\right)^2 = \frac{b^2 - 4ac}{4a^2}$$

$$x + \frac{b}{2a} = \pm\sqrt{\frac{b^2 - 4ac}{4a^2}}$$

$$x = \frac{\pm\sqrt{b^2 - 4ac}}{2a} - \frac{b}{2a}$$

$$x = \frac{-b \pm \sqrt{b^2 - 4ac}}{2a}$$

The Quadratic Formula

The solutions of a quadratic equation in standard form,
$ax^2 + bx + c = 0$, where $a > 0$, are given by this formula.

$$x = \frac{-b \pm \sqrt{b^2 - 4ac}}{2a}$$

EXAMPLE 1 Find the solution set of $2x^2 + x - 10 = 0$ by the quadratic formula.

Plan The equation is in standard form. Determine the values of a, b, and c, and substitute them into the quadratic formula.

Solution $2x^2 + x - 10 = 0 \longleftarrow a = 2, b = 1, c = -10$

$$x = \frac{-b \pm \sqrt{b^2 - 4ac}}{2a}$$

$$x = \frac{-1 \pm \sqrt{1^2 - 4 \cdot 2 \cdot (-10)}}{2 \cdot 2}$$

$$x = \frac{-1 \pm \sqrt{1 + 80}}{4}$$

$$x = \frac{-1 \pm \sqrt{81}}{4}$$

$$x = \frac{-1 \pm 9}{4}$$

$x = \dfrac{-1 + 9}{4}$ or $x = \dfrac{-1 - 9}{4}$

$x = \dfrac{8}{4}$ $\qquad$ $x = \dfrac{-10}{4}$

$x = 2$ $\qquad\qquad$ $x = -\dfrac{5}{2}$

Each solution checks in the original equation. Thus the solution set is $\left\{2, -\dfrac{5}{2}\right\}$. The check is left for you.

TRY THIS 1. Use the quadratic formula to find the solution set of
$3x^2 - 2x - 5 = 0$.

You could solve the equation in Example 1 by factoring, since
$2x^2 + x - 10 = (2x + 5)(x - 2)$. However, some quadratic

equations cannot be solved by factoring, or they may be difficult to factor. In such cases, the formula is the best method for solution.

EXAMPLE 2 Solve $2y + 1 = 2y^2$ by the quadratic formula.

Plan First put the equation in standard form. Then use the quadratic formula.

Solution

$$2y + 1 = 2y^2$$

$$2y^2 - 2y - 1 = 0 \quad \longleftarrow a = 2, b = -2, c = -1$$

$$y = \frac{-b \pm \sqrt{b^2 - 4ac}}{2a}$$

$$y = \frac{-(-2) \pm \sqrt{(-2)^2 - 4 \cdot 2 \cdot (-1)}}{2 \cdot 2}$$

$$y = \frac{2 \pm \sqrt{4 + 8}}{4}$$

$$y = \frac{2 \pm \sqrt{12}}{4}$$

$$y = \frac{2 \pm 2\sqrt{3}}{4} \quad \longleftarrow \sqrt{12} = 2\sqrt{3}$$

$$y = \frac{\overset{1}{\cancel{2}}(1 \pm \sqrt{3})}{\underset{1}{\cancel{2}} \cdot 2} = \frac{1 \pm \sqrt{3}}{2}$$

Thus, the solutions are $\dfrac{1 \pm \sqrt{3}}{2}$.

TRY THIS **2.** Solve $6x = 2 - 5x^2$ by the quadratic formula.

The solutions in Example 2 are given in *simplest radical form*. The solutions can be approximated to the nearest tenth by using a table of square roots or the square root key on a calculator.

$$\frac{1 + \sqrt{3}}{2} \approx \frac{1 + 1.732}{2} = \frac{2.732}{2} = 1.366 \quad \longleftarrow 1.4 \text{ to the nearest tenth}$$

$$\frac{1 - \sqrt{3}}{2} \approx \frac{1 - 1.732}{2} = \frac{-0.732}{2} = -0.366 \quad \longleftarrow -0.4 \text{ to the nearest tenth}$$

Thus, the solutions are 1.4 and -0.4, to the nearest tenth.
The portion of the quadratic formula that is under the radical sign, $b^2 - 4ac$, is called the **discriminant**.

Before using the quadratic formula, it is wise to see whether $b^2 - 4ac$ is negative. If the discriminant is negative, the equation will have no real number solutions. In other words, if $b^2 - 4ac < 0$, the solution set of the quadratic equation is the empty set, or $\varnothing$.

EXAMPLE 3   Solve $x^2 = 3x - 8$.

Solution $x^2 - 3x + 8 = 0$ ⟵ standard form; $a = 1, b = -3, c = 8$
$b^2 - 4ac = (-3)^2 - 4 \cdot 1 \cdot 8 = 9 - 32 = -23$

The discriminant is negative, so there are no real number solutions.

TRY THIS   3. Solve $6 = 4y - y^2$.

Classroom Exercises

For each equation, give the value of a, b, and c.

1. $3x^2 - 2x + 1 = 0$ **2.** $y^2 - y - 1 = 0$ **3.** $2y^2 + 3 = 4y$
4. $d^2 = 5d - 2$ **5.** $p^2 - 2p = 0$ **6.** $-3x^2 = 5x$

Find the value of $b^2 - 4ac$, for the given values of a, b, and c.

7. $a = 1, b = 5, c = 5$ **8.** $a = 1, b = -5, c = 5$ **9.** $a = 1, b = 2, c = 4$

Each expression represents two numbers. Simplify, if possible.

10. $4 \pm \sqrt{12}$ **11.** $-2 \pm \sqrt{18}$ **12.** $0 \pm \sqrt{9}$
13. $\dfrac{8 \pm 4\sqrt{3}}{2}$ **14.** $\dfrac{-4 \pm 8\sqrt{2}}{4}$ **15.** $\dfrac{-7 \pm \sqrt{11}}{3}$

Solve by using the quadratic formula.

16. $x^2 + 7x + 6 = 0$ **17.** $y^2 - y - 12 = 0$ **18.** $3c - 8 = -2c^2$

Written Exercises

Solve by using the quadratic formula. Give irrational solutions in simplest radical form.

1. $x^2 - 7x + 10 = 0$ **2.** $c^2 + 6c + 8 = 0$ **3.** $x^2 - 9x + 14 = 0$
4. $d^2 + 2d - 3 = 0$ **5.** $y^2 + 4y - 3 = 0$ **6.** $x^2 - 9x + 8 = 0$
7. $2x^2 + 1 = 3x$ **8.** $x^2 - 7x = -3$ **9.** $x^2 - 1 = 7x$
10. $x^2 = 1 - x$ **11.** $2x + x^2 + 7 = 0$ **12.** $3 = y^2 + 5y$
13. $y = 6y^2 - 3$ **14.** $11x = 5x^2 - 3$ **15.** $4 = 3y^2 - 5y$
16. $-x^2 - 4 = 2x$ **17.** $x^2 + 4x + 2 = 8$ **18.** $-y^2 + 2 = -6y$

19. $2x - 1 + x^2 = 1$ **20.** $2x(x - 2) = 3$ **21.** $(x + 1)^2 = (2x - 3)^2$

22. $x^2 + (x - 1)^2 = 2$ **23.** $3x^2 = (3x)^2 - 2x + 1$ **24.** $(x + 2)^2 = 7 - x^2$

Solve, to the nearest tenth, by using the quadratic formula.

25. $3x^2 + 2x + 1 = -7$ **26.** $4d^2 = 5d + 2$ **27.** $4x = -x^2 - 2$

Solve each problem.

28. Twice the square of a number is 4 more than the opposite of the number. Find the number.

29. If twice a number is decreased by 1, the result is equal to 3 times the square of the number. Find the number.

Solve by using the quadratic formula.

30. $\frac{3}{2}y + y^2 = \frac{5}{2}$ **31.** $\frac{1}{2}x^2 - 2 = -\frac{1}{2}x$ **32.** $1 + \frac{x - 4}{x - 3} = \frac{3}{x - 1}$

33. $\frac{4}{3y + 4} - -1 + \frac{4}{y}$ **34.** $2r\sqrt{2} = r^2 - 6$ **35.** $4x + 2\sqrt{6} = x^2\sqrt{6}$

36. In a golden rectangle whose length is 1 unit and whose width is x units, the following proportion is always true. Find x correct to three decimal places.

$$\frac{x}{1} = \frac{1 - x}{x}$$

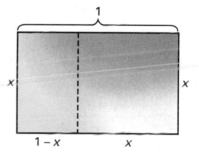

37. Write an explanation of why Exercise 36 enables you to conclude that in any golden rectangle, the width is a little more than six-tenths of the length.

38. Explain why a quadratic equation has no real solutions if $4ac > b^2$.

Mixed Review

Add or subtract. *8.5, 8.6, 8.7*

1. $\frac{7x}{3} + \frac{2x}{3}$ **2.** $\frac{6y^2}{7} - \frac{y^2}{7}$ **3.** $\frac{x^2}{3x - 9} + \frac{6x}{3x - 9}$

4. $\frac{x + 3}{2x} + \frac{2x + 1}{4x}$ **5.** $\frac{y + 2}{3y} - \frac{y + 3}{2y}$ **6.** $\frac{7}{10n} - \frac{5}{2n^2}$

7. $\frac{3}{n - 4} - \frac{5}{n^2 - 4n}$ **8.** $\frac{x}{x - 4} + \frac{3}{x + 4}$ **9.** $\frac{5}{y - 6} - \frac{1}{y^2 - 2y - 24}$

10. y varies directly as x. y is 12 when x is 4. Find x when y is 14. *10.6*

11. One machine can complete an order in 10 h. Another takes 15 h. How long will it take both machines working together? *9.5*

14.4 Choosing a Method of Solution

Objective	To solve quadratic equations using the most appropriate method

You have learned four methods for solving quadratic equations.

(1) Square Root Property   (3) Completing the Square
(2) Factoring   (4) Quadratic Formula

You can use Methods 3 and 4 for any quadratic equation. However, Methods 1 and 2 are used when an equation has no middle term.

EXAMPLE 1   Solve $x^2 = 98$.

Solutions

Method 1: Square Root Property

$$x^2 = 98$$
$$x = \sqrt{98} \quad or \quad x = -\sqrt{98}$$
$$x = 7\sqrt{2} \qquad\quad x = -7\sqrt{2}$$

Method 2: Factoring

$$x^2 = 98$$
$$x^2 - 98 = 0$$
$$(x - \sqrt{98})(x + \sqrt{98}) = 0$$
$$x = \sqrt{98} \quad or \quad x = -\sqrt{98}$$
$$x = 7\sqrt{2} \qquad\quad x = -7\sqrt{2}$$

Thus, the solutions are $7\sqrt{2}, \; -7\sqrt{2}$.

If a quadratic equation can be solved by factoring, then that is usually a simpler method than completing the square or using the formula.

EXAMPLE 2   Solve $2x^2 = 9x + 5$.

Solutions   **Method 2:** Factoring

$$2x^2 - 9x - 5 = 0$$
$$(2x + 1)(x - 5) = 0$$
$$2x + 1 = 0 \quad or \quad x - 5 = 0$$
$$2x = -1 \qquad\qquad x = 5$$
$$x = -\frac{1}{2}$$

Method 4: Quadratic Formula

For $2x^2 - 9x - 5 = 0$, $a = 2$, $b = -9$, and $c = -5$.

$$x = \frac{-(-9) \pm \sqrt{(-9)^2 - 4 \cdot 2 \cdot (-5)}}{2 \cdot 2}$$

$$x = \frac{9 \pm \sqrt{121}}{4} = \frac{9 \pm 11}{4}$$

$$x = 5 \quad or \quad x = -\frac{1}{2}$$

Thus, the solutions are 5 and $-\frac{1}{2}$.

TRY THIS   1. Solve $3x^2 - 2x = 1$.

When neither the Square Root Property nor factoring can be applied, then completing the square or the quadratic formula should be used.

EXAMPLE 3

A pellet is to be shot upward from the earth's surface at an initial velocity of 25 m/s. Use the formula $h = 25t - 5t^2$ to find the height h in meters of the pellet t seconds after it is shot upward. After how many seconds will the pellet be 10 m above the ground? Give answers correct to the nearest tenth of a second.

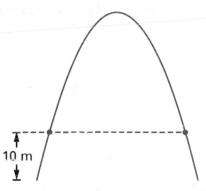

Plan

Substitute 10 for h in $h = 25t - 5t^2$. Solve for t.

There will be two solutions, one for the number of seconds for the flight upward and one for the number of seconds downward.

Solution

Substitute 10 for h.
Write in standard form.
Factoring won't work.
Use the quadratic formula.

$$h = 25t - 5t^2$$
$$10 = 25t - 5t^2$$
$$5t^2 - 25t + 10 = 0$$
$$t = \frac{-b \pm \sqrt{b^2 - 4ac}}{2a}$$

$a = 5, b = -25, c = 10$

$$t = \frac{-(-25) \pm \sqrt{(-25)^2 - 4 \cdot 5 \cdot 10}}{2 \cdot 5}$$

$$t = \frac{25 \pm \sqrt{625 - 200}}{10} = \frac{25 \pm \sqrt{425}}{10}$$

$$t \approx \frac{25 - 20.616}{10} \quad \text{or} \quad t \approx \frac{25 + 20.616}{10}$$

$$t \approx \frac{4.384}{10} \qquad\qquad t \approx \frac{45.616}{10}$$

$$t \approx 0.4 \qquad\qquad t \approx 4.6$$

THINK: 0.4 s seems reasonable for the pellet to rise to 10 m, and 4.6 s seems reasonable for it to peak and fall to 10 m.

Thus, the pellet will rise to 10 m after 0.4 s and will fall to 10 m after 4.6 s.

TRY THIS

2. After how many seconds (nearest tenth of a second) will the pellet in Example 3 be 5 m above the ground? Use the formula $h = 25t - 5t^2$.

Focus on Reading

Below are four steps for solving a quadratic equation. Put the steps in the most logical order.

1. Use the quadratic formula.
2. Write the equation in standard form.
3. Try factoring the equation.
4. Check to see whether the discriminant is negative.

Classroom Exercises

Which method would you use to solve each equation?

1. $x^2 = 49$ **2.** $x^2 - 5x + 6 = 0$ **3.** $(y - 6)^2 = 81$

4. $x^2 + 4x - 9 = 0$ **5.** $(x + 2)^2 = 13$ **6.** $3c^2 + 11c = 4$

7. $-2a - 10 = -a^2$ **8.** $y^2 - 12y + 36 = 0$ **9.** $2r^2 + 12r = -9$

10–18. Solve each equation in Classroom Exercises 1–9.

Written Exercises

Solve each equation. Give irrational solutions in simplest radical form.

1. $x^2 = 64$ **2.** $a^2 + 8a + 7 = 0$ **3.** $3x^2 + 7x + 3 = 0$

4. $2x^2 - 3x - 4 = 0$ **5.** $2d^2 - 5d - 12 = 0$ **6.** $(x - 2)^2 = 64$

7. $y^2 - 3y = 28$ **8.** $y^2 - 50 = 0$ **9.** $6x^2 + 11x - 10 = 0$

10. $4x^2 + x = 2$ **11.** $r^2 - 8r + 16 = 0$ **12.** $y^2 - 2y = 5$

13. $(y - 8)^2 = 17$ **14.** $-3 = y - 4y^2$ **15.** $x^2 - 3x = 0$

16. $r^2 - 81 = 0$ **17.** $6x - 1 = 2x^2$ **18.** $2 = 2y^2 - y$

19. $4x^2 + 12x + 9 = 0$ **20.** $5x + x^2 = 0$ **21.** $5c^2 + 2c - 1 = 0$

Solve each equation. Approximate irrational solutions to the nearest tenth.

22. $-2x - 2 = -x^2$ **23.** $y^2 + 22 = 10y$ **24.** $25n^2 = 4{,}225$

25. $7 - x^2 = 4x + 4$ **26.** $12 - 4y^2 = 0$ **27.** $3y^2 + 2 = 5y + 6$

In the polygon with n sides, the number of diagonals, d, is given by the formula $d = \dfrac{n^2 - 3n}{2}$. Use this formula for Exercises 28–31.

28. Find the number of diagonals in a polygon with 8 sides.

29. Find the number of diagonals in a polygon with 27 sides.

30. If a polygon has 14 diagonals, how many sides does it have?

31. If a polygon has 35 diagonals, how many sides does it have?

The formula $h = 40t - 5t^2$ can be used to find the height in meters of an object shot upward at an initial velocity of 40 m/s after t seconds. Use this formula for Exercises 32–34. Approximate irrational answers to the nearest tenth of a second.

A baseball pitcher can throw a ball with an initial velocity of 40 m/s.

32. If the pitcher throws the ball straight up, when will its height be 20 m from where he threw it?

33. When will the height of the ball be 80 m from where the pitcher threw it?

34. After how many seconds will the ball be at the height from which the pitcher threw it?

The sum S of the first n positive integers is given by the formula $S = \dfrac{n^2 + n}{2}$.

For example, for the first 10 positive integers $(1, 2, 3, \cdots, 8, 9, 10)$,

$$S = \frac{10^2 + 10}{2} = \frac{100 + 10}{2} = \frac{110}{2} = 55.$$

Use this formula for Exercises 35–37.

35. Find the sum of the first 25 positive integers.

36. Starting with 1, how many consecutive integers must be used to obtain a sum of 136?

37. Starting with 1, how many consecutive integers must be used to obtain a sum of 210?

The formula $h = 60t - 5t^2$ can be used to find the height in meters of an object shot upward at an initial velocity of 60 m/s after t seconds. Use this formula for Exercises 38–41.

From the top of a building 10 m tall, a pellet is launched at an initial velocity of 60 m/s.

38. When will the pellet be 110 m above the ground?

39. When will the pellet fall to the level of the top of the building?

40. When will the pellet be 190 m above the ground?

41. Why do you think there is only one answer to Exercise 40?

42. Keith wrote a quadratic equation that had $\sqrt{7}$ and $2\sqrt{7}$ as its roots. What was the equation?

43. Eva wrote a quadratic equation that had $2\sqrt{11}$ as its only root. What was the equation?

Midchapter Review

Give all irrational solutions in simplest radical form.

Solve each equation.   *14.1*

1. $x^2 = 34$ **2.** $(r - 3)^2 = 64$ **3.** $6(y + 2)^2 = 30$

Complete the square. Show the result as the square of a binomial.   *14.2*

4. $y^2 - 14y$ **5.** $x^2 + 24x$ **6.** $n^2 + \frac{1}{2}n$

Solve by completing the square.   *14.2*

7. $x^2 + 6x + 7 = 0$ **8.** $y^2 - 8y - 48 = 0$ **9.** $5x^2 = 2x + 1$

Solve by using the quadratic formula.   *14.3*

10. $x^2 - 9x + 14 = 0$ **11.** $2y^2 - 2y - 4 = 0$ **12.** $x^2 - 5x - 2 = 0$
13. $5 = c^2 + 3c$ **14.** $y^2 - 4y = 6$ **15.** $-x^2 - 4 = 3x$

Solve each equation.   *14.4*

16. $x^2 - 14 = 0$ **17.** $a^2 - 4a - 45 = 0$ **18.** $3y^2 - 2y = 1$
19. $r^2 + 7r = 0$ **20.** $x^2 - 8x = 5$ **21.** $2c^2 = -6c - 1$

Solve.   *14.1, 14.2*

22. If the length of each side of a square is doubled, then the area is 144 cm². Find the length of each side of the original square.

23. The square of a number is 9 more than 5 times the number. Find the number.

Application: *Stopping Distance for a Car*

You can estimate the stopping distance, s, needed for a car going x mph by adding the reaction distance (x feet) and the braking distance $\left(\frac{x^2}{20}\right)$.

$$s = x + \frac{x^2}{20}$$

1. You are driving at 30 mph and you see an animal in the road. How many feet will the car travel before you can stop?

2. A police officer estimates the stopping distance for a car as 206.25 ft. Is the car traveling at a speed greater than, or less than, 60 mph?

14.5 Problem Solving: Quadratic Equations and Geometry

Objective   To solve geometric problems that lead to quadratic equations

You are now able to choose from four methods when you solve problems that lead to quadratic equations.

EXAMPLE 1   The rectangular floor of a tree house is constructed so that its perimeter is 42 ft. and its area is 104 ft². Find the width and the length of the floor.

Plan   Draw a diagram and represent the data. If you need to solve a quadratic equation, try factoring first. If that is not successful, use the quadratic formula.

Solution   Let w = the width and l = the length.
The perimeter formula is $p = 2l + 2w$.
$$42 = 2l + 2w$$
$$21 = l + w$$
So, $l = 21 - w$.

$$A = lw$$
$$104 = (21 - w)w \quad \longleftarrow \text{The area is 104 ft}^2.$$
$$104 = 21w - w^2$$
$$w^2 - 21w + 104 = 0$$
$$(w - 13)(w - 8) = 0$$
$$w = 13 \text{ or } w = 8 \quad \longleftarrow \text{Width: 13 ft or 8 ft}$$

If $w = 13$, $l = 21 - 13$, or 8.
If $w = 8$, $l = 21 - 8$, or 13.

Check   Is the perimeter 42 ft? Yes, since $2 \cdot 13 + 2 \cdot 8 = 26 + 16 = 42$.
Is the area 104 ft²? Yes, since $13 \cdot 8 = 104$.
Thus, the width of the floor is 8 ft and the length is 13 ft.

TRY THIS   **1.** The perimeter of a rectangular garden is 80 m and its area is 76 m². Find the width and length.

Some applications of the Pythagorean Theorem lead to quadratic equations. When these applications involve geometric figures, it is important to *draw a diagram* to represent the given information as you begin to solve each problem.

EXAMPLE 2 The distance between two opposite corners of a rectangular garden is 14 m. The length of the garden is 2 m longer than the width. Find the length and the width of the garden.

Solution Let w = the width.
Then $w + 2$ = the length.
Use the Pythagorean Theorem.

$$a^2 + b^2 = c^2$$
$$w^2 + (w + 2)^2 = 14^2$$
$$w^2 + w^2 + 4w + 4 = 196$$
$$2w^2 + 4w - 192 = 0 \quad \longleftarrow \text{Divide each side by 2.}$$
$$w^2 + 2w - 96 = 0$$

$$w = \frac{-2 \pm \sqrt{2^2 - 4 \cdot 1 \cdot (-96)}}{2 \cdot 1} \quad \longleftarrow \begin{array}{l}\text{Use the quadratic formula.} \\ a = 1, b = 2, c = -96\end{array}$$

$$w = \frac{-2 \pm \sqrt{4 + 384}}{2}$$

$$w = \frac{-2 \pm \sqrt{388}}{2}$$

$$w = \frac{-2 \pm 2\sqrt{97}}{2} \quad \longleftarrow \sqrt{388} = \sqrt{4} \cdot \sqrt{97} = 2\sqrt{97}$$

$$w = -1 \pm \sqrt{97} \quad \longleftarrow \text{Reject the negative solution.}$$

$$w = -1 + 9.8 \quad \longleftarrow \sqrt{97} \approx 9.849 \approx 9.8$$

$$w = 8.8 \text{ and } w + 2 = 10.8$$

Calculator check: (Check that $\sqrt{8.8^2 + 10.8^2} \approx 14$.)

8.8 $\boxed{x^2}$ $\boxed{+}$ 10.8 $\boxed{x^2}$ $\boxed{=}$ $\boxed{\sqrt{x}}$ display $\longrightarrow$ 13.931259 $\approx$ 14

Thus, the length is about 10.8 m, and the width is about 8.8 m.

TRY THIS 2. The diagonal of a rectangle is 8 mm. The length is 5 mm longer than the width. Find the width and the length.

3. The distance between the opposite corners of a rectangular pool is 12 yd. The length of the pool is 4 yd longer than the width. Find the width and the length.

Classroom Exercises

Use the data from each figure to write an equation in one variable.

1.

A = 117, w, 2w − 5

2.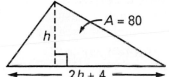

A = 80, h, 2h + 4

3.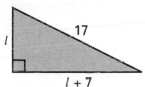

17, l, l + 7

4–6. Solve the equations in Classroom Exercises 1–3.

Solve each problem.

7. Opposite corners of a rectangle are 30 ft apart. The length is 6 ft longer than the width. Find the length and the width.

8. The area of a rectangle is 72 ft² and its perimeter is 34 ft. Find the length and the width of the rectangle.

Written Exercises

Solve each problem.

1. Jaime's bedroom floor is the shape of a rectangle. The distance between two opposite corners is 15 ft. The length is 3 ft longer than the width. Find the length and the width of the floor.

2. Opposite sides of a square are increased by 3 cm. The other sides are increased by 2 cm. The area of the resulting rectangle is 72 cm². Find the length of a side of the original square.

3. The perimeter of a rectangular floor is 38 ft and area of the floor is 90 ft². Find the length and the width of the floor.

4. The number of square centimeters in the area of a square is 42 more than the number of centimeters in the length of each side. Find the length of each side.

5. The distance between opposite corners of a rectangular deck is 25 ft. The length is 3 ft shorter than 3 times the width. Find the length and the width of the deck.

6. A patio is in the shape of a triangle. The area of the patio is 28.5 m². The base of the triangle is 2.5 m less than twice the height. Find the base and the height.

7. Refer to Exercises 1–6 to give an example of a number that is a solution to an equation used to solve a problem, even though it is not a solution to that problem. Explain in writing why the number is not a solution to the problem.

Solve. Give irrational answers to the nearest tenth.

8. The length of a rectangular piece of cloth is 8 cm more than the width. The area is 50 cm². Find the length and the width.

9. A windowpane is in the shape of a right triangle. The area of the glass is 4 ft². One leg of the triangle measures 1 ft more than 3 times the other leg. Find the length of each leg.

10. A wire 28 cm long can be bent to form a rectangle with an area of 42 cm². Find the length and the width of the rectangle.

11. A rectangular plot of ground measures 14 m by 10 m. A path is to be constructed within the plot so that a 72 m² garden can be planted with the path surrounding it. Find the width of the path.

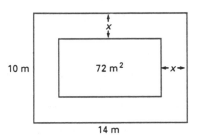

12. The dimensions of a rectangle are 16 ft by 12 ft. If each dimension of the rectangle is decreased by the same amount, the area of the resulting rectangle is 32 ft². Find the length and the width of the resulting rectangle.

13. The diagonal of a square piece of glass is 5 in. longer than the length of a side. Find the length of a side.

14. A ladder is leaning against a tree so that it touches the tree 8 ft above the ground and touches the ground 6 ft from the base of the tree. How much should the ladder be lowered so that the distance from the top of the ladder to the ground will equal the distance from the bottom of the ladder to the base of the tree?

Mixed Review

Graph each point in the same coordinate plane. *10.1*

1. $A(1, 3)$
2. $B(-4, -4)$
3. $C(-2, 0)$
4. $D(4, -1)$

Graph each equation. *10.5, 11.3*

5. $x + y = 8$
6. $y = 3x - 2$

Solve. *4.7*

7. 48 is what percent of 150?
8. 96 is 120% of what number?

9. y varies inversely as x. y is 8 when x is 3. Find y when x is -2. *10.7*

Simplify. *13.2*

10. $\sqrt{98}$
11. $\sqrt{196}$
12. $8\sqrt{12}$
13. $-2\sqrt{32}$
14. $\sqrt{5} \cdot \sqrt{2}$
15. $\sqrt{10} \cdot \sqrt{20}$
16. $\sqrt{50} \cdot \sqrt{2}$
17. $\sqrt{7} \cdot \sqrt{7}$

Problem Solving Strategies

Checking Assumptions

Carla and Joann have two large identical buckets. Carla fills hers with glass marbles that are $\frac{1}{2}$ inch in diameter. Joann fills hers with larger marbles that are 1 inch in diameter. Whose bucket has the most marbles in it?

Then Carla and Joann each fill their buckets (with the marbles in them) with water to the brim. Whose bucket has more water in it? Whose bucket has more glass in it?

Many people assume that one bucket will have more water (or glass) than the other. This is not so. In theory, the proportion of water to glass is the same in both buckets.

Mathematics provides a way to check out some assumptions such as this one to determine the truth of what appears to be so.

Exercises

Use the strategy of Checking Assumptions to solve these problems.

1. Betsy uses a square piece of paper, 11 inches on a side, to paint the design on the left. Rafael uses paper of the same size to paint the design on the right. Whose paper had more of its area covered with paint?

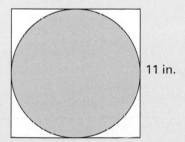 11 in.   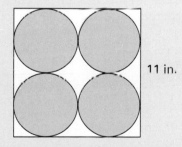 11 in.

2. Bob sold half his hamsters, plus an additional one-half a hamster to George. Then Bob sold half of the hamsters that remained plus one-half a hamster to Joe. Bob had exactly one hamster left. Did Bob have to divide a hamster in half?

3. How many hamsters did Bob have to start with?

14.6 Quadratic Functions

Objectives

To graph quadratic functions

To find the coordinates of the vertex and the equation of the axis of symmetry of a parabola

To find the minimum or maximum value of a quadratic function

Below are the graphs of two functions with domain $\{-2, -1, 0, 1, 2\}$.

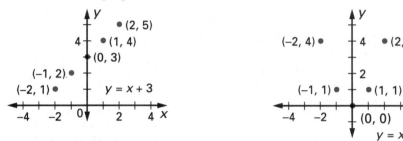

The equation $y = x + 3$ is a linear equation. The equation $y = x^2$ is a quadratic equation.

An equation of the form $y = ax^2 + bx + c$ $(a \neq 0)$ defines a **quadratic function**. To graph a quadratic function, select several values of x, find the corresponding values of y, graph the ordered pairs, and draw a smooth curve through the points. In all examples in this lesson, use the set of real numbers as the domain of x.

EXAMPLE 1   Graph $y = x^2 + 2x - 3$.

Plan   Make a table of values. Then graph the ordered pairs and draw the curve.

Solution

x	$x^2 + 2x - 3$	y	Ordered pairs
0	$0^2 + 2 \cdot 0 - 3$	-3	$(0, -3)$
1	$1^2 + 2 \cdot 1 - 3$	0	$(1, 0)$
2	$2^2 + 2 \cdot 2 - 3$	5	$(2, 5)$
-1	$(-1)^2 + 2(-1) - 3$	-4	$(-1, -4)$
-2	$(-2)^2 + 2(-2) - 3$	-3	$(-2, -3)$
-3	$(-3)^2 + 2(-3) - 3$	0	$(-3, 0)$
-4	$(-4)^2 + 2(-4) - 3$	5	$(-4, 5)$

TRY THIS   1. Graph $y = x^2 - 2x - 3$.   2. Graph $y = x^2 + x - 6$.

Any equation of the form $y = ax^2 + bx + c$ $(a \neq 0)$ has a graph that is a **parabola**. In Example 1, the parabola opens upward. The point $(-1, -4)$ is the **vertex**, or the *turning point*, of the parabola. The y-coordinate of the vertex, -4, is the **minimum value** (least value) of the function. Thus, the vertex A is called a **minimum point**.

Notice that the parabola described by $y = x^2 + 2x - 3$ is symmetric with respect to the dashed vertical line that contains the vertex, $(-1, -4)$. This line is called the **axis of symmetry** of the parabola and its equation is $x = -1$.

EXAMPLE 2   Graph $y = -x^2 + 6x - 5$.

Solution

x	y	Ordered pair
0	-5	$(0, -5)$
1	0	$(1, 0)$
2	3	$(2, 3)$
3	4	$(3, 4)$
4	3	$(4, 3)$
5	0	$(5, 0)$
6	-5	$(6, -5)$

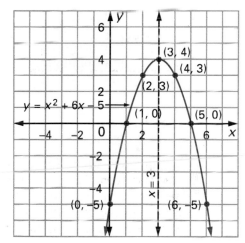

TRY THIS   3. Graph $y = -x^2 - 2x + 3$.

For the function in Example 2, $y = -x^2 + 6x - 5$, the coefficient of x^2 is a negative number, -1. This causes the parabola to open downward. The vertex $(3, 4)$ is a **maximum point**, and the y-coordinate of the vertex, 4, is the **maximum value** (greatest value) of the function. The axis of symmetry with equation $x = 3$ contains the vertex, $(3, 4)$.

The graph of a quadratic function $y = ax^2 + bx + c$ is made up of pairs of points with the same y-coordinate (except for the vertex). In Example 2, notice that pairs of points such as $(2, 3)$, $(4, 3)$, and $(1, 0)$, $(5, 0)$ have the same y-coordinate.

The axis of symmetry contains the vertex and lies halfway between any two points with the same y-coordinate. Thus, the x-coordinate of the vertex is the *arithmetic mean*, or average, of the x-coordinates of any two points with the same y-coordinate.

Pairs of points	Mean of x-coordinates
$(1, 0)$, $(5, 0)$	$\frac{1}{2}(1 + 5) = \frac{1}{2} \cdot 6 = 3$
$(2, 3)$, $(4, 3)$	$\frac{1}{2}(2 + 4) = \frac{1}{2} \cdot 6 = 3$

→ x-coordinate of vertex

The values of a and b in $y = ax^2 + bx + c$ can be used to find the x-coordinate of the vertex of its graph as well as the equation of the axis of symmetry of its graph.

x-coordinate of the vertex: $\quad -\dfrac{b}{2a}$

equation of the axis of symmetry: $\quad x = -\dfrac{b}{2a}$

EXAMPLE 3

For the function $y = 2x^2 - 8x + 5$:
a. find the coordinates of the vertex of the parabola,
b. find the equation of the axis of symmetry,
c. find the minimum or maximum value, and
d. graph the function.

Solution

$a = 2, b = -8$

x-coordinate of vertex $= -\dfrac{b}{2a} = -\left(\dfrac{-8}{2 \cdot 2}\right) = -\left(\dfrac{-8}{4}\right) = 2$

Substitute 2 for x and solve for y.
$$y = 2x^2 - 8x + 5$$
$$y = 2 \cdot 2^2 - 8 \cdot 2 + 5$$
$$y = -3$$

Thus, the coordinates of the vertex are $(2, -3)$. The equation of the axis of symmetry is $x = 2$. Since $a = 2$ and $2 > 0$, the parabola opens upward, and the minimum value is -3.

x	y	Ordered pairs
2	-3	$(2, -3)$
3	-1	$(3, -1)$
4	5	$(4, 5)$
1	-1	$(1, -1)$
0	5	$(0, 5)$

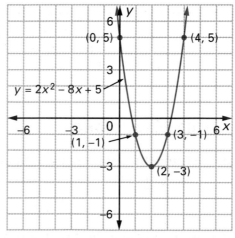

TRY THIS

4. For the function $y = -3x^2 + 6x - 9$, find the coordinates of the vertex, the equation of the axis of symmetry, the maximum or minimum value, and graph the function.

EXAMPLE 4   Mrs. Truro sells packages of towels. She uses the following formula to approximate her profits per day.

$$p = -x^2 + 50x - 350$$

In the formula, p is the profit derived from selling x packages of towels. How many packages of towels must she sell to make a maximum profit? What is the maximum profit?

Plan   Use the characteristics of the graphs of quadratic functions. The graph of $p = -x^2 + 50x - 350$ will have a maximum since the coefficient of x^2 is negative. Use the formula $x = -\frac{b}{2a}$ to find the value of x that makes p a maximum.

Solution $a = -1, b = 50, c = -350$

$$x = -\frac{b}{2a} = \frac{-50}{2(-1)} = \frac{-50}{-2} = 25 \quad \longleftarrow \begin{array}{l} \text{number of packages per day} \\ \text{to give maximum profit} \end{array}$$

To find the maximum profit, let $x = 25$ in $p = -x^2 + 50x - 350$.

$p = -1x^2 + 50x - 350$
$p = -1(25)^2 + 50 \cdot 25 - 350$
$p = -625 + 1,250 - 350$
$p = 275$

Thus, she must sell 25 packages per day to make a maximum profit of $275.

TRY THIS   **5.** Use the formula $p = x^2 - 14x + 89$ to find how many packages of towels must be sold to make a minimum profit and to find the minimum profit.

Classroom Exercises

Tell whether the function has a maximum or a minimum value.

1. $y = -x^2 + 5x + 2$ **2.** $y = 3x^2 + 7x - 1$ **3.** $y = 12 - x^2$
4. $2 + 3x^2 = y$ **5.** $y = x^2 + x$ **6.** $2x - 4x^2 + 1 = y$

For each quadratic function: (a) find the coordinates of the vertex of the parabola, (b) find the equation of the axis of symmetry, (c) find the minimum or maximum value, and (d) graph the function.

7. $y = 3x^2$ **8.** $y = -x^2 + 2$ **9.** $y = x^2 - 5x + 4$

Written Exercises

Graph each function.

1. $y = x^2$

2. $y = -2x^2$

3. $y = \frac{1}{2}x^2$

4. $y = -x^2 + 1$

5. $y = 3x^2 + 2x$

6. $y = x^2 + 2x + 4$

For each quadratic function, (a) find the coordinates of the vertex of the parabola, (b) find the equation of the axis of symmetry, (c) find the minimum or maximum value, and (d) graph the function.

7. $y = 3x^2 + 2$

8. $y = -x^2 - 6x - 8$

9. $y = x^2 - 4x + 3$

10. $y = x^2 - 8x + 7$

11. $y = \frac{1}{2}x^2 - x - 2$

12. $y = -4x^2 + 16x - 6$

13. The formula for the cost of running a taco stand is $c = x^2 - 12x + 60$. How many units x of tacos must be sold to keep costs at a minimum? Find the minimum cost.

14. The cost c of producing x units of radios is $c = x^2 - 12x + 72$. How many radios should be made to produce the minimum cost? What is the minimum cost?

15. The formula for the height s reached by a rocket fired straight up from the ground with an initial velocity of 96 ft/s is $s = -16t^2 + 96t$. Find the time t for the rocket to reach a maximum height. Find this height.

16. The owner of a new company finds that the profit p is related to the number x of items sold by $p = 200 + 800x - x^2$. How many items must be sold for the maximum profit? What is the maximum profit?

17. A hair dryer manufacturer determines that the total profit p (in dollars) of manufacturing x hair dryers is $p = -0.18x^2 + 36x + 4,000$. How many must be sold for the maximum profit?

18. A biologist's formula to predict the number of impulses fired after stimulation of a nerve is $i = -x^2 + 30x - 50$, where i is the number of impulses per millisecond and x is the number of milliseconds after stimulation. Find the time for the maximum number of impulses.

19. Graph each function on the same set of axes.

    a. $y = x^2$
    b. $y = x^2 + 2$
    c. $y = x^2 - 3$

    d. For the function $y = x^2 + k$, where k is constant, explain what happens to the resulting parabolas when k increases.

    e. For the function $y = x^2 + k$, where k is a constant, give the coordinates of the vertex of the parabola. Give the minimum value.

20. Graph each function on the same set of axes.

    a. $y = x^2$
    b. $y = (x - 1)^2$
    c. $y = (x + 3)^2$

    d. For the function $y = (x - h)^2$, where h is a constant, explain what happens to resulting parabolas as h increases.

    e. For the function $y = (x - h)^2$, where h is a constant, give the coordinates of the vertex of the parabola and the minimum value.

21. Graph each function on the same set of axes.

    a. $y = (x + 2)^2 - 3$ **b.** $y = (x - 1)^2 - 1$ **c.** $y = (x - 3)^2 + 2$

    d. For the function $y = (x - h)^2 + k$, where h and k are constants, give the coordinates of the vertex. Give the minimum value.

Consider the quadratic function $y = ax^2 + bx + c$ $(a \neq 0)$ for Exercises 22–23.

22. Give the coordinates of the vertex of the parabola.

23. Give the maximum or minimum value.

24. Use your answer to Exercise 23 to give the maximum value of $y = 4 - \frac{1}{2}x^2 + x$.

Refer to the relation $x = y^2$ for Exercises 25–27.

25. Make a table of values and graph the relation.

26. Do any two ordered pairs have the same first coordinate? If your answer is yes, give an example to support it.

27. Is the equation a function? Explain your answer.

28. Write an inequality to describe each shaded region below.

    a.
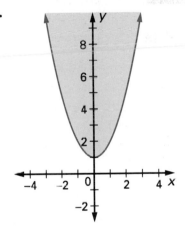

    b.
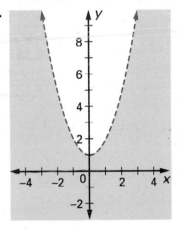

Mixed Review

Solve.   *3.3, 3.4*

1. $-2x + 5 = -7$ **2.** $8n + 19 = -4$ **3.** $y + 4 = 7y + 5 - 10y$

Graph each equation. Is the relation a function?   *10.5*

4. $y = 3$ **5.** $x = 4$ **6.** $x \cdot y = 3$

7. Find the slope of the line determined by $A(-2, 3)$ and $B(5, -1)$.   *11.1*

8. For the relation $\{(-3, 1), (6, 1), (3, -1), (4, 2)\}$, give the domain and range. Is the relation a function?   *10.2*

14.7 Quadratic Functions and the Discriminant

Objectives

To find the x-intercepts of a quadratic function

To determine the number of real-number solutions of a quadratic equation by using the discriminant

You have learned that the quadratic equation $x^2 - 4x + 3 = 0$ is related to the quadratic function $y = x^2 - 4x + 3$. The solutions of the equation can be found by factoring.

$$x^2 - 4x + 3 = 0$$
$$(x - 3)(x - 1) = 0$$
$$x = 3 \ or \ x = 1$$

Notice that the graph of the function $y = x^2 - 4x + 3$ crosses the x-axis at points $(3, 0)$ and $(1, 0)$. The x-coordinates of these two ordered pairs are the two solutions of the equation $x^2 - 4x + 3 = 0$.

Recall that the x-coordinate of a point where a graph crosses the x-axis is called an x-*intercept* of the graph. Thus, the x-intercepts of the parabola, 3 and 1, are the solutions of the equation.

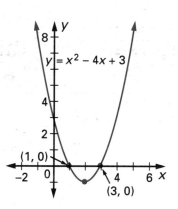

EXAMPLE 1   Find the x-intercepts of the graph of $y = 2x^2 - 3x - 5$.

Plan   Find the solutions of $2x^2 - 3x - 5 = 0$.
Try factoring.

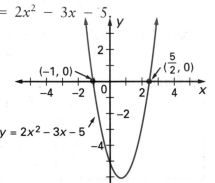

Solution
$$2x^2 - 3x - 5 = 0$$
$$(2x - 5)(x + 1) = 0$$
$$x = \frac{5}{2} \ or \ x = -1$$

Thus, the x-intercepts are $\frac{5}{2}$ and -1.

TRY THIS   1. Find the x-intercepts of the graph of $y = -3x^2 + 14x - 8$.

Examine the relationships in the table below.

Function	$y = x^2 - 6x + 5$	$y = x^2 - 6x + 9$	$y = x^2 - 6x + 11$
Graph			
Number of x-intercepts	2	1	0
Related equation	$x^2 - 6x + 5 = 0$	$x^2 - 6x + 9 = 0$	$x^2 - 6x + 11 = 0$
Discriminant $b^2 - 4ac$	$(-6)^2 - 4 \cdot 1 \cdot 5$ $= 36 - 20$ $= 16$ (positive)	$(-6)^2 - 4 \cdot 1 \cdot 9$ $= 36 - 36$ $= 0$ (zero)	$(-6)^2 - 4 \cdot 1 \cdot 11$ $= 36 - 44$ $= -8$ (negative)
Number of real number solutions	2	1	0

The relationship between the discriminant and the number of real number solutions of a quadratic equation is summarized below.

If $b^2 - 4ac > 0$, there are two solutions. They are $\dfrac{-b \pm \sqrt{b^2 - 4ac}}{2a}$.

If $b^2 - 4ac = 0$, there is one solution. The solution is $-\dfrac{b}{2a}$.

If $b^2 - 4ac < 0$, there is no real number solution.

EXAMPLE 2   Use the discriminant to determine the number of real number solutions.
a. $x^2 - 7x - 2 = 0$ **b.** $5x^2 + 4x + 1 = 0$ **c.** $-x^2 + 10x - 25 = 0$

Solutions

a. $b^2 - 4ac$
$= (-7)^2 - 4 \cdot 1 \cdot (-2)$
$= 49 + 8$
$= 57 \leftarrow$ positive
Two solutions

b. $b^2 - 4ac$
$= 4^2 - 4 \cdot 5 \cdot 1$
$= 16 - 20$
$= -4 \leftarrow$ negative
No solution

c. $b^2 - 4ac$
$= 10^2 - 4(-1)(-25)$
$= 100 - 100$
$= 0 \leftarrow$ zero
One solution

TRY THIS   **2.** Use the discriminant to determine the number of real number solutions of $-4x^2 - 3x + 6 = 0$.

Classroom Exercises

For each quadratic function graphed below, give the related quadratic equation and its real number solution(s), if they exist. Tell whether the discriminant is positive, negative, or zero.

1. $y = x^2 - 4x + 7$

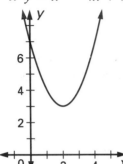

2. $y = -x^2 - 2x + 3$

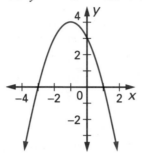

3. $y = 4x^2 - 4x + 1$

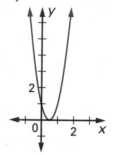

Use the related quadratic equation to find the x-intercepts of each quadratic function.

4. $y = x^2 - 8x + 16$ **5.** $y = x^2 + 9x - 2$ **6.** $y = 3 - 2x^2 + x$

Use the discriminant to determine the number of real number solutions of each equation. Do not solve.

7. $y = x^2 - 8x + 4$ **8.** $y = 2x^2 + 5x + 3$ **9.** $y = 1 + 4x^2 - 4x$

Written Exercises

Use the related quadratic equation to find the x-intercepts of each quadratic function.

1. $y = x^2 - 7x - 18$ **2.** $y = x^2 + 12x + 36$ **3.** $y = x^2 + 5x - 24$

4. $y = 64 - x^2$ **5.** $y = 3x^2 + 11x - 4$ **6.** $y = -4x^2 - 4x + 3$

7. $y = x^2 + 7x - 4$ **8.** $y = x - 2x^2 + 5$ **9.** $-6 + 3x^2 - 2x = y$

Use the discriminant to determine the number of real number solutions of each equation. Do not solve.

10. $x^2 - 5x + 7 = 0$ **11.** $x^2 - 8x + 16 = 0$ **12.** $x^2 + 4x + 2 = 0$

13. $x^2 - 2x + 9 = 0$ **14.** $-3x^2 + 2x - 4 = 0$ **15.** $4x^2 - 6x - 1 = 0$

16. $-9 = 6x + x^2$ **17.** $-x^2 + 40 = 0$ **18.** $3x^2 - 7x = 0$

19. $\frac{1}{2}x^2 + x + 1 = 0$ **20.** $0 = 2x^2 - \frac{1}{2}x + 3$ **21.** $x^2 + \frac{1}{4} = x$

22. $x^2 + 2.1x = -1.1025$ **23.** $0.5x = x^2 - 0.14$ **24.** $x^2 + 2.25 = 0$

25. For what value(s) of c will the graph of $y = x^2 - 18x + c$ have exactly one x-intercept?

26. For what value(s) of c will the vertex of $y = 16x^2 + 24x + c$ lie on the x-axis?

27. For what value(s) of c will the graph of $y = x^2 - 6x + c$ have no x-intercepts?

28. For what value(s) of c will the graph of $y = x^2 - 8x + c$ have two x-intercepts?

29. Explain in writing how the discriminant can be used to determine whether the solutions of $ax^2 + bx + c = 0$ are rational or irrational. Give examples to illustrate your statements.

30. What is the relationship between b^2 and $4ac$ if $ax^2 + bx + c = 0$ has just one solution?

31. Explain why the sign of b has no effect on the number of solutions of $ax^2 + bx + c = 0$.

32. Show that the quadratic function $y = ax^2 + bx + c \ (a \neq 0)$ will have two x-intercepts if $a > 0$ and $c < 0$.

33. In Exercise 32, what conclusion can you draw about the number of x-intercepts if $a < 0$ and $c > 0$?

Mixed Review

Simplify.   *6.1, 6.2*

1. $(4x^2)^2$

2. $(-2y^2)^3$

3. $(-3xy^2)(5x^4y^2)$

Solve. Check for extraneous solutions.   *9.1, 9.2*

4. $\dfrac{3}{4} - \dfrac{1}{x} = \dfrac{5}{12}$

5. $\dfrac{x}{9} = \dfrac{4}{x}$

6. $\dfrac{x-3}{2} = \dfrac{-5}{x+4}$

Solve.   *4.4, 12.8*

7. The width of a rectangle is 6 cm less than the length. The perimeter of the rectangle is 54 cm. Find the length and the width.

8. Abu has 18 coins, all dimes and quarters. The total value of the coins is $3.30. How many of each type are there?

9. Given that $g(x) = 4x^2 - 3$, find $g(-2)$.   *10.3*

◢◢◢/Brainteaser

When $\frac{1}{4}$ of the adults left a beach party, the ratio of adults to children was 1:2. When 30 of the children left, the ratio of the children to adults was then 4:3. How many people remained at the beach?

Chapter 14 Review

Key Terms

axis of symmetry (p. 559)
completing the square (p. 539)
discriminant (p. 545)
maximum point (p. 559)
maximum value (p. 559)
minimum point (p. 559)

minimum value (p. 559)
parabola (p. 559)
quadratic formula (p. 544)
quadratic function (p. 558)
Square Root Property (p. 535)
vertex of a parabola (p. 559)

Key Ideas and Review Exercises

14.1   To solve an equation of the form $x^2 = c$, use the Square Root Property. If $x^2 = c$, where $c > 0$, then $x = \sqrt{c}$ or $x = -\sqrt{c}$.

Solve each equation. Give irrational solutions in simplest radical form.

1. $y^2 = 14$

2. $2x^2 = 36$

3. $-z^2 = -121$

4. $-4 = 19 - x^2$

5. $(r - 2)^2 = 81$

6. $(2a + 1)^2 - 3 = 4$

14.2   To solve an equation by completing the square, write it in the form $x^2 + bx = -c$, take $\frac{1}{2}$ of b, square it, and add the result to each side of the equation. The left side is now a perfect square, $\left(x + \frac{b}{2}\right)^2$. Then solve by using the Square Root Property.

Solve by completing the square. Give irrational solutions in simplest radical form.

7. $x^2 + 10x - 24 = 0$

8. $y^2 - 8y = -16$

9. $x^2 + 2x - 35 = 0$

10. $x^2 - 6x - 2 = 0$

11. $10 - 6y = y^2$

12. $x^2 + 7x + 10 = 0$

14.3   To solve a quadratic equation by using the quadratic formula, write the equation in standard form, $ax^2 + bx + c = 0$, where $a > 0$. Then use the formula, $x = \dfrac{-b \pm \sqrt{b^2 - 4ac}}{2a}$. If the discriminant $b^2 - 4ac$ is negative, the equation has no real number solutions.

Solve by using the quadratic formula. Give irrational solutions in simplest radical form.

13. $c^2 - 9c + 20 = 0$

14. $x^2 + 8x = 12$

15. $2x^2 = -4x - 1$

16. $a^2 - 5a + 1 = 0$

17. $-y^2 + 6y = 4$

18. $2x - 4 = -x^2$

14.4 Solve a quadratic equation by (1) using the Square Root Property, (2) factoring, (3) completing the square, or (4) by using the quadratic formula.

Solve. Give irrational solutions in simplest radical form.

19. $5x^2 = 100$ **20.** $y^2 + 10y = -24$ **21.** $r^2 - 12r + 36 = 0$

22. $4x^2 + x - 3 = 0$ **23.** $x^2 + 5x = 3$ **24.** $x^2 - 2 = 6x$

25. If a ball is thrown straight up at an initial velocity of 40 m/s, when will its height be 50 m from where it was thrown? Use the formula $h = 40t - 5t^2$. Give answers correct to the nearest tenth of a second.

14.5 To solve a geometric problem that leads to a quadratic equation, draw and label a figure. Then solve an equation by any appropriate method.

26. The distance between two opposite corners of a rectangular patio is 13 m. The length of the patio is 3 m shorter than 3 times the width. Find the length and the width of the patio.

27. The perimeter of a picture frame is 38 in. and its area is 84 in². Find the length and the width of the frame.

14.6 For the parabola $y = ax^2 + bx + c$ $(a \neq 0)$:

(1) The x-coordinate of the vertex is $-\frac{b}{2a}$. To find the y-coordinate of the vertex, substitute the x-value in the equation and solve for y.

(2) The equation of the axis of symmetry is $x = -\frac{b}{2a}$.

(3) The maximum or minimum value is the y-coordinate of the vertex.

For each quadratic function: (a) find the coordinates of the vertex of the parabola, (b) find the equation of the axis of symmetry, (c) find the minimum or maximum value, and (d) graph the function.

28. $y = -x^2$ **29.** $y = 2x^2 - 1$ **30.** $y = x^2 - 6x + 11$

14.7 The x-intercepts of the graph of $y = ax^2 + bx + c$ are the solutions of $ax^2 + bx + c = 0$. For the equation $ax^2 + bx + c = 0$, there are two solutions if $b^2 - 4ac > 0$; there is one solution if $b^2 - 4ac = 0$; and there are no real number solutions if $b^2 - 4ac < 0$.

Use the related quadratic equation to find the x-intercepts.

31. $y = x^2 - 4x - 21$ **32.** $y = 3x^2 - 14x + 8$ **33.** $-3x + 2x^2 - 1 = y$

Use the discriminant to find the number of solutions. Do not solve.

34. $x^2 - 6x + 3 = 0$ **35.** $-2x^2 + 3x + 5 = 0$ **36.** $25 + 10x = -x^2$

37. Given the function $y = x^2 - 20x + c$, write an explanation of how to find the value(s) of c such that the graph will have exactly one x-intercept.

Solve each equation. Give irrational solutions in simplest radical form.

1. $x^2 = 35$

2. $3x^2 - 48 = 0$

3. $(c - 2)^2 = 17$

4. $-(2x - 3)^2 + 9 = 2$

Solve by completing the square. Give irrational solutions in simplest radical form.

5. $x^2 + 2x - 3 = 0$

6. $x^2 + 8x - 20 = 0$

7. $y^2 - 8y + 48 = 0$

8. $3z^2 = 3 - 2z$

Solve by using the quadratic formula. Give irrational solutions in simplest radical form.

9. $x^2 - 7x + 12 = 0$

10. $2c^2 = 5c + 1$

11. $3 - x^2 = 5x$

12. $2y + y^2 = -4$

Use the quadratic function $y = x^2 - 4x + 5$ for Items 13–16.

13. Find the coordinates of the vertex of the parabola.

14. Write the equation of the axis of symmetry of the parabola.

15. Find the maximum or minimum value.

16. Graph the function.

Use the discriminant to determine the number of solutions for each equation. Do not solve.

17. $x^2 + 3x + 3 = 0$

18. $25x^2 - 10x - 1 = 0$

19. $4x^2 + 9 = 12x$

20. $-\frac{1}{2}x^2 + 3x - 1 = 0$

21. The formula $h = 50t - 5t^2$ can be used to find the height in meters of an object shot upward at an initial velocity of 50 m/s after t seconds. If a pellet is shot upward at an initial velocity of 50 m/s, when will its height be 70 m from where it was shot? Give answers to the nearest tenth of a second.

22. The distance between two opposite corners of a rectangular deck is 13 ft. The length is 7 ft longer than the width. Find the length and the width.

23. Solve $\dfrac{x^2 - 4}{2} - 1 = -x - 2$

24. What is the solution of the quadratic equation $ax^2 + bx + c = 0$ ($a \neq 0$) if the discriminant is equal to zero?

Choose the *one* best answer to each question or problem.

1. If x and y are positive integers with a difference of 9, what is the least possible value of $x + y$?
   (A) 8   (B) 9   (C) 10   (D) 11
   (E) 18

2. If $4y + 3y = 35$, then $(2y - 1)^2 = \underline{\ ?\ }$.
   (A) 81   (B) 25   (C) 9   (D) 6
   (E) 5

3. If three-thirds of $5\frac{1}{3}$ is subtracted from $5\frac{1}{3}$, the result is $\underline{\ ?\ }$.
   (A) $10\frac{2}{3}$ (B) $5\frac{1}{3}$ (C) 1
   (D) 0   (E) -1

4. For what value(s) of y is the statement $\frac{5^y}{5^6} > 1$ true?
   (A) $y > 1$ (B) $y > 6$
   (C) $y > 0$ (D) $y = 6$
   (E) $y < 6$

5. Solve $10 = \dfrac{5 - \frac{x}{y}}{4}$ for x.
   (A) $35y$ (B) $\dfrac{5 - \frac{x}{y}}{40}$
   (C) $\dfrac{5y - x}{40}$ (D) $-35y$
   (E) $35 - \dfrac{x}{y}$

6. If $\frac{2}{3}$ of a number is 12, what is $\frac{5}{6}$ of the number?
   (A) 15   (B) 10   (C) 8   (D) $\frac{20}{3}$
   (E) None of these

7. Carrie cycled 10 mi at 20 mi/h. How much time would she have saved if she had cycled at 25 mi/h?
   (A) $\frac{1}{2}$ h   (B) $\frac{2}{5}$ h   (C) 10 min
   (D) 5 min   (E) 6 min

8. What is the maximum possible area of the rectangle (in square units)?

   (A) 7   (B) 14   (C) 49
   (D) 196   (E) It cannot be determined from the information given.

9. If $0 < c < 1$, then $\dfrac{1}{\frac{1}{c}}$ is $\underline{\ ?\ }$.
   (A) greater than 1   (B) less than 0
   (C) between 0 and 1   (D) equal to 0
   (E) It cannot be determined from the information given.

10. If $x + y = 15$ and $x - y = 7$, then what is the value of y^2?
    (A) 22   (B) 16   (C) 11   (D) 4
    (E) 121

11. The equation $x^2 - 12x + c = 0$ has just one solution if $c = \underline{\ ?\ }$.
    (A) 0   (B) -24 (C) 24
    (D) -36 (E) 36

12. For what value(s) of x is it true that $4 + 5x \neq 6x$?
    (A) 4 only   (B) Every value except 4
    (C) $\frac{4}{11}$ only   (D) $\frac{11}{4}$ only
    (E) -4 only

13. If $\frac{2}{3}x = \frac{3}{2}y$ and $y \neq 0$, then $\frac{x}{y} = \underline{\ ?\ }$.
    (A) 1   (B) $\frac{9}{4}$ (C) $\frac{4}{9}$
    (D) $\frac{2}{3}$ (E) $\frac{3}{2}$

14. The area of a square is quadrupled if each side is $\underline{\ ?\ }$.
    (A) increased by 2
    (B) increased by 4   (C) doubled
    (D) quadrupled   (E) None of these

Cumulative Review   (Chapters 1–14)

1. Evaluate $16 - 5x$ for $x = 3$.   *1.2*

2. Which property is illustrated?   *1.5*
$(6 + 3x) + x = 6 + (3x + x)$

3. Simplify $8y + 2(6 + 3y) + 8$.   *1.7*

4. Simplify $-|10 - 8|$.   *2.2*

5. Evaluate $-2x^3 + 7x$ *2.8*
for $x = -1$.

6. Simplify.   *2.10*
$7(3 - 2x) - 4(x + 6)$

Solve.

7. $y - 9 = -4$ *3.1*

8. $-\frac{3}{5}c = 21$ *3.2*

9. $(r - 6)3 = 4(2r - 1) + 1$ *3.5*

10. $\frac{2}{3}x - \frac{1}{2} = \frac{3}{4}$ *4.5*

11. $2.4 - 1.6y = 3.2y$ *4.6*

12. $-5a + 15 > -20$ *5.2*

13. $|14 - x| = -2$ *5.6*

Graph the solution set.

14. $y \le 4$ *and* $y > -1$ *5.4*

15. $7 - |2x - 5| \le -2$ *5.7*

Simplify. (Exercises 16–18)

16. $2x^2y(-3xy^3)^2$ *6.2*

17. $\dfrac{5a^2bc^3}{-15ab^4c}$ *6.3*

18. $3a^3 - 2a + 7 - 4a^3 - a^2 + 9a$ *6.6*

19. Subtract $-3x^2 + 5x - 2$ *6.7*
from $6x^2 - 7x - 1$.

20. Multiply $(2x - 8)(3x + 1)$.   *6.9*

Factor completely. (Exercises 21–23)

21. $x^2 - 3x - 28$ *7.3*

22. $c^2 - 81$ *7.5*

23. $2y^2 + 10y - 48$ *7.6*

24. Solve $r^2 + 7r = -10$.   *7.7*

Simplify.

25. $\dfrac{y + 3}{y - 1} \div \dfrac{y^2 - 9}{y^2 - 6y + 5}$ *8.4*

26. $\dfrac{-3x - 9}{x^2 - 3x} + \dfrac{2x}{x - 3}$ *8.7*

27. $\dfrac{1 + \dfrac{1}{x}}{\dfrac{x}{2} - \dfrac{1}{2x}}$ *8.9*

Solve for x.

28. $\dfrac{x + 1}{x - 3} = \dfrac{3}{x} + \dfrac{12}{x^2 - 3x}$ *9.1*

29. $\dfrac{y + 7}{5} = \dfrac{y - 3}{4}$ *9.2*

30. $3x - 3b = 5x - a$ *9.3*

Give the domain and the range of each relation. Is the relation a function?

31.   *10.2*

32. $\{(-1, 0), (0, 1), (-1, 2), (2, 3)\}$

33. If $f(x) = -2x^2 + 9$, find   *10.3*
$f(-3)$.

34. Graph $2x - 3y = 9$.   *10.5*

35. Find the slope of the line de-   *11.1*
termined by $A(2, -6)$ and
$B(3, 2)$.

36. Write an equation determined   *11.2*
by points $R(4, 3)$ and
$S(0, -1)$.

37. Find the slope of the line.   *11.3*
$y = -\frac{4}{5}x - 3$

Solve each system. (Exercises 38 and 39).

38. $3x - 2y = 8$ **12.2**
   $y = -2$

39. $x - 2y = 9$ **12.4**
   $-3x + 2y = 5$

Solve by graphing.

40. $y > x - 2$ **12.10**
   $y \le -x + 4$

41. Write a fraction $\frac{a}{b}$, where a **13.1**
and b are integers, for $0.6\overline{2}$.

Simplify. (Exercises 42–44)

42. $\sqrt{28}$ **13.2**

43. $-\sqrt{27x^3y^8}$ **13.5**

44. $8\sqrt{2} - \sqrt{50}$ **13.6**

45. Approximate $\sqrt{87}$ to the   **13.3**
nearest tenth.

46. Solve $3x^2 - 2 = 5$.   **14.1**

47. Solve $x^2 - 2x + 7 = 0$.   **14.3**

48. Solve $3x^2 + x - 5 = 0$.   **14.6**

49. Find the coordinates of the   **14.6**
vertex of the parabola
$y = x^2 + 4x - 10$. Graph
the function.

50. If 142 is 7 more than 3 times
a number, find the number.   **3.3**

51. A train went 147 mi in $3\frac{1}{2}$h.   **3.6**
What was the average rate in
miles per hour?

52. The sum of two consecutive   **4.3**
odd integers is -76. Find the
integers.

53. The base of an isosceles tri-   **4.4**
angle is 8 cm longer than a
leg. The perimeter is 104 cm.
Find the length of each side.

54. In a class of 180 students,   **4.7**
45% are boys. Find the num-
ber of boys and the number
of girls in the class.

55. The price of a stock dropped
from $12\frac{1}{2}$ to $11\frac{1}{2}$. What was
the percent decrease?

56. Forty-eight is 12% of what
number?

57. Jane earns $250 a week, plus   **4.8**
a 5% commission on her to-
tal sales. Last week she
earned $671. What were her
total sales for the week?

58. The length of a rectangular   **7.9**
garden is 3 ft less than twice
the width. The area is 54 ft^2.
Find the length and the width
of the garden.

59. Separate a 72-cm board into   **9.2**
two parts with lengths in the
ratio 3:5. Find the lengths of
the two parts.

60. One machine can complete an   **9.5**
order in 6 h while another
machine takes 9 h. How long
will it take both machines to
complete this order working
together?

61. If y varies inversely as x and   **10.7**
y is 24 when x is 9, find x
when y is 6.

62. One pencil and 3 erasers cost   **12.3**
79¢. Two pencils and 5 eras-
ers cost $1.48. Find the cost
of a pencil and the cost of an
eraser.

63. The tens digit of a two-digit   **12.6**
number is 3 more than the
units digit. If the digits are reversed, the new number is 27
less than the original number.
Find the original number.

64. A rectangular lot measures 12   **13.4**
yd by 16 yd. How many yards
farther is it to walk the length
and the width of the lot than
to walk from one corner to
the opposite corner?

Bill Grove, of Whitenoise, plays the saxophone, which is a wind instrument. The music made by wind instruments, such as the clarinet, flute, and trombone, is produced by sound waves vibrating inside a tube.

15.1 Similar Triangles

Objective

To find the lengths of sides of similar triangles

Some distances are impossible to measure directly. In such cases, *similar triangles* can often be used to measure distances indirectly. An ancient method of measuring heights is called *shadow reckoning*. This makes use of similar triangles that involve the sun's rays, two vertical objects, and the shadows of these objects.

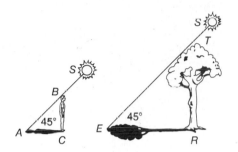

Similar triangles have the same shape. If all pairs of **corresponding angles** have the same measure, then the two triangles are **similar triangles.** In the figure at the right below, △ABC is similar to △DEF, or △ABC ~ △DEF.

The symbol "∠" means *angle.* The symbol "m ∠" means *measure of an angle.*

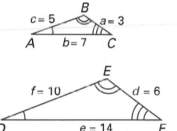

Notice the same markings for pairs of corresponding angles, ∠A and ∠D, ∠B and ∠E, ∠C and ∠F. This indicates that m ∠A = m ∠D, m ∠B = m ∠E, and m ∠C = m ∠F.

The sides opposite pairs of corresponding angles are called **corresponding sides.** Thus, $\overline{AC}$ (opposite ∠B) and $\overline{DF}$ (opposite ∠E) are corresponding sides.

In △ABC, *a*, *b*, and *c* denote the lengths of the sides. Compare the ratios of the lengths of corresponding sides in △ABC and △DEF.

$$\frac{a}{d} = \frac{3}{6}, \text{ or } \frac{1}{2}$$

$$\frac{b}{e} = \frac{7}{14}, \text{ or } \frac{1}{2}$$

$$\frac{c}{f} = \frac{5}{10}, \text{ or } \frac{1}{2}$$

Each ratio is equal to $\frac{1}{2}$. This illustrates an important property of similar triangles.

In *similar triangles, the lengths of all three pairs of corresponding sides have the same ratio.*

EXAMPLE 1 $\triangle ABC \sim \triangle RST$, $a = 8$, $r = 12$, and $c = 10$. Find t.

Plan   Write a proportion using a, r, c, and t, since a and r are lengths of corresponding sides, and c and t are lengths of corresponding sides.

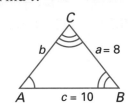

Solution
$$\frac{a}{r} = \frac{c}{t}$$
$$\frac{8}{12} = \frac{10}{t}$$
$$8t = 12 \cdot 10 \quad \longleftarrow \text{If } \frac{a}{b} = \frac{c}{d}, \text{ then } ad = bc.$$
$$8t = 120$$
$$t = 15$$

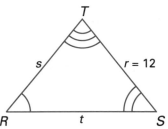

EXAMPLE 2   A pole that is 2 m high casts a shadow that is 3 m long. At the same time, a nearby building casts a shadow that is 36 m long. Find the height of the building.

Plan   Draw a diagram to show two similar right triangles. Let x represent the height of the building. Write a proportion to find the height.

Solution
$$\frac{x}{2} = \frac{36}{3}$$
$$3x = 72$$
$$x = 24$$

(The triangles are not shown in true relative size.)

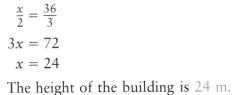

The height of the building is 24 m.

TRY THIS   1. Jane is 5 ft tall. She casts a 7-ft shadow at the same time that a nearby pole casts a 15-ft shadow. How high is the pole?

Focus on Reading

$\triangle EFG \sim \triangle KLM$. Tell whether each statement is true or false.

1. $\angle E$ corresponds to $\angle K$.
2. $\angle G$ corresponds to $\angle L$.
3. $\overline{EG}$ corresponds to $\overline{KL}$.
4. $\overline{FG}$ corresponds to $\overline{LM}$.
5. $\frac{e}{k}$ and $\frac{f}{l}$ must be equal.
6. $\frac{m}{g}$ and $\frac{l}{f}$ must be equal.

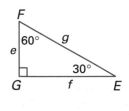

Classroom Exercises

$\triangle ABC \sim \triangle DEF$. Complete the proportion.

1. $\frac{c}{f} = \frac{a}{?}$

2. $\frac{c}{f} = \frac{?}{e}$

3. $\frac{e}{b} = \frac{d}{?}$

4. $\frac{?}{c} = \frac{d}{a}$

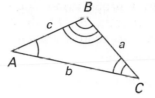

Find the missing length.

5. $c = 12$, $f = 8$, and $b = 9$. Find e.

6. $a = 16$, $d = 12$, and $c = 8$. Find f.

7. $d = 8$, $a = 16$, and $f = 9$. Find c.

8. $e = 10$, $b = 15$, and $d = 12$. Find a.

Written Exercises

In Exercises 1–8, $\triangle ABC \sim \triangle XZY$.
Find the missing length.

1. $b = 8$, $z = 4$, $a = 12$. Find x.

2. $a = 12$, $x = 6$, and $b = 8$. Find z.

3. $z = 16$, $b = 4$, and $x = 12$. Find a.

4. $y = 5$, $b = 6$, and $z = 15$. Find c.

5. $b = 250$, $y = 200$, and $c = 150$. Find z.

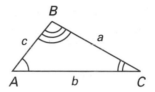

6. $a = 40$, $x = 30$, and $b = 36$. Find z.

7. $b = 12.5$, $y = 10.0$, and $c = 8.5$. Find z.

8. $y = 4.5$, $b = 6.0$, and $z = 6.6$. Find c.

In Exercises 9–12, $\triangle DEF \sim \triangle RST$.

9. $\angle E$ corresponds to which angle in $\triangle RST$?

10. $\angle D$ corresponds to which angle in $\triangle RST$?

11. $\angle F$ corresponds to which angle in $\triangle RST$?

12. What is the degree measure of $\angle F$?

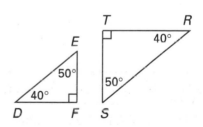

Solve each problem.

13. A 2-m stick casts a 10-m shadow. At the same time, a nearby building casts a 40-m shadow. Find the height of the building.

14. Mr. Forbes is 6 ft tall. He casts a 4-ft shadow at the same time that a nearby flagpole casts an 18-ft shadow. How high is the flagpole?

15. A 30-m ladder touches the side of a building at a height of 25 m. At what height would a 12-m ladder touch the building if it makes the same angle with the ground?

16. Tony stands so that his shadow just reaches the tip of the shadow of a tree. His height is 5 ft and the length of his shadow is 8 ft. The length of the shadow of the tree is 40 ft. What is the height of the tree?

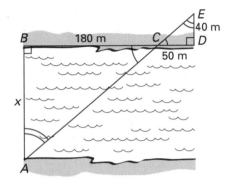

17. Ms. Carter wants to find the height of one of her trees. When she holds a yardstick in a vertical position, touching the ground, it casts a shadow 2 ft long. At the same time, the tree's shadow is 32 ft long. What is the height of the tree?

18. In the figure at the right, $BC = 180$ m, $CD = 50$ m, and $ED = 40$ m. Angles B and D are right angles, and $\triangle ABC \sim \triangle EDC$. Use this information to find x, the distance across the river.

Round lengths to the nearest tenth.

19. The lengths of three sides of a triangle are 5 cm, 8 cm, and 9 cm. The shortest side of a similar triangle is 9 cm. Find the other lengths.

20. The lengths of three sides of a triangle are 12 cm, 14 cm, and 16 cm. The longest side of a similar triangle is 30 cm. Find the other lengths.

21. In $\triangle ABC$, m $\angle A = 62$ and m $\angle B = 28$. In $\triangle XYZ$, m $\angle X = 62$ and m $\angle Z = 90$. Are the two triangles similar? Explain.

22. In right $\triangle DEF$, m $\angle D = 36$. In right $\triangle JKL$, m $\angle K = 53$. Are the two right triangles similar? Explain.

Mixed Review

Divide. *8.4*

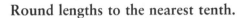

1. $\dfrac{x^2 - 1}{y + 2} \div \dfrac{(x - 1)^2}{2y - 8}$

2. $\dfrac{n^2 + 4n - 21}{n^2 + n - 20} \div \dfrac{n^2 + 8n + 7}{n^2 + 6n + 5}$

Simplify. *13.2, 13.7*

3. $\sqrt{3} \cdot \sqrt{11}$

4. $3\sqrt{8y^5} \cdot 5\sqrt{2y}$

5. $\sqrt{2}(\sqrt{8} + 3\sqrt{2})$

6. $(4\sqrt{5} - \sqrt{2})(5\sqrt{5} - 3\sqrt{2})$

7. Find two consecutive odd integers whose product is 399. *7.9*

8. The sum of a number and its reciprocal is $\frac{25}{12}$. Find the number. *9.1*

15.2 Trigonometric Ratios

Objectives

To compute or find the value of the sine, cosine, and tangent of acute angles of right triangles

To explain why corresponding angles of similar right triangles have the same trigonometric ratios

Recall that in a right triangle, the side opposite the right angle is called the *hypotenuse*. The other sides are called the *legs*.

In right triangle ABC, leg a is opposite $\angle A$; leg b is opposite $\angle B$. $\angle A$ and $\angle B$ are acute angles, since each has a degree measure between 0 and 90. Each leg is also referred to as *adjacent to an acute angle*. Thus, leg a is adjacent to $\angle B$ and leg b is adjacent to $\angle A$.

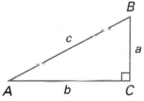

The figure below shows two similar right triangles.

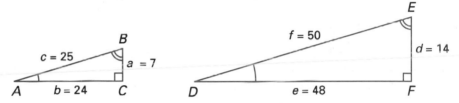

Corresponding sides of the two similar triangles are proportional.

$$\frac{a}{d} = \frac{c}{f} \qquad \frac{b}{e} = \frac{c}{f} \qquad \frac{a}{d} = \frac{b}{e}$$

In $\frac{a}{d} = \frac{c}{f}$, the means ($c$ and d) can be interchanged, as shown below.

$$\frac{a}{d} = \frac{c}{f} \qquad\qquad \left(\frac{7}{14} = \frac{25}{50}\right)$$

Use the Proportion Property. $a \cdot f = d \cdot c$

Divide each side by $c \cdot f$. $\dfrac{a \cdot f}{c \cdot f} = \dfrac{d \cdot c}{c \cdot f}$

A new proportion is obtained. $\dfrac{a}{c} = \dfrac{d}{f}$ $\left(\dfrac{7}{25} = \dfrac{14}{50}\right)$

Notice that the left side of the above proportion involves sides of $\triangle ABC$ and the right side involves sides of $\triangle DEF$. In a similar way, you can rewrite $\frac{b}{e} = \frac{c}{f}$ as $\frac{b}{c} = \frac{e}{f}$, and $\frac{a}{d} = \frac{b}{e}$ as $\frac{a}{b} = \frac{d}{e}$.

The ratios $\frac{a}{c}$, $\frac{b}{c}$, and $\frac{a}{b}$ in right triangle ABC are called, respectively, the *sine ratio* of angle A, the *cosine ratio* of angle A, and the *tangent ratio* of angle A. These ratios, abbreviated as *sin A*, *cos A*, and *tan A*, are defined as follows.

Definition

For all right triangles ABC with **right angle C** and sides a, b, and c:

$$\sin A = \frac{\text{length of opposite side}}{\text{length of hypotenuse}} = \frac{a}{c}$$

$$\cos A = \frac{\text{length of adjacent side}}{\text{length of hypotenuse}} = \frac{b}{c}$$

$$\tan A = \frac{\text{length of opposite side}}{\text{length of adjacent side}} = \frac{a}{b}$$

EXAMPLE 1

For right triangle ABC, find the trigonometric ratios for $\angle A$ and $\angle B$ to three decimal places.

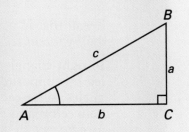

Plan

Use the definitions of sine, cosine, and tangent.

Solutions

$\sin A = \frac{\text{opp}}{\text{hyp}} = \frac{6}{10}$, or 0.600 $\qquad$ $\sin B = \frac{\text{opp}}{\text{hyp}} = \frac{8}{10}$, or 0.800

$\cos A = \frac{\text{adj}}{\text{hyp}} = \frac{8}{10}$, or 0.800 $\qquad$ $\cos B = \frac{\text{adj}}{\text{hyp}} = \frac{6}{10}$, or 0.600

$\tan A = \frac{\text{opp}}{\text{adj}} = \frac{6}{8}$, or 0.750 $\qquad$ $\tan B = \frac{\text{opp}}{\text{adj}} = \frac{8}{6}$, or 1.333

EXAMPLE 2

For right triangle PQR, find $\sin P$, $\cos P$, and $\tan P$. Find $\sin Q$, $\cos Q$, and $\tan Q$. Leave the answers in fraction form.

Plan

Use the definitions of sine, cosine, and tangent.

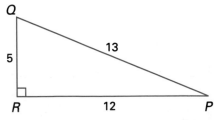

Solutions

$\sin P = \frac{5}{13}$ $\qquad$ $\sin Q = \frac{12}{13}$

$\cos P = \frac{12}{13}$ $\qquad$ $\cos Q = \frac{5}{13}$

$\tan P = \frac{5}{12}$ $\qquad$ $\tan Q = \frac{12}{5}$

EXAMPLE 3   For right triangle RST, find sin R, cos R, and tan R.

Plan   First use the Pythagorean Theorem to find the length, t.

Solution

$$t^2 = r^2 + s^2$$
$$t^2 = 2^2 + 1^2 = 5$$
$$t = \sqrt{5}$$

Thus, sin $R = \dfrac{2}{\sqrt{5}}$, or $\dfrac{2\sqrt{5}}{5}$

$\cos R = \dfrac{1}{\sqrt{5}}$, or $\dfrac{\sqrt{5}}{5}$

$\tan R = \dfrac{2}{1}$, or 2

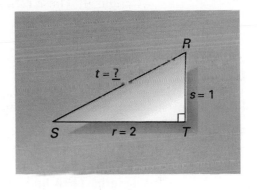

TRY THIS   For right triangle RST in Example 3, find sin S, cos S, and tan S if $s = 2$ and $r = 6$.

Classroom Exercises

Refer to the figure at the right.
1. Name the hypotenuse.
2. Name the leg opposite $\angle M$.
3. Name the leg adjacent to $\angle M$.
4. Name the leg adjacent to $\angle N$.
5. Name the leg opposite $\angle N$.

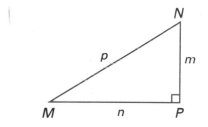

Find each of the following to three decimal places.

6. sin D	7. cos D	8. tan D
9. sin E	10. cos E	11. tan E

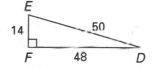

Written Exercises

Find each of the following to three decimal places.

1. sin A	2. cos A	3. tan A
4. sin B	5. cos B	6. tan B

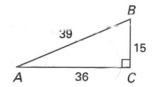

Find each of the following to three decimal places.

7. sin *J*   **8.** cos *J*   **9.** tan *J*

10. sin *K*   **11.** cos *K*   **12.** tan *K*

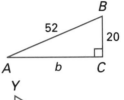

Find each of the following values. Leave answers in fraction form.

13. sin *Y*   **14.** cos *Y*   **15.** tan *Y*

16. sin *X*   **17.** cos *X*   **18.** tan *X*

Find the missing length. Then find the trigonometric ratios.

19. *b*   **20.** sin *A*   **21.** cos *A*

22. tan *A*   **23.** sin *B*   **24.** cos *B*

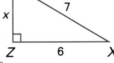

Find the missing length. Then find the trigonometric ratios. Rationalize denominators if necessary.

25. *x*   **26.** sin *X*   **27.** cos *X*

28. tan *X*   **29.** cos *Y*   **30.** tan *Y*

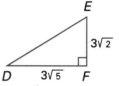

Refer to right triangle *DEF* at the right. Find the trigonometric ratios. Rationalize denominators if necessary.

31. sin *D*   **32.** cos *D*   **33.** tan *D*

34. sin *E*   **35.** cos *E*   **36.** tan *E*

In right triangle *QRS*, angles *Q* and *R* are acute angles. The leg adjacent to $\angle Q$ is 12 cm long. The leg opposite $\angle Q$ is 9 cm long.

37. Find the length of $\overline{QR}$.   **38.** Find tan *Q*.   **39.** Find cos *R*.

Triangle *ABC* is an *isosceles* right triangle. The two legs have the same length, and the measure of each acute angle is 45.

40. Find the length of the hypotenuse.

41. Find sin 45, cos 45, and tan 45. Rationalize denominators if necessary.

Mixed Review

Factor.   **7.4, 7.5**

1. $2x^2 + x - 6$ **2.** $y^2 - 24y + 144$ **3.** $n^2 - 25$

Solve each equation.   **7.7**

4. $x^2 - 9 = 0$ **5.** $x^2 - 7x + 10 = 0$ **6.** $2x^2 - 8x = 0$

15.3 Trigonometric Tables

Objectives

To find the value of the sine, cosine, and tangent of an acute angle using a trigonometric table or a calculator

To find the measure of an angle using a trigonometric table or a calculator

To find the values of trigonometric ratios for angles with degree measures between 0 and 90, use the trigonometric table on page 643. Although the table gives *approximations* to four decimal places, the symbol = is used instead of ≈ for convenience.

EXAMPLE 1

Find each value.

a. sin 12

b. tan 47

Plan

Find the appropriate number in the Angle Measure column. Then read across to the correct column.

Solutions

a.

Angle Measure	sin	cos	tan
10	.1736	.9848	.1763
11	.1908	.9816	.1944
12 →	.2079	.9781	.2126
13	.2250	.9744	.2309

Thus, sin 12 = 0.2079.

b.

Angle Measure	sin	cos	tan
46	.7193	.6947	1.036
47 —	.7314	.6820 →	1.072
48	.7431	.6691	1.111
49	.7547	.6561	1.150

Thus, tan 47 = 1.072.

TRY THIS

Find each value: 1. tan 10   2. cos 49

You can also use a trigonometric table to find the measure of an angle, given a trigonometric ratio of the angle.

EXAMPLE 2

Find m∠B if cos B = 0.2419.

Solution

Read down the cos column until you find 0.2419. Then read across to the Angle Measure column to find the correct angle measure.
Thus, m ∠B = 76.

Angle Measure	sin	cos	tan
75	.9659	.2588	3.732
76 ←	.9703	.2419	4.011
77	.9744	.2250	4.332
78	.9781	.2079	4.704

TRY THIS

3. Find m∠A if sin A = .9744.

If the trigonometric ratio of an angle does not appear in the table, use the closest value to find the measure of the angle.

EXAMPLE 3 Find m ∠A to the nearest degree if cos A = 0.9710.

Plan Locate the value closest to 0.9710 in the cos column. Then read across to find the angle measure.

Solution

Angle Measure	sin	cos	tan	
11	.1908	.9816	.1944	
12	.2079	.9781	.2126	
13	.2250	.9744	.2309	
14 ⟵	.2419	.9703	.2493	⟵ .9710 is closer to .9703 than to .9744.

Thus, m ∠A = 14, to the nearest degree.

TRY THIS 4. Find m ∠B to the nearest degree if sin B = .1937.

Classroom Exercises

Use the tables in Example 1 to find the value of the trigonometric ratio.

1. sin 10   **2.** cos 13   **3.** tan 11
4. cos 48   **5.** tan 49   **6.** sin 46

Use the table in Example 2 to find the measure of angle A.

7. tan A = 4.704   **8.** cos A = 0.2588   **9.** sin A = 0.9781

Written Exercises

Find the value of the trigonometric ratio to four decimal places.
Use the table on page 643.

1. sin 36   **2.** cos 8   **3.** tan 73
4. cos 15   **5.** tan 31   **6.** cos 54
7. tan 12   **8.** sin 81   **9.** tan 43
10. sin 48   **11.** tan 4   **12.** sin 79
13. cos 21   **14.** sin 2   **15.** cos 86

Find m ∠A to the nearest degree. Use the table on page 643.

16. cos A = 0.9877   **17.** tan A = 0.5543   **18.** sin A = 0.9925
19. tan A = 0.0875   **20.** sin A = 0.7193   **21.** cos A = 0.5000

22. $\sin A = 0.9205$ **23.** $\cos A = 0.4067$ **24.** $\tan A = 3.732$

25. $\cos A = 0.8740$ **26.** $\tan A = 2.500$ **27.** $\sin A = 0.6460$

28. $\tan A = 9.001$ **29.** $\sin A = 0.0299$ **30.** $\cos A = 0.1351$

31. $\cos 60 + \sin 30$ **32.** $\sin 70 - \cos 20$ **33.** $\sin 25 + \cos 65$

34. $(\sin 30)^2 + (\cos 30)^2$ **35.** $(\sin 40)^2 + (\cos 40)^2$ **36.** $(\sin 70)^2 + (\cos 70)^2$

37. Determine the degree measure of $\angle A$ if $\sin A = \cos A$.

38. Describe the relationship between m $\angle A$ and m $\angle B$ if $\sin A = \cos B$.

39. Show by choosing three measures of $\angle A$ from the table that $\sin A = \cos (90 - A)$.

40. Show by choosing three measures of $\angle A$ from the table that $\tan A = \dfrac{\sin A}{\cos A}$.

Midchapter Review

In Exercises 1–4, $\triangle ABC \sim \triangle DEF$. Find the missing length.   *15.1*

1. $a = 10$, $d = 6$, $c = 15$. Find f.

2. $b = 9$, $e = 5$, and $a = 18$. Find d.

3. $a = 15$, $b = 9$, and $d = 10$. Find e.

4. $e = 14$, $d = 16$, and $b = 7$. Find a.

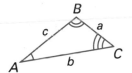 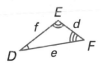

Find each of the following to three decimal places.   *15.2*

5. $\sin A$ **6.** $\cos A$

7. $\tan A$ **8.** $\sin B$

9. $\cos B$ **10.** $\tan B$

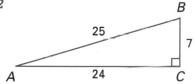

Find each of the following. Leave the answer in the fraction form.   *15.2*

11. $\sin A$ **12.** $\cos A$

13. $\tan A$ **14.** $\sin B$

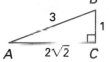

Find the value of the trigonometric ratio.   *15.3*

15. $\sin 38$ **16.** $\cos 9$ **17.** $\tan 41$

Find the measure of $\angle A$ to the nearest degree.   *15.3*

18. $\cos A = 0.8192$ **19.** $\tan A = 4.103$ **20.** $\sin A = 0.8301$

21. A 3-m stick casts a 5-m shadow. At the same time, a nearby tree casts a 15-m shadow. Find the height of the tree.   *15.1*

15.4 Right-Triangle Solutions

Objectives   To find the lengths of the sides of a right triangle to the nearest tenth
To find the measures of the acute angles of a right triangle to the nearest degree

In this lesson, you will see how trigonometric ratios can be used to find the lengths of sides or the measures of angles in a right triangle.

EXAMPLE 1   In $\triangle ABC$, if m $\angle A = 24$ and $b = 32.0$, find a to the nearest tenth.

Plan   You know m $\angle A$ and the length of b, the leg adjacent to $\angle A$. To find the length a of the leg opposite $\angle A$, use the definition $\tan A = \dfrac{\text{opp}}{\text{adj}}$.

Solution
$$\tan 24 = \frac{a}{32}$$
$$32 \tan 24 = a$$
$$32(0.4452) = a$$
$$14.2464 = a$$

So, $a = 14.2$ to the nearest tenth.

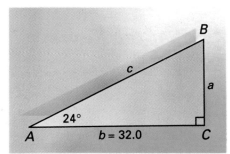

EXAMPLE 2   In $\triangle ABC$, if m $\angle B = 50$ and $b = 37.0$, find c to the nearest tenth.

Plan   You know the measure of $\angle B$ and the length of the leg opposite $\angle B$. To find the length of the hypotenuse, use $\sin B = \dfrac{\text{opp}}{\text{hyp}}$.

Solution
$$\sin 50 = \frac{37}{c}$$
$$c(\sin 50) = 37$$
$$c = \frac{37}{\sin 50}$$
$$c = \frac{37}{0.7660} = 48.30$$

So, $c = 48.3$ to the nearest tenth.

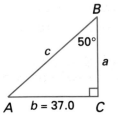

TRY THIS   In right triangle ABC in Example 2, if m $\angle A = 17$ and $c = 23.0$, find b to the nearest tenth.

In Examples 1 and 2, a trigonometric ratio was used to find *the length of a side* of a right triangle when the following facts were known:

the measure of an acute angle in the triangle

the length of another side in the triangle

In the next example, you will see how a trigonometric ratio can be used to find *the measure of an acute angle* in a right triangle when the following facts are known:

lengths of *any two sides* of the triangle

EXAMPLE 3   If a = 2.0 and b = 3.0, find m $\angle A$ to the nearest degree.

Plan   You know the length of the leg opposite $\angle A$ and the length of the leg adjacent to $\angle A$. Use $\tan A = \dfrac{\text{opp}}{\text{adj}}$ to find the measure of $\angle A$.

Solution $\tan A = \dfrac{2}{3} = 0.6667$

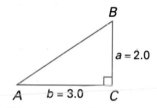

The value closest to 0.6667 in the tangent column is $\tan 34 = 0.6745$.

So, m $\angle A = 34$, to the nearest degree.

Classroom Exercises

For Exercises 1–5, refer to $\triangle ABC$.

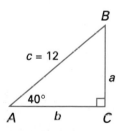

1. Identify the leg opposite $\angle A$.
2. Identify the leg adjacent to $\angle A$.
3. Identify the hypotenuse of the triangle.
4. What trigonometric ratio would you use to find b?
5. Find b to the nearest tenth.

In Exercises 6–8, find the length of the indicated side to the nearest tenth, or the measure of the indicated angle to the nearest degree.

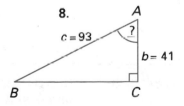

6.

7.

8.

Written Exercises

Find the length of the indicated side to the nearest tenth.

1.

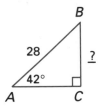

2.

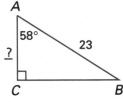

3.

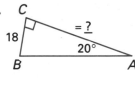

Find the measure of the indicated angle to the nearest degree.

4.

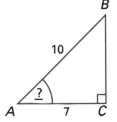

5.

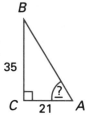

6.

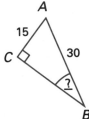

Find the missing lengths of sides to the nearest tenth and the missing measures of angles to the nearest degree.

7. If $a = 14$ and m $\angle A = 60$, find b.

8. If $b = 32$ and m $\angle B = 15$, find c.

9. If $a = 93$ and m $\angle B = 52$, find c.

10. If $c = 18$ and m $\angle B = 33$, find a.

11. If $b = 72$ and $c = 96$, find m $\angle A$.

12. If $a = 31$ and $b = 46$, find m $\angle B$.

13. If $a = 44$ and $c = 77$, find m $\angle A$.

14. If $a = 15$ and $b = 16$, find m $\angle B$.

15. If $a = 33.6$ and m $\angle B = 12$, find c.

16. If $a = 76.3$ and $c = 98.7$, find m $\angle A$.

17. If $b = 86.8$ and m $\angle A = 46$, find a.

18. If $b = 49.6$ and $c = 76.4$, find m $\angle B$.

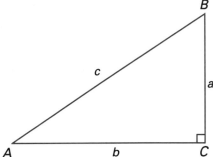

Find all the missing measures (lengths of sides to nearest tenth and measures of angles to nearest degree).

19.

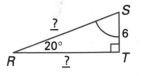

20.

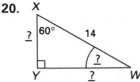

21.

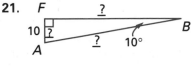

Solve.

22. Anna drew a right triangle ABC with legs 4.0 cm and 5.0 cm long. What is the measure of $\angle A$?

23. Georgio drew a right triangle DEF with $\angle F$ the right angle. The degree measure of $\angle D$ was 38 and DF was 12.0 cm. What was the length of the hypotenuse?

24. Shoshana drew a right triangle GHI with $\angle I$ the right angle. GI was 3.6 cm and IH was 4.8 cm. What was the measure of $\angle G$?

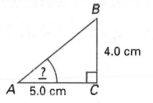

Figure $ABCD$ is a rhombus. A rhombus is a parallelogram whose diagonals bisect each other and are perpendicular to each other. The diagonals of $ABCD$ are $\overline{BD}$ and $\overline{AC}$. m $\angle DAC = 25$ and $DE = 4.0$.

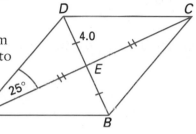

Find the indicated lengths to the nearest tenth and angle measures to the nearest degree.

25. AD 26. BC 27. EC
28. AE 29. BE 30. m $\angle DCE$
31. m $\angle EBA$ 32. AB 33. DC

Mixed Review

Add or subtract.   *8.5, 8.6, 8.7*

1. $\dfrac{8y}{5} + \dfrac{3y}{5}$
2. $\dfrac{9}{10n} - \dfrac{5}{2n^2}$
3. $\dfrac{4}{x - 6} - \dfrac{1}{x^2 - 2x - 24}$

Solve by using the quadratic formula. Write irrational solutions in simplest radical form.   *14.3*

4. $x^2 - 7x + 3 = 0$
5. $2x + 7 = -x^2$
6. $3 = 5x^2 - 11x$

Solve.   *4.7*

7. Ninety-two percent of 150 is what number?
8. Thirty-eight percent of what number is 19?
9. Thirty-two is what percent of 80?

▰▰▰/Brainteasers

1. If x is a real number, what is the least value of this product?
   $(x + \sqrt{2} + \sqrt{3})(x + \sqrt{2} - \sqrt{3})(x - \sqrt{2} + \sqrt{3})(x - \sqrt{2} - \sqrt{3})$
2. Solve for x if $x^2 + |x| = 30$.
3. Find all values of x such that $|x| + 2 = |x - 2|$.

15.5 Problem Solving: Applying Trigonometry

Objective   To solve problems using trigonometric ratios

The following examples illustrate applications of trigonometric ratios. All answers are rounded and given as approximations.

EXAMPLE 1   Find the distance across the pond to the nearest meter.

Plan   Use $\tan D = \dfrac{\text{opp}}{\text{adj}}$.

Solution
$$\tan 36 = \frac{x}{32}$$
$$x = 32(\tan 36) = 32(0.7265), \text{ or } 23.25$$
So, the distance across the pond is 23 m, to the nearest meter.

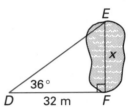

An **angle of elevation** is an angle formed by a horizontal line and the line of sight to a point at a higher elevation. An **angle of depression** is an angle formed by a horizontal line and the line of sight to a point at a lower elevation. For any given line of sight, the measure of the angle of elevation equals the measure of the angle of depression.

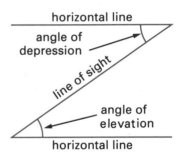

EXAMPLE 2   A ship is 335 m from the base of a cliff. The degree measure of the angle of elevation from the ship to the top of the cliff is 34. Find the distance from the ship to the top of the cliff. Give the answer to the nearest 10 meters.

Plan   Use $\cos S = \dfrac{\text{adj}}{\text{hyp}}$.

Solution
$$\cos 34 = \frac{335}{x}$$
$$x(\cos 34) = 335$$
$$x = \frac{335}{\cos 34} = \frac{335}{0.8290}, \text{ or } 404.1013$$

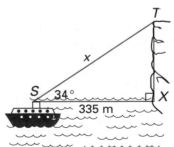

So the distance from the ship to the top of the cliff is about 400 m.

Classroom Exercises

The figure at the right shows a pond and right triangle XYZ. Identify each given side as the leg opposite ∠X, the leg adjacent to ∠X, or the hypotenuse.

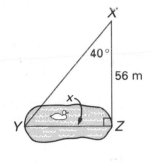

1. $\overline{XY}$
2. $\overline{XZ}$
3. $\overline{YZ}$
4. In right triangle XYZ, which trigonometric ratio would you use to find x, the distance across the lake?
5. In right triangle XYZ, find x.

For Classroom Exercises 6–7, use right triangle ABC.

6. What is the degree measure of the angle of elevation?
7. Find the height of the tree to the nearest foot.

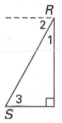

8. In the figure at the right, identify which angle is the angle of depression from point R to point S.

Written Exercises

1. Find the length x of the ladder to the nearest foot.

5 ft

2. Find the height x of the flagpole to the nearest foot.

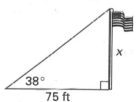

3. Find the length x of the ladder to the nearest meter.

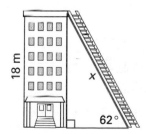

4. Find the distance x from the ship to the lighthouse to the nearest meter.

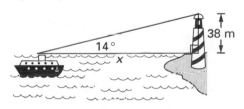

Solve each problem. Find lengths to the nearest integer and angle measures to the nearest degree.

5. A kite is flying at the end of a 220-m string. How high above the ground is the kite if the string has an angle of elevation of measure 55?

6. A tree casts a 30-m shadow when the degree measure of the angle of elevation of the sun is 24. How tall is the tree?

7. The degree measure of the angle of depression from the top of a lighthouse 120 ft high to an object in the water is 63. How far from the base of the lighthouse is the object? The foot of the lighthouse is at sea level.

8. A straight road up a hill is 430 m long and has an angle of elevation of degree measure 12. Find the height of the hill.

9. A plane flying at an altitude of 9,400 m makes an angle of depression with its carrier that has degree measure 28. How far is the plane from its carrier?

10. A ramp is 156 m long. It rises a vertical distance of 31 m. Find the measure of the angle of elevation.

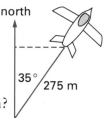

11. An airplane flies in a northeasterly direction making an angle with the north line that has degree measure 35. If the plane flies a distance of 275 mi, how many miles east will it fly?

12. In Exercise 11, suppose the plane flies in a northeasterly direction at an angle of degree measure 42 from the north line. How many miles would it have to fly to be 215 mi east of the starting position?

Suppose that a rectangular park is labeled *ABCD*. A straight diagonal path from *B* to *D* is 85 ft long and makes an angle of degree measure 22 with each of the longer sides of the rectangle.

13. Find the length of the park to the nearest foot.

14. Find the area of the park to the nearest hundred square feet.

Mixed Review

Simplify if possible.   *6.1, 6.2, 6.3*

1. $-4xy^2z(5x^3y^5z)$ 2. $(-3a^4)^2$ 3. $-(4m^9)^4$ 4. $\dfrac{-18a^4b^2}{3ab^2}$

Solve the system of equations.   *12.4, 12.5*

5. $x + y = 12$
   $x - y = 6$

6. $-3x + 2y = 1$
   $-x - y = 2$

7. $5x - 4y = 1$
   $3x + 2y = 5$

You have now used a number of problem-solving strategies. Here are some of them.

Checking Assumptions	Making a Graph
Defining the Variables	Making a Table
Drawing a Diagram	Solving a Simpler Problem
Estimating Before Solving	Using Formulas
Guessing and Checking	Working Backwards

Use one or more of these strategies to solve these problems.

1. Twenty-four is what percent of 60?

2. Eighty is 32% of what number?

3. If $8,000 is invested at a simple interest rate of 8.4% per year for 3 years, how much interest is earned?

4. An isosceles triangle has a vertex angle with degree measure 42. What is the degree measure of a base angle?

5. Find three consecutive even integers whose sum is 72.

6. Express the number of seconds in a 12-hour day in scientific notation.

7. The area of a garden that is circular is 64π ft². What is the diameter of the garden?

8. The area of a square is 27 cm². Find the length of a side to the nearest tenth.

9. A hiker walked 6 mi south and then 8 mi east. How far was the hiker from the starting point?

10. Find the area of a rectangle if its length is $8\sqrt{2}$ cm and its width is $5\sqrt{3}$ cm.

11. The bending of a beam varies directly as its mass. A beam is bent 20 mm by a mass of 40 kg. How much will the beam bend with a mass of 100 kg?

12. It takes Karen 3 h to cut the grass. Scott takes $3\frac{1}{2}$ h to cut the same area. How long will it take them to cut the grass together?

13. Write an equation of the line with slope $\frac{1}{2}$ and y-intercept the same as that of the line described by the equation $y = -\frac{2}{3}x + 5$.

14. Walt has $3.30 in dimes and quarters. The number of dimes is 2 less than the number of quarters. How many coins of each type does he have?

15. Cashews cost $11.25/kg. Pecans cost $13/kg. A box contains a mixture that will sell for $136.00. The number of kilograms of cashews in the box is 3 less than the number of kilograms of pecans. How many kilograms of each are in the box?

16. Two cities are 1,630 mi apart. Flying with the wind, a jet took 2 h 30 min to travel from one city to the other. On the return trip, the jet flew against the same wind and took 3 h. Find the rate of the jet in still air and the rate of the wind.

Chapter 15 Review

Key Terms

angle of depression   (p. 590)
angle of elevation   (p. 590)
corresponding angles   (p. 575)
corresponding sides   (p. 575)

cosine ratio   (p. 580)
similar triangles   (p. 575)
sine ratio   (p. 580)
tangent ratio   (p. 580)

Key Ideas and Review Exercises

15.1   In similar triangles, all pairs of corresponding sides have the same ratio. To find the length of a side in one of two similar triangles, use a proportion involving the known lengths and the unknown length.

In the figures below, $\triangle ABC \sim \triangle DEF$.

1. If $a = 12$, $c = 10$, and $d = 6$, find f.
2. If $d = 12$, $e = 18$, and $b = 24$, find a.

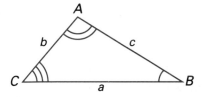
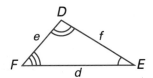

15.2   Three trigonometric ratios are defined.

$$\text{sine} = \frac{\text{opposite}}{\text{hypotenuse}} \qquad \text{cosine} = \frac{\text{adjacent}}{\text{hypotenuse}} \qquad \text{tangent} = \frac{\text{opposite}}{\text{adjacent}}$$

Find each of the following to three decimal places.

3. $\sin A$
4. $\cos A$
5. $\tan A$

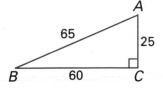

Find the missing length. Then find the trigonometric ratios. Rationalize the denominator if necessary.

6. x
7. $\cos Y$
8. $\tan X$

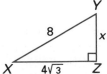

15.3   Use trigonometric tables or a calculator to find the sine, cosine, or tangent of an acute angle, or to find the measure of an acute angle when its trigonometric ratio is given.

Find the value of the trigonometric ratio.

9. sin 38

10. tan 42

11. cos 62

12. sin 28

Find m ∠C to the nearest degree.

13. cos C = 0.7193

14. sin C = 0.8387

15. tan C = 0.5310

16. cos C = 0.4700

15.4   To find the length of a side or the measure of an acute angle in a right triangle, use trigonometric ratios.

Find the length of the indicated side to the nearest tenth, or the measure of the indicated angle to the nearest degree.

17. If a = 16 and m ∠A = 32, find c.

18. If b = 45 and a = 17, find m ∠B.

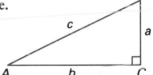

19. Write in your own words how to find the measure of an acute angle of a right triangle when
a. the length of a leg and the length of the hypotenuse are known.
b. the lengths of the two legs are known.

15.5   Use trigonometric ratios to solve problems involving angle measures and lengths of sides in a right triangle.

20. Find the height of the tent pole to the nearest foot. Refer to the figure at the right.

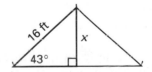

21. The height of a building is 40 m. How far from the building would you be if the degree measure of your angle of elevation to the top of the building were 38? Give your answer to the nearest meter.

In Exercises 1 and 2, $\triangle ABC \sim \triangle DEF$.

1. If $a = 22$, $c = 8$, and $f = 4$, find d.
2. If $b = 24$, $c = 12$, and $e = 6$, find f.
3. A 3-m stick casts a 12-m shadow while a tree casts a 16-m shadow. How high is the tree?

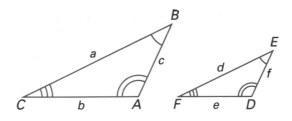

Find each of the following to three decimal places.

4. $\sin A$
5. $\cos A$
6. $\tan B$

Find each of the following. Leave the answers in fraction form.

7. $\tan M$
8. $\cos M$
9. $\sin N$

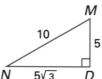

10. Refer to $\triangle RST$ at the right. Find the missing length. Then find $\cos R$. Rationalize the denominator if necessary.

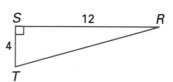

Find each value.

11. $\sin 34$
12. $\cos 81$
13. $\tan 14$

Find m $\angle B$ to the nearest degree.

14. $\sin B = 0.6018$
15. $\cos B = 0.3907$
16. $\tan B = 9.500$

Find the length of the indicated side to the nearest tenth, or the measure of the indicated angle to the nearest degree.

17. If $a = 8$ and m $\angle A = 21$, find c.
18. If $b = 14$ and $a = 7$, find m $\angle A$.
19. If $b = 4.8$ and $c = 11.2$, find m $\angle B$.

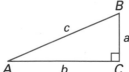

20. A plane flying at an altitude of 7,000 ft makes an angle of depression of degree measure 32 with its carrier. To the nearest hundred feet, how far is the plane from the carrier?

21. Use the figure at the right to show that $\tan A = \dfrac{\sin A}{\cos A}$.

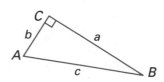

Choose the *one* best answer to each question or problem. (The figures in this test may not be drawn to scale.)

1. x, y, and z are in the ratio of 3:1:2. Find z.

(A) 30   (B) 60   (C) 90
(D) 15   (E) 45

Find the true statement.

2.

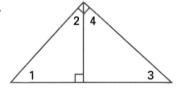

(A) m $\angle 1$ = m $\angle 3$
(B) m $\angle 3$ = m $\angle 4$
(C) m $\angle 1$ + m $\angle 2$ = m $\angle 3$ + m $\angle 4$
(D) m $\angle 2$ = m $\angle 4$
(E) m $\angle 1$ = m $\angle 4$

3.

(A) $x > y$ (B) $x < y$
(C) $x + y = 150$ (D) $x > 30$
(E) $x + y = 90$

4. $\tan W =$ _____

(A) $\frac{\sqrt{6}}{2}$ (B) $\frac{\sqrt{6}}{6}$ (C) $\frac{\sqrt{3}}{3}$
(D) $\frac{\sqrt{2}}{2}$ (E) 1

5. $\sin T =$ _____

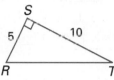

(A) $\frac{1}{2}$ (B) $\frac{\sqrt{5}}{5}$ (C) $\frac{\sqrt{3}}{3}$
(D) $\frac{\sqrt{2}}{2}$ (E) 1

6.

(A) $\sin A = \cos B$
(B) $\sin A = \cos A$
(C) $\tan A = \tan B$
(D) $\sin B = \cos B$
(E) $\cos A = \cos B$

7. $\overline{AC}$ and $\overline{XZ}$ are straight lines; $b = 10°$, $y = 170°$

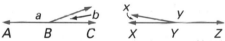

(A) $x + y = x + b$
(B) $y + b = y + a$
(C) $a + b = x + a$
(D) $y + a = 180$ (E) $x + b = 90$

8.

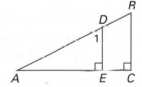

(A) m $\angle 1$ = m $\angle B$
(B) m $\angle A$ = m $\angle B$
(C) $\dfrac{AB}{AD} = \dfrac{AE}{AC}$ (D) $\dfrac{BC}{AD} = \dfrac{DB}{AE}$
(E) m $\angle A$ = m $\angle 1$

Mae Jamison, an astronaut, is pictured here during ejection seat training at Vance Air Force Base. Before joining the space shuttle program, Dr. Jamison worked in engineering, with computers, and as a medical officer in Africa.

16.1 Probability of an Event

Objectives   To determine the probability of an event
To determine the probability of an event that is certain to happen and one that cannot happen

Probability is the study of the chances that particular events will occur.

When a coin is tossed, there are 2 *possible outcomes*: heads or tails. These are *equally likely* outcomes if the coin is "fair." Assume that you want tails as the outcome. Then tails is called a *favorable* or *successful* outcome. Out of 2 possible outcomes, there is one way to get the outcome *tails*. So the probability of getting tails is $\frac{1}{2}$. A way to determine the probability of an event is given in the following formula.

$$\textbf{Probability} \text{ of an event} = \frac{\text{number of successful outcomes}}{\text{total number of possible outcomes}}$$

In symbols, $P(E) = \frac{s}{t}$.

EXAMPLE 1   In one throw of a *die* (singular for *dice*), what is the probability of each event?

a. The upper face will show 4 dots.
b. The upper face will show an even number of dots.

Since there are 6 possible outcomes, $t = 6$.
Find the successful outcomes s for the event.
Then use $P(E) = \frac{s}{t}$.

Solutions   **a.** The upper face will show 4 dots.
1 successful outcome (4); so, $s = 1$.

$P(4) = \frac{s}{t} = \frac{1}{6}$

b. The upper face will show an even number of dots.
3 successful outcomes (2, 4, or 6); so, $s = 3$.

$P(\text{even number}) = \frac{s}{t} = \frac{3}{6} = \frac{1}{2}$

TRY THIS   In one throw of a die, what is the probability of each event?

1. The upper face will show one dot.
2. The upper face will show an odd number of dots.
3. The upper face will show three or more dots.

EXAMPLE 2   A bag contains 12 marbles, 10 are white marbles and 2 are blue marbles. One marble is drawn from the bag. Find the probability of each event.

   a. A white marble is drawn.   **b.** A blue marble is drawn.

Plan   There are 12 possible outcomes; so, $t = 12$. Find the successful outcomes s for the event. Then use $P(E) = \frac{s}{t}$.

Solutions
   a. A white marble is drawn.
   10 successful outcomes;
   so, $s = 10$.

   $P(\text{white}) = \frac{s}{t} = \frac{10}{12}$, or $\frac{5}{6}$

   b. A blue marble is drawn.
   2 successful outcomes;
   so, $s = 2$.

   $P(\text{blue}) = \frac{s}{t} = \frac{2}{12}$, or $\frac{1}{6}$

EXAMPLE 3   A bag contains 8 dimes. One coin is drawn from the bag. Find each probability.

   a. $P(\text{dime})$ **b.** $P(\text{quarter})$

Plan   There are 8 possible outcomes; so, $t = 8$. Use $P(E) = \frac{s}{t}$.

Solutions
   a. $P(\text{dime})$
   8 successful outcomes;
   so, $s = 8$.

   $P(\text{dime}) = \frac{s}{t} = \frac{8}{8}$, or 1

   b. $P(\text{quarter})$
   no successful outcomes;
   so, $s = 0$.

   $P(\text{quarter}) = \frac{s}{t} = \frac{0}{8}$, or 0

TRY THIS   One marble is drawn from a bag containing two yellow and six red marbles. Find the probability of each event.

   4. A red marble is drawn.

   5. A yellow marble is drawn.

   6. A white marble is drawn.

Example 3 illustrates two important ideas.

If an event is *certain* to happen, its probability is 1: $P(E) = 1$.
If an event *cannot happen*, its probability is 0: $P(E) = 0$.

All probabilities fall in the interval from 0 to 1. Notice that in Example 2, the probability of drawing a white marble is $\frac{5}{6}$. The probability of *not drawing* a white marble is $\frac{1}{6}$. Thus,

$$P(\text{white}) + P(\text{not white}) = \frac{5}{6} + \frac{1}{6} = 1$$

In general, if $P(E)$ is the probability of an event E occurring and $P(\text{not } E)$ is the probability of E not occurring, then

$$P(E) + P(\text{not } E) = 1 \quad \text{and} \quad P(\text{not } E) = 1 - P(E).$$

Classroom Exercises

A bag contains 4 white marbles and 6 blue marbles. One marble is drawn. Find the probability of each event.

1. A white marble is drawn.　　**2.** A blue marble is drawn.

3. A red marble is drawn.　　**4.** A red marble is not drawn.

A person spins the pointer of this spinner. Find each probability.

5. $P(4)$　　　　　　　　**6.** $P(1)$

7. $P(\text{a number less than 6})$　　**8.** $P(\text{a number less than 14})$

Written Exercises

In one throw of a die, what is the probability of each event?

1. The upper face will show 3 dots.

2. The upper face will show 5 dots.

3. The upper face will show an odd number of dots.

4. The upper face will show less than 5 dots.

5. The upper face will show 2 dots.

6. The upper face will not show 2 dots.

Refer to the spinner at the right. Find the probability of each event.

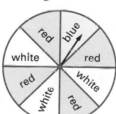

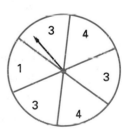

7. $P(\text{white})$

8. $P(\text{red})$

9. $P(\text{blue})$

10. $P(\text{not white})$

11. $P(\text{not red})$

12. $P(\text{not blue})$

13. $P(3)$

14. $P(4)$

15. $P(2)$

16. $P(1)$

17. $P(\text{even number})$

18. $P(\text{not 5})$

A bag contains 20 marbles; 4 are white, 10 are blue, and 6 are red. One marble is drawn. Find the probability of each event.

19. $P(\text{white})$　　**20.** $P(\text{blue})$　　**21.** $P(\text{red})$　　**22.** $P(\text{green})$

23. $P(\text{not white})$　　**24.** $P(\text{not blue})$　　**25.** $P(\text{not red})$　　**26.** $P(\text{not green})$

27. If the probability that it will snow is $\frac{3}{10}$, what is the probability that it will not snow?

In a scientific experiment, a gerbil is placed in a large space with 5 exits labeled A, B, C, D, and E.

28. What is the probability that the gerbil will use Exit C?

29. What is the probability that the gerbil will *not* use Exit C?

30. If the gerbil uses an exit, what is the probability that it will use one of the five labeled exits?

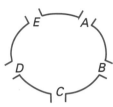

The relative chances that an event E will occur are often expressed in terms of the *odds* in favor of E. The odds that an event E will occur are defined by the ratio $\dfrac{\text{number of successful outcomes}}{\text{number of unsuccessful outcomes}}$.

Example: What are the odds of spinning a prime number on this spinner? Five numbers are prime (2, 3, 7, 11, 13); three numbers are not prime (4, 9, 21).

So, the odds of spinning a prime number are $\frac{5}{3}$.

Refer to the spinner. Find each of the following.

31. the odds of spinning an even number

32. the odds of spinning a number that is not even

33. the odds of spinning a number that is less than 15

34. the odds of spinning a number that is a factor of 42

35. Show that the odds that an event E will occur can be found by using the ratio $\dfrac{P(E)}{P(\text{not } E)}$.

Mixed Review

Solve. Check the solutions.   *4.5, 5.6, 5.7, 7.7, 14.1, 14.3, 14.4*

1. $|x + 3| = 2$

2. $|x - 5| = -1$

3. $|x - 3| \le 9$

4. $x^2 + x - 12 = 0$

5. $\frac{x}{6} + \frac{x}{2} = 9$

6. $(x - 2)^2 = 41$

7. $4x^2 = 30$

8. $y^2 - 1 = 7y$

9. $4 = 2x^2 - x + 2$

10. If the length of each side of a square is tripled, then the area is 225 cm². Find the length of each side of the original square.   *14.1*

11. The square of a number is 22 more than 9 times the number. Find the number.   *7.8*

16.2 Probability: Compound Events

Objectives

To determine the probability of independent events
To determine the probability of compound events

In many situations, you need to make a systematic listing of all the outcomes. The set of all possible outcomes is called a **sample space**. Below are the 6 outcomes in the sample space for rolling a die.

$$\{1, 2, 3, 4, 5, 6\}$$

An event is a subset of the sample space. The event "roll a 3, 4, or 6" is {3, 4, 6}. Note that *outcome* and *event* have different meanings.

There are 2 different roads from East-vale to Centerton. There are 4 different roads from Centerton to Westvale. Suppose you want to list all the possible routes from Eastvale to Westvale by way of Centerton.

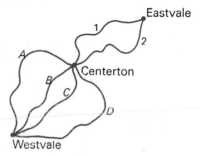

A diagram called a **tree diagram** can be used to determine all possible routes (outcomes).

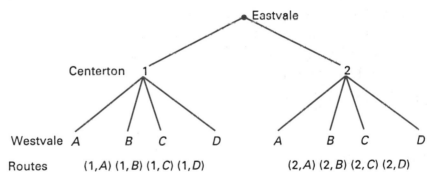

If you use Road 1 to Centerton, you can use any of the 4 roads to Westvale: *A, B, C,* or *D.*

If you use Road 2 to Centerton, you can use any of the 4 roads to Westvale: *A, B, C,* or *D.*

The sample space of possible routes from Eastvale to Westvale is {(1,*A*), (1,*B*), (1,*C*), (1,*D*), (2,*A*), (2,*B*), (2,*C*), (2,*D*)}.

Note that each route is shown as an *ordered pair.*

EXAMPLE 1   Suppose you toss one coin and roll one die. What is the probability of getting a tail on the coin and a 6 on the die?

Plan   Make a tree diagram and list the sample space.

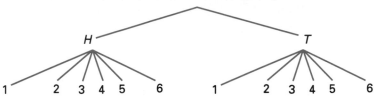

Solution   Sample space: {(H,1), (H,2), (H,3), (H,4), (H,5), (H,6), (T,1), (T,2), (T,3), (T,4), (T,5), (T,6)}

There are 12 outcomes. In the sample space, there is only one successful outcome: (T,6). Since all the outcomes are equally likely,

$$P\,[(T,6)] \;=\; \tfrac{1}{12}, \text{ or } P(T \text{ and } 6) \;=\; \tfrac{1}{12}.$$

So, the probability of getting a tail on the coin and a 6 on the die is $\tfrac{1}{12}$.

The outcome of rolling a die does not affect the outcome of tossing a coin. Similarly, the outcome of tossing a coin does not affect the outcome of rolling a die. Such events are called **independent events**.

In Example 1, you can see that $P(T) = \tfrac{1}{2}$ and that $P(6) = \tfrac{1}{6}$. Note that $\tfrac{1}{2} \cdot \tfrac{1}{6} = \tfrac{1}{12}$, which is equal to $P(T \text{ and } 6)$. This suggests the following rule.

Probability of A and B
If A and B are independent events, then $P(A \text{ and } B) = P(A) \cdot P(B)$.

EXAMPLE 2   A red die and a white die are rolled. What is the probability of getting a 3 on the red die and a 5 on the white die?

Plan   The two events are independent. Use $P(A \text{ and } B) = P(A) \cdot P(B)$.

Solution $P(r = 3) = \tfrac{1}{6} \qquad P(w = 5) = \tfrac{1}{6} \qquad P(r = 3 \text{ and } w = 5) = \tfrac{1}{6} \cdot \tfrac{1}{6} = \tfrac{1}{36}$

So, the probability of getting a 3 on the red die and a 5 on the white die is $\tfrac{1}{36}$.

TRY THIS   A blue die and a red die are rolled. What is the probability of getting an even number on the blue die and a 3 on the red die?

EXAMPLE 3

In a roll of two dice, a small one and a big one, find $P(s \le 3 \text{ or } b \le 2)$.

Plan

Make a sample space of ordered pairs. Count the number of outcomes in which $s \le 3$ and the number of outcomes in which $b \le 2$, and then subtract the number of ordered pairs common to both sets. They cannot be counted twice.

Solution

The sample space is shown at the right. There are 36 possible outcomes.

There are 18 outcomes in which $s \le 3$ and 12 outcomes in which $b \le 2$.

Big

6	(1,6)	(2,6)	(3,6)	(4,6)	(5,6)	(6,6)
5	(1,5)	(2,5)	(3,5)	(4,5)	(5,5)	(6,5)
4	(1,4)	(2,4)	(3,4)	(4,4)	(5,4)	(6,4)
3	(1,3)	(2,3)	(3,3)	(4,3)	(5,3)	(6,3)
2	(1,2)	(2,2)	(3,2)	(4,2)	(5,2)	(6,2)
1	(1,1)	(2,1)	(3,1)	(4,1)	(5,1)	(6,1)

    1   2   3   4   5   6

Small

However, 6 ordered pairs are common to both sets and must not be counted twice. So, the number of these common ordered pairs must be subtracted. For $s \le 3$ or $b \le 2$, there are $18 + 12 - 6$, or 24 successful outcomes.

$P(s \le 3 \text{ or } b \le 2) = \frac{24}{36}$, or $\frac{2}{3}$

In Example 3, $P(s \le 3 \text{ or } b \le 2) = \frac{18}{36} + \frac{12}{36} - \frac{6}{36} = \frac{24}{36}$, or $\frac{2}{3}$.

This suggests the following.

Probability of A or B

For two events A and B, $P(A \text{ or } B) = P(A) + P(B) - P(A \text{ and } B)$.

Note that if the two sets are *mutually exclusive*, or do not overlap, then $P(A \text{ or } B) = P(A) + P(B)$.

The events A *and* B and A *or* B are called *compound events* since each contains more than one element of the sample space.

EXAMPLE 4

A bag contains 4 white, 8 green, and 6 red beads. A bead is drawn. Find the probability that the bead is white or green.

Plan

Use $P(A \text{ or } B) = P(A) + P(B)$ since the two sets are mutually exclusive.

Solution

$P(\text{white or green}) = P(w) + P(g) = \frac{4}{18} + \frac{8}{18} = \frac{12}{18}$, or $\frac{2}{3}$

So, the probability that the bead is white or green is $\frac{2}{3}$.

Classroom Exercises

Use the tree diagram in Example 1. Find the probability of each event.

1. P(H and 2)   **2.** P(T and 5)   **3.** P(T and 1)   **4.** P(H and 8)

A red die and a blue die are rolled.

5. Find the probability of a 4 on the red die and a 2 on the blue die.

6. Find the probability of a 2 on the red die and a 2 on the blue die.

7. Find $P(r > 4 \text{ and } b > 4)$.

8. Find $P(r > 4 \text{ or } b > 4)$.

Written Exercises

Suppose you toss a coin and spin this spinner.

1. Make a tree diagram and list the sample space.

2. What is the probability of getting a head on the coin and a 3 on the spinner?

3. What is the probability of getting a tail on the coin and a 5 on the spinner?

4. What is the probability of getting a tail on the coin and a 2 on the spinner?

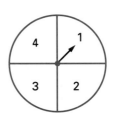

Refer to the two spinners at the right. Find the probability of each event.

5. P(blue and 4)
6. P(red and 1)
7. P(white and 4)
8. P(white and 1)
9. P(red and 2)
10. P(blue and 3)

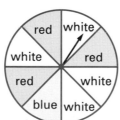 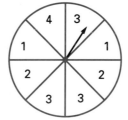

A small die and a big die are rolled. Find each of the following. (Use the sample space in Example 3.)

11. $P(s \geq 4 \text{ or } b \leq 2)$ **12.** $P(s \leq 2 \text{ or } b \leq 2)$

13. $P(s \geq 5 \text{ or } b \geq 5)$ **14.** $P(s \leq 3 \text{ or } b \geq 5)$

15. $P(s < 3 \text{ or } b < 3)$ **16.** $P(s > 5 \text{ or } b > 5)$

17. $P(s < 1 \text{ or } b > 6)$ **18.** $P(s < 7 \text{ or } b > 0)$

A bag contains 3 white, 6 green, and 9 red beads. One bead is drawn.

19. Find P(white or red).   **20.** Find P(green or red).

This set of cards is mixed and placed in a bag. Find the probability that the number drawn is

| 1 | 2 | 3 | 4 |

| 5 | 6 | 7 |

| 8 | 9 |

| 10 |

21. even *and* greater than 7.

22. even *or* greater than 7.

23. odd *and* prime.

24. odd *or* prime.

25. a factor of 3 *or* a factor of 7.

26. a factor of 6 *and* a factor of 9.

The Gallon Organization is taking a survey of families with 3 children. The order of birth of boys (*B*) and girls (*G*) in a given family can be shown as *GBG*, which indicates this outcome: a girl was born first, a boy was born second, and a girl was born third.

27. Make a tree diagram and list all the possible outcomes in a family with three children. How many possible outcomes are there?

28. Assume that the outcomes are equally likely. Find the probability of three girls *or* three boys.

29. Find the probability of two girls *and* a boy. (HINT: This does *not* mean that the girls were born before the boy. The order is *not* significant in this problem.)

30. Find the probability that the oldest child is a boy *or* the youngest child is a girl.

Mixed Review

Simplify.   *13.2, 13.5, 13.7*

1. $\sqrt{12} \cdot \sqrt{12}$

2. $-8\sqrt{800}$

3. $\sqrt{30} \cdot \sqrt{50}$

4. $\sqrt{x^6}$

5. $2\sqrt{x^5 y^7}$

6. $8\sqrt{36x^6 y^{12} z^7}$

7. $5\sqrt{3} \cdot 7\sqrt{3}$

8. $3\sqrt{5} \cdot 6\sqrt{2}$

9. $-5\sqrt{12a} \cdot 2\sqrt{3a}$

10. The first side of a triangle is 2 in. longer than the second. The second side is 3 times as long as the third side. The perimeter is 28 in. How long is each side?   *4.4*

11. The selling price of a compact disc player is $889. The profit is 40% of the cost. Find the cost.   *4.8*

▰▰/Brainteaser

The mean (average) of the numbers in a set of $3n$ numbers is 50. The set is subdivided into two disjoint sets, one containing $2n$ of the numbers, the other containing the remaining n numbers. The mean of the numbers in the larger subset is twice the mean of the numbers in the smaller. Find the mean of the numbers in the smaller subset.

16.3 Mean, Median, and Mode

Objectives

To find the mean, the median, and the mode for a set of data

To construct a frequency table and find the mean, the median, and the mode for the data in the table

---

In statistics, the average of a set of numbers is called the *arithmetic mean*, or simply *mean* of the numbers, or *data*. Often the data in statistics are called *scores*.

The **mean** of a set of data is found by adding the scores and dividing the sum by the number of scores.

$$\text{mean of a set of data} = \frac{\text{sum of the scores}}{\text{number of scores}}$$

The symbol $\bar{x}$ (read "*x*-bar") is often used to represent the mean.

One advantage of using the mean is that it provides a way of using a single number to represent a set of data. However, the mean may be misleading if there are some extreme scores. Extreme scores are scores that are much greater or much less than most of the other scores.

EXAMPLE 1 Carol scored 98, 96, 88, 92, and 86 on her mathematics tests. Find the mean of her scores.

Solution

$$\bar{x} = \frac{\text{sum of the scores}}{\text{number of scores}}$$

$$= \frac{98 + 96 + 88 + 92 + 86}{5}$$

$$= \frac{460}{5}$$

$$= 92$$

TRY THIS Susan, José, and Lucia received these scores on five tests. Compute the mean score for each student.

1. Susan: 75, 83, 91, 94, 87
2. José: 84, 86, 70, 85, 90
3. Lucia: 84, 96, 96, 70, 79

There are other numbers, apart from the mean, that can be used to represent a set of data. One such number is called the *median*.

The **median** of a set of data is found by arranging the data in order and choosing the middle score. If the data contain an even number of items, the mean of the two middle scores is the median.

One advantage of using the median is that it is not influenced by extreme scores.

EXAMPLE 2 Find the median 3:00 P.M. temperature for a week when the Fahrenheit temperatures at 3:00 P.M. were 48, 43, 51, 63, 49, 50, and 68.

Plan Arrange the temperatures in order and choose the middle temperature.

Solution 43   48   49   50   51   63   68

So, the median is 50.

TRY THIS **4.** This list shows the number of students attending the seven high schools in Orange County. Find the median.

539   625   517   525   415   560   478

To find the median of an *even number of scores*, you find the mean of the two middle scores.

EXAMPLE 3 Find the median of these six temperatures: 97, 94, 86, 89, 92, 90.

Plan Arrange the temperatures in order. Since there is an even number of scores, find the mean of the two middle numbers.

Solution 86   89   90   92   94   97

$$\text{Median} = \frac{90 + 92}{2}$$

$$= \frac{182}{2}, \text{ or } 91$$

So, the median is 91.

TRY THIS **5.** The price in cents of a pint-size carton of 10 brands of orange juice is given below. Find the median price.

69   71   68   70   65   71   69   75   72   67

Sometimes it is important to know the most frequent score, or *mode*, of a set of data.

The **mode** of a set of data is the score that occurs most frequently.

To find the mode, list each number as many times as it occurs and then choose the number or numbers that occur most frequently. If each item appears an equal number of times, there is no mode.

EXAMPLE 4   The test scores for a student were 90, 95, 90, 85, 100, 95, 80, 90, 100, 80. Find the mode.

Plan   Arrange the scores in order. Group the same scores together.

Solution

80, 80,	85,	90, 90, 90,	95, 95,	100, 100
twice	once	three times	twice	twice

So, the mode is 90.

Notice, in Example 4, that if the test scores had included three 80s as well as three 90s, there would have been two modes, 80 and 90.

The three types of statistical measures you have just studied—mean, median, and mode—are called **measures of central tendency**. They help tell about the data and identify its "middle" points or representative numbers.

A **frequency table** is often used to summarize and represent a set of data. The table below shows the frequency of runs scored per game by a baseball team in its 50-game schedule.

In this table, the runs are the scores s; the Tally column is used to record the times each score occurred; and the Frequency column gives the total number of times each score occurred.

The column headed $f \cdot s$ (frequency × score) is not an essential part of every frequency table, but it is useful in calculating the mean, as shown in Example 5. To calculate the mean, find the sum of the products $f \cdot s$, then divide by the sum of the frequencies.

Runs (s)	Tally	Frequency (f)	$f \cdot s$
0	II	2	0
1	IIII	5	5
2	III	3	6
3	IIII I	6	18
4	IIII IIII II	12	48
5	IIII IIII	9	45
6	I	1	6
7	IIII	4	28
8	II	2	16
9	IIII	4	36
10	II	2	20
		Sum: 50	Sum: 228

EXAMPLE 5   Find the mean, the median, and the mode for the runs scored per game by the baseball team. Use the table preceding this example.

Solution

$$\text{mean} = \frac{\text{sum of the products } f \cdot s}{\text{sum of the frequencies}} = \frac{228}{50}, \text{ or } 4.56$$

So, the mean of the scores is 4.56 runs per game.

The median is the middle score. Count to find the 25th and 26th scores. They occur in the row that has frequency 12—the row for 4 runs. So, the median is 4 runs per game.

The mode is the most frequently occurring score. So, the mode is 4 runs per game.

Summary   Note that a frequency table is helpful in determining the median and the mode as well as the mean. An $f \cdot s$ column is also useful in many situations.

To construct a frequency table:

1. label the columns;
2. tally the data; and
3. find the frequency of each score.

Focus on Reading

True or false?

1. The mean is always a number that appears in the set of data.
2. The median is always the middle score in a set of scores.
3. There is no mode in this set of data: 1, 2, 3, 4, 6, 8, 10.
4. The mode and the median can never be the same number.

Classroom Exercises

Find the mean of each set of data.

1. 3, 4, 5, 5, 8   2. 4, 3, 4, 2, 7   3. 6, 9, 8, 10, 7, 3
4–6. Find the median of each set of data in Exercises 1–3.
7–9. Find the mode of each set of data in Exercises 1–3.

Written Exercises

Find the mean of each set of data.

1. 18, 15, 12, 14, 16

2. 5, 10, 12, 13, 10

3. 16, 24, 19, 36, 35

4. 96, 94, 97, 93, 95

5. 46, 48, 87, 95, 85

6. 77, 76, 70, 72, 68, 69

7. 91, 72, 73, 89, 73, 83

8. 87, 99, 100, 96, 99, 95

Find the median.

9. 98, 93, 97, 100, 92

10. 49, 43, 40, 41, 48

11. 105, 100, 98, 104, 110

12. 12, 13, 9, 8, 14, 15

13. 91, 93, 98, 87, 90

14. 100, 98, 103, 95, 96, 100

Find the mode.

15. 91, 90, 91, 98, 97, 100

16. 38, 36, 37, 36, 39

17. 50, 48, 50, 48, 55

18. 100, 101, 98, 103, 105

19. 98, 97, 98, 100, 96, 98

20. 85, 80, 85, 100, 80

A class had the following test scores:
90, 95, 85, 100, 100, 95, 80, 95, 100, 75, 70, 75, 90, 95, 100, 85, 80, 70, 85, 90, 100, 90, 85, 75, 70, 75, 95, 100, 90, and 90. **(Exercises 21–24)**

21. Make a frequency table.

22. Find the mean.

23. Find the median.

24. Find the mode.

Solve.

25. Frankie scored 48.5, 43.2, 38.7, 53.1, and 49.3 on a battery of tests. What is the mean of these scores?

26. In her music auditions, Linda Sue received scores of 98.3, 89.1, 96.5, 93.4, 91.9, and 95.8. Find the mean of these scores.

27. Kris has a bowling average of 210. One day she bowled 190 three times and 200 twice. What must she bowl in her next game to maintain her average?

28. Wally's test grades so far are 85, 80, 75, and 90. He expects to get the same grade on each of the remaining tests and to have an average of 87 on a total of ten tests. What is that grade?

29. Find the mean of this set of data. $x + 3, x + 2, x + 5, 2 + x$

30. Find the median and the mode of the set of data in Exercise 29.

31. Find the value(s) of x for the set of data if the mean of $8x^2$, $4x$, $2x$, 7, -8, $-7x^2$, $-3x$, 2, $-x$ is 1.

32. Find the value(s) of t for the set of data if the mean of t^2, $-3t$, t, $5t^2$ is 0.

33. The mean of 20 students' scores is 88. If the 2 lowest and the 2 highest scores are removed, the mean of the remaining scores is 84. What is the mean of the removed scores?

34. The mean of 48 students' test scores is 94. If the 4 lowest and the 4 highest scores are removed, the mean of the remaining scores is 96. What is the mean of the removed scores?

Midchapter Review

A bag contains 8 red marbles and 10 white marbles. One marble is drawn. Find the probability of each event.

1. $P(\text{red})$　　　　　**2.** $P(\text{green})$　　　　　**3.** $P(\text{not yellow})$

Refer to the spinner at the right. Find the probability of each event.

4. $P(1)$

5. $P(4)$

6. $P(\text{even number})$

7. $P(5)$

Suppose you spin both of these spinners. Find the indicated probability.

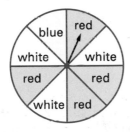 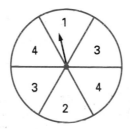

8. $P(\text{white } and \text{ 4})$　　　**9.** $P(\text{red } and \text{ 3})$

10. $P(\text{blue } and \text{ 1})$　　　**11.** $P(\text{white } and \text{ 2})$

A blue die and a green die are rolled. Make a sample space of ordered pairs. Find the probability of each event.

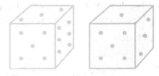

12. $P(b < 2 \text{ or } g < 2)$　　　**13.** $P(b \geq 3 \text{ or } g \leq 3)$

A football team scored the following points in its games: 13, 6, 14, 20, 14, 7, and 10. Use this data for Exercises 14–16.

14. Find the mean.　　　**15.** Find the median.　　　**16.** Find the mode.

16.4 Statistical Graphs

Objectives   To read and interpret scatter plots and histograms

Although the mean, median, and mode of a set of data help to characterize the data, it is often convenient to use a graph to show how two sets of data vary relative to each other.

The list below gives ordered pairs (heights, weights) for twenty young male adults (*A* to *T*) with medium frames. The heights are in inches and the weights are in pounds.

A: (67,146)   *E:* (70,157)   *I:* (67,145)   *M:* (69,151)   *Q:* (68,147)

B: (68,151)   *F:* (70,156)   *J:* (69,153)   *N:* (71,160)   *R:* (70,154)

C: (66,145)   *G:* (67,148)   *K:* (68,149)   *O:* (66,141)   *S:* (67,145)

D: (71,158   *H:* (69,155)   *L:* (66,142)   *P:* (66,144)   *T:* (71,159)

You can probably see that the greater the height, the greater the weight seems to be. However, a graph called a **scatter plot** can be used to learn more about the relationship and to make predictions about data.

To make a scatter plot, plot each ordered pair as a point in the coordinate plane. Then you see whether or not the points suggest a clear relationship.

In this figure, the points seem to suggest a linear relation, although they obviously do not lie exactly on a line. Some points are above the line that has been drawn; other points are below it. In general, they cluster around the line. So, the line can be used to make judgments or predictions about data for weights and heights of male adults with medium frames.

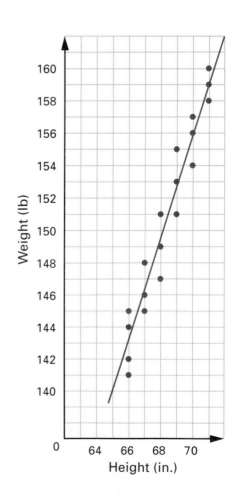

EXAMPLE 1 Use the graph on the preceding page to answer the questions.

a. Approximately what weight would you predict for a young male adult (medium frame) whose height is 65 in?

b. Approximately what weight would you predict for a young male adult (medium frame) whose height is 72 in?

Solutions a. approximately 140 pounds

b. approximately 162 pounds

TRY THIS Approximately what weight would you predict for a young male adult (medium frame) whose height is 70 inches?

Note in Example 1 that the answers are approximate. Data obtained from a graph are usually approximate.

Another type of useful graph is a *histogram*. A histogram is often used to represent the data in a frequency table. The table below represents the distribution of semester grades in English for 460 juniors in a high school. The scores are grouped in intervals (50–60, 60–70, 70–80, 80–90, 90–100) with each boundary score assigned to the lesser interval. For example, a score of 80 would be assigned to the interval 70–80.

Interval	Frequency
90–100	98
80–90	150
70–80	100
60–70	83
50–60	29

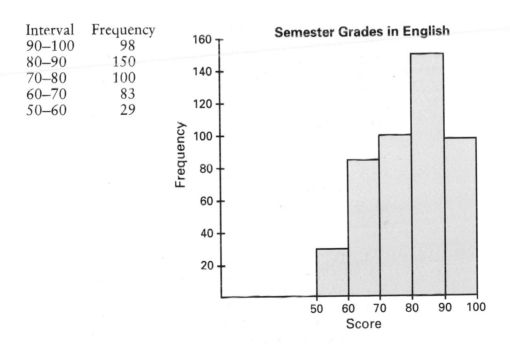

The **histogram** for the set of data is shown above at the right. Notice that a histogram is a kind of bar graph. The horizontal axis is used to indicate the intervals for the scores. The vertical axis is used to indicate the frequencies of the scores in the given interval.

EXAMPLE 2 From the histogram for the 460 students, answer each question.

    a. Approximately how many scores were above 90?

    b. Approximately how many scores were above 80?

Plan Find the correct interval or intervals on the horizontal axis. Then determine the appropriate frequency or frequencies.

Solutions

a. For all scores above 90, use the interval 90–100. Approximately 100 scores were in this interval.

b. There are two appropriate intervals: 80–90 and 90–100. The number of scores in these two intervals was approximately 100 + 150, or 250.

Classroom Exercises

Use the scatter plot that precedes Example 1 for Exercises 1–2.

1. What point on the line has 67 as its *x*-coordinate?

2. Complete this ordered pair for the point on the line: (69, __?__).
Tell what the ordered pair means in the problem situation.

The histogram below represents a number of students and their scores on a social studies exam. Each boundary score is assigned to the lesser interval.

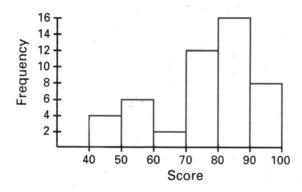

3. How many students had scores above 90?

4. How many students had scores above 80?

5. How many students had scores of 50 or less?

6. How many students had scores of 60 or less?

7. In which interval did the greatest number of scores occur?

8. In which interval did the least number of scores occur?

Written Exercises

A group of scientists kept a record of the number of chirps that crickets made at various temperatures. The scatter plot at the right shows points for the ordered pairs (temperature Fahrenheit, number of chirps per minute); it also shows the line around which the points cluster. Use the line to answer the questions in Exercises 1–4.

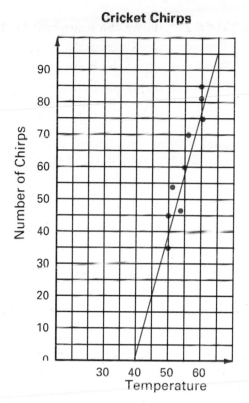

Cricket Chirps

1. When the temperature is 50°F, what is the number of chirps per minute?

2. When the temperature is 60°F, what is the number of chirps per minute?

3. Approximately what number of chirps per minute would you predict for a temperature of 65°F?

4. Approximately what number of chirps per minute would you predict for a temperature of 40°F?

The histogram below represents the numbers of hours that 250 bulbs burned. Each boundary score is assigned to the lesser interval.

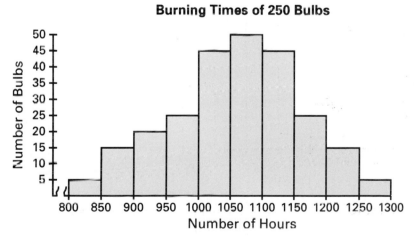

Burning Times of 250 Bulbs

5. How many bulbs burned 800–850 h?

6. How many bulbs burned 1,250–1,300 h?

7. Approximately how many bulbs burned longer than 1,200 h?

8. In which interval did the greatest number of hours occur?

9. Approximately how many bulbs burned longer than 1,050 h?

10. Approximately how many bulbs burned 1,050 h or less?

11. What percent of the bulbs burned 1,050–1,100 h?

12. What percent of the bulbs burned longer than 1,150 h?

13. What percent of the bulbs burned 900 h or less?

14. Suppose 625 bulbs had been used and the same percents of the total number occurred in the same intervals. How many bulbs would have burned 1,050–1,100 h?

15. Write a short description of a scatter plot.

Suppose that many families with 4 children were surveyed to find the sexes of the 4 children. The results can be summarized by using a "representative sample" of 16 families and displaying the data in this histogram. Note that order of birth is not significant in these data. For example, a family that has 3 girls and 1 boy includes the following possible outcomes (in terms of orders of birth): GGGB, GGBG, GBGG, BGGG.

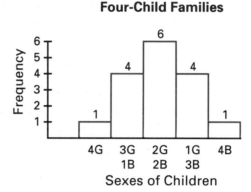

Four-Child Families

Use the histogram to answer the questions in Exercises 16–18.

16. What is the probability that a 4-child family will have 4 girls?

17. What is the probability that a 4-child family will have 2 girls and 2 boys?

18. If 8,000 families with 4 children were included in the survey, approximately how many would you expect to have more than 2 girls?

Mixed Review

Factor completely. 7.2–7.6

1. $x^2 - 9x + 8$

2. $y^2 + 6y + 9$

3. $4n^3 - 4n$

4. $6x^3 - 15x$

5. $x^2 - x - 12$

6. $6x^2 + 19x + 10$

Solve by factoring. 7.7

7. $8y^2 - 32 = 0$

8. $9t^3 - 16t = 0$

9. $3a^2 - 2a = 5$

10. Doug's age is 6 years less than his brother's age. If his age is increased by twice his brother's age, the result is 39 years. Find each of their ages. *12.3*

16.5 Range and Standard Deviation

To calculate and interpret the range and the standard deviation

Scores in a set of data may vary widely or they may cluster close to the mean. Therefore, a study of the spread, or *dispersion* of the data, is important. The simplest measure of dispersion is the **range**, which is the difference between the highest and lowest scores.

For example, the range of this set of data is 95–60, or 30.

$$95, 85, 75, 70, 60$$

The *standard deviation* measures the extent to which scores deviate from the mean. A small standard deviation indicates that most scores are close to the mean. A large standard deviation indicates that most scores are not close to the mean.

The **standard deviation** of a set of data, $x_1, x_2, x_3, \cdots, x_n$, with a mean $\bar{x}$, is

$$s = \sqrt{\frac{(x_1 - \bar{x})^2 + (x_2 - \bar{x})^2 + (x_3 - \bar{x})^2 + \cdots + (x_n - \bar{x})^2}{n}}.$$

EXAMPLE 1   Find the standard deviation for the set of data: 12, 10, 8, 13, 9, 8.

Plan   First find the mean $\bar{x}$. Then find the standard deviation s.

Solution $\bar{x} = \dfrac{12 + 10 + 8 + 13 + 9 + 8}{6} = \dfrac{60}{6}$, or 10

$$s = \sqrt{\frac{(x_1 - \bar{x})^2 + (x_2 - \bar{x})^2 + (x_3 - \bar{x})^2 + \cdots + (x_n - \bar{x})^2}{n}}$$

$$s = \sqrt{\frac{(12 - 10)^2 + (10 - 10)^2 + (8 - 10)^2 + (13 - 10)^2 + (9 - 10)^2 + (8 - 10)^2}{6}}$$

$$s = \sqrt{\frac{2^2 + 0^2 + (-2)^2 + 3^2 + (-1)^2 + (-2)^2}{6}}$$

$$s = \sqrt{\frac{4 + 0 + 4 + 9 + 1 + 4}{6}} = \sqrt{\frac{22}{6}} \approx 1.91$$

TRY THIS   Find the standard deviation for this set of data:

$$14 \quad 18 \quad 16 \quad 15 \quad 12$$

Classroom Exercises

Find the range for each set of data.

1. 18, 16, 21, 10, 14 **2.** 99, 100, 98, 97, 80 **3.** 50, 65, 60, 70, 55

Find the standard deviation for each set of data.

4. 6, 8, 10, 12 **5.** 10, 5, 14, 3 **6.** 3, 2, 4, 5, 2

7. 2, 4, 6, 4 **8.** 1, 8, 7, 4 **9.** 4, 5, 6, 3, 2

Written Exercises

Find the range for each set of data.

1. 21, 16, 19, 27, 25 **2.** 60, 58, 59, 56, 57 **3.** 75, 70, 80, 90, 100

Find the standard deviation for each set of data.

4. 15, 13, 19, 17 **5.** 3, 2, 4, 6, 5 **6.** 72, 79, 93, 70, 82, 61

7. 24, 42, 36, 30 **8.** 22, 25, 28, 32, 18 **9.** 98, 97, 86, 75, 91, 92

10. 5.68, 2.84, 4.26 **11.** 43.1, 52.6, 48.4, 36.3, 49.7 **12.** 110.7, 98.6, 101.3, 99.3, 102.8

The weights of 9 objects used in a scientific experiment were:

15 g, 6 g, 9 g, 8 g, 15 g, 11 g, 6 g, 9 g, 11 g

13. Find the range of the set of data.

14. Find the standard deviation.

The heights of 10 players on a basketball team were:

5.8 ft, 6.2 ft, 5.7 ft, 5.9 ft, 6.3 ft, 6.1 ft, 6.4 ft, 5.7 ft, 6.2 ft, 6.0 ft

15. Find the range of the set of data.

16. Find the standard deviation.

17. The lengths (in centimeters) of a set of line segments were:

$x + 2.2, x + 2.5, x - 0.5, x - 1.5, x + 1.8, x + 0.9$

Find the range, the mean, and the standard deviation for this set of data.

18. Elena kept a record of the number of errors she made in each softball game. After 7 games, the range for the set of data, the mean, the median, the mode, and the standard deviation were all the same number. What was that number?

There is a special bell-shaped graph that happens to fit the plots of some kinds of statistical measures—for example, the heights of pea plants, test scores on an examination, and lifespans of organisms of a particular species—where large numbers of data are used. This curve is called a **normal curve**. The highest point of the curve corresponds to the mean of the measures. For data that are normally distributed:

- 50% of the data lie on each side of the mean;
- about 68.2% of the measures fall within 1 standard deviation from the mean;
- about 95.4% of the measures fall within 2 standard deviations from the mean; and
- about 99.6% of the measures fall within 3 standard deviations from the mean.

The life expectancy of a certain auto mobile approximately fits the normal curve. The mean life is 80,000 mi with one standard deviation of 12,000 mi. Thus, the probability that a car of this kind will last between 80,000 mi and 92,000 mi is 34.1%, or 0.341.

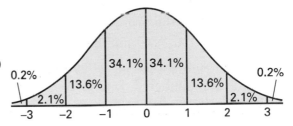

19. What is the probability that a car will last between 68,000 and 92,000 mi?

20. What is the probability that a car will not last 80,000 mi?

21. What is the probability that a car will last more than 92,000 mi?

22. What is the probability that a car will last less than 68,000 mi?

Mixed Review

Solve each system of equations. *12.2, 12.4, 12.5*

1. $3y = x$
   $5x - 2y = 13$

2. $4x - 3y = 14$
   $5x + 3y = 4$

3. $-x \quad 5y \quad 3$
   $2x - y - 5$

Simplify. *13.8*

4. $\dfrac{\sqrt{18}}{\sqrt{2}}$

5. $\dfrac{\sqrt{32a^5}}{\sqrt{8a}}$

6. $\dfrac{16x^2y}{\sqrt{8x^5y^3}}$

7. Four times the tens digit of a two-digit number, increased by the units digit, is 16. If the digits are reversed, the new number is 2 less than 3 times the original number. Find the original number. *12.6*

Chapter 16 Review

Key Terms

event (p. 603)
frequency table (p. 610)
histogram (p. 615)
independent events (p. 604)
mean (p. 608)
measures of central tendency (p. 610)
median (p. 609)

mode (p. 609)
probability (p. 599)
range (p. 619)
sample space (p. 603)
scatter plot (p. 614)
standard deviation (p. 619)
tree diagram (p. 603)

Key Ideas and Review Exercises

16.1 To find the probability of an event E, use

$$P(E) = \frac{s}{t} = \frac{\text{number of favorable outcomes}}{\text{total number of possible outcomes}}.$$

Ten cards are numbered consecutively from 1 to 10 and placed in a box. One card is drawn from the box. Find the probability of each event.

1. P(even number)   **2.** P(odd number)   **3.** $P(5)$ **4.** P(not 8)

16.2 To find the probability of $P(A \text{ and } B)$, use
$P(A \text{ and } B) = P(A) \cdot P(B)$, if A and B are independent events.
To find the probability of $P(A \text{ or } B)$, use
$P(A \text{ or } B) = P(A) + P(B) - P(A \text{ and } B)$. If A and B are mutually exclusive events, use $P(A \text{ or } B) = P(A) + P(B)$.

A red die and a white die are rolled.

5. Give a sample space of ordered pairs.

6. Find $P(r = 5 \text{ and } w = 1)$.

7. Find $P(r < 4 \text{ and } w \geq 2)$.

8. Find $P(r \leq 3 \text{ or } w = 6)$.

A pouch contains 6 red marbles, 4 white marbles, and 5 pink marbles. A marble is drawn.

9. Find P(red marble *or* white marble).

10. Find P(pink marble *or* white marble).

16.3 To find the mean of a set of data, add the scores and divide the sum by the number of scores.
To find the median of a set of data, arrange the scores in order and choose the middle score. If the data contains an even number of scores, use the mean of the two middle scores as the median.
To find the mode of a set of data, find the score that occurs most frequently. A set of data may have more than one mode.

Find the mean, the median, and the mode of each set of data.

11. 8, 12, 10, 8, 16, 9

12. 98, 99, 97, 98, 96, 100

The ages of 20 students on a camping trip were: 17, 15, 16, 15, 16, 15, 15, 16, 17, 15, 18, 15, 17, 16, 17, 16, 15, 18, 15, 16.

13. Make a frequency table for the data. **14.** Find the mean.

15. Find the median. **16.** Find the mode.

17. In a short paragraph, explain the advantages and the disadvantages of using the mean, the median, and the mode. Use examples to illustrate your explanation.

16.4   To interpret a scatter plot, see p. 614.
         To construct or to use a histogram, see p. 615.

The histogram at the right represents the weights of a freshman football team. Each boundary score is assigned to the lesser interval.

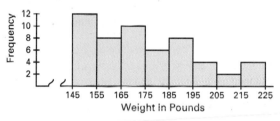

18. How many players weigh between 195 lb and 205 lb?

19. How many players weigh more than 205 lb?

The scatter plot at the right represents the number of hours students studied for their final exam and their scores.

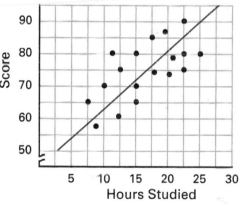

20. A student studies about 5 h. What score did this student probably receive?

21. A student's score was close to 95. About how many hours did this student study for the exam?

16.5   To find the range of a set of data, find the difference between the highest and lowest scores.

To find the standard deviation of a set of data, use

$$s = \sqrt{\frac{(x_1 - \overline{x})^2 + (x_2 - \overline{x})^2 + \cdots + (x_n - \overline{x})^2}{n}}$$

For Exercises 22–23, use the set of data: 18, 24, 26, 13, 19.

22. Find the range. **23.** Find the standard deviation.

A bag contains 15 red marbles, 10 white marbles, and 5 yellow marbles. One marble is drawn. Find the probability of each event.

1. $P(\text{red})$ **2.** $P(\text{yellow})$ **3.** $P(\text{not white})$ **4.** $P(\text{not yellow})$

5. $P(\text{blue})$ **6.** $P(\text{not red})$ **7.** $P(\text{white})$ **8.** $P(\text{not blue})$

A white die and a black die are rolled.

9. Give a sample space of ordered pairs.

10. Find $P(w = 6 \text{ and } b = 3)$.

11. Find $P(b \geq 3 \text{ and } w = 1)$.

12. Find $P(w = 4 \text{ or } b > 2)$.

Find the mean, the median, and the mode of each set of data.

13. 12, 10, 10, 20, 8

14. 96, 95, 96, 97, 94, 90

Two columns of a frequency table are shown at the right. Use the scores in this table for Exercises 15–17.

Scores	Frequency
8	6
9	4
10	5
11	3
12	2

15. Find the mean.

16. Find the median.

17. Find the mode.

The histogram at the right represents the SAT scores of a college class. Each boundary score is assigned to the lesser interval.

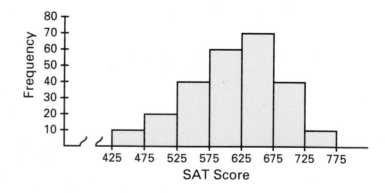

18. How many scores are between 675 and 725?

19. How many scores are between 425 and 525?

20. How many scores are 575 or less?

For Exercises 21–22, use the following set of data: 16, 14, 23, 27, 30.

21. Find the range.

22. Find the standard deviation.

23. A green die and a red die are rolled. Find $P(g + r = 7 \text{ or } g + r = 11)$.

24. When a die is rolled, what are the odds that the upper face will show 5 dots?

College Prep Test

Choose the one best answer to each question or problem.

1. What is the decimal for
$60 + 4 + \frac{3}{5} + \frac{2}{50}$?
(A) 70.04   (B) 64.64
(C) 64.46   (D) 64.44
(E) 64.05

2. What is the decimal for
$90 + 5 + \frac{3}{10} + \frac{6}{25}$?
(A) 95.90   (B) 95.84
(C) 95.98   (D) 95.27
(E) 95.54

3. What is the sum of all the whole number factors of 48?
(A) 124   (B) 75   (C) 48
(D) 26   (E) 14

4. How many numbers between 1 and 100 inclusive are divisible by either 2 or 3 or both?
(A) 99   (B) 98   (C) 67
(D) 66   (E) 16

5. How many numbers between 1 and 100 inclusive are divisible by either 5 or 12 but not both?
(A) 30   (B) 28   (C) 27
(D) 26   (E) 1

6. How many numbers between 1 and 100 inclusive are divisible by both 3 and 8?
(A) 45   (B) 33   (C) 12   (D) 4
(E) 0

7. If two dice are rolled, the probability that neither lands with 4 dots up is ___?___.
(A) $\frac{25}{36}$ (B) $\frac{11}{12}$ (C) $\frac{5}{6}$ (D) $\frac{1}{36}$
(E) $\frac{1}{12}$

8. In the formula $A = \frac{bh}{2}$, for $A = 48$ and $b = 8$, find the mean of b and h.
(A) 52   (B) 28   (C) 12
(D) 10   (E) 7

9.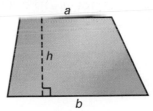

The formula for the area of the trapezoid is $A = \frac{1}{2}h(a + b)$, where a and b are the lengths of the bases and h is the height. Find the mean of the bases if the area is 198 in² and the height is 22 in.
(A) 4,356   (B) 36   (C) 18
(D) 9   (E) 4.5

10. In 1984, a company transported 15,000 boxes of fruit per month. In 1990, it transported 75,000 boxes of fruit per month. What was the average increase in monthly shipments per year?
(A) 10,000   (B) 12,000
(C) 15,000   (D) 5,000   (E) 857

11. The average of 22 students' scores is 86. If the two highest and the two lowest scores are removed, the mean of the remaining scores is 82. What is the mean of the removed scores?
(A) 172   (B) 416   (C) 105
(D) 104   (E) 4

12. If $-1 < x < 0$ and $x < y$, then the mean of x and y is ___?___.
(A) less than x
(B) greater than x
(C) greater than y
(D) less than -1
(E) It cannot be determined from the information given.

1. Evaluate $8 - 2x$ for $x = 2$. **1.2**

2. Which property is illustrated? **1.5**
   $6 + (-a) = -a + 6$

3. Simplify $6m + 3(5 + 2m) + 4$. **1.7**

4. Simplify $-6 \cdot 9 - 4^2$. **2.8**

5. Evaluate $-4y + 6y^3$ for
   $y = -2$.

6. Simplify $6(p - 3) - 2(1 + 4p)$. **2.10**

7. Pam plans to ride her bike $4\frac{1}{3}$ **3.6**
   mi for 40 min. At what rate
   must she travel?

Solve each equation or inequality.

8. $r + 15 = -15$ **3.1**

9. $2x - 8 = 17 + 3x$ **3.4**

10. $\frac{3}{4}x + \frac{1}{3} = \frac{2}{3}x - 1\frac{2}{3}$ **4.5**

11. $|x - 4| = 7$ **5.6**

12. $-2x - 5 < 13$ **5.7**

13. $6x^2 + 13x - 5 = 0$ **7.7**

Simplify.

14. $(2a^3b^2)(-5ab^5)$ **6.1**

15. $(-3x^2yz^4)^4$ **6.2**

16. $\dfrac{16x^{-2}y^{-1}}{-4xy^{-2}}$ **6.4**

17. $\dfrac{a - 3}{a^2 - 3a}$ **8.1**

Find each answer.

18. $(5x^2 - 5x - 3)$ **6.7**
    $+ (-3x^2 - x + 5)$

19. $(4x^2 - 9x + 3)$
    $- (-2x^2 + 8x - 1)$

20. $-3x(2x^3 - 5x + 1)$ **6.8**

21. $(2x - 3y)(3x + 4y)$ **6.9**

22. $\dfrac{x - 2}{x} \div \dfrac{3x - 6}{x^4}$ **8.4**

23. $\dfrac{a + 3}{9a} - \dfrac{4a + 2}{3a}$ **8.6**

24. $\dfrac{x}{x + 5} + \dfrac{8x + 15}{x^2 + 5x}$ **8.7**

25. $(4a^3 - 7a + 3) \div (2a - 1)$ **8.8**

26. Factor $4x^2 - 12x + 28$. **7.2**

27. Factor $3a^2 - 9a - 30$. **7.6**

**Solve for x. Check for extraneous
solutions, if necessary.**

28. $\dfrac{x + 5}{x - 4} = \dfrac{3}{x} + \dfrac{36}{x^2 - 4x}$ **9.1**

29. $\dfrac{x + 7}{6} = \dfrac{3}{x}$ **9.2**

30. $7 - 2x = mx$ **9.3**

31. Is the relation $\{(-2, 3),$ **10.2**
    $(-1, 5), (1, 3), (7, 1)\}$ a func-
    tion? Explain your reasoning.

32. Given $f(x) = 2x^2 - 9$, find **10.3**
    $f(-1)$.

33. Find the slope of the line de- **11.1**
    termined by the points $P(2,3)$
    and $Q(7,-6)$.

34. Write an equation in the form **11.2**
    $Ax + By = C$ for the line
    that includes the point
    $A(-4, 3)$ and with a slope of $-\frac{2}{5}$.

35. Solve. $\begin{array}{l} x + y = 4 \\ 3x - 2y = 2 \end{array}$ **12.5**

Simplify.

36. $-\sqrt{18x^7y^{12}} \ (x > 0, y > 0)$ **13.5**

37. $4\sqrt{3} \cdot 2\sqrt{75}$ **13.7**

38. $\sqrt{2}\,(\sqrt{2} - 3\sqrt{6})$

39. $\dfrac{-5}{3 - \sqrt{3}}$ **13.8**

40. In right triangle ABC, $a = 4$ and $b = 6$. Find the length of the hypotenuse c.   *13.4*

41. Use the quadratic formula to solve $x^2 + 4x + 2 = 0$.   *14.3*

42. If $\triangle ABC \sim \triangle XYZ$, find z for $a = 14, c = 10, x = 7$.   *15.1*

Refer to the figure to name each trigonometric ratio in fraction form.

43. $\sin A$ *15.2*

44. $\cos B$

45. $\tan A$

Find the median and the mode, if any, for the given data.

46. 16, 14, 36, 32, 38   *16.3*

47. 98, 97, 98, 96, 97, 98

For the set of data 12, 8, 6, 10, 16, 8, find each of the following.

48. the range   *16.5*

49. the standard deviation

Solve each problem.

50. The length of a rectangle is twice the width. The perimeter is 45 cm. Find the length and the width.   *4.4*

51. Twenty percent of 45 is what number?   *4.7*

52. Six is what percent of 30?

53. Ten percent of what number is 20?

54. The selling price of a television set is $260. The profit is 30% of the cost. Find the cost.   *4.8*

55. The square of a number is 12 less than 8 times the number. Find the number.   *7.8*

56. Two cars started toward each other at the same time from towns 170 km apart. One car's rate was 45 km/h, and the other car's rate was 40 km/h. After how many hours did they meet?   *9.4*

57. To do a job alone takes Rose 4 h, Bob 3 h, and Shelly 5 h. How long would the job take if they all worked together?   *9.5*

58. The cost of a metal varies directly as its mass. If 5 kg cost $15, find the cost of 8 kg.   *10.6*

59. y varies inversely as x. y is 20 when x is -4. Find y when x is -16.   *10.7*

60. The cost of an adult ticket to a school play was $2.00. A student ticket cost $1.50. The number of student tickets sold was 50 more than twice the number of adult tickets. The total income from tickets was $800. How many tickets of each type were sold?   *12.3*

61. The sum of the digits of a two-digit number is 8. If the digits are reversed, the new number is 36 less than the original number. Find the original number.   *12.6*

62. Mark has 6 more quarters than dimes. He has $3.25 in all. How many coins of each type does he have?   *12.8*

63. What is the probability that if a letter is picked from the alphabet, it will be a vowel?   *16.1*

64. A bag contains 20 colored disks. There are 12 red disks and 3 blue disks. What is the probability of picking a disk that is either red or blue?   *16.2*

Computer Investigations: Algebra 1

The following is a listing of the computer investigations that are included in *Holt Algebra 1*. The related textbook page for each investigation is also indicated. For each investigation, you will need the *Investigating Algebra with the Computer* software.

Title	Appendix Page	Related Text Page
SLOPE–INTERCEPT FORM OF A LINE	629	424
GRAPHING $y = \lvert Ax + B \rvert$	631	424
GRAPHING $y = \lvert Ax + B \rvert + C$	633	424
GRAPHING SYSTEMS OF EQUATIONS	635	445
GRAPHING QUADRATIC FUNCTIONS	637	558
MAXIMUM AND MINIMUM	638	558
THE DISCRIMINANT	639	564
USING STATISTICS: PREDICTING	641	614

Investigation: Slope-Intercept Form of a Line

Program: SLOPEINT

Objectives: To use the computer to graph equations of the form $y = Mx + B$

To predict the slope and y intercept of a line before graphing

Part 1

1. **a.** With BASIC loaded into the computer and the disk in drive 1 (or drive A), run the program SLOPEINT by typing the appropriate command.
   Apple: RUN SLOPEINT   IBM: RUN "SLOPEINT"
   Be sure to press the RETURN key after typing the command.

   b. Road the opening messages of the program.

2. Use the program to draw the graph of $y = 2x + 3$.

   a. Type 2 for M and press RETURN.

   b. Enter 3 for B (and press RETURN).

3. With the graph on the screen, answer the following questions.

   a. Is the graph a straight line?

   b. What is the y coordinate of the point where the graph crosses the y axis? This value is called the y intercept of the graph.

   c. Use the point $(-1,1)$ and the point where the graph crosses the y axis to compute the slope. What is the slope of the graph?

4. **a.** Answer Y (yes) to the questions ANOTHER GRAPH? and CLEAR THE SCREEN?.

   b. Graph the equation $y = 4x - 1$. Enter 4 for M and -1 for B.

   c. What is the y intercept?

   d. Use the y intercept and the point $(1,3)$ to compute the slope. What is the slope?

5. Answer Y to ANOTHER GRAPH? and Y to CLEAR THE SCREEN?. Then, before having the computer graph $y = -3x + 2$, predict the y intercept and the slope of the graph.

   a. y intercept?   **b.** slope?

6. Now have the computer graph $y = -3x + 2$. (M = -3 and B = 2.)

   a. Was your prediction for the y intercept correct?

   b. Was your prediction for the slope correct?

7. Repeat steps 5 and 6 for the equation $y = .5x - 3$. Do not leave the previous graph on the screen. Were your predictions correct?

8. *Complete*: For the graph of the equation $y = Mx + B$, the slope equals __?__ and the y intercept equals __?__.

Try These

Have the computer graph the following equations. In each case, predict the slope and *y* intercept before seeing the graph. Clear the screen before each graph is drawn.

9. $y = -.5x - 4$ **10.** $y = x + 5$

11. $y = 1.5x - 2$ **12.** $y = -x + 2.5$

Part 2   **1.** Clear the screen and graph $y = 3x$. That is, enter 3 for M and 0 for B.

      a. Does the graph go through the origin?

      b. What is the *y* intercept of the graph?

      c. Does the *y* intercept equal the value of B in the equation?

      d. What is the slope of the line?

      e. Does the slope equal the value of M in the equation?

    2. a. Before graphing $y = -2x$, predict the *y* intercept and the slope.

      b. Now clear the screen and graph $y = -2x$. Were your predictions correct?

Try These

Have the computer graph the following equations. In each case, predict the slope and *y* intercept before seeing the graph. Clear the screen before each graph is drawn.

    3. $y = 2x$ **4.** $y = -3x$ **5.** $y = 2.5x$ **6.** $y = -4x$

Part 3   **1.** Clear the screen and graph $y = 4$. In this case, M = 0 and B = 4.

      a. The graph is what kind of straight line?

      b. What is the *y* intercept of the graph?

      c. Does the *y* intercept equal the value of B?

      d. What is the slope of the line?

      e. Does the slope equal the value of M for this equation?

    2. a. Before graphing $y = -2$, predict the *y* intercept and the slope.

      b. Now graph $y = -2$. (Enter 0 for M.) Were your predictions correct?

Try These

Have the computer graph these equations. In each case, predict the slope and *y* intercept before seeing the graph. Clear the screen before each graph is drawn.

    3. $y = 1$ **4.** $y = -5$ **5.** $y = 2.5$ **6.** $y = -1$

Investigation: Graphing $y = |Ax + B|$

Program: ABSVAL1

Objectives: To use the computer to graph equations of the form $y = |Ax + B|$
To predict the x intercept of the graph of an equation of the form $y = |Ax + B]$
To predict the slopes of the arms of the graph of an equation of the form $y = |Ax + B|$

Part 1

1. **a.** With BASIC loaded into the computer and the disk in drive 1 (or drive A), run the program ABSVAL1 by typing the appropriate command.
   Apple: RUN ABSVAL1   IBM: RUN "ABSVAL1"
   Be sure to press the RETURN key after typing the command.

2. Have the computer graph the equation $y = |x|$. Enter 1 for A and 0 for B. With the graph on the screen, answer the following questions.
   a. The graph is shaped like what letter of the alphabet?
   b. The graph lies in which quadrants?
   c. What is the x intercept of the graph?
   d. What are the slopes of the two "arms" or "branches" of the graph?

3. **a.** Answer Y (yes) to ANOTHER GRAPH? and N (no) to CLEAR THE SCREEN?.
   b. Have the computer graph the equation $y = |2x|$. That is, enter 2 for A and 0 for B.
   c. The graph is shaped like what letter?
   d. The graph lies in which quadrants?
   e. What is the x intercept?   **f.** What are the slopes of the arms?

4. Before having the computer graph $y = |3x|$, predict the x intercept and the slopes of the arms of the graph.
   a. x intercept?   **b.** slopes?

5. Without clearing the screen, graph $y = |3x|$. (Use A = 3 and B = 0.)
   a. Was your prediction for the x intercept correct?
   b. Was your prediction for the slopes correct?

6. Answer Y to ANOTHER GRAPH? and Y to CLEAR THE SCREEN?. Then graph $y = |-2x|$. (A = -2, B = 0)
   a. What is the x intercept?   **b.** What are the slopes of the arms?
   c. The graph is the same as that of what equation graphed earlier?

7. *Complete:* For the graph of $y = |ax|$, the x intercept is __?__ and the slopes of the arms are __?__ and __?__ .

Try These Clear the screen each time and have the computer graph the following equations. In each case, predict the slopes of the arms before seeing the graph.

8. $y = |.5x|$ **9.** $y = |-4x|$ **10.** $y = |-x|$ **11.** $y = |5x|$

Part 2 **1.** Clear the screen and graph $y = |x + 1|$. Enter 1 for A and 1 for B.

  a. The graph is shaped like what letter?

  b. The graph is in which quadrants?

  c. What is the x intercept? **d.** What are the slopes of the arms?

2. Graph $y = |x - 2|$. Do not clear the screen. (Enter 1 for A and -2 for B.)

  a. What is the x intercept? **b.** What are the slopes of the arms?

3. Before graphing $y = |x + 3|$, predict the x intercept and the slopes of the arms. **a.** x intercept? **b.** slopes?

4. Without clearing the screen, graph $y = |x + 3|$. Were your predictions for the x intercept and the slopes correct?

Try These Clear the screen and have the computer graph the following equations on the same axes. In each case, predict the x intercept before seeing the graph.

5. $y = |x - 1|$ **6.** $y = |x - 3|$

7. $y = |x + 2|$ **8.** $y = |x + 4|$

Part 3 **1.** Clear the screen. Then graph $y = |2x - 4|$. (Enter 2 for A and -4 for B.)

  a. The graph is shaped like what letter?

  b. The graph is which quadrants?

  c. What is the x intercept? **d.** What are the slopes of the arms?

2. Repeat step 1 for $y = |3x + 6|$. **a.** x intercept? **b.** slopes?

3. Before seeing the graph of $y = |2x + 8|$, predict the x intercept and the slopes of the arms. **a.** x intercept? **b.** slopes?

4. Clear the screen and graph $y = |2x + 8|$. Were your predictions correct?

5. Repeat steps 3–4 for $y = |-2x + 6|$. **a.** x intercept? **b.** slopes?

6. Repeat steps 3–4 for $y = |-x + 4|$. **a.** x intercept? **b.** slopes?

7. *Complete:* The graph of $y = |Ax + B|$ (with $a \neq 0$) is shaped like the letter __?__ and lies in quadrants __?__ and __?__. The x intercept is __?__ and the slopes of the arms are __?__ and __?__.

Try These Predict the x intercept and the slopes of the arms of the graph of each equation. Then clear the screen and have the computer graph the equation. Correct your predictions if they were wrong.

8. $y = 2x + 1$ **9.** $y = 3x = 2$ **10.** $y = -5x - 4$

Investigation: Graphing $y = |Ax + B| + C$

Program: ABSVAL2

Objectives: To use the computer to graph equations of the form $y = |Ax + B| + C$
To predict the coordinates of the vertex and the slopes of the arms of the graph.

Part 1

1. **a.** With BASIC loaded into the computer and the disk in drive 1 (or drive A), run the program ABSVAL2 by typing the appropriate command.
   Apple: RUN ABSVAL2   IBM: RUN "ABSVAL2"
   Be sure to press the RETURN key after typing the command.
   b. Road the opening messages of the program.

2. **a.** Have the computer graph the equation $y = |x|$. Enter 1 for A, 0 for B, and 0 for C.
   b. The vertex of the graph is the endpoint where the two arms meet. What are the coordinates of the vertex of the graph? (_?_ , _?_)
   c. What are the slopes of the arms of the graph?

3. **a.** Answer Y (yes) to ANOTHER GRAPH and N (no) to CLEAR THE SCREEN?.
   b. Have the computer graph $y = |x| + 3$. That is, enter 1 for A, 0 for B, and 3 for C.
   c. What are the coordinates of the vertex?
   d. What are the slopes of the arms?

4. **a.** Before having the computer graph $y = |x| - 2$, predict the coordinates of the vertex and the slopes of the arms.
   b. Without clearing the screen, graph $y = |x| - 2$. ($A = 1$, $B = 0$, $C = -2$)
   c. Were your predictions for the vertex and the slopes correct?

5. Answer Y to ANOTHER GRAPH? and Y to CLEAR THE SCREEN?. Then graph $y = |2x| + 4$. ($A = 2$, $B = 0$, $C = 4$) Give the following.
   a. coordinates of the vertex?   **b.** slopes of the arms?

6. Repeat step 5 for $y = |-3x| - 1$. ($A = -3$, $B = 0$, $C = -1$)

7. **a.** Before graphing $y = |4x| - 6$, predict the coordinates of the vertex and the slopes of the arms of the graph.
   b. Without clearing the screen, graph $y = |4x| - 6$. Were your predictions correct?

8. Repeat step 7 for $y = |-2x| + 5$.

Try These   Clear the screen and graph the following equations on the same screen. In each case, predict the coordinates of the vertex and the slopes of the arms before seeing the graph. Then check your predictions from the graph.

9. $y = |x| + 2$ **10.** $y = |x| + 5$ **11.** $y = |x| - 3$ **12.** $y = |x| - 7$
13. $y = |5x| + 6$ **14.** $y = |-4x| + 1$ **15.** $y = |-5x| - 7$ **16.** $y = |.5x| - 8$

Part 2

1. Clear the screen and graph $y = |x + 1| + 2$. (A = 1, B = 1, and C = 2.)
   a. What are the coordinates of the vertex?
   b. What are the slopes of the arms?

2. Repeat step 1 for $y = |x - 2| + 3$. Do not clear the screen. (A = 1, B = -2, C = 3)

3. a. Before having the computer graph $y = |x + 3| - 4$, predict the coordinates of the vertex and the slopes of the arms.
   b. Without clearing the screen, graph $y = |x + 3| - 4$. Were your predictions for the intercepts and the slopes correct?

4. Clear the screen and graph $y = |2x - 4| - 5$. Give the following.
   a. coordinates of the vertex?   **b.** slopes of the arms?

5. Without clearing the screen, repeat step 4 for $y = |3x - 9| + 1$.

6. a. Before graphing $y = |4x + 12| - 2$, predict the coordinates of the vertex and the slopes of the arms.
   b. Without clearing the screen, graph $y = |4x + 12| - 2$. Were your predictions correct?

7. Repeat step 6 for $y = |-3x + 6| - 7$.

8. *Complete*: For the graph of $y = |Ax + B| + C$ (A ≠ 0), the vertex is (__?__, __?__) and the slopes of the arms are __?__ and __?__.

Try These   Clear the screen and graph the following equations on the same screen. In each case, predict the coordinates of the vertex and the slopes of the arms before seeing the graph. Then check your predictions from the graph.

9. $y = |x - 1| + 4$ **10.** $y = |x + 6| + 2$
11. $y = |2x + 8| - 1$ **12.** $y = |3x - 15| - 6$
13. $y = |-4x - 12| + 5$ **14.** $y = |-.5x + 4| - 8$

Investigation: Graphing Systems of Equations

Program: SYSTEMS

Objective: To use the computer to solve systems of two linear equations by graphing

1. **a.** With BASIC loaded into the computer and the disk in drive 1 (or drive A), run the program SYSTEMS by typing the appropriate command.
      Apple: RUN SYSTEMS   IBM: RUN "SYSTEMS"
      Be sure to press the RETURN key after typing the command.
   b. Read the opening messages of the program.

2. Use the program to draw the graph of these two equations on the same axes.

$$\begin{cases} x + 2y = 5 \\ 3x - y = 1 \end{cases}$$

   a. For the first equation enter 1 for A, 2 for B, and 5 for C.
   b. Is the graph of the first equation a straight line?
   c. For the second equation enter 3 for A, −1 for B, and 1 for C.
   d. Is the graph of the second equation a straight line?
   e. At what point do the two graphs intersect? (_?_ , _?_)
   f. Substitute the x and y coordinates of the point of intersection into the first equation. Does a true sentence result?
   g. Substitute the coordinates of the intersection point into the second equation. Does a true sentence result?

3. **a.** Enter Y (yes) to the question ANOTHER SYSTEM?.
   b. Have the computer graph these equations on the same axes.

   $$\begin{cases} 3x - 2y = 14 \\ 2x + 3y = -8 \end{cases}$$
   A = 3, B = −2, C = 14
   A = 2, B = 3,   C = −8

   c. What is the point of intersection of the two lines? (_?_ , _?_)
   d. Substitute the x and y coordinates of this point into the first equation. Do you get a true sentence?
   e. Substitute the x and y coordinates of this point into the second equation. Do you get a true sentence?

4. Repeat step 3 for this system. $$\begin{cases} -3x + y = 4 \\ 10x - 7y = 5 \end{cases}$$

   a. What is the point of intersection of the two lines?
   b. Substitute the x and y coordinates of the intersection point into both equations. Are both sentences true?

5. Repeat step 3 for this system. $\begin{cases} 6x - 2y = 12 \\ 3x - y = -4 \end{cases}$

    a. Do the two lines intersect?

    b. Do the two equations have any common solution?

6. Repeat step 3 for this system. $\begin{cases} x + y = 6 \\ 2x + 2y = 12 \end{cases}$

    a. What do you notice about the graphs of the two equations?

    b. How many common solutions do the two equations have?

Try These

Have the computer graph each pair of equations on the same axes. Write the coordinates of the point of intersection of each pair or, if the lines do not intersect, write <u>no common point</u>. Check by substitution that the coordinates of the point of intersection make both equations true.

7. $\begin{cases} 3x + y = 11 \\ 2x - 3y = 11 \end{cases}$ **8.** $\begin{cases} x + y = 7 \\ 2x - 3y = 14 \end{cases}$

9. $\begin{cases} 4x - 3y = 18 \\ -8x + 6y = 11 \end{cases}$ **10.** $\begin{cases} -9x + 7y = -59 \\ 11x + 12y = 31 \end{cases}$

11. $\begin{cases} 2x = 14 \\ x - 2y = 3 \end{cases}$ (NOTE: B = 0)   **12.** $\begin{cases} 10y = -30 \\ 4x + 2y = -2 \end{cases}$ (NOTE: A = 0)

Put each equation in the form $Ax + By = C$. Then use the program to determine the common solution, if any, of each system. Check each solution by substitution.

13. $\begin{cases} y = 3x + 2 \\ y = 6x - 1 \end{cases}$ **14.** $\begin{cases} 4x = 9y - 7 \\ 3 = 3x - 4y \end{cases}$

15. $\begin{cases} 2y = 11x + 15 \\ y + 3x = 0 \end{cases}$ **16.** $\begin{cases} 16 = -2x \\ 20 + x = 2y \end{cases}$

17. $\begin{cases} 3x - y = 7 \\ 4y = 12x - 15 \end{cases}$ **18.** $\begin{cases} y = 5x - 2 \\ 15x - 3y = 6 \end{cases}$

Investigation: Graphing Quadratic Functions

Program: PARA1

Objectives: To use the computer to graph equations of the form $y = Ax^2 + Bx + C$ and discover that the graph is a parabola

To read the zeros of a quadratic function from its graph

1. **a.** With BASIC loaded into the computer and the disk in drive 1 (or drive A), run the program PARA1 by typing the appropriate command.

   Apple: RUN PARA1   IBM: RUN "PARA1"

   Be sure to press the RETURN key after typing the command.

   b. Read the opening messages of the program.

2. Use the program to draw the graph of $y = x^2$, as follows.

   a. Enter 1 for A and press RETURN.

   b. Enter 0 for B (and press RETURN).

   c. Enter 0 for C.

   d. Is the graph a straight line?

3. The graph of $y = x^2$ is called a **parabola.** Where does the parabola touch the x axis; that is, what is its x intercept?

4. **a.** Enter Y to ANOTHER GRAPH? and N to CLEAR THE SCREEN?.

   b. Graph $y = -3x^2$. Enter -3 for A, 0 for B, and 0 for C.

5. Answer these questions about the graph of $y = -3x^2$.

   a. Is the graph a parabola?

   b. What is the x intercept?

   c. The **zeros** of a function are the values for x which make the function equal zero. List any zeros of the function $y = -3x^2$.

6. **a.** Answer Y to ANOTHER GRAPH? and Y to CLEAR THE SCREEN?.

   b. Graph $y = x^2 + 2x$. Enter 1 for A, 2 for B, and 0 for C.

7. Answer these questions about the graph of $y = x^2 + 2x$.

   a. Is the graph a parabola?

   b. How many zeros (x intercepts) does this function have?

   c. List the zeros.

8. Clear the screen and graph $y = x^2 - 3x$. Enter $A = 1$, $B = -3$, and $C = 0$. What are the zeros of this function?

9. Clear the screen and graph $y = x^2 - x - 2$. ($A = 1$, $B = -1$, $C = -2$)

   a. How many zeros does this function have?   **b.** List the zeros.

Try These
Have the computer graph the following functions, each on a separate screen. List the zeros of each function. Estimate any zeros that are not integers to the nearest tenth.

10. $y = x^2 + 2x - 8$

11. $y = -x^2 + 4x$

12. $y = 2x^2 - 11x - 6$

13. $y = x^2 - 12x + 36$

Investigation: Maximum and Minimum

Program: PARA3

Objectives: To use the computer to graph functions of the form $y = Ax^2 + Bx + C$ and draw the axis of symmetry

To discover that the parabola opens upward when $A > 0$ and downward when $A < 0$

To discover that the x coordinate of the vertex is $\frac{-B}{2A}$ and the equation of the axis of symmetry is $x = \frac{-B}{2A}$

1. **a.** With BASIC loaded into the computer and the disk in drive 1 (or drive A), run the program PARA3 by typing the appropriate command.
    Apple: RUN PARA3   IBM: RUN "PARA3"
    Be sure to press the RETURN key after typing the command.
    b. Read the opening messages of the program.

2. **a.** Have the computer graph $y = x^2$. Enter 1 for A, 0 for B, and 0 for C.
    b. The computer graphs the parabola and draws the **axis of symmetry.** It also prints the equation of the axis of symmetry and the coordinates of the turning point or **vertex** of the parabola.
    c. Does the parabola open upward or downward?
    d. What are the coordinates of the vertex? (_?_ , _?_)
    e. What is the equation of the axis of symmetry? $x =$ _?_

3. **a.** Enter Y (yes) for ANOTHER GRAPH?.
    b. Have the computer graph $y = -2x^2$. Enter -2 for A, 0 for B, and 0 for C.
    c. Does the parabola open upward or downward?
    d. What are the coordinates of the vertex?
    e. What is the equation of the axis of symmetry?

4. Repeat step 3 for $y = x^2 - 2x + 3$. ($A = 1$, $B = -2$, $C = 3$)
    a. open upward or downward?   **b.** coordinates of the vertex?
    c. equation of the axis of symmetry?

5. **a.** For the function $y = x^2 - 2x + 3$ above, compute $\frac{-B}{2A}$.
    b. What connection does this value have to the vertex of the parabola?
    c. What connection does this value have to the axis of symmetry equation?

6. **a.** For $y = 2x^2 - 16x + 35$, compute $\frac{-b}{2a}$.

b. Before graphing the function, predict whether it will open up or down.

c. Predict the equation of the axis of symmetry.

7. Have the computer graph $y = 2x^2 - 16x + 35$.

a. Does the parabola open the way you predicted?

b. Was your prediction of the equation of the axis of symmetry correct?

c. What are the coordinates of the vertex?

8. Before graphing $y = -3x^2 + 6x - 2$, make predictions about the graph.

a. open upward or downward?   **b.** equation of the axis of
c. x coordinate of the vertex?   symmetry?

9. Have the computer graph $y = -3x^2 + 6x - 2$. Were your predictions correct?

10. Complete for the parabola $y = Ax^2 + Bx + C$. ($A \neq 0$)

a. The parabola opens upward if $A > \underline{\ ?\ }$.

b. The parabola opens downward if $\underline{\ ?\ }$.

c. The x coordinate of the vertex of the parabola equals $\underline{\ ?\ }$.

d. The equation of the axis of symmetry is $\underline{\ ?\ }$.

Try These   Before having the computer graph each parabola, predict whether it will open upward or downward. Also predict the x coordinate of the vertex and the equation of the axis of symmetry. Check your predictions from the computer's graph. Also list the y coordinate of the vertex.

11. $y = x^2 + 6x + 7$ 12. $y = -2x^2 - 4x - 3$
13. $y = -5x^2 - 30x - 45$ 14. $y = x^2 + 2$
15. $y = 4x^2 - 8x$ 16. $y = -3x^2 + 4$

Investigation: The Discriminant

Program: PARA2

Objectives: To use the computer to graph equations of the form $y = Ax^2 + Bx + C$
To use the discriminant to predict the number of zeros of the function before seeing its graph

1. **a.** With BASIC loaded into the computer and the disk in drive 1 (or drive A), run the program PARA2 by typing the appropriate command.
Apple: RUN PARA2   IBM: RUN "PARA2"
Be sure to press the RETURN key after typing the command.

b. Read the opening messages of the program.

2. a. Use the program to graph the function $y = 3x^2 - 8x - 3$. Enter 3 for A, -8 for B, and -3 for C.

b. After the graph is displayed, count the number of **zeros** of the function. That is, count the number of points where the graph crosses the x axis. How many zeros does it have?

c. For a quadratic function $y = Ax^2 + Bx + C$, the value of $B^2 - 4AC$ is called the **discriminant** of the function. Compute the value of $B^2 - 4AC$ for $y = 3x^2 - 8x - 3$. Enter this value into the computer. If your value is incorrect, the computer will tell you to try again. What is the correct value?

d. Based on the discriminant, the computer prints the number of zeros of this function. Does this number agree with your answer to part **b** above?

3. Answer Y (yes) to ANOTHER GRAPH? . Then repeat step 2 for the function $y = x^2 + x + 2$. (A = 1, B = 1, C = 2). Be sure to count the zeros from the graph before computing the discriminant.

a. number of zeros?   **b.** discriminant?

4. Repeat step 2 for the function $y = x^2 + 4x + 4$. (A = 1, B = 4, C = 4)

a. number of zeros?   **b.** discriminant?

5. a. What is the discriminant of $y = 2x^2 - x - 6$? (A = 2, B = -1, C = -6)

b. Predict the number of zeros of the graph of $y = 2x^2 - x - 6$.

c. Have the computer graph the function. Was your prediction correct?

d. Enter your value for the discriminant. Was it correct?

6. Repeat step 5 for the function $y = 4x^2 - 4x + 1$.

a. discriminant?   **b.** number of zeros?

7. Repeat step 5 for the function $y = -x^2 + 3x - 4$. Notice that A = -1.

a. discriminant?   **b.** number of zeros?

8. *Complete*: For the quadratic function $y = Ax^2 + Bx + C$,

a. if the discriminant is positive, the function has _?_ zero(s);

b. if the discriminant is negative, the function has _?_ zero(s);

c. if the discriminant is zero, the function has _?_ zero(s).

Try These   Compute the discriminant of each function and predict the number of zeros. Then have the computer graph the function. Check your predictions.

9. $y = x^2 + 2x + 7$ **10.** $y = 2x^2 - 5x$ (NOTE: C = 0.)

11. $y = 3x^2 + 5x - 2$ **12.** $y = 6x^2 + 5$ (NOTE: B = 0.)

13. $y = -3x^2 + 4x + 6$ **14.** $y = -x^2 - 6x - 9$

Investigation: Using Statistics: Predicting

Program: SCATPLOT

Objectives: To use the computer to draw scatterplots and draw the median line of fit
To have the computer predict a *Y* value on the median line of fit for any given *X* value

1. **a.** With BASIC loaded into the computer and the disk in drive 1 (or drive A), run the program SCATPLOT by typing the appropriate command.
     Apple: RUN SCATPLOT   IBM: RUN "SCATPLOT"
   Be sure to press the RETURN key after typing the command.

   b. Read the opening messages of the program.

2. Enter the pairs of values at the right into the computer. Be sure to type the comma between the pairs. Also press RETURN after entering each pair. After typing the last pair, answer PAIR #11? by typing 999, 999 (and pressing RETURN).

0.2, 70	1.1, 75
1.2, 80	1.5, 79
1.6, 83	1.9, 84
2.2, 86	2.4, 86
2.7, 89	3.0, 91

3. **a.** The computer draws the **scatterplot.** After studying the plot, press any key to see the **median line of fit.**

   b. What is the equation of the line of fit?

   c. To the question PREDICT Y VALUE FOR WHICH X VALUE? enter 3.5 (and press RETURN).

   d. What is the predicted *Y* value on the line of fit for *X* = 3.5?

   e. To ANOTHER GRAPH? enter Y (yes).

4. **a.** Enter the pairs of values below. Enter 999,999 to end the list.

      1,4   2,7   3,6   5,9   6,10   7,12   9,12   10,13   11,15   12,16

   b. Press any key to see the median line of fit.

   c. What is the equation of the line of fit?

   d. To PREDICT Y VALUE FOR WHICH X VALUE? enter 15.

   e. What is the predicted *Y* value for *X* = 15?

Try These   Use the computer to draw the scatterplot of each set of data. In each case record the equation of the line of fit. Then enter the *X* value and record the predicted *Y* value for that *X* value.

5.
X	10	20	20	25	30	35	40	45	50	60
Y	10	12	11	14	18	23	30	29	31	35

Predict *Y* for *X* = 53.

6.
X	17.5	18.0	19.0	19.5	20.5	21.0	22.5	23.5	25.0	27.0
Y	8.7	8.5	8.4	7.9	7.8	8.0	7.4	7.1	6.8	6.1

Predict *Y* for *X* = 18.0.

Table of Roots and Powers

No.	Sq.	Sq. Root	Cube	Cu. Root	No.	Sq.	Sq. Root	Cube	Cu. Root
1	1	1.000	1	1.000	51	2,601	7.141	132,651	3.708
2	4	1.414	8	1.260	52	2,704	7.211	140,608	3.733
3	9	1.732	27	1.442	53	2,809	7.280	148,877	3.756
4	16	2.000	64	1.587	54	2,916	7.348	157,564	3.780
5	25	2.236	125	1.710	55	3,025	7.416	166,375	3.803
6	36	2.449	216	1.817	56	3,136	7.483	175,616	3.826
7	49	2.646	343	1.913	57	3,249	7.550	185,193	3.849
8	64	2.828	512	2.000	58	3,364	7.616	195,112	3.871
9	81	3.000	729	2.080	59	3,481	7.681	205,379	3.893
10	100	3.162	1,000	2.154	60	3,600	7.746	216,000	3.915
11	121	3.317	1,331	2.224	61	3,721	7.810	226,981	3.936
12	144	3.464	1,728	2.289	62	3,844	7.874	238,328	3.958
13	169	3.606	2,197	2.351	63	3,969	7.937	250,047	3.979
14	196	3.742	2,744	2.410	64	4,096	8.000	262,144	4.000
15	225	3.875	3,373	2.466	65	4,225	8.062	274,625	4.021
16	256	4.000	4,096	2.520	66	4,356	8.124	287,496	4.041
17	289	4.123	4,913	2.571	67	4,489	8.185	300,763	4.062
18	324	4.243	5,832	2.621	68	4,624	8.246	314,432	4.082
19	361	4.359	6,859	2.668	69	4,761	8.307	328,509	4.102
20	400	4.472	8,000	2.714	70	4,900	8.357	343,000	4.121
21	441	4.583	9,261	2.759	71	5,041	8.426	357,911	4.141
22	484	4.690	10,648	2.802	72	5,184	8.485	373,248	4.160
23	529	4.796	12,167	2.844	73	5,329	8.544	389,017	4.179
24	576	4.899	13,824	2.884	74	5,476	8.602	405,224	4.198
25	625	5.000	15,625	2.924	75	5,625	8.660	421,875	4.217
26	676	5.099	17,576	2.962	76	5,776	8.718	438,976	4.236
27	729	5.196	19,683	3.000	77	5,929	8.775	456,533	4.254
28	784	5.292	21,952	3.037	78	6,084	8.832	474,552	4.273
29	841	5.385	24,389	3.072	79	6,241	8.888	493,039	4.291
30	900	5.477	27,000	3.107	80	6,400	8.944	512,000	4.309
31	961	5.568	29,791	3.141	81	6,561	9.000	531,441	4.327
32	1,024	5.657	32,768	3.175	82	6,724	9.055	551,368	4.344
33	1,089	5.745	35,937	3.208	83	6,889	9.110	571,787	4.362
34	1,156	5.831	39,304	3.240	84	7,056	9.165	592,704	4.380
35	1,225	5.916	42,875	3.271	85	7,225	9.220	614,125	4.397
36	1,296	6.000	46,656	3.302	86	7,396	9.274	636,056	4.414
37	1,369	6.083	50,653	3.332	87	7,569	9.327	658,503	4.431
38	1,444	6.164	54,872	3.362	88	7,744	9.381	681,472	4.448
39	1,521	6.245	59,319	3.391	89	7,921	9.434	704,969	4.465
40	1,600	6.325	64,000	3.420	90	8,100	9.487	729,000	4.481
41	1,681	6.403	68,921	3.448	91	8,281	9.539	753,571	4.498
42	1,764	6.481	74,088	3.476	92	8,464	9.592	778,688	4.514
43	1,849	6.557	79,507	3.503	93	8,649	9.644	804,357	4.531
44	1,936	6.633	85,184	3.530	94	8,836	9.695	830,584	4.547
45	2,025	6.708	91,125	3.557	95	9,025	9.747	857,375	4.563
46	2,116	6.782	97,336	3.583	96	9,216	9.798	884,736	4.579
47	2,209	6.856	103,823	3.609	97	9,409	9.849	912,673	4.595
48	2,304	6.928	110,592	3.634	98	9,604	9.899	941,192	4.610
49	2,401	7.000	117,649	3.659	99	9,801	9.950	970,299	4.626
50	2,500	7.071	125,000	3.684	100	10,000	10.000	1,000,000	4.642

Table

Trigonometric Ratios

Angle Measure	Sin	Cos	Tan	Angle Measure	Sin	Cos	Tan
0°	0.000	1.000	0.000	46°	.7193	.6947	1.036
1°	.0175	.9998	.0175	47°	.7314	.6820	1.072
2°	.0349	.9994	.0349	48°	.7431	.6691	1.111
3°	.0523	.9986	.0524	49°	.7547	.6561	1.150
4°	.0698	.9976	.0699	50°	.7660	.6428	1.192
5°	.0872	.9962	.0875	51°	.7771	.6293	1.235
6°	.1045	.9945	.1051	52°	.7880	.6157	1.280
7°	.1219	.9925	.1228	53°	.7986	.6018	1.327
8°	.1392	.9903	.1405	54°	.8090	.5878	1.376
9°	.1564	.9877	.1584	55°	.8192	.5736	1.428
10°	.1736	.9848	.1763	56°	.8290	.5592	1.483
11°	.1908	.9816	.1944	57°	.8387	.5446	1.540
12°	.2079	.9781	.2126	58°	.8480	.5299	1.600
13°	.2250	.9744	.2309	59°	.8572	.5150	1.664
14°	.2419	.9703	.2493	60°	.8660	.5000	1.732
15°	.2588	.9659	.2679	61°	.8746	.4848	1.804
16°	.2756	.9613	.2867	62°	.8829	.4695	1.881
17°	.2924	.9563	.3057	63°	.8910	.4540	1.963
18°	.3090	.9511	.3249	64°	.8988	.4384	2.050
19°	.3256	.9455	.3443	65°	.9063	.4226	2.145
20°	.3420	.9397	.3640	66°	.9135	.4067	2.246
21°	.3584	.9336	.3839	67°	.9205	.3907	2.356
22°	.3746	.9272	.4040	68°	.9272	.3746	2.475
23°	.3907	.9205	.4245	69°	.9336	.3584	2.605
24°	.4067	.9135	.4452	70°	.9397	.3420	2.747
25°	.4226	.9063	.4663	71°	.9455	.3256	2.904
26°	.4384	.8988	.4877	72°	.9511	.3090	3.077
27°	.4540	.8910	.5095	73°	.9563	.2924	3.271
28°	.4695	.8829	.5317	74°	.9613	.2756	3.487
29°	.4848	.8746	.5543	75°	.9659	.2588	3.732
30°	.5000	.8660	.5774	76°	.9703	.2419	4.010
31°	.5150	.8572	.6009	77°	.9744	.2250	4.331
32°	.5299	.8480	.6249	78°	.9781	.2079	4.704
33°	.5446	.8387	.6494	79°	.9816	.1908	5.145
34°	.5592	.8290	.6745	80°	.9848	.1736	5.671
35°	.5736	.8192	.7002	81°	.9877	.1564	6.314
36°	.5878	.8090	.7265	82°	.9903	.1392	7.115
37°	.6018	.7986	.7536	83°	.9925	.1219	8.144
38°	.6157	.7880	.7813	84°	.9945	.1045	9.514
39°	.6293	.7771	.8098	85°	.9962	.0872	11.43
40°	.6428	.7660	.8391	86°	.9976	.0698	14.30
41°	.6561	.7547	.8693	87°	.9986	.0523	19.08
42°	.6691	.7431	.9004	88°	.9994	.0349	28.64
43°	.6820	.7314	.9325	89°	.9998	.0175	57.29
44°	.6947	.7193	.9657	90°	1.000	0.000	
45°	.7071	.7071	1.000				

Glossary

absolute value: The distance between x and 0 on a number line. (p. 46)

acute angle: An angle with a degree measure less than 90. (p. 579)

addition method: A method for solving a system of linear equations in two variables, based on the Addition Property. (p. 460)

algebraic expression: An expression that contains one or more operations with one or more variables. (p. 1)

angle of elevation: An angle formed by a horizontal line and the line of sight to a point at a higher elevation. (p. 590)

angle of depression: An angle formed by a horizontal line and the line of sight to a point at a lower elevation. (p. 590)

area: A measurement of the number of square units that a geometric figure contains. (p. 13)

arithmetic mean: The average of a set of numbers. (p. 69)

average: The sum of the members of the set divided by the number of members. (p. 69)

axis of symmetry: An imaginary line about which a curve is symmetric. (p. 559)

binomial: A polynomial with two terms. (p. 218)

boundary line: A line that separates a coordinate plane into two regions. (p. 433)

central tendency: The "middle points" of statistical data, measured by the *mean, mode,* and *median.* (p. 610)

coefficient: See *numerical coefficients.* (p. 26)

completing the square: A method for solving quadratic equations. (p. 539)

complex fraction: A fraction with at least one fraction in its numerator, denominator, or in both. (p. 325)

complex rational expression: A rational expression with at least one rational expression in its numerator, denominator, or in both. (p. 326)

composite number: A positive integer with two or more positive factors other than 1 (not prime). (p. 243)

conclusion: The *then* clause in a conditional statement. (p. 116)

conditional: A statement written in *if-then* form. (p. 116)

conjugates: Binomial expressions that differ only in the sign of the second term. (p. 523)

conjunction: The logical union of two statements, which are connected by the word *and.* (p. 175)

constant linear function: A function of the form $f(x) = c$, where c is constant and whose graph is a horizontal line. (p. 393)

constant of variation: The constant k in the equation $y = kx$ or $xy = k$, where k is a nonzero real number. (pp. 397, 401)

conversion fractions: Fractions equal to 1 that are used to convert units of measurement. (p. 364)

coordinate: The number, or number pair, that corresponds to a point on a number line. (pp. 41, 373)

coordinate plane: A plane that has a vertical axis and a horizontal axis that intersect in a point called the origin. (p. 373)

corresponding angles: Angles of two similar figures, which have the same measure. (p. 575)

corresponding sides: Sides, proportional in length, that lie opposite the pairs of corresponding angles in similar figures. (p. 575)

cosine ratio: The cosine of an acute angle of a right triangle is the ratio of the length of the side that is adjacent to the acute angle to the length of the hypotenuse. (p. 580)

degree of a monomial: The sum of the exponents of all its variables. (p. 219)

degree of a polynomial: The degree of a polynomial is the same as that of the greatest degree term. (p. 219)

difference of two squares: A perfect square minus another perfect square: $a^2 - b^2$. (p. 259)

dimensional analysis: The use of conversion fractions to convert units of measurement. (p. 364)

direct variation: A linear function defined by an equation of the form $y = kx$, where k is a nonzero real number. (p. 397)

discriminant: A portion of the quadratic formula that is under a radical sign, $b^2 - 4ac$. (p. 545)

disjunction: A logical intersection of two statements connected by the word *or*. (p. 176)

domain: The set of all first coordinates of a relation. (p. 378)

double root: A root which appears twice as a factor. (p. 269)

empty set: The only set containing no members, symbolized by $\varnothing$. (p. 32)

equation: Two expressions with an equals symbol between them. (p. 30)

equivalent equations: Equations that have the same solution set. (p. 89)

equivalent expressions: Expressions that are equal for all values of their variables for which the expressions have meaning. (p. 19)

even integer: An integer divisible by 2. (p. 135)

event: A specific outcome which is a subset of the sample space. (p. 603)

exponent: The number which tells how many times the base of a power, such as 3^2, is used as a factor. (p. 9)

extraneous solution: A solution of a derived equation that is not a solution of the original equation. (pp. 338, 526)

extremes: The numbers a and d in the equation $\frac{a}{b} = \frac{c}{d}$, where $b \neq 0$ and $d \neq 0$. (p. 343)

factoring by grouping: A method of grouping terms to find a common binomial factor. (p. 264)

factors: Numbers or groups of numbers that are multiplied. (p. 9)

formula: In a formula, variables and symbols are used to show how quantities are related. (p. 9)

frequency table: A representation used to summarize statistical data. (p. 610)

function: A relation in which no two ordered pairs have the same first coordinate. (p. 378)

graph: The set of points on a number line or in a coordinate plane that correspond to a number, an ordered pair, or a relation. (p. 41)

greatest common factor (GCF): The largest integer that is a common factor of two or more integers. (p. 244)

grouping symbols: Parentheses ( ) and brackets [ ] that are used to clarify or to change the order of operations. (p. 5)

half-planes: Two regions of a coordinate plane that are separated by a boundary line. (p. 433)

histogram: A type of bar graph that is used to illustrate a set of data. (p. 615)

hypothesis: The *if* clause in a conditional statement. (p. 116)

hypotenuse: The side that is opposite the right angle in a right triangle. (p. 579)

identity: An equation that is true for any value from the replacement set of the variable. (p. 103)

independent events: Separate events whose outcomes do not affect each other. (p. 604)

inequality: Two expressions with an inequality symbol between them. (p. 30)

integers: The set of whole numbers and their opposites: $\{..., -3, -2, -1, 0, 1, 2, 3, ...\}$. (p. 41)

inverse variation: A function defined by an equation of the form $xy = k$, or $y = \dfrac{k}{x}$, where k is a nonzero real number. (p. 401)

irrational number: A number that cannot be expressed as the quotient of two integers. (p. 497)

isosceles triangle: A triangle with two congruent sides. (p. 140)

least common denominator (LCD): The LCM of all denominators in a group of fractions by which the fractions can be multiplied to eliminate the denominators. (p. 144)

least common multiple (LCM): The smallest number that is divisible by a group of numbers. (p. 144)

like terms: Terms that include the same variables and their corresponding exponents. (p. 26)

linear combination method: A method for solving a system of linear equations in two variables using addition with multiplication. (p. 464)

linear function: A function of one variable, which has a line as its graph. (p. 392)

literal equation: An equation with more than one variable in which one of the variables can be expressed in terms of the other variables. (p. 349)

mathematical sentence: A statement that indicates a relationship between numerical or variable expressions. (p. 30)

maximum point: A point on a curve whose y-coordinate is greater than or equal to the y-coordinate of every other point on the curve. (p. 559)

maximum value: The y-coordinate of the maximum point. (p. 559)

mean: See *Arithmetic mean*. (p. 608)

means: In the equation $\dfrac{a}{b} = \dfrac{c}{d}$, where $b \neq 0$ and $d \neq 0$, the means are b and c. (p. 343)

median: The middle score or the mean of two middle scores of an ordered set of data. (p. 609)

minimum point: A point on a curve whose y-coordinate is less than or equal to the y-coordinate of every other point on the curve. (p. 559)

minimum value: The y-coordinate of the minimum point. (p. 559)

mode: The value that occurs most frequently in a set of data. (p. 609)

monomial: A variable, or a product of a numeral and one or more variables. (p. 201)

null set: See *empty set*. (p. 31)

numerical coefficient: A number by which a variable or a product of variables is multiplied; also simply called a *coefficient*. (p. 26)

numerical expression: An expression that contains one or more numbers involving one or more operations. (p. 1)

odd integer: An integer that is not divisible by 2. (p. 136)

open half-plane: A half-plane that does not include the boundary line. (p. 433)

open sentence: A mathematical sentence that contains at least one variable. (p. 31)

opposites: Like numbers with opposite signs whose sum is zero. (p. 45)

ordered pair: A pair of numbers that corresponds to a point in a coordinate plane. (p. 373)

origin: The point at which the axes intersect in a coordinate plane. (p. 373)

parabola: A graph of any equation of the form $y = ax^2 + bx + c$, where $a \neq 0$. (p. 559)

parallel lines: Coplanar lines with equal slopes. The lines do not intersect. (p. 429)

percent: *per hundred*, or *hundredths*. For example, 6% means six per hundred, or six hundredths. (p. 150)

perfect square: A positive rational number whose principal square root is rational. (p. 501)

Perfect Square Trinomial: A trinomial that can be factored as a perfect square of binomials.
$a^2 + 2ab + b^2 = (a + b)^2$
$a^2 - 2ab + b^2 = (a - b)^2$. (p. 260)

perimeter: A measure of the distance around the boundary of a figure. (p. 13)

perpendicular lines: Lines that have slopes whose product is -1, and intersect at an angle of measure 90. (p. 430)

point-slope form: The form of an equation of a line with slope m and containing point $P(x_1, y_1)$: $y - y_1 = m(x - x_1)$. (p. 418)

polynomial: A monomial or the sum of two or more monomials. (p. 218)

power: The third power of 5 is written as 5^3. The raised three is called an exponent. An exponent indicates how many times a number is used as a factor. (p. 9)

prime factorization: A factorization in which all the factors are prime numbers. (p. 244)

prime number: An integer greater than 1 whose only positive factors are 1 and itself. (p. 243)

principal square root: The positive *square root* of a number. (p. 500)

probability of an event: A ratio between 0 and 1 that describes how likely it is that a particular event will occur. (p. 599)

proportion: An equation which states that two ratios are equal. (p. 343)

Proportion Property: For all real numbers a, b, c, and d, if $\frac{a}{b} = \frac{c}{d}$, then $ad = bc$. The product of the *extremes* equals the product of the *means*. (p. 343)

Pythagorean Theorem: If triangle ABC is a right triangle with c the length of the hypotenuse and a and b the lengths of the legs, then $c^2 = a^2 + b^2$. (p. 508)

quadrant: One-fourth of a coordinate plane, as divided by the x-and y-axes. (p. 374)

quadratic equation: A second degree equation of the form $ax^2 + bx + c = 0$, where $a \neq 0$. (p. 268)

quadratic formula: The solutions of a quadratic equation of the form $ax^2 + bx + c = 0$, where $a \neq 0$, are given by this formula: $x = \frac{-b \pm \sqrt{b^2 - 4ac}}{2a}$. (p. 544)

quadratic function: An equation of the form $y = ax^2 + bx + c$, where $a \neq 0$. (p. 558)

quadratic polynomial: A polynomial of degree 2. (p. 268)

radical: The expression $\sqrt{49}$, is called a *radical*. The $\sqrt{}$ is a *radical sign,* and the number under the radical sign is called the *radicand*. (p. 500)

range of a relation: The set of all second coordinates of the relation. (p. 378)

range of a set of data: The difference between the greatest and least values in a set of data. (p. 619)

ratio: the comparison of two numbers by division. (p. 343)

rational equation: An equation that contains one or more rational expressions. (p. 337)

rational number: A real number that can be expressed in the form $\frac{a}{b}$, where a and b are integers and $b \neq 0$. (p. 495)

real number: The set of positive and negative numbers including all rational numbers, all irrational numbers, and 0. (pp. 42, 497)

reciprocal: Two numbers are called reciprocals, or *multiplicative inverses*, of each other if their product is 1; 4 and $\frac{1}{4}$ are reciprocals, since $4 \cdot \frac{1}{4} = 1$. (p. 68)

relation: A set of ordered pairs. (p. 378)

replacement set: The set of numbers that can replace a variable. (p. 30)

right triangle: A triangle with one angle of measure 90. (p. 508)

rise: The vertical change from one point to another in the slope of a line. (p. 413)

roots: The solutions of an open sentence. (p. 268)

run: The horizontal change from one point to another in the slope of a line. (p. 413)

sample space: The set of all possible outcomes. (p. 603)

scatter plot: A graph of ordered pairs that indicates the kind of relation that may exist between variables. When the relation is linear, a line approximating the points is drawn and then used to make predictions. (p. 614)

scientific notation: A number in the form $a \times 10^n$, where $1 < a < 10$ and n is an integer. (p. 214)

similar triangles: Triangles that have the same shape based on corresponding congruent angles. (p. 575)

sine ratio: The sine of an acute angle of a right triangle is the ratio of the length of the side that is opposite the acute angle to the length of the hypotenuse. (p. 580)

slope: A description of the steepness of a line, defined by the ratio of the vertical distance to the horizontal distance between any two points on the line. (p. 414)

slope-intercept form: If a line has slope m and y-intercept b, then the slope-intercept form of an equation of the line is $y = mx + b$. (p. 424)

solution set: The set of all numbers from a given replacement set that make an open sentence true. (p. 31)

square root: One of two equal factors of a number. (p. 500)

standard deviation: A measure s of the dispersion of a set of data, $x_1, x_2, x_3, \ldots$ x_n about the mean x for that set, defined by

$$s = \sqrt{\frac{(x_1 - x)^2 + (x_2 - x)^2 + (x_3 - x)^2 + \ldots + (x_n - x)^2}{n}}$$

where n is the number of values in the set. (p. 619)

subset: If all members of a set X are also members of a set Y, then X is said to be a subset of Y. (p. 498)

substitution method: A method for solving a system of linear equations in two variables, based on the Substitution Property. (p. 452)

supplementary: When the sum of the measures of two angles is 180, the angles are supplementary. (p. 346)

system of linear equations: A set of two or more linear equations in the same variables. (p. 445)

tangent ratio: The tangent of an acute angle of a right triangle is the ratio of the length of the side that is opposite the acute angle to the length of the side adjacent to the angle. (p. 580)

term: In the expression $7x^2 + 8xy + 9$, $7x^2$, $8xy$, and 9 are the terms of the expression. (p. 26)

then-clause: The conclusion in a conditional statement. (p. 116)

tree diagram: A diagram that can be used to determine or illustrate a *sample space*. (p. 603)

trinomial: A polynomial with three terms. (p. 218)

truth table: A summary of the truth values of a conjunction or a disjunction. (p. 176)

value of a function: A member of the range of a function. (p. 383)

variable: A symbol that is used to represent one or more numbers. (p. 1)

vertex of a parabola: The maximum or minimum point of the graph of a parabola. (p. 559)

volume: The number of cubic units contained in a solid figure. (p. 14)

x- and y-axes: The horizontal and vertical number lines in a coordinate plane which intersect at the *origin*. (p. 373)

x- and y-coordinates: In an ordered pair of numbers, the x-coordinate is the first number in the pair and the y-coordinate is the second number. (p. 374)

x-intercept: The x-coordinate of the point where a line intersects the x-axis. (p. 424)

y-intercept: The y-coordinate of the point where a line intersects the y-axis. (p. 424)

zero exponent: For each nonzero real number b, $b^0 = 1$ (0^0 is undefined). (p. 210)

Selected Answers

Answers are provided to the odd-numbered problems for the Written Exercises, the Midchapter Reviews, the Mixed Problem Solving, and the Problem Solving Strategies.

Chapter 1

Written Exercises, pages 3–4

1. 63 **3.** 8 **5.** 20 **7.** 15 **9.** 42 **11.** 4
13. $0.89y$ **15.** $\frac{x}{7}$ **17.** $365 - s$ **19.** $\frac{2}{3}g$
21. $c + 3$ **23.** $\frac{3}{4}s$ **25.** $\frac{1}{3}b$ **27.** $0.2p$
29. 30.7 **31.** 30.6 **33.** 3 **35.** 1.2 **37.** 5.2
39. 90 **41.** 0.0351 **43.** 4.1 **45.** $\frac{3}{4}$ **47.** $\frac{7}{20}$
49. 15.5 **51.** $x + 4$ **53.** $3d$

Written Exercises, pages 7–8

1. 114 **3.** 8 **5.** 0 **7.** 45 **9.** 4 **11.** 9
13. 9 **15.** 2 **17.** 7 **19.** 1 **21.** 3 **23.** 45
25. 20 **27.** 22 **29.** 28 **31.** 5.5 **33.** 1.5
35. 38 **37.** 0 **39.** 12 **41.** 20 **43.** 4
45. $360 - 8w$ **47.** $10p + 65t$ **49.** Some calculators obey the order of operations, others do not.

Written Exercises, pages 11–12

1. 81 **3.** 100,000 **5.** 54 **7.** 1,000
9. 52 **11.** 1,600 **13.** 400 **15.** 9
17. 84 **19.** 66 **21.** 4,600 **23.** 2
25. 8 **27.** 0 **29.** 7 **31.** 3 **33.** 5 m
35. 180 m **37.** 11.25 m **39.** 9 **41.** 6
43. 148 **45.** 0 **47.** 405 **49.** 1
51. 100 ft **53.** 16 ft **55.** 64 ft **57.** 196 ft
59. 14 **61.** 162 **63.** $\frac{1}{64}$

Written Exercises, pages 15–16

1. 36 ft **3.** 20.8 cm **5.** 42 ft **7.** 64 yd^2
9. $\frac{1}{4}$ in^2 **11.** 176 m^2 **13.** 10 ft^2 **15.** 25 cm^2
17. 56 ft^2 **19.** 60 m^2 **21.** 343 ft^3
23. 0.512 cm^3 **25.** $p = 49$ m, $A = 137$ m^2
27. $A = 20$ m^2 **29.** 57 in **31.** 19 yd
33. 63 in **35.** 254 in^2 **37.** 13 yd^2
39. 452 ft^2 **41.** Perimeter is doubled.
43. It will be multiplied by 8.

Midchapter Review, page 16

1. 17 **3.** 27 **5.** 28 **7.** 10 **9.** $x + 7$, or $7 + x$ **11.** $79y$ **13.** $p = 22$ in, $A = 28$ in^2

Written Exercises, page 20

1. Comm Prop Add **3.** Assoc Prop Mult
5. $299 + 73 + 1 = 299 + 1 + 73 = 300 + 73 = 373$ **7.** $15 \cdot 7 \cdot 2 = 15 \cdot 2 \cdot 7 = 30 \cdot 7 = 210$
9. $50 \cdot 14 \cdot 2 = 50 \cdot 2 \cdot 14 = 100 \cdot 14 = 1,400$
11. $20 \cdot 43 \cdot 5 = 20 \cdot 5 \cdot 43 = 100 \cdot 43 = 4,300$
13. $\frac{1}{4} + 18 + \frac{3}{4} = \frac{1}{4} + \frac{3}{4} + 18 = 1 + 18 = 19$
15. $\frac{2}{3} \cdot 17 \cdot 3 = \frac{2}{3} \cdot 3 \cdot 17 = 2 \cdot 17 = 34$
17. $32m$ **19.** $15k$ **21.** $42y$ **23.** $64d$
25. Assoc Prop Add **27.** Comm Prop Add
29. $299 + 57 + 3 + 1 = 299 + 1 + 57 + 3 = 300 + 60 = 360$ **31.** $688 + 289 + 12 + 11 = 688 + 12 + 289 + 11 = 700 + 300 = 1,000$
33. $(0.5) \cdot 27 \cdot 2 = (0.5) \cdot 2 \cdot 27 = 1 \cdot 27 = 27$
35. $2\frac{3}{7} + 399 + 3\frac{4}{7} + 1 = 2\frac{3}{7} + 3\frac{4}{7} + 399 + 1 = 6 + 400 = 406$ **37.** $\frac{1}{2} \cdot 25 \cdot 12 \cdot 4 = \frac{1}{2} \cdot 12 \cdot 25 \cdot 4 = 6 \cdot 100 = 600$ **39.** $96y$ **41.** $1,300g$
43. $60b$ **45.** No. By the Assoc Prop Mult, $6(3x) = (6 \cdot 3)x = 18x$. Thus, the two expressions, $6(3x)$ and $18x$ are equivalent and they are equal for all values of x. **47.** No. Let $a = 1$ and $b = 2$. In this case, $a \div b \neq b \div a$; $1 \div 2 \neq 2 \div 1 \left(\frac{1}{2} \neq 2\right)$.

Written Exercises, pages 24–25

1. $8 \cdot 7 + 8 \cdot 6$; 104 **3.** $4 \cdot 3 + 8 \cdot 3$; 36
5. $\frac{1}{2} \cdot 8 + \frac{1}{2} \cdot 4 + \frac{1}{2} \cdot 2$; 7 **7.** $\frac{1}{4} \cdot 28 - \frac{1}{4} \cdot 16$; 3
9. $8(7 + 3)$; 80 **11.** $(8 + 12)4$; 80
13. $(4 + 5 + 8)7$; 119 **15.** $4 \cdot 3a - 4 \cdot 9$; $12a - 36$ **17.** $x \cdot 4 - 5 \cdot 4$; $4x - 20$ **19.** $\frac{3}{4} \cdot 8x + \frac{3}{4} \cdot 12$; $6x + 9$ **21.** $\frac{2}{3} \cdot 6x - \frac{2}{3} \cdot 12$; $4x + 8$ **23.** $1.5 \cdot 2x + 1.5 \cdot 3$; $3x + 4.5$
25. $3 \cdot 4.1x - 6 \cdot 3$; $12.3x - 18$ **27.** $4c \cdot 1.5 - 2b \cdot 1.5 + 1 \cdot 1.5$; $6c - 3b + 1.5$ **29.** $6 \cdot 40 + 6 \cdot 3$; 258 **31.** $7 \cdot 49 = 7 \cdot 50 - 7 \cdot 1 = 350 - 7 = 343$ **33.** $49 \cdot 3 + 49 \cdot 7 = 49(3 + $

7) $= 49 \cdot 10 = 490$ **35.** $\frac{1}{2} \cdot 47 + \frac{1}{2} \cdot 3 = \frac{1}{2}(47 +$

3) $= \frac{1}{2} \cdot 50 = 25$ **37.** $15 \cdot \frac{3}{4} + 5 \cdot \frac{3}{4} = (15 +$

5) $\frac{3}{4} = 20 \cdot \frac{3}{4} = 15$ **39.** Answers will vary.

41. Distr Prop   **43.** Comm Prop of Add
45. Assoc Prop Mult   **47.** Assoc Prop Mult
49. Distr Prop   **51.** No. Examples will vary.
53. Yes.

Written Exercises, pages 28–29

1. $5m$ **3.** Not possible   **5.** $10x$ **7.** $7a + 7$
9. $12y$ **11.** $15a$ **13.** $20 + 7a$
15. $11x + 10y$ **17.** $11m + 6$ **19.** $16x + 24$
21. $9y + 14$ **23.** $2b + 5$ **25.** $-3x - 4$
27. $3x + 9$ **29.** $7\frac{1}{5}c$ **31.** $14\frac{1}{4}m + 10\frac{1}{4}$
33. $20x + 20$ **35.** $12x + 42$ **37.** $8x + 9$
39. $4a + 12$ **41.** $22a + 19$; 129
43. $21b + 40$; 124   **45.** $25y + 18$, 243
47. $202x + 149$ **49.** $229k + 120$

Written Exercises, pages 33–34

1. T   **3.** F   **5.** T   **7.** T   **9.** T
11. {0, 1, 2, 3}   **13.** $\emptyset$ **15.** {0, 1, 3}
17. {5}   **19.** {3, 5}   **21.** $\emptyset$ **23.** {5}   **25.** {5}
27. {5}   **29.** {5, 10}   **31.** {0, 5}   **33.** {5}
35. F; if $x = 1$ and $y - 2$, $x - y \neq y - x$.
37. F   **39.** T   **41.** {2}   **43.** $\emptyset$

Problem Solving Strategies, page 35

1. a. number of people, total cost
   b. How much is each person's share?
   c. dollars
3. a. the total observation time, how the three
   students share the observation time
   b. How many hours must Ed observe the
   experiment?
   c. hours

Chapter 2

Written Exercises, pages 43–44

1. -3 **3.** 2   **5.** $\frac{1}{4}$ **7.** $-1\frac{3}{4}$

9, 11, 13, 15.

17. 20   **19.** 8   **21.** -3 **23.** $3\frac{1}{2}$
25. 236.25   **27.** -4.2 **29.** $>$ **31.** $<$
33. $<$ **35.** $>$ **37.** $<$ **39.** $>$ **41.** $>$
43. $<$ **45.** $>$ **47.** $>$ **49.** $>$ **51.** $<$
53. $>$ **55.** $<$ **57.** T   **59.** F   **61.** T
63. T   **65.** T   **67.** F

Written Exercises, pages 47–48

1. -2 **3.** 0   **5.** 3   **7.** -0.5 **9.** 10
11. -2 **13.** -7 **15.** -17 **17.** 3   **19.** 1
21. 1   **23.** 0.8   **25.** -3 **27.** 3   **29.** 3
31. 5   **33.** 54   **35.** -6 **37.** 11   **39.** 12
41. 12   **43.** 48   **45.** 18   **47.** 8   **49.** -5;
gaining 5 lb; 5   **51.** 8; 8-degree increase; 8
53. 12; 12 ft below sea level; -12 **55.** F,
$-6 < -2$ **57.** T, $-2 < 2$ **59.** T, $8 = 8$
61. F, $\frac{3}{4} > \frac{1}{2}$ **63.** T, $16 = 16$ **65.** T, $0 < 1$
67. $=$ **69.** $<$ **71.** $=$ **73.** $>$ **75.** $=$
77. $>$ **79.** If $x < 0$ then $|x| = -x$. Absolute
value of a number may equal the opposite of the
number.   **81.** T   **83.** F; for $x < 0$, $|x| - x$.
85. T   **87.** F; for $x < 0$, then $x < -x$.

Written Exercises, pages 51–52

1. 10   **3.** 15   **5.** -3 **7.** 0   **9.** -1
11. -10 **13.** 0   **15.** 0   **17.** -3 **19.** 0
21. 0   **23.** -9 **25.** 0   **27.** 2   **29.** 0
31. 10   **33.** -16 **35.** -3 **37.** Let a and b
be any positive real number; $-a + (-b) =$
$-(a + b)$, -161 **39.** No, let $a = 2$ and
$b = -1$; then $|a + b| = |2 + (-1)| = |1| = 1$.
Yet $|a| + |b| = |2| + |-1| = 2 + 1 = 3$. Not true
for all numbers.

Written Exercises, page 55–56

1. 13   **3.** -13 **5.** -2 **7.** -8 **9.** -8
11. -17 **13.** 0   **15.** -3.6 **17.** 7.7
19. -10.8 **21.** 5.3   **23.** 18   **25.** 3-yd loss
27. 4-lb loss   **29.** -7 **31.** $4\frac{1}{5}$ **33.** $4\frac{5}{6}$
35. -3 **37.** -17 **39.** 10   **41.** 5
43. -26 **45.** 26   **47.** $7.5 + (-0.9) = 6.6$;
$-0.9 + 7.5 = 6.6$ **49.** $(2.6 + (-1.4)) +$
$(-0.7) = 1.2 + (-0.7) = 0.5$ **51.** 197 ft
below sea level.   **53.** 5:17 P.M.

Written Exercises, pages 59–60

1. 6 **3.** −8 **5.** 9 **7.** −6 **9.** −15
11. 0 **13.** −16 **15.** 18 **17.** 0
19. −34 **21.** −14 **23.** 24 **25.** 40
27. −68 **29.** −6.5 **31.** 2.2 **33.** 2.6
35. 3.8 **37.** $\frac{1}{4}$ **39.** $-\frac{3}{8}$ **41.** −2 **43.** 10
45. −16 **47.** −13 **49.** −3 **51.** 15
53. 101 **55.** −40 **57.** 12 **59.** 2 **61.** 6
63. 1 **65.** −1 **67.** 19 **69.** 2.25 kg
71. −219°C **73.** 7 **75.** −7 **77.** 7
79. 7 **81.** 19 **83.** −3 **85.** They are
opposites (add inverses). **87.** No. If $a = 2$,
then $2 - e = e - 2$, only if $e = 2$. Since e is
unique, its value must be 2 for all values of a. If
$a = 5, 5 - 2 = 3$ and $2 - 5 = -3$. Since $3 \neq$
$-3, 5 - 2 \neq 2 - 5$, that is, $5 - e \neq e - 5$.
Since "$a - e = e - a$" is not true for $a = 5$, it
is not true for all real numbers. **89.** No; let a
and b equal any two whole numbers such that a
$< b$. Then $a - b < 0$. A negative number is not
in the set of whole numbers. Therefore, the set
of whole numbers is not closed under subtraction.

Midchapter Review, page 60

1. 5 **3.** 4 **5.** 15 **7.** −14.3 **9.** −3
11. 42 **13.** −15 **15.** 5 **17.** −15
19. 65,200 ft

Written Exercises, pages 65–66

1. 0 **3.** 30 **5.** 0 **7.** −81 **9.** 24
11. 48 **13.** −3 **15.** 2 **17.** 3.2 **19.** 0
21. 8 **23.** −45 **25.** 90 **27.** 144
29. −6 **31.** −20 **33.** 25 **35.** 36
37. −120 **39.** 100 **41.** −19 **43.** 3
45. 400 **47.** −500 **49.** 49 **51.** 9
53. 945 **55.** −120 **57.** 40 **59.** 27
61. −864 **63.** 288 **65.** 14°F **67.** −512
69. 80 **71.** −216 **73.** −68 **75.** F; the
square of a negative number equals the product
of 2 negative numbers which is always a positive
number. **77.** T; a negative number raised to
an even power equals the product of an even
number of negative numbers. This results in a
product of a string of positive numbers; result
always positive. **79.** F; result always zero.

Written Exercises, pages 70–71

1. 4 **3.** −4 **5.** −4 **7.** −5 **9.** −25
11. 0 **13.** −6 **15.** 20 **17.** −2
19. Undef **21.** $-\frac{3}{2}$ **23.** $-\frac{1}{6}$ **25.** −21

27. $\frac{1}{2}$ **29.** 1 **31.** 9 **33.** −9 **35.** $675
profit **37.** $-\frac{3}{40}$ per day **39.** $4\frac{2}{3}$ **41.** $-1\frac{1}{5}$
43. −1 **45., 47.** Answers will vary.

Written Exercises, page 74

1. 25 **3.** −22 **5.** −43 **7.** 24 **9.** −6
11. −9 **13.** −7 **15.** 12 **17.** 0 **19.** 6
21. 24 **23.** 9 **25.** 18 **27.** −1 **29.** 0
31. −3 **33.** 22 **35.** 82 **37.** 15
39. −616 **41.** 1

Written Exercises, pages 77–78

1. $5y$ **3.** $-6a$ **5.** $-3a$ **7.** $-7x$
9. $-5r$ **11.** $-11c$ **13.** $2b$ **15.** $11c$
17. $-6x$ **19.** $1.6c$ **21.** $-5z - 10$
23. $2y + 1$ **25.** $3b - 4$ **27.** $-4b + 2$
29. $-b - 7$ **31.** $8x$ **33.** $-5a$
35. $2b + 4$ **37.** $-b + 4$ **39.** $-c + 5$
41. $-k - m$ **43.** $x - 6$ **45.** $-7r + s$
47. $-3y$ **49.** $-0.9g - t$ **51.** 6 **53.** −5
55. 6 **57.** $p = 6x - 2y$ **59.** $p = 18a + 4b - 8$
61. $A = 2hs + s^2$ **63.** $x + 2y$, 8.6
65. $-x + 9, 6\frac{2}{5}$ **67.** $-a - b, -3\frac{1}{2}$
69. $-0.06x - 4.1z + 4.3$, 4.2836
71. $-0.08x + 0.3y + 3z + 2.3$, 3.062

Written Exercises, pages 80–81

1. $-21 - 28x$ **3.** $a - 2b - 8$ **5.** $7x - 20$
7. $-5p - 19$ **9.** $-19d + 42$ **11.** $5x - 5$
13. $-a - 2$ **15.** $7z - 12$ **17.** $-3a - 2$
19. $-33x + 14$ **21.** $-29y + 33$
23. $-27x - 48$ **25.** $-x - 1$; −6
27. $-2z - 3$; −3.4 **29.** $33 - 23y$; 56
31. $-4z - 2$; −1.2 **33.** $22z - 39$; −83
35. $7r - 1$; −15.7 **37.** $-10n - 10$; −2
39. $7m + 22$ **41.** $-7x + 10$ **43.** $2x - 7$
45. $7x + 14$ **47.** $2y - 46$ **49.** $3ax - ay$
51. $-ax$ **53.** $2ce - de$

Chapter 3

Written Exercises, pages 92–93

1. 53 **3.** 17 **5.** 5 **7.** −9 **9.** −2
11. −1 **13.** 0 **15.** −3 **17.** −4 **19.** 6
21. 0 **23.** $n + 9 = 42$; 33 **25.** $p - 35 = 85$;
$120 **27.** 13.9 **29.** −6.0 **31.** 5.3
33. $18\frac{2}{3}$ **35.** 903.12 **37.** 774.06 **39.** The

new equation, $0 = x + 2$, does not have x alone on one side. **41.** $\{2, -2\}$ **43.** The set of real numbers **45.** $\emptyset$ **47.** $\{12\}$

Written Exercises, pages 96–97

1. 5 **3.** -12 **5.** 6 **7.** -24 **9.** 21
11. -40 **13.** 24 **15.** -18 **17.** $7n = -84$; -12 **19.** $5x = 15$; 3 h **21.** $5(43)n = 10,000$; 47 days **23.** $\frac{2}{21}$ **25.** $\frac{1}{12}$
27. -8 **29.** 6 **31.** -20 **33.** 4 **35.** 0
37. To divide by a number is to multiply by its reciprocal. **39.** $\{27, -27\}$ **41.** $\emptyset$
43. $\{-15, 15\}$ **45.** The set of real numbers < 0

Written Exercises, pages 99–100

1. -5 **3.** 2 **5.** 1 **7.** -2 **9.** -2
11. 6 **13.** 9 **15.** 7 **17.** -4 **19.** 20
21. -27 **23.** -5 **25.** 12 **27.** 11 **29.** 8
31. $5n - 6 = 34$; 8 **33.** $3c + 35 = 347$; \$104
35. $5m - 17 = 28$; 9 **37.** $3x + 2 = 17$; 5 h

39. 9 **41.** 1.5 **43.** $-\frac{1}{24}$ **45.** -0.02

47. -0.2 **49.** $\frac{3}{4}$ **51.** $\frac{1}{8}$ **53.** $-\frac{13}{14}$

55. 0

Midchapter Review, page 100

1. 12 **3.** 7 **5.** -6 **7.** 4 **9.** $3\frac{1}{3}$ **11.** 4

13. $\frac{1}{3}n = 18$; 54

Problem Solving Strategies, page 101

Answers will vary. Possible answers are given.
1. c, e, f **3.** d, e **5.** a, b, e

Written Exercises, pages 104–105

1. 3 **3.** 4 **5.** -5 **7.** 5 **9.** -12 **11.** 3
13. 11 **15.** 6 **17.** -14 **19.** -2 **21.** -2
23. -2 **25.** $x + 30 = 2x$; \$30
27. $2x + 10 = 4x$; 5 **29.** $5x - 3 - 3x + 37$; 20 yr old **31.** $120 + 150x = 180x$; 4 cars
33. 11 **35.** The set of real numbers
37. $\left\{-1\frac{1}{2}\right\}$ **39.** $\emptyset$ **41.** The set of real numbers **43.** $\emptyset$ **45.** $\{2, -2\}$ **47.** $\emptyset$
49. $\emptyset$

Written Exercises, pages 107–108

1. 1 **3.** -8 **5.** 2 **7.** 2 **9.** -1 **11.** 2
13. -4 **15.** 1 **17.** -3 **19.** $5(x + 3) = 35$; 4 **21.** $x + 5 = 4(x + 8)$; -9
23. $2(x + 5) = x + 38$; 28 yr **25.** $10 + 4(x - 2) = 50$; 12 tables **27.** $-\frac{1}{6}$ **29.** 4

31. $-1\frac{2}{9}$

Written Exercises, pages 112–113

1. 216 tickets **3.** 450 **5.** 50 mi/h **7.** $\frac{1}{5}$ h, or 12 min **9.** 2 **11.** 2.3 **13.** 20 lb/in^2
15. 8 in **17.** 46.7 mi/h **19.** Approximately 18.3 blocks

Written Exercises, pages 117–118

1. Subt Prop Eq; Add Inverse Prop; Add Identity Prop; Mult Prop Eq; Mult Inverse Prop; Mult Identity Prop **3.** Given; Add Prop Eq; Assoc Prop Add; Add Inverse Prop; Add Identity Prop

5.

	Statements	Reasons
1.	$5x - 3 = 18$	1. Given
2.	$5x - 3 + 3 = 18 + 3$	2. Add Prop Eq
3.	$5x + 0 = 21$	3. Add Inverse Prop
4.	$5x = 21$	4. Add Identity Prop
5.	$\frac{5x}{5} = \frac{21}{5}$	5. Div Prop Eq
6.	$1 \cdot x = 4\frac{1}{5}$	6. Mult Inverse Prop
7.	$x = 4\frac{1}{5}$	7. Mult Identity Prop

7.

	Statements	Reasons
1.	$7 - 5a = 4$	1. Given
2.	$7 + (-5a) = 4$	2. Def Subt
3.	$-7 + 7 + (-5a) = -7 + 4$	3. Add Prop Eq
4.	$0 + (-5a) = -3$	4. Add In Prop
5.	$-5a = -3$	5. Add Id Prop
6.	$\frac{-5a}{-5} = \frac{-3}{-5}$	6. Div Prop Eq
7.	$1 \cdot a = \frac{3}{5}$	7. Mult In Prop
8.	$a = \frac{3}{5}$	8. Mult Id Prop

9.

Statements	Reasons
1. $a = b$	1. Given
2. $a - c = a - c$	2. Reflex Prop
3. $a - c = b - c$	3. Sub Prop

Thus, if $a = b$, then $a - c = b - c$.

11.

Statements	Reasons
1. $(ax + b) + ay = (b + ax) + ay$	1. Comm Prop Add
2. $\quad = b + (ax + ay)$	2. Assoc Prop Add
3. $\quad = b + a(x + y)$	3. Dist Prop
4. $\quad = a(x + y) + b$	4. Comm Prop Add
5. $(ax + b) + ay = a(x + y) + b$	5. Trans Prop of Eq

13.

Statements	Reasons
1. $mx + (a + x) = mx + (x + a)$	1. Comm Prop Add
2. $\quad = (mx + x) + a$	2. Assoc Prop Add
3. $\quad = (m + 1)x + a$	3. Dist Prop
4. $\quad = a + (m + 1)x$	4. Comm Prop Add
5. $mx + (a + x) = a + (m + 1)x$	5. Trans Prop of Eq

Mixed Problem Solving, page 119

1. $6.40/h   **3.** $90   **5.** 16,600   **7.** 9   **9.** 4
11. $301.33

Chapter 4

Written Exercises, pages 127–128

1. Let x = the amount of time Jeanie worked. Then $x - 2$ = time Bill worked.   **3.** Let x = the number of Bob's fish. Then $\frac{1}{2}x$ = number of Kate's fish.   **5.** $3m - 2$
7. $3s + 1$ **9.** Let x = Ron's points. Then $\frac{1}{3}x$ = Jason's points.   **11.** Let x = Josie's earnings. Then $2x + 5$ = Kyle's earnings.
13. Let l = last year's price. Then $l + \frac{1}{5}l$ = this year's price.   **15.** Pennies   **17.** n **19.** Cheese

21. $s + 4.50$ **23.** Let x = length of the second side. Then $x + 3.2$ = length of the first side and $x + 2$ = length of the third side.
25. $1,200 + 60n$ **27.** $330 - 15t$

Written Exercises, pages 132–134

1. 13, 52   **3.** Brian, 16; Gus, 23   **5.** Barry, 16 h; Clyde, 24 h   **7.** Dan: 90; Aaron: 168   **9.** 6 swordtails, 17 guppies   **11.** First, $420; second, $140   **13.** Cost: $60; profit: $70   **15.** Bessie: 9; Jean: 18   **17.** $28
19. Pump: $23; valve: $8   **21.** 8   **23.** Last month: $23.48; this month: $20.97   **25.** $65
27. Amy: $168; Katie: $42   **29.** 16   **31.** 77
33. First: -8; second: -2, third: 7   **35.** Shirt: $17, tie: $7, jacket: $60   **37.** Twin: $160, double: $240

Written Exercises, pages 137–138

1. 37, 38   **3.** 38, 40   **5.** No solution
7. No solution   **9.** 89, 91, 93   **11.** No solution   **13.** $-2, 0, 2, 4$ **15.** Never
17. Never   **19.** Always   **21.** No solution
23. Yes   **25.** n = integer; s = sum; $n = \dfrac{s - 6}{4}$

Written Exercises, pages 142–143

1. $l = 19.5$ cm; $w = 6.5$ cm   **3.** $l = 12$ ft; $w = 5$ ft   **5.** $l = 4$ ft; $w = 10$ ft   **7.** 60
9. Base: 9 km; legs: 13 km   **11.** First: 19 in; second: 12 in; third: 14 in   **13.** 13 yd, 18 yd, 21 yd   **15.** $A : 63°$; $B : 32°$; $C : 85°$ **17.** $l = 15$ cm; $w = 8$ cm   **19.** 232 ft

Midchapter Review, page 143

1. 37, 39, 41   **3.** Vertex: 85°; bases: 47.5°

Written Exercises, page 146

1. $c = 20$ **3.** $c = \dfrac{5}{6}$ **5.** $y = 2\dfrac{8}{9}$ **7.** $x = 3$
9. $x = 36$ **11.** $x = 6$ **13.** 30 yr   **15.** $500
17. $a = -1\dfrac{1}{9}$ **19.** $y = 24$ **21.** 16 and 18
23. $x = 6$

Written Exercises, pages 148–149

1. $x = 9$ **3.** $y = 7$ **5.** $c = 8$ **7.** $d = 34$
9. $r = 0.6$ **11.** $d = 172$ **13.** $q = 61$
15. $x = 1,240$ **17.** $z = 0.17$ **19.** $y = -60$
21. $n = -0.2$ **23.** $x = 10.02$ **25.** 9
27. $106,000   **29.** 0.02, 0.018   **31.** $12.50
33. 3°K

Written Exercises, pages 152–153

1. 9 **3.** 20% **5.** 50 **7.** 25.6 **9.** $57\frac{1}{7}$%

11. 700 **13.** 33.54 **15.** 37.5% **17.** 5.25
19. 75% **21.** 80% **23.** $1,125,000
25. $1,984 **27.** 20% **29.** $368 **31.** $4,000
33. 17% **35.** 2,232 **37.** No. 1988 earnings
were 280 + (0.15)(280) = $322; 1989 earnings
= 322 − (0.15)(322) = $273.70

Written Exercises, page 156

1. $169.34 **3.** $7.65 **5.** $300 **7.** $120
9. $13.60 price; $3.40 discount **11.** $1,000
13. 42 h **15.** $120

Problem Solving Strategies, page 157

1. 6h **3.** 17 and 19 **5.** 12, 14, 16

Chapter 5

Written Exercises, pages 168–169

1. $x > -3$

3. $z < -10$

5. $r < -7$

7. $y < 2\frac{1}{4}$

9. $d > -3\frac{2}{3}$

11. $y < -2\frac{1}{2}$

13. $y < -14.3$

15. $z > -10\frac{3}{4}$

17. $s + 6.25 < 50$; $s < 43.75 where $s =$
amount in savings before **19.** s 13 < 90;
$s < 103$ copies

21. $x < 26$

23. $c > 2.4$

25. No. 2 ≯ 2 **27.** By Add Prop Ineq, if $a <
b$, then $a + c < b + c$ and if $a > b$, then $a + c >
a + b$. Let $c = (-d)$. If $a < b$, then $a + (-d) <
b + (-d)$. Thus, $a - d < b - d$. If $a > b$, then
$a + (-d) > b + (-d)$. Thus, $a - d > b - d$.

Written Exercises, page 174

1. $y < 6$

3. $z > \frac{2}{7}$

5. $a < -15$

7. $x < -1$

9. $z > 2$

11. $y > -4\frac{1}{2}$

13. $x < -27$

15. $x > 3$

17. $\emptyset$

19. $x < -2$

655

21. $c > 1$

23. $\emptyset$

25. $c < 5$

27. $2x > 63$; $x > \$31.50$ **29.** $\frac{1}{3}x > 62$; $x > \$186$ **31.** $x > 16$ **33.** $c < -1$ **35.** $c > 8$
37. $x > -\frac{3}{5}$ **39.** $y > -1$ **41.** $x < b - a$

43. If $(a + b) > 0$ and $c > 0$ then $x < \frac{cd}{a + b}$;
if $(a + b) > 0$ and $c < 0$ then $x > \frac{cd}{a + b}$; if
$(a + b) < 0$ and $c > 0$ then $x > \frac{cd}{a + b}$; if
$(a + b) < 0$ and $c < 0$ then $x < \frac{cd}{a + b}$.

Written Exercises, pages 177–178

1. T **3.** F **5.** F **7.** T **9.** T **11.** $x > 110$ and $x < 115$ **13.** $x = 150$ or $x > 150$
15. 3 **17.** 0; (Answers 17–26 may vary.)
19. 0 **21.** 4 **23.** −4 **25.** No such value

27.

p	q	$\sim p$	$\sim q$	$\sim p$ and $\sim q$
T	T	F	F	F
T	F	F	T	F
F	T	T	F	F
F	F	T	T	T

29.

p	q	$\sim p$	$\sim q$	$\sim p$ or $\sim q$
T	T	F	F	F
T	F	F	T	T
F	T	T	F	T
F	F	T	T	T

31.

p	q	$\sim p$	$\sim p$ or q
T	T	F	T
T	F	F	F
F	T	T	T
F	F	T	T

Written Exercises, pages 183–184

1.

3.

5.

7.

9.

11.

13.

15.

17.

19.

21.

23.

25.

27.

29.

31.

33.

$-15 \quad -13 \quad -11$

35. 42, 56 **37.** $170 < d < 230$; 200 ± 30

39.

$\quad\quad 5$
$0 \quad 10 \quad 20$

41.

$-8 \quad 0 \quad 8$

43.

$\quad -9$
$-12 \quad -6 \quad 0 \quad 6$

45.

$\quad\quad 3$
$0 \quad 2 \quad 4$

47.

$a \quad 0 \quad -a$

49.

$b \quad\quad a$

51.

$a \quad 0 \quad b$

Midchapter Review, page 184

1. $x < 6$

$-6 \quad 0 \quad 6$

3. $x > -2$

$-2 \quad 0 \quad 2$

5. $y \geq -13$

$\quad -13$
$-26 \quad 0 \quad 26$

7. T **9.** F
11.

$\quad\quad 7$
$0 \quad 14 \quad 28$

13.

$-11 \quad -5$
$-12 \quad -8 \quad -4 \quad 0$

Problem Solving Strategies, page 185

1. Units are missing from answer; 4π ft^2
3. Answer doesn't make sense; 1181.8

Written Exercises, pages 188–189

1. $3x + 5 \geq 95$ **3.** $x + 4x \leq 40$
5. $x \geq 75$ **7.** $x \geq 9$ **9.** (1,2); (2,3); (3,4);
(4,5); (5,6); (6,7) **11.** (6,8); (4,6); (2,4)
13. $5 < x \leq 7$ **15.** $-2 < x < 5$

17. $75{,}000 < x < 137{,}500$ **19.** $-34 < x < 6$
21. "3 less than x" is written as $x - 3$. "3 is
less than x" is written as $3 < x$. The expressions
are not the same.

Written Exercises, page 191

1. $4, -4$ **3.** $3, -3$ **5.** $9, -1$ **7.** No
solution **9.** $3, -3$ **11.** No solution
13. $6, -2$ **15.** $-4, -6$ **17.** $3, 11$ **19.** $=$

Written Exercises, page 194

1.

$-4 \quad 0 \quad 4$

3.

$-4 \quad 0 \quad 4$

5.

$-11 \quad\quad 3$
$-12 \quad -6 \quad 0 \quad 6$

7.

$1 \quad\quad 7$
$0 \quad 4 \quad 8$

9.

$-3 \quad\quad 7$
$-4 \quad 0 \quad 4 \quad 8$

11.

$-7 \quad\quad 3$
$-8 \quad -4 \quad 0 \quad 4$

13.

$\quad 1$
$-6 \quad 0 \quad 6$

15.

$-5 \quad\quad 9$
$-6 \quad 0 \quad 6 \quad 12$

17.

$-\frac{1}{2} \quad\quad 5\frac{1}{2}$
$-4 \quad 0 \quad 4 \quad 8$

19.

$\frac{1}{2}$
$0 \quad 2 \quad 4$

21. $|x| < 8$

$-8 \quad 0 \quad 8$

23. $|x - 10{,}000| < 2{,}000$

$\quad 10{,}000$
$8{,}000 \quad 12{,}000$

25.

27.

29.

31.

33.

Mixed Problem Solving, page 195

1. \$1,730 **3.** 5° F **5.** 4.7 km **7.** 10 weeks
9. 59° **11.** $x - 2, x + 2$ **13.** Apprentice:
\$19; electrician: \$25.50

Chapter 6

Written Exercises, page 203

1. $2x^4$ **3.** $4a^4b^2$ **5.** z^4 **7.** $12a^7$
9. $-50yz^3$ **11.** $-12b^8$ **13.** $-10x^3y^3$
15. x^2y^2 **17.** $-6x^4y^3z^2$ **19.** $30x^6$
21. $-42z^7$ **23.** $-3x^2y^4z$ **25.** $32x^3y^2$
27. $-12x^3y^3z^2$ **29.** $x^3y^2; -4$ **31.** x^{a+b}
33. z^{2x-1} **35.** 3 **37.** Example answers may
vary. F; $x = 2$

Written Exercises, pages 205–206

1. y^{12} **3.** y^7 **5.** $9c^2$ **7.** -729 **9.** $-r^3$
11. $-c^5$ **13.** $25y^6$ **15.** a^8b^4 **17.** x^4y^4
19. $x^4y^2z^6$ **21.** $32a^{20}b^5c^{10}$ **23.** $-125x^6y^9z^3$
25. $4x^7$ **27.** a^8b^2 **29.** $\frac{1}{3}a^3$ **31.** $-24c^4d^3$
33. $72x^{17}$ **35.** $-3a^9b^7$ **37.** $x^{10}y^2; 9$
39. $8x^{12}y^3; 216$ **41.** Pos **43.** Zero
45. Pos **47.** 2 **49.** 2 **51.** 3,6

Written Exercises, page 209

1. 25 **3.** 1 **5.** $\frac{1}{z^8}$ **7.** $\frac{d^2}{c}$ **9.** $\frac{1}{2}$ **11.** $\frac{-r}{9}$
13. $\frac{1}{343x^3}$ **15.** $\frac{1}{2x}$ **17.** $\frac{-3}{ab}$ **19.** $\frac{ab^2}{7}$
21. $\frac{4a^5}{3b}$ **23.** $9r^6$ **25.** 1 **27.** $\frac{2}{5}$ **29.** y^{2n}
31. $\frac{3x^ny^{m-4}}{2}$

Written Exercises, page 213

1. $\frac{2}{243}$ **3.** $\frac{1}{21}$ **5.** 1 **7.** $\frac{1}{64}$ **9.** $-3b$
11. $\frac{1}{m^{11}}$ **13.** $-6x$ **15.** $8x^5$ **17.** $\frac{1}{3a^5}$
19. $\frac{1}{243}$ **21.** -8 **23.** $\frac{2a^{24}}{b^8}$ **25.** $\frac{2d^{19}}{3c^3}$
27. 2 **29.** 0 **31.** $-\frac{3}{5}$
33. $\left(\frac{a}{b}\right)^m = (ab^{-1})^m$ (Def Neg Exp)
$\qquad = a^m(b^{-1})^m$ (Power of a Product Prop)
$\qquad = a^mb^{-m}$ (Power of a Product Prop)
$\qquad = \frac{a^m}{b^m}$ (Def Neg Exp)

Written Exercises, page 216

1. 5.62×10^6 **3.** 5.002×10^0 **5.** 6.7×10^{-6}
7. 9.142×10^7 **9.** 1.86×10^5 mi/s
11. 7.725×10^7 m **13.** 0.00031 **15.** 0.01
17. 1,000 **19.** 20 **21.** 3,634,000
23. 0.0352 **25.** 4.32×10^8
27. 1.8247×10^2 **29.** 9.6424×10^7

Written Exercises, pages 220–221

1. Yes **3.** Yes **5.** Binomial **7.** Monomial
9. $-3y^2 + 2y + 1; 2$ **11.** $-d^3; 3$
13. $-3x^3 + 3x^2 + 3x + 1; 3$ **15.** $4y^6 + 3y +$
$7; 6$ **17.** $2a^2 + 10a - 6; -6 + 10a + 2a^2$
19. $11x^2 - 2x + 2; 2 - 2x + 11x^2$
21. $6x^4 - 3x^2; -3x^2 + 6x^4$ **23.** $-4r^4 +$
$4r - 2; -2 + 4r - 4r^4$ **25.** $12a^3 -$
$3a^2 - 9a - 4; -4 - 9a - 3a^2 + 12a^3$
27. $5y^4 - 10y^3 + 2y^2 + y - 5; -5 + y +$
$2y^2 - 10y^3 + 5y^4$ **29.** $-2a^2 + 3b^2 + 10a + 6b$
31. $-16a^2b^2 - 10a^2b^3$ **33.** Sample answer:
$2x^3 + x^2 + 6x - 7$ **35.** Sample answer:
$-7x^3y^2$ **37.** F; since $x^2 + x^3 \neq x^5$ for the
real value $x = 1$.

Midchapter Review, page 221

1. $2y^5$ **3.** $-\frac{2}{y}$ **5.** a^3b^6 **7.** $-48bc^3d^3$
9. $\frac{y^2}{z}$ **11.** $\frac{1}{2x^3}$ **13.** $\frac{125x^2}{7}$ **15.** $\frac{2}{3x}$
17. 3.2×10^7 **19.** 6.5×10^{-3}

Written Exercises, pages 224–225

1. $8x^2 - 5x$ **3.** $-a^2 - 11a + 11$ **5.** $-7b^2 -$
$7b - 5$ **7.** $-6x^4 + x^3 + 8x^2 - 4x + 2$
9. $-y^3 + 3y^2 - 1$ **11.** $-2x^3 - 6x^2 - 3$
13. 17 **15.** $10r^2 + 5$ **17.** $-x^3 - 5x$

19. $y^3 - \frac{5}{8}y^2 - \frac{2}{3}y + \frac{1}{4}$ **21.** $13.41x^3 -$
$11.1x^2 + 6.3x + 0.7$ **23.** $8.5x^5 - 4.2x^4 -$
$7.6x^3 + 10.1x - 0.2$ **25.** $19y - 2$
27. $-8y^3 - 6xy^2 - 2x^2y$

Written Exercises, pages 227–228

1. $15y^2 - 10y$ **3.** $3r^2 + 7r$ **5.** $-2x^3 -$
$8x^2 + 2x$ **7.** $7x^4 - 4x^3 + x^2$
9. $-3a^4 + a^3 - a^2$ **11.** $-8y^5 + 6y^4 + 2y^3$
13. $8b^5 - 6b^4 + 2b^3$ **15.** $-4y^5 - 8y^4 - 4y^3$
17. $6c^2 - 3c$ **19.** $16c^2$ **21.** $-7a^2 + 8a + 11$
23. $5y^2 - 4y - 6$ **25.** $4x^2 + 2x + 4$
27. $-5y^3 - 14y$ **29.** $-3a^3b + 6a^2b^2 - 3ab^3$
31. $-r^4s - 2r^3s^2 + 5r^2s^3$ **33.** $-6a^5b^2 -$
$15a^3b^3 + 3a^2b^5$ **35.** $-2x^4y - 6x^3y^2 +$
$10x^2y^3 - 8xy^4$ **37.** $38x^2 + 28x$
39. $-9a^3b - a^2b^2 + 28ab^3$

Written Exercises, page 231

1. $x^2 - x - 72$ **3.** $y^2 - 14y + 40$
5. $c^2 - 12c + 36$ **7.** $2x^2 + 7x + 5$
9. $2y^2 - 10y + 12$ **11.** $6y^2 + 17y + 5$
13. $8x^2 - 8x - 6$ **15.** $2r^2 - 11r - 40$
17. $2y^2 - 11y + 12$ **19.** $4x^2 + 7xy - 2y^2$
21. $2r^2 - rs - 3s^2$ **23.** $10y^2 + 13yz - 3z^2$
25. $x^3 + 10x^2 + 23x - 6$ **27.** $12x^3 - 8x^2 -$
$3x + 2$ **29.** $14y^3 - 17y^2 + y + 2$
31. $x^4 + 3x^2 - 10$ **33.** $c^4 - 4c^2 - 12$
35. $16y^6 - 1$ **37.** $4m^2 + 12x + 9$
39. $6x^2 - x - 2$ **41.** $21y^6 + 11x^2y^3 - 2x^4$
43. $ax - ay + bx - by$ **45.** $7a^4 - 4a^3b -$
$a^2b^2 + 4ab^3 - 6b^4$ **47.** $a^2 + 2ab + b^2 - 9$

Written Exercises, page 235

1. $y^2 - 12y + 36$ **3.** $c^2 - 16c + 64$
5. $y^2 + 20y + 100$ **7.** $r^2 - 144$
9. $-x^2 + 49$ **11.** $49y^2 - 1$ **13.** $100d^2 - 4$
15. $-36y^2 + 1$ **17.** $4r^2 - 4rs + s^2$
19. $4p^2 - 9q^2$ **21.** $49x^2 - y^2$
23. $16r^2 + 8rs + s^2$ **25.** $-25c^2 + 9$
27. $49x^2 - 14xy + y^2$ **29.** $y^4 - 10y^2 + 25$
31. $9x^4 - 12x^2 + 4$ **33.** $49y^6 - 4$
35. $x^2 - \frac{1}{2}x + \frac{1}{16}$ **37.** $x^2 - 0.2x + 0.01$
39. $y^2 + y + 0.25$ **41.** $x = -1$ **43.** $a = -4$
45. $y = 3$ **47.** $r = 5$

Chapter 7

Written Exercises, pages 246–247

1. $2^3 \cdot 5$ **3.** $3^2 \cdot 5$ **5.** 7^2 **7.** $2^2 \cdot 7$

9. $2^2 \cdot 3 \cdot 5$ **11.** $2^3 \cdot 5^2$ **13.** 3 **15.** 4
17. 6 **19.** 9 **21.** 6 **23.** 17 **25.** 2 **27.** 1
29. 2 **31.** 12 **33.** $2m^4$ **35.** $3 \cdot$ **37.** $7x^3$
39. $3x$ **41.** $2a^3$ **43.** $5y$ **45.** x **47.** $2m^2$
49. a^6 **51.** $\frac{b^7}{n}$ **53.** $-3m^5$ **55.** $-3a^7$
57. $9c^2$ **59.** $-16y^6$ **61.** $-6a^3b$
63. $-13m$ **65.** $20ab$
67. 7×14 **69.** $18a^{m-2}b^{2n-2}$ **71.** $6x^{2a}y^{3b}$

Written Exercises, pages 250–251

1. $2(x^2 - 4x - 3)$ **3.** $5(t^2 - 3t + 5)$
5. $4(x^2 - 3x - 9)$ **7.** $4(7y^2 - 5y - 6)$
9. $2x^2 + 11x - 4$ **11.** $8(a^2 + 2a + 1)$
13. $3(2x^2 - 7x - 4)$ **15.** $2(2b^2 + 13b - 7)$
17. $5b^2 + 12b - 60$ **19.** $a(a^2 + 3a - 1)$
21. $m^2(m^2 - 3m - 7)$ **23.** $a^2(a^4 - a^2 - 2)$
25. $3a(3a^2 - a + 2)$ **27.** $3a(a - 7)$
29. $5r^2 - 36$ **31.** $4y(y^2 - 5y + 6)$
33. $9x(x^4 + 9x^2 - 3)$ **35.** $3x(x^2 - 11x + 28)$
37. $5a^5 - b^5$ **39.** $2y(y^2 - 2y - 24)$
41. $3f^2(2 - 5f)$ **43.** $2t^3(1 - 64t^2)$
45. $8a^2 + b^2 + ab$ **47.** $4a^2(2a^2 + a - 3)$
49. $r^2(4 - \pi)$ **51.** $r^2(4 + \pi)$
53. $2x^2y^3(3 - 10x^2y^2 + 18x^5y^3)$
55. $4x^5y^4(2x^4 - 5x^2y^4 + 3y^5)$
57. $5d^2c^2(7c^2 + 9cd - 10d^2)$
59. $2y^n(y + 2)$ **61.** $3w^{2n}(3 + 7w)$
63. $r^{6n-27}(3r^{3n} - 13r^9)$

Written Exercises, pages 254–255

1. $(x + 4)(x - 1)$ **3.** $(a - 7)(a - 2)$
5. $(r + 3)(r - 2)$ **7.** $(t - 6)(t + 4)$
9. $(y^2 - 9y + 22)$ **11.** $(h + 3)(b - 9)$
13. $(x + 4)(x + 3)$ **15.** $(y - 17)(y - 1)$
17. $(x - 4)(x - 12)$ **19.** $(y + 9)(y + 8)$
21. $(a + 9)(a + 6)$ **23.** $(c - 8)(c + 7)$
25. $(x + 4), (x + 9)$ **27.** $(x - 4)$
29. $(x + d)(x + e)$ **31.** $(x + 3)(x + n)$
33. $(x^{3a} + 12)(x^{3a} + 9)$ **35.** $(y^{3b} + 15)$
$(y^{3b} + 12)$ **37.** $(t^{4n} - 32)(t^{4n} + 5)$

Written Exercises, page 258

1. $(2x - 1)(x + 3)$ **3.** $(5x - 1)(x - 2)$
5. $(2b - 3)(b - 1)$ **7.** Irreducible
9. $(5a - 1)(2a + 3)$ **11.** $(3b + 2)(b - 1)$
13. $(3y - 2)(2y + 3)$ **15.** Irreducible
17. $(3x - 5)(2x + 1)$ **19.** $(3t - 5)(2t + 3)$
21. $(2x - 3)^2$ **23.** $(4m + 7)(2m + 5)$
25. $(3a - 3)(5a + 2)$ **27.** $(6c + 7)(6c - 5)$
29. $(2b + 9)(b - 5)$ **31.** $(4t + 7)(2t + 7)$
33. $(10a - 1)(a - 9)$ **35.** $(-5a + 2)(3a + 8)$

37. $(2x + 3)(-5x + 6)$ **39.** $(5b + 2)$
$(-3b + 10)$ **41.** $(8x - 3)(x - 4)$
43. $(4x - 3)(2x - 1)$ **45.** $(8d - 5)(5d + 8)$
47. $(2a + 8)(2a + 1)$ **49.** $b = -15$

Written Exercises, pages 261–262

1. $(a - 5)(a + 5)$ **3.** $(t - 6)(t + 6)$
5. $(5 - r)(5 + r)$ **7.** $(3 - g)(3 + g)$
9. $(7u - 5)(7u + 5)$ **11.** $(7 - 4y)(7 + 4y)$
13. $(2e - 1)(2e + 1)$ **15.** $(12 - h)(12 + h)$
17. No **19.** Yes; $(t - 2)^2$ **21.** No
23. Yes; $(3a - 1)^2$ **25.** No **27.** Yes;
$(7u - 1)^2$ **29.** $(7t - 15y)(7t + 15y)$
31. $(16a - 15b)(16a + 15b)$ **33.** $(2y - 2x + 5)$
$(2y + 2x - 5)$ **35.** $(9t + 5v)^2$
37. $(7r + 3t)^2$ **39.** $(2y + 7x)^2$
41. $3a - 4b; 3$ **43.** $\pi(R^2 - r^2); 374$
45. $[(5t + 6) - (t - 3)] [(5t + 6) + (t - 3)];$
$(4t + 9)(6t + 3)$ **47.** $(a + b - 3)(a + b + 3)$
$(a^2 + 2ab + b^2 + 9)$

Midchapter Review, page 262

1. 2 **3.** 3 **5.** $4a^6$ **7.** $3(a^2 - 3a + 5)$
9. $4a^2b(2a^2b - 12b^2 + a)$ **11.** $(a + 5)(a - 4)$
13. $(2a + 5)(a - 1)$ **15.** $(4t - 1)(4t + 1)$
17. $(a + 2)(a + 4)$

Written Exercises, page 265

1. $2(x + 4)(x + 1)$ **3.** $2(a - 4)(a - 3)$
5. $3y(y + 4)(y + 1)$ **7.** $3(x + 5)(x - 5)$
9. $-2(a - 7)(a + 7)$ **11.** $3(x + 2)^2$
13. $3(3p - q)(p + 4q)$ **15.** $6(x + 2y)$
$(x - 5y)$ **17.** $2(5y - 7x)(5y + 7x)$
19. $2(4m - 13n)(m + n)$ **21.** $2(2a - b)^2$
23. $(2 + b)(x + y)$ **25.** $(5a + 3b)(x + y)$
27. $(r + s)(t - 3)$ **29.** $(y - 2)(p - 5)(p + 5)$
31. $3(4r + 1)(r - 4)$ **33.** $-3(f + 4)(f - 2)$
35. $2a(12 - 5a)(12 + 5a)$ **37.** $2s(5s + 7)$
$(3s - 2)$ **39.** $2y(5y - 4)(2y + 1)$ **41.** $(x - 2)$
$(x + 2)(m + 1)$ **43.** $4ay(3y - a)(a^2 + 16y^2)$
45. $(a + 2)(a - 1)(a^2 - a + 2)$
47. $(6x - 3s - 4)(2x - s + 3)$ **49.** $(2x - 5y)$
$(2x + 5y + 1)$ **51.** $(8a^2 - 4a + 1)$
$(8a^2 + 4a + 1)$

Written Exercises, page 270

1. $\{2, 3\}$ **3.** $\{-1, 3\}$ **5.** $\{4, -4\}$ **7.** $\{0, 12\}$
9. $\left\{-\frac{1}{3}, 2\right\}$ **11.** $\left\{-\frac{1}{2}, 1\right\}$ **13.** $\left\{0, -\frac{1}{4}\right\}$
15. $\{\pm 7\}$ **17.** $\left\{-1, \frac{1}{4}\right\}$ **19.** $\left\{\frac{2}{3}, -7\right\}$

21. $\left\{\frac{1}{2}, 7\right\}$ **23.** $\left\{\frac{2}{3}\right\}$ **25.** $\left\{\frac{1}{4}, -6\right\}$
27. $\left\{\frac{5}{2}, -4\right\}$ **29.** $\left\{-\frac{5}{3}, -8\right\}$ **31.** $\left\{-\frac{8}{3}, -\frac{1}{2}\right\}$
33. $\{0, +6\}$ **35.** $\{0, \pm 2\}$ **37.** $\left\{0, \frac{1}{2}, -2\right\}$
39. $\left\{0, \frac{7}{4}\right\}$ **41.** $\{0, \pm 11\}$ **43.** $\{0, \pm 2, \pm 4\}$
45. $\left\{0, \pm \frac{3}{2}\right\}$ **47.** $\{0, \pm 2, \pm 5\}$
49. $\left\{0, \pm \frac{5}{2}, \pm 1\right\}$ **51.** $\{0, \pm 7, \pm 1\}$

Written Exercises, pages 275–276

1. $\{-5, -8\}$ **3.** $\{-5, 0\}$ **5.** $\{-3, 7\}$
7. $\{-2, 10\}$ **9.** $\{2\}$ **11.** $\left\{\frac{2}{3}, -4\right\}$
13. $\{-4, 7\}$ **15.** $\left\{\frac{1}{3}, -2\right\}$ **17.** $\left\{\pm \frac{7}{5}\right\}$
19. $\left\{-\frac{7}{4}, -6\right\}$ **21.** $\left\{-\frac{1}{2}, \frac{3}{4}\right\}$ **23.** $\left\{-3, \frac{7}{6}\right\}$
25. Sample answer: Write in standard form:
$4x^3 - 15x^2 - 9x = 9$. Factor:
$x(4x^2 - 15x + 9) = 0; x(4x - 3)(x - 3) = 0$.
Set each factor equal to zero: $x = 0$;
$4x - 3 = 0, x - 3 = 0$. Solve for x: $x = 0$ or
$x = \frac{3}{4}$ or $x = 3$. So, the solution set is $\left\{0, \frac{3}{4}, 3\right\}$
27. $\left\{5, -\frac{15}{2}\right\}$ **29.** $\left\{\frac{6}{5}, -1\right\}$ **31.** $\left\{\frac{1}{3}, 5\right\}$
33. $\{2, -4\}$ **35.** $\left\{-\frac{2}{3}, -3\right\}$ **37.** $\{-a, c\}$

Written Exercises, pages 280–281

1. $\{-6, -8\}$ or $\{6, 8\}$ **3.** 6,8 **5.** $\{-3, -5\}$
or $\{3, 5\}$ **7.** $l = 9$ in, $w = 6$ in **9.** $l = 11$ cm,
$w = 4$ cm **11.** 5, 7, 9 **13.** 6, 8, 10
15. 4 m **17.** 9 ft $\times$ 10 ft **19.** 8 in

Problem Solving Strategies, page 282

1. 8 **3.** First game matches: AB in one gym,
CD in other. Only 4 distinct possible pairs for
second game.

Mixed Problem Solving, page 283

1. 34.8 cm; 75.69 cm^2 **3.** First: $232, second:
$58 **5.** 3,065 **7.** 5 h 10 min **9.** First =
29 cm, second = 21 cm, third = 26 cm
11. First: 36 students, second: 12 students
13. vertex: 98°, bases: 41° **15.** Last:
$3,020; present: $2,400

Chapter 8

Written Exercises, pages 292–293

1. -3 **3.** 4 **5.** $-2, -3$ **7.** $1, 3$ **9.** $\dfrac{2k}{3}$

11. $\dfrac{3}{5}$ **13.** 2 **15.** $\dfrac{y-7}{y-3}$ **17.** $\dfrac{a-2}{2a+1}$

19. NP **21.** NP **23.** $\dfrac{m+2}{2}$ **25.** $\dfrac{1}{8.96}$

27. 8 **29.** 0 **31.** $\dfrac{p-2}{2p^2+6p}$ **33.** ~~NP~~ y^2-5y-4 $2y^2-14y$

35. $\dfrac{x+7}{5x+5}$ **37.** $\dfrac{x+4}{3x^2-12x}$ **39.** $\dfrac{2ax-ay^2}{2b^2x-3b^2}$

41. $\dfrac{mx-m}{6n}$ **43.** $x+3$ **45.** e^3 **47.** $\dfrac{6}{e}$

49. $\dfrac{rh}{2r+2h}$ **51.** $\dfrac{x^2-x-6}{x}$

53. $\dfrac{5y^4-3y^3-2y^2}{3}$ **55.** $\dfrac{a-3b}{a-3}$

Written Exercises, page 296

1. $-\dfrac{1}{x+5}$ **3.** $\dfrac{-1}{a-6}$ **5.** $-x+2$

7. $-x-1$ **9.** $\dfrac{-1}{x+3}$ **11.** $\dfrac{-1}{c-9}$ **13.** $\dfrac{-x+3}{2x-3}$

15. $\dfrac{-p-2}{p-2}$ **17.** $\dfrac{-2b+3}{b-4}$ **19.** $\dfrac{-x+5}{x-6}$

21. $\dfrac{-2m-16}{m+7}$ **23.** $\dfrac{-x+5}{2x-8}$

25. $\dfrac{-py-5p}{m^3}$ **27.** $\dfrac{-2s-7}{s^2-6s}$ **29.** $\dfrac{-a}{6a-10}$

31. $-x+3-2y$

Written Exercises, pages 300–301

1. $\dfrac{45}{88}$ **3.** $\dfrac{6a^3}{35}$ **5.** $\dfrac{-8b^3}{33a}$ **7.** $\dfrac{a^2+2a-15}{6}$

9. $\dfrac{15z}{y}$ **11.** $\dfrac{-x}{7}$ **13.** $\dfrac{3a^2b}{c}$ **15.** $\dfrac{y-5}{11}$

17. $\dfrac{15}{2}$ **19.** $5x+15$ **21.** $\dfrac{5}{y+1}$

23. $\dfrac{2a-12}{a+5}$ **25.** $\dfrac{-4b^3}{3ax+9a}$ **27.** $\dfrac{-5b^4}{2x+2}$

29. $\dfrac{y+5}{-9b}$ **31.** $\dfrac{-1}{3x+2}$

33. $\dfrac{-x^2-6xy-5y^2}{x^2-3xy+2y^2}$ **35.** $\dfrac{-2x-10}{x-5}$

37. $\dfrac{x-1}{x^2+5x+6}$ **39.** $\dfrac{-2x+3}{x-1}$ **41.** $\dfrac{3}{13}$

43. $\dfrac{8x^3-12x^2+6x-1}{27}$

Written Exercises, pages 304–305

1. $\dfrac{35}{18}$ **3.** $\dfrac{9}{49x}$ **5.** $\dfrac{-5a^2}{8bst^2}$ **7.** $\dfrac{3}{2xy}$

9. $\dfrac{n^2}{n^2-1}$ **11.** $-\dfrac{b}{3}$ **13.** $\dfrac{a+2}{4a+12}$

15. $\dfrac{7x-28}{2}$ **17.** $\dfrac{3}{4x}$ **19.** $\dfrac{-9}{20b^2}$

21. $\dfrac{-35m}{3mn+9n}$ **23.** $\dfrac{x^2-x-20}{10}$

25. $\dfrac{x-5}{3x^2+15x}$ **27.** $\dfrac{1}{5x^2-5x}$ **29.** $3y$

31. $\dfrac{3x-3y}{5(x^2+2xy+y^2)}$ or $\dfrac{3(x-y)}{5(x+y)^2}$ **33.** a^3-

$8a^2+16a$ or $a(a-4)^2$ **35.** $\dfrac{3k^3+15k^2}{16}$ or

$\dfrac{3k^2(k+5)}{16}$ **37.** $\dfrac{3b}{2}$ **39.** $\dfrac{3x^2+9x}{-x-8}$

41. $\dfrac{a^3-a^2}{a^2-9}$ **43.** $\dfrac{3a-2b}{a^4}$ **45.** $\dfrac{3(4a+b)}{5}$

47. $\dfrac{x-4}{x^2+x-12}$ **49.** $x+3$

51. $\dfrac{5x+y+4}{x+1}$

Written Exercises, pages 308–309

1. $\dfrac{11a}{5}$ **3.** $2x^3$ **5.** $\dfrac{2}{x^2}$ **7.** $\dfrac{6}{x}$ **9.** $\dfrac{11}{x}$

11. 1 **13.** $\dfrac{x+1}{2}$ **15.** $\dfrac{a+17}{a}$ **17.** $\dfrac{5b}{7}$

19. $\dfrac{2y}{2y-3}$ **21.** $\dfrac{3}{4}$ **23.** $\dfrac{x+3}{4}$ **25.** $\dfrac{3}{a}$

27. $\dfrac{2}{a-6}$ **29.** $\dfrac{x+8}{2}$ **31.** $\dfrac{1}{x+4}$

33. $\dfrac{2x-3}{x-8}$ **35.** $\dfrac{2b-3c}{3}$ **37.** $\dfrac{2x-3}{2}$

39. $\dfrac{26}{x}$ **41.** $x-6+2y$

Midchapter Review, page 310

1. 3 **3.** 2 **5.** ±3 **7.** $\dfrac{18a^5}{-7b^2}$ **9.** $\dfrac{a}{2a+1}$

11. $\dfrac{-1}{a-1}$ **13.** $\dfrac{-2b^3}{a}$ **15.** $\dfrac{-y}{3}$ **17.** $\dfrac{9a+6}{4}$

Written Exercises, pages 314–315

1. $\dfrac{x}{2}$ **3.** $\dfrac{29b}{63}$ **5.** $\dfrac{19a}{24}$ **7.** $\dfrac{3k}{2}$ **9.** $\dfrac{5x+10}{12}$

11. $\dfrac{6}{7a}$ **13.** $\dfrac{m^2+7m+2}{4m^3}$

15. $\dfrac{-10x^2+4x+21}{12x^3}$ **17.** $\dfrac{14y+17}{12y}$

19. $\dfrac{4a+5}{6a}$ **21.** $\dfrac{22b-17}{36}$ **23.** $-\dfrac{5x+1}{3}$

25. $\dfrac{22a - 11}{6a}$ **27.** $\dfrac{31k - 17}{30}$ **29.** $\dfrac{19y - 8}{15}$

31. $\dfrac{12x + 11}{12}$ **33.** Answers will vary.   **35.** $\dfrac{7x}{5}$

37. 2   **39.** $\dfrac{6x^2 + 4x + 10xy - 4y + 3y^2}{12xy}$

41. $\dfrac{17a^2 - 8a + 26}{20a}$ **43.** $\dfrac{-2}{5a + 2}$

Written Exercises, page 319

1. $\dfrac{x + 7}{x^2 - x - 2}$ **3.** $\dfrac{5a + 13}{a^2 + 4a - 5}$ **5.** $\dfrac{15m - 2}{m}$

7. $\dfrac{x^2 + x + 1}{x - 2}$ **9.** $\dfrac{5a + 3}{a^2 - 9a}$

11. $\dfrac{-2x^2 + 6x + 5}{x^2 + x}$ **13.** $\dfrac{3x - 2}{x - 1}$

15. $\dfrac{x^2 - 4x + 10}{x - 3}$ **17.** $\dfrac{y^3 + 3y^2 - 9y + 27}{y^3 - 9y}$

19. $\dfrac{x + 2}{x}$ **21.** $\dfrac{4x + 13}{x^2 - 2x - 24}$ **23.** $\dfrac{7}{a - 9}$

25. $\dfrac{a + 4}{a^2 - 6a + 8}$ **27.** $\dfrac{2}{a - 4}$

29. $\dfrac{2b^2 + 14b + 6}{b^2 - 25}$ **31.** $\dfrac{x^2 + 3x - 7}{x^2 - 5x + 6}$

33. $\dfrac{6}{a - 4}$ **35.** $\dfrac{y^2 - 4y - 8}{2y^2 - 5y - 12}$

37. $\dfrac{13x^2 + 15x - 7}{5x - 2}$ **39.** $\dfrac{a + 6}{a - 2}$

41. $\dfrac{x^4 + 9x - 252}{x^2 - 16}$

Written Exercises, page 323

1. $15a^4 + 6a^2 - 8a$ **3.** $4n^2 - 3n + 6$

5. $3x + 1$ **7.** $3y - 1 - \dfrac{3}{y + 2}$ **9.** $3a + 2 +$

$\dfrac{4}{2a - 3}$ **11.** $4x - 5 - \dfrac{3}{3x + 1}$ **13.** $3t - 6 +$

$\dfrac{4}{4t + 3}$ **15.** $5y + 6$ **17.** $2x^2 + x - 2$

19. $2t^2 - t + 5$ **21.** $2a + 3 + \dfrac{13}{2a - 1}$

23. $t^2 + 4t - \dfrac{16}{3} + \dfrac{97}{9t + 12}$ **25.** $(a + 3)$

$(a - 4)(a + 1)$ **27.** $(4a^2 + 6a + 9)(2a - 3)$

29. $k = 2$

Problem Solving Strategies, page 324

1. 30%   **3.** Impossible

Written Exercises, pages 328–329

1. $\dfrac{21}{64}$ **3.** $\dfrac{2x}{5x - 1}$ **5.** $\dfrac{14}{23}$ **7.** $\dfrac{12a + 1}{a + 4}$

9. $\dfrac{54m - 2m^2}{3m^2 + 36}$ **11.** $\dfrac{-3x + 8}{11x + 1}$ **13.** $\dfrac{a + 3}{2a + 2}$

15. $-\dfrac{y - 3}{2y - 10}$ **17.** $\dfrac{3a^2 + 2a - 1}{4a^2 - 3a - 1}$

19. $\dfrac{2a + 11}{11a + 2}$ **21.** 3   **23.** $\dfrac{-5a - 4}{5a - 6}$

25. $x^2 + x - 6$ **27.** $\dfrac{3}{r}$

Chapter 9

Written Exercises, pages 341–342

1. $x = 6$ **3.** $x = \dfrac{1}{6}$ **5.** $y = -\dfrac{5}{3}$ **7.** $n = 2$

9. $x = 9$ **11.** $n = -20$ **13.** $a = 31$

15. $y = 7$ **17.** $x = -6$ **19.** $x = \pm 3$ **21.** No

solution   **23.** $n = 7$ **25.** 7.2 cm   **27.** $\dfrac{4}{3}, \dfrac{3}{4}$

29. $\dfrac{7}{12}$ **31.** $-\dfrac{15}{4}$

Written Exercises, page 347

1. E: 5, x; M: 10, 2   **3.** E: x, 4; M: 3, 7
5. E: 3, n; M: $n + 6$, 2   **7.** E: n, $n - 5$;

M: 3, 2   **9.** $x = 4$ **11.** $x = 5\dfrac{1}{4}$ **13.** $x = 2\dfrac{1}{7}$

15. $n = 7\dfrac{1}{5}$ **17.** $x = 5$ **19.** $n = 3$

21. $-6, 10$ **23.** $-5, 8$ **25.** ± 4 **27.** -27
29. ± 3 **31.** 4, -6 **33.** 45,000 people
35. 11, -5 **37.** 2, -4 **39.** 0, -1

41. $-\dfrac{3}{5}, 2$ **43.** 25 muffins   **45.** 140, 40

47. 25, 65   **49.** 3:4

Written Exercises, pages 352–353

1. $x = \dfrac{5}{b}$ **3.** $x = b - 2c$ **5.** $x = yz$

7. $x = \dfrac{3s}{r}$ **9.** $x = \dfrac{c - b}{6}$ **11.** $x = \dfrac{n - m}{a}$

13. $x = \dfrac{c}{a + b}$ **15.** $x = \dfrac{c}{a - b}$

17. $x = \dfrac{36}{b + d}$ **19.** $x = \dfrac{18}{c - d}$

21. $x = \dfrac{3a + t}{2}$ **23.** $x = \dfrac{5bk}{j}$

25. $l = \dfrac{p - 2w}{2}$; $l = 18.4$ cm   **27.** $x = 5c$

29. $x = \dfrac{4e + f + cd}{k}$ **31.** $x = \dfrac{6p + q}{r - p}$

33. $x = \dfrac{ab}{a + b}$ **35.** Answers will vary.

37. $x = r - 9s$ **39.** $a = \dfrac{s}{1 + r}$

41. $r = 1 + t$ **43.** $x_2 = \dfrac{Bx_1}{A - Vx_1}$

Midchapter Review, page 353

1. $x = 12$ **3.** $a = \dfrac{1}{8}$ **5.** $x = \pm 6$ **7.** $-2, 1$

9. $x = \dfrac{5b + 3}{a}$ **11.** $x = \dfrac{c}{b - a}$ **13.** $\dfrac{5}{6}, \dfrac{6}{5}$

Written Exercises, pages 357–358

1. 4 km/h; 9 km/h **3.** 2 h **5.** 6 h **7.** L: 10 km/h; M: 14 km/h **9.** 65 km/h; 77.5 km/h
11. 10 h **13.** 8:00 A.M., the next day

15. $t = \dfrac{x}{y + z}$

Written Exercises, pages 362–363

1. $\dfrac{3}{8}$ **3.** $\dfrac{3}{4}$ **5.** $6\dfrac{6}{13}$ h **7.** $9\dfrac{5}{19}$ h **9.** $37\dfrac{1}{3}$ h

11. D: $10\dfrac{1}{2}$ days; A: 21 days **13.** $2\dfrac{122}{191}$ h

15. $1\dfrac{37}{47}$ h **17.** 72 h **19.** 4 h

Written Exercises, page 366

1. 60 ft **3.** 2.25 lb **5.** 2.5 m
7. 0.05 mi/min **9.** 270 ft^2 **11.** 800 lb/min
13. 0.8 qt/s **15.** 0.135 T/h **17.** $20\dfrac{4}{9}$ yd^3

Mixed Problem Solving, page 367

1. $-43, -41$ **3.** 4, 18 **5.** K; 32; S: 76
7. vertex: 98, bases: 41 **9.** 21 in., 25 in.,
32 in **11.** $\dfrac{1}{3}$ **13.** $27.64 **15.** First: 63;
second: 24

Chapter 10

Written Exercises, pages 376–377

1. $(2, 1)$ **3.** $(-3, 3)$ **5.** $(4, -4)$
7. $(-2, 0)$ **9.** $(-4, -2)$ **11.** $(0, -3)$
13. A, D **15.** B, H, L
17., 19., 21., 23.

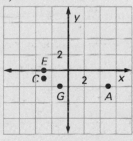

25.

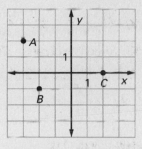

27.

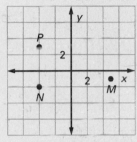

29.

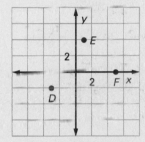

31. $(-1, 4)$

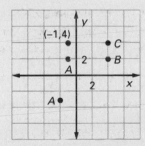

33. $(3, 5)$

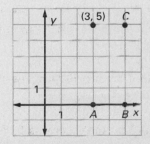

35. *D, F*   **37.** *A, B, C, G*   **39.** *A, B*
41. (3, 3)

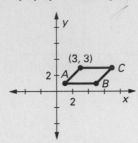

43. (1, 4)

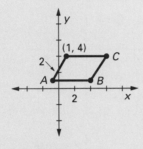

45. (11, 3), (3, 3), (−1, −1)   **47.** (11, 4),
(1, 4), (−3, −2)   **49.** (12, 2), (0, 2)

Written Exercises, pages 379–381

1. D: {−3, 0, 3, 5}; R: {−3, −2, −1, 1};

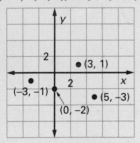

3. D: {−1, 2, 4}; R: {−3, 2, 3, 4};

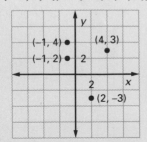

5. D: {−6, −4, 5, 7}; R: {−3, 7, 10}; yes
7. D: {−3, 2, 3}; R: {−4, −3, −2, 5}; no

9. {(1, 2), (3, 1), (−1, 3), (−2, −2), (2, −3)};
yes   **11.** A function   **13.** Not a function
15. Not a function   **17.** {(monkey, 15),
(elephant, 35), (beaver, 5), (bear, 25)}; D: {monkey,
elephant, beaver, bear}; R: {15, 35, 5, 25}
19. 3   **21.** Answers will vary.   **23.** −1, 7
25. −7, 5

27.

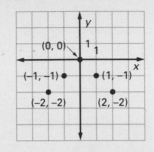

29.

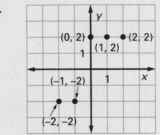

Written Exercises, pages 384–385

1. Not a function   **3.** 4   **5.** 3   **7.** 4
9. −4   **11.** 5   **13.** 17   **15.** −5   **17.** −8
19. 1   **21.** −7   **23.** R: {−8, −5, 4}
25. R: {−4, 4, 14}   **27.** R: {−6, −5, −1}
29. R: {−3.9984, 194.81, 439.5236}   **31.** 980
33. R: {1, 7, 17}   **35.** R: {0, 3, 4}
37. R: {25, 49, 121}   **39.** $f(x) = 2x$

Written Exercises, pages 388–389

1. (1, 2), (2, 6)   **3.** (2, 0), (4, 5)   **5.** Two of (6, 0),
(4, 1), (0, 3), (2, 4)   **7.** (0, 3), (2, 6)   **9.** (3, 2), (4, 4)
11. (0, 3), (3, 5)   **13.** (5, 0), (2, 1)   **15.** (0, 3),
(3, 1)   **17.** {(1, 12), (2, 6), (3, 4), (4, 3), (6, 2),
(12, 1)}   **19.** {(1, 16), (2, 8), (4, 4), (8, 2), (16, 1)}
21. {(1, 25), (5, 5), (25, 1)}   **23.** {(0, 4), (4, 0)}
25. $lw = 32$; {(1, 32), (2, 16), (4, 8), (8, 4),
(16, 2), (32, 1)}   **27.** $x + y = 10$; {(0, 10), (2, 8),
(4, 6), (6, 4), (8, 2), (10, 0)}   **29.** {(9, 1), (7, 2),
(5, 3), (3, 4), (1, 5)}   **31.** {(−78, 99), (−76, 96),

$(-74, 93), (-72, 90), (-70, 87), (-68, 84), (-66,$
$81), (-64, 78), (-62, 75), (-60, 72), (-58,$
$69), (-56, 66), (-54, 63), (-52, 60), (-50,$
$57), (-48, 54), (-46, 51), (-44, 48), (-42,$
$45), (-40, 42), (-38, 39), (-36, 36), (-34, 33),$
$(-32, 30), (-30, 27), (-28, 24), (-26, 21),$
$(-24, 18), (-22, 15), (-20, 12)\}$

Midchapter Review, page 389

1. $(1, 2)$　　**3.** $(-1, 1)$　　**5.** $(3, 0)$　　**7.** $(-3, 3)$
9., 11.

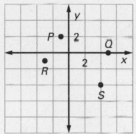

13. D: $\{-1, 1, 3\}$; R: $\{-2, 3, 6\}$; no　　**15.** 1
17. 6　　**19.** $f(-2) = 16$; $f(0) = 2$; $f(3) = 26$
21. $\{(2, 1), (5, 3)\}$　　**23.** $\{6, 6\}$

Problem Solving Strategies, page 390

1. 5 h　　**3.** 72 mi/h

Written Exercises, pages 395–396

1.

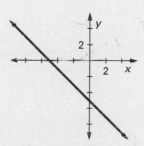

3.

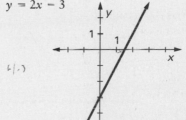

5.

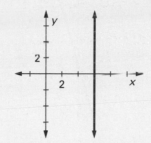

7.

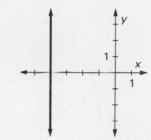

9. $y = 2x$

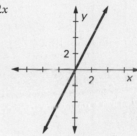

11. $y = x$

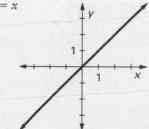

13. $y = 2x - 3$

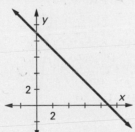

15. $y = 4x - 1$

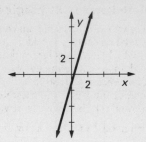

17. Linear

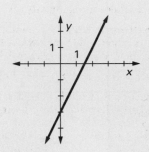

19.

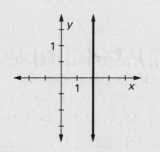

21. Linear

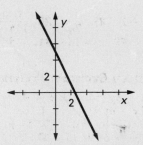

23. Constant linear

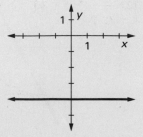

25. Not a function   **27.** A function
29.

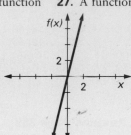

31.

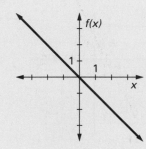

33. $y = -2x + 10$

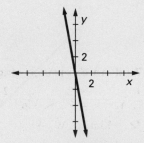

35. $y = -6x$

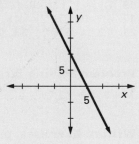

37. $y = 4x - 6$

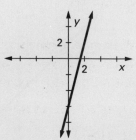

39.

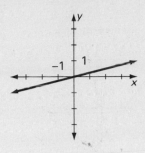

41.

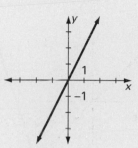

43.

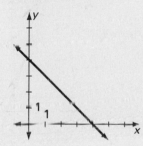

Problem Solving Strategies, page 405

Answers will vary. Sample answers are given.
1. Let n be any integer. Add 1 to n, to get $n + 1$, which is always larger than n. (Students may add any positive integer to n, for example 3, 100, or even a general form like k, where k is any positive integer.)   **3.** Restatements: For any rational number, we can always find a smaller rational number or for any $\frac{p}{q}$, we can find a smaller rational number $\frac{p}{q} - 1$.

5. Restatement: Let x be a number greater than 3 but less than 4. We can always find a number smaller than x but greater than 3 by calculating the average of 3 and x: $\frac{3 + x}{2}$. Proof that the average of any two numbers (a and b, where a is the larger) is less than a and greater than b:

$$a > b \qquad\qquad a > b$$
$$2a > a + b \qquad a + b > 2b$$
$$a > \frac{a + b}{2} \qquad \frac{a + b}{2} > b$$

Chapter 11

Written Exercises, pages 416–417

1. -2 **3.** 0   **5.** 1   **7.** 0   **9.** Undef   **11.** 0; horiz   **13.** $-\frac{1}{4}$; down to right   **15.** 0; horiz

17. Undef; vert   **19.** AB: 1; BC: -4; AC: $-\frac{2}{3}$

21. -1 **23.** $\frac{r}{7n}$ **25.** $\frac{3r + 3}{11n - 4}$ **27.** $\overleftrightarrow{AD}$, $\overleftrightarrow{BC}$ **29.** $a = 16$ **31.** 0, 5   **33.** $-5, -3$

Written Exercises, pages 399–400

1. $y = 18$ **3.** $y = -162$ **5.** $x = 48$
7. Yes; $k = 4$ **9.** No   **11.** $11.50
13. 440 mi   **15.** 40 m   **17.** 50 L   **19.** $y = 11\frac{37}{49}$
21. 1,620 m

Written Exercises, page 403–404

1. $y = 2$ **3.** $y = 4$ **5.** $x = 1$ **7.** $x = 4$
9. No   **11.** No   **13.** $66\frac{2}{3}$ amps   **15.** 21 cm
17. 16 in   **19.** 11 cm   **21.** $8\frac{1}{3}$ m
23. $310\frac{10}{289}$ lb

Written Exercises, pages 421–422

1. $x + 3y = 9$ **3.** $x + 4y = 30$ **5.** $5x + y = 0$
7. $3x - 4y = -15$ **9.** $3x + y = 10$
11. $4x + 3y = 8$ **13.** $5x - y = -11$
15. $3x - 5y = 15$ **17.** $2x + y = -4$
19. $2x - y = 0$ **21.** $3x + y = 2$
23. $12x - 4y = 5$ **25.** $12x - 24y = 35$
27. $x - 2y = -7$

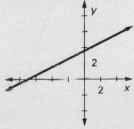

29. $4x - y = -d$ **31.** $12gx + 3y = 4g$
33. $(2 + 2r)x + (3 - r)y = 2r^2 + 6$ **35.** Line
$l: 4x - 3y = 0$, line $m: 2x + 3y = 0$, line $n:$
$5x + 4y = 0$. The value of C is zero in each
equation. The three lines intersect at the origin.

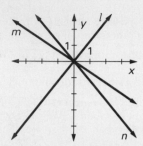

Written Exercises, pages 427–428

1. $y = 5x + 2$, or $5x - y = -2$ **3.** $y = \frac{1}{2}x - 4$,

or $x - 2y = 8$ **5.** $y = -\frac{1}{9}x - 7$, or

$x + 9y = -63$ **7.** $y = -4x + \frac{4}{3}$, or $12x +$

$3y = 4$ **9.** $y = \frac{1}{3}$, or $3y = 1$ **11.** Slope:

$-\frac{5}{3}$, y-intercept: -4 **13.** Slope: $\frac{4}{3}$,

y-intercept: -5 **15.** Slope: -1, y-intercept: 9

17. Slope: $\frac{3}{5}$, y-intercept: -4

19. Slope: 2, y-intercept: -3

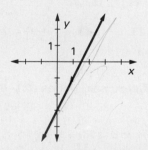

21. Slope: -3, y-intercept: 1

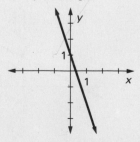

23. Slope: $-\frac{4}{3}$, y-intercept: -2

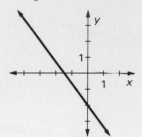

25. Slope: 3, y-intercept: 0

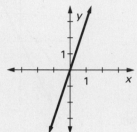

27. Slope: -4, y-intercept: 0

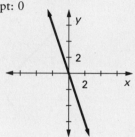

29.

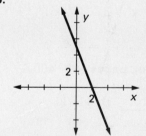

31.

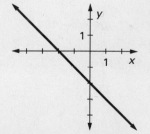

33.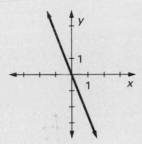

35. $y = -\dfrac{5}{2}x$

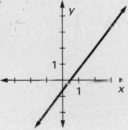

37. $y = \dfrac{4}{3}x - \dfrac{2}{3}$

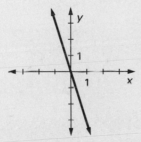

39. $y = -3x$

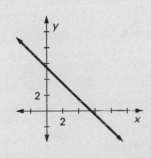

41. $y = -x + 4$ **43.** $y = 2x + 4$
45. $y = -3x - 5$
47. $y = -x + \dfrac{11}{2}$

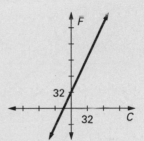

49. $y = \dfrac{10}{3}x$

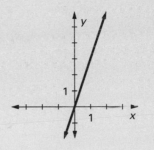

51.

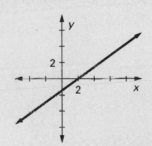

Midchapter Review, page 138

1. $-\dfrac{2}{5}$; down to right   **3.** $\dfrac{5}{3}$; up to right

5. $\dfrac{3}{5}$ **7.** $2x + 3y = 16$ **9.** $2x - y = 5$

11. $y = -5x + \dfrac{4}{3}$

13. $y = \dfrac{4}{5}x - \dfrac{8}{5}$

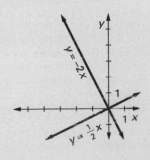

Written Exercises, pages 431–432

1. Perpendicular

669

3. Parallel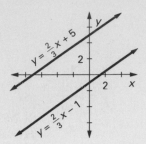

5. Parallel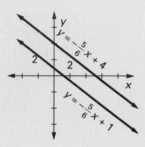

7. Perpendicular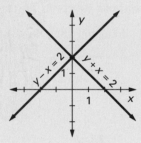

9. Perpendicular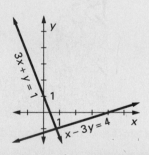

11. Perpendicular   **13.** Neither   **15.** Parallel
17. Perpendicular   **19.** Two lines in a coordinate plane are parallel if the two lines have equal slopes or if both lines are vertical. Two lines in a coordinate plane are perpendicular if the product of the slopes of the two lines is -1, or if one line is horizontal ($m = 0$) and the other line is vertical (m is undefined). If two lines do not possess one of the three characteristics above, then the two lines are neither parallel nor perpendicular.   **21.** Answers will vary.

23. Let $k = 3$. Then $y = -\frac{4}{3}x + 1$. Let

$k = 12$. Then $y = -\frac{4}{3}x + 4$. As k increases the slopes of the graphs remain equal and the y-intercepts increase.

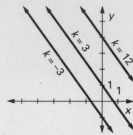

25. Collinear   **27.** Not Collinear
29. Collinear

Written Exercises, page 437

1.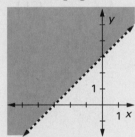

3.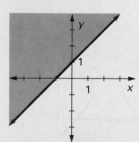

5.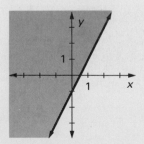

7.

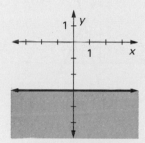

9.

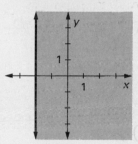

11.

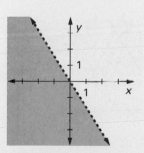

13.

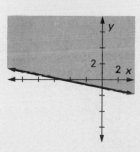

15.

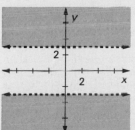

17.

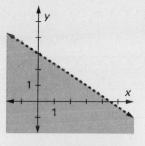

19.

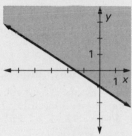

21.

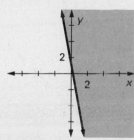

23.

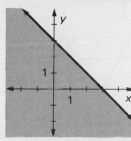

25. $y \leq \frac{1}{2}x + 1$ **27.** $x > -3$

29. y = perimeter, x = shortest side; $y \geq 4x$

31.

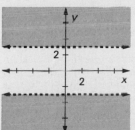

671

33.

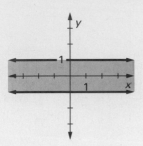

Problem Solving Strategies, page 438

1. $(5, 3)$ **3.** You could fail to get more *yes* than *no* answers.

Mixed Problem Solving, page 439

1. 60 mi/h **3.** $l = 18$ cm, $w = 8$ cm
5. Craig: 12 points; Kyle: 30 points **7.** 71, 73
9. $2,960 **11.** $14/h **13.** 1, 6 **15.** 12, 14
or $\{-12, -14\}$ **17.** $\frac{2}{5}$ h, or 24 min **19.** $17.08

Chapter 12

Written Exercises, pages 449–450

1. $(1, -3)$ **3.** $(-5, 3)$ **5.** No solution
7. $(-3, 5)$
9. $(-2, 4)$

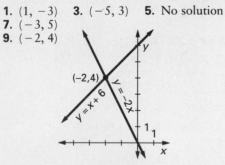

11. $\left(\frac{3}{2}, \frac{3}{2}\right)$

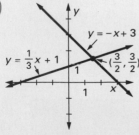

13. $(4, -2)$

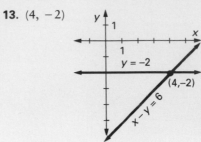

15. $(2, 5)$

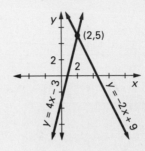

17. 0 **19.** 1 **21.** Infinitely many **23.** 1
25. $(2,0)$

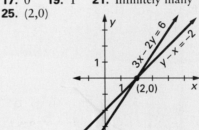

27. $(2, 1)$

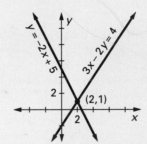

29. $\left(3, \frac{5}{2}\right)$

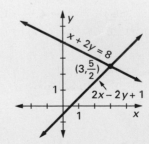

31. $\left(\frac{3}{2}, 2\right)$

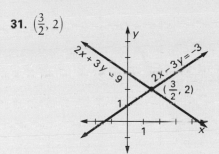

33. Fractions hard to read on a graph
35. Infinitely many *or* 1   **37.** 1 *or* 0   **39.** (0,0), (0,3), (3,0), (1,4)   **41.** Answers will vary.

Problem Solving Strategies, page 451

1. 21.5 mi   **3.** 2:30

Written Exercises, pages 454–455

1. (−2, −2)   **3.** (4, 8)   **5.** (−4, 4)
7. (2, −8)   **9.** (−3, 0)   **11.** (0, 1)   **13.** $\left(\frac{1}{2}, \frac{1}{2}\right)$
15. (3, 7)   **17.** (4, 0)   **19.** (−7, 3)   **21.** (4, 2)
23. $\left(4, \frac{10}{3}\right)$ **25.** (−2, −1)   **27.** (3, 2)
29. $\left(\frac{8}{7}, \frac{6}{7}\right)$ **31.** $\left(\frac{13}{12}, \frac{7}{12}\right)$ **33.** (12, 8)
35. $(u, r) = \left(-\frac{23}{30}, \frac{7}{15}\right)$ **37.** If $-\frac{1}{3}x + 5$ is substituted for *y* in the second equation, a false sentence such as 15 = 9 is obtained. The system has no solution.   **39.** (2, 1, −1)

Written Exercises, pages 458–459

1. Bob: 19 yr; Hank: 8 yr   **3.** *l* = 20 m; *w* = 3m   **5.** $27, $47   **7.** Mr. Hernandez: 210 lb; Carlos: 70 lb   **9.** Jane: 28 yr; Karen: 7 yr   **11.** Jack: 20; Igor: 7   **13.** *l*: 19 in; *w*: 7 in   **15.** 11, 9   **17.** Sneed: $240; Johnson: $120   **19.** −40   **21.** 32, 58   **23.** 63, 55
25. Nicole: 524 km; Melissa: 756 km

Written Exercises, pages 462–463

1. (3, 2)   **3.** (1, 0)   **5.** (1, 2)   **7.** (−7, 2)
9. $\left(-\frac{4}{3}, 2\right)$ **11.** $\left(5, -\frac{9}{7}\right)$ **13.** $\left(2, \frac{5}{3}\right)$
15. (10, 4)   **17.** Jane: 97 lb; Pat: 105 lb
19. House: $57,200; lot: $21,300
21. $14.95, $17.95   **23.** (−6, 10)
25. (−5, 1)   **27.** $\left(\frac{5}{3}, 30\right)$ **29.** *r* = 3; *s* = −1
31. (2, 4)   **33.** (2, 2)   **35.** $\left(-\frac{5}{7}, -\frac{73}{84}\right)$

37. $y = \dfrac{C + E}{B + D}$

Written Exercises, pages 466–467

1. (3, 1)   **3.** (2, 3)   **5.** (4, 0)   **7.** (−2, −1)
9. (−9, −5)   **11.** (4, 3)   **13.** (2, 1)   **15.** (1, 1)
17. (1, −4)   **19.** $\left(\frac{1}{3}, -\frac{1}{2}\right)$ **21.** (−4, 0)
23. (2, 0)   **25.** Socks: $3; sneakers: $24
27. 25 yd, 40 yd   **29.** Jacket: $75; trousers: $39   **31.** (2, −1)   **33.** $\left(\frac{1}{3}, \frac{1}{7}\right)$ **35.** (2, 1)
37. (3.2, 2.25)

Midchapter Review, page 467

1. (−1, 2)   **3.** (1, 1)   **5.** $\left(-\frac{19}{17}, \frac{8}{17}\right)$
7. (2, −3)   **9.** 6, 9   **11.** 7 hits, 19 misses
13. Mary: 65 h; Victor: 21 h

Written Exercises, pages 470–471

1. 93   **3.** 25   **5.** 28   **7.** 93   **9.** 96
11. $100h + 10t + u$; $100u + 10t + h$
13. 584   **15.** Let *t* = the tens digit and *u* = the units digit. Then $10t + u$ = a two-digit number and $10u + t$ = that two-digit number with the digits reversed. $10t + u + 10u + t = 11t + 11u = 11(t + u)$. This is divisible by 11 since $\frac{11(t + u)}{11} = t + u$.   **17.** 59, 67, 75, 83, 91

Written Exercises, pages 473–474

1. Sean: 21; Mrs. O'Malley: 49   **3.** Kim: 18; Shirley: 62   **5.** Al: 20; Mary: 28   **7.** Denise: 27; Jack: 13   **9.** Regina: 6; Morti 10
11. Ian: 4; Judy: 32   **13.** Penelope: $6\frac{1}{2}$; William: 13   **15.** Clint: 20; Fern: 12; Geri: 8

Written Exercises, pages 477–478

1. 9 dimes, 3 quarters   **3.** Pecans: 1 lb; walnuts: 3 lb   **5.** 10%: 12 oz; 18%: 20 oz
7. 7 nickels, 6 dimes   **9.** 4%: $6\frac{1}{4}$ g; 2%: $3\frac{3}{4}$ g
11. Plums: 2 kg; cherries: 5 kg   **13.** 18.75 lb
15. $\frac{105}{47}$ or $2\frac{11}{47}$ L

Written Exercises, pages 481–482

1. 10 h   **3.** 33 mi/h   **5.** 140 mi/h   **7.** 5 h
9. 45 mi/h   **11.** 8 mi   **13.** 150 mi/h

15. $r + c$ = downstream rate of boat
$= r + c + c - c$
$= r - c + c + c$
$= (r - c) + 2c$
= rate upstream + 2(rate of current)

Written Exercises, page 485

1.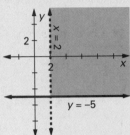

3. No solution

5.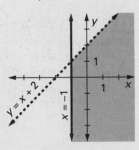

7.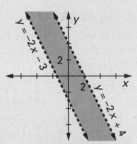

9.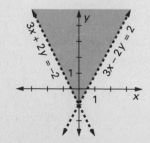

11.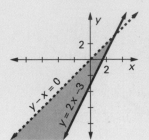

13.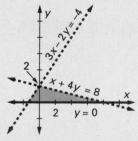

15.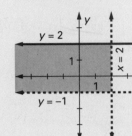

17.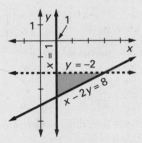

19.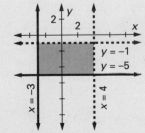

21. No solution

674

23.

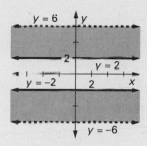

Chapter 13

Written Exercises, pages 498–499

1. $\frac{1}{1}$ **3.** $\frac{-23}{8}$ **5.** $\frac{-7}{1}$ **7.** $0.\overline{6}$, repeating

9. $-0.1\overline{6}$, repeating **11.** $-2.\overline{7}$, repeating

13. $\frac{17}{3}$ **15.** $\frac{13}{3}$ **17.** $\frac{62}{99}$ **19.** $\frac{34}{45}$ **21.** $\frac{182}{999}$

23. $\frac{28,640}{9,999}$ **25.** $\frac{522,683}{9,999}$ **27.** $\frac{5,252}{999}$

29. $1.\overline{306}$, repeating **31.** 0.1875, terminating
33. T; all integers are also rational. **35.** T; irrational numbers are subset of real numbers. **37.** T; whole numbers are subset of real numbers. **39.** F; 0 not a natural number. **41.** T; rational numbers are subset of real numbers. **43.** The set of integers is a subset of the set of rational numbers. This means that *every* number in the set of integers is also a number in the set of rational numbers.

45. $0.\overline{3} = \frac{1}{3}$; $0.\overline{6} = \frac{2}{3}$; $\frac{1}{3} + \frac{2}{3} = 1 = 0.\overline{9}$ **47.** In general, the decimal will be irrational since the sequences of blocks of 2's will not all be the same length as the decimal is extended indefinitely.

Written Exercises, pages 502–503

1. 2 **3.** 4 **5.** $-3\sqrt{2}$ **7.** 12 **9.** 8
11. $3\sqrt{3}$ **13.** $4\sqrt{2}$ **15.** $6\sqrt{3}$ **17.** $-2\sqrt{2}$
19. $-6\sqrt{2}$ **21.** $\sqrt{21}$ **23.** $\sqrt{77}$ **25.** 15
27. 7 **29.** $-24\sqrt{5}$ **31.** $-60\sqrt{6}$
33. $40\sqrt{14}$ **35.** $72\sqrt{7}$ **37.** $6\sqrt{7}$ **39.** $4\sqrt{2}$
41. 16 ft **43.** $l = 24$ cm, $w = 8$ cm
45. $-12\sqrt{14}$ **47.** $45\sqrt{3}$ **49.** $\frac{6}{7}\pi$ s

51. 2π s

Written Exercises, pages 506–507

1. 4.4 **3.** 6.9 **5.** 7.9 **7.** 8.5 **9.** 9.2
11. 3.6 **13.** 6.2 **15.** 8.1 **17.** 9.9

19. 15.7 **21.** 15.7 **23.** 23.5 **25.** 4, 9, 16, 25, 36, 49, 64, 81 **27.** 4.2 cm **29.** 5.6
31. $l = 42.0$ m, $w = 10.5$ m **33.** 0.6
35. 4 m/s

Written Exercises, pages 510–512

1. 5 m **3.** $2\sqrt{3}$ **5.** $2\sqrt{5}$ **7.** $2\sqrt{85}$
9. $\sqrt{34}$ **11.** $\sqrt{74}$ **13.** $\sqrt{105}$
15. $b = \sqrt{39}$ **17.** $b = 40$ **19.** $b = 12$
21. $b = 6\sqrt{2}$ **23.** $a = 12$ **25.** $c = \sqrt{149}$
27. Yes **29.** Yes **31.** Yes **33.** No
35. Yes **37.** Yes **39.** Yes **41.** $b = \sqrt{22}$
43. $c = 6\sqrt{5}$ **45.** $b = \sqrt{46}$ **47.** $a = 7$
49. $c = \sqrt{443}$ **51.** 25.5 cm **53.** 130 yd
55. 10.8 km **57.** Yes **59.** In Exercise 58
$(a + b)^2 = 4(\frac{1}{2}ab) + c^2$ is given where c is the length of the hypotenuse and a and b are the lengths of the legs. Thus, $a^2 + 2ab + b^2 = 2ab + c^2$. Subtract $2ab$ from each side of this equation to obtain $a^2 + b^2 = c^2$, the Pythagorean Relation. **61.** An equilateral triangle can be separated into 2 congruent triangles. In one of these right triangles let s equal the length of the hypotenuse, and h equal the length of one leg. Then $\frac{1}{2}s$ equals the length of the other leg. Then apply the Pythagorean Theorem: $h^2 + (\frac{1}{2}s)^2 = s^2$. Solve this equation for h. The result is $h = \frac{1}{2}s\sqrt{3}$.

Written Exercises, pages 514–515

1. $2x^{12}$ **3.** $-4y^8$ **5.** $70y^{14}$ **7.** $45b^{15}$
9. $3a^3\sqrt{a}$ **11.** $4y\sqrt{y}$ **13.** $-12c^2\sqrt{c}$
15. $-4a^4\sqrt{3a}$ **17.** $x^4y^3\sqrt{xy}$
19. $-3m^3n^2\sqrt{5mn}$ **21.** $-2y^2\sqrt{10xy}$
23. $12a^8b^7\sqrt{2ab}$ **25.** $2a^5b^6$ **27.** $-7a^6b^5$
29. $24x^7y^{20}$ **31.** $72x^{12}y^{18}$ **33.** $27a^7b^4\sqrt{3ab}$
35. $20x^{10}y^{16}\sqrt{6xy}$ **37.** $-15a^5b^5\sqrt{3}$
39. $-15a^6b^{12}\sqrt{2}$ **41.** $54a^5b^{14}\sqrt{2ab}$
43. $42a^{10}b^{15}\sqrt{ab}$ **45.** $24e^6f^4\sqrt{3f}$
47. $12x^5y^3z^5$ **49.** $10xz^2\sqrt{11xy}$
51. $-8x^6y^7z^4\sqrt{15xy}$ **53.** $40a^{20}b^{19}c^{11}\sqrt{2a}$
55. $-6a^{15}b^{12}c^{18}\sqrt{7b}$ **57.** $-27a^{20}b^{40}c^{50}\sqrt{3}$

Midchapter Review, page 515

1. 0.2, terminating **3.** $3.\overline{6}$, repeating **5.** $\frac{41}{9}$

7. $\frac{379}{99}$ **9.** 9 **11.** $5\sqrt{2}$ **13.** 3.9 **15.** 8.9

17. 11.6 **19.** $c = 5\sqrt{2}$ **21.** $a = 10\sqrt{3}$
23. Yes **25.** No **27.** $-24a^9$
29. $24x^6y^9\sqrt{y}$

Written Exercises, pages 517–518

1. $23\sqrt{2}$ **3.** $-\sqrt{5}$ **5.** $11\sqrt{2}$ **7.** $-\sqrt{7}$
9. $13\sqrt{11}$ **11.** $5\sqrt{a}$ **13.** $-12\sqrt{ab}$
15. $11\sqrt{cd}$ **17.** $19\sqrt{3xy}$ **19.** $27\sqrt{2mn}$
21. $8xy\sqrt{x}$ **23.** $(ab - 5b)\sqrt{ab}$
25. $6x^2\sqrt{2y}$ **27.** $25xy\sqrt{5} + 32xy\sqrt{5xy}$
29. $10x^2\sqrt{2y}$ **31.** $6 + 10\sqrt{2} + 2\sqrt{5}$
33. $16\sqrt{2}$ **35.** $l = 2\sqrt{26}$ cm, $p = 8\sqrt{26}$ cm
37. $\sqrt{2} + \sqrt{5} + \sqrt{7}$

Written Exercises, page 521

1. $30\sqrt{5}$ **3.** $16\sqrt{35}$ **5.** $30\sqrt{10}$ **7.** $12x$
9. $60x$ **11.** $60x^3\sqrt{2x}$ **13.** $-70x^3\sqrt{3x}$
15. $28y^7$ **17.** $9\sqrt{35} - 15\sqrt{14}$
19. $-9\sqrt{30} + 135\sqrt{2}$ **21.** $40\sqrt{3} - 24$
23. $11 - 5\sqrt{10}$ **25.** $-36 - 21\sqrt{2}$ **27.** 94
29. 10 **31.** $16 + 26\sqrt{6}$ **33.** $-169 + 28\sqrt{15}$
35. $77 + 24\sqrt{10}$ **37.** $17 + 4\sqrt{15}$ **39.** $167 + 28\sqrt{15}$ **41.** $25\sqrt{2} - 6\sqrt{5}$ **43.** $8\sqrt{15}$ cm^2

Written Exercises, pages 524–525

1. $\sqrt{7}$ **3.** $5x$ **5.** $3a^2$ **7.** $\dfrac{-2\sqrt{3}}{3}$
9. $7\sqrt{2}$ **11.** $\dfrac{7\sqrt{3}}{3}$ **13.** $-8\sqrt{3}$
15. $-36\sqrt{6}$ **17.** $\dfrac{\sqrt{6a}}{3a}$ **19.** $\dfrac{\sqrt{3x}}{x^2}$ **21.** $\dfrac{4\sqrt{a}}{a^2}$
23. $\dfrac{8\sqrt{5a}}{5a^4}$ **25.** $9 + 3\sqrt{7}$ **27.** $\dfrac{4\sqrt{7} + 16}{3}$
29. $\dfrac{24\sqrt{b}}{ab}$ **31.** $48c^2d\sqrt{d}$ **33.** $18x^3y^2\sqrt{xy}$
35. $\dfrac{a^3b^3\sqrt{6b}}{2}$ **37.** $-\dfrac{3a\sqrt{5b}}{b^3}$ **39.** $\dfrac{c^4\sqrt{6a}}{a^2b}$
41. $\dfrac{\sqrt{6}}{2}$ **43.** $\dfrac{\sqrt{15}}{3}$ **45.** $\dfrac{15\sqrt{5} + 5}{44}$
47. $\dfrac{60 - 36\sqrt{2}}{7}$ **49.** $\dfrac{-45\sqrt{5} - 15}{44}$
51. $\dfrac{3\sqrt{2} - 6\sqrt{3}}{-10}$ **53.** $2\sqrt{2}$ in.
55. $12\sqrt{2}$ cm

Written Exercises, page 528

1. $x = 25$ **3.** No solution **5.** $y = 81$
7. $x = 23$ **9.** No solution **11.** No solution
13. $y = 10$ **15.** $x = 8$ **17.** $x = 9$
19. $y = 1$ **21.** No solution **23.** No solution
25. $y = 2$ **27.** No solution **29.** $y = 2$
31. $a = 5$ **33.** $y = 3$ **35.** 2 **37.** $x = 25$

39. $a = 9$ **41.** No solution **43.** $A = \pi r^2$
45. $h = \dfrac{3V}{\pi r^2}$

Mixed Problem Solving, page 529

1. 104 **3.** $l = 18$ in, $w = 2$ in **5.** $36\dfrac{12}{13}$ cm
7. 320 **9.** 10 quarters, 25 dimes **11.** 20%
13. $1,008 **15.** 12, 14, or $-14, -12$
17. 7, 9, 11 or $-3, -1, 1$ **19.** $30\dfrac{6}{7}$ m^3

Chapter 14

Written Exercises, pages 537–538

1. $x = \pm 7$ **3.** $a = 0$ **5.** $\pm\sqrt{26}$ **7.** $\pm 2\sqrt{6}$
9. $\pm 5\sqrt{3}$ **11.** $y = \pm 10\sqrt{3}$ **13.** $x = \pm 8$
15. $z = \pm 4\sqrt{2}$ **17.** $x = \pm 5$ **19.** $a =$
$\pm\dfrac{\sqrt{15}}{5}$ **21.** $x = \pm\dfrac{4\sqrt{3}}{3}$ **23.** $x = \pm\dfrac{3\sqrt{2}}{2}$
25. $x = \pm\dfrac{\sqrt{105}}{7}$ **27.** $a = \pm\dfrac{\sqrt{2}}{2}$
29. $-6, 14$ **31.** $6, 10$ **33.** $-5, 3$
35. $x = -8 \pm 2\sqrt{3}$ **37.** $x = \dfrac{4 \pm 3\sqrt{2}}{3}$
39. $c = \dfrac{3 \pm \sqrt{2}}{4}$ **41.** $a = \dfrac{5 \pm \sqrt{6}}{6}$ **43.** $x = -\dfrac{1}{2}$
45. $-\dfrac{1}{3}, 1$ **47.** 5.7 s **49.** 6 m
51. $y = -7 \pm \sqrt{6}$ **53.** No real-number
solution **55.** $y = \dfrac{3}{7}$

Written Exercises, page 542

1. $(x + 7)^2$ **3.** $(x + 9)^2$ **5.** $\left(y - \dfrac{15}{2}\right)^2$
7. $\left(y + \dfrac{3}{10}\right)^2$ **9.** $6, -4$ **11.** $5, 1$
13. $1, -3$ **15.** $5, -3$ **17.** $7, -3$
19. $1, -7$ **21.** $11, 7$ **23.** $6, 12$
25. $4 \pm \sqrt{11}$ **27.** $-7 \pm \sqrt{43}$ **29.** $3 \pm \sqrt{13}$
31. $-3 \pm \sqrt{19}$ **33.** $1, 2$ **35.** $-6, 5$ **37.** $7, 8$
39. $-4, \dfrac{1}{2}$ **41.** $\dfrac{1}{2}, -\dfrac{1}{3}$ **43.** $4, \dfrac{1}{4}$
45. $\dfrac{-3 \pm \sqrt{145}}{4}$ **47.** $\dfrac{-1 \pm \sqrt{10}}{3}$ **49.** $\dfrac{3}{2}, -1$
51. $1 \pm \sqrt{5}$

Written Exercises, pages 546–547

1. $5, 2$ **3.** $7, 2$ **5.** $-2 \pm \sqrt{7}$ **7.** $1, \dfrac{1}{2}$
9. $\dfrac{7 \pm \sqrt{53}}{2}$ **11.** No real-number solution

13. $\dfrac{1 \pm \sqrt{73}}{12}$ **15.** $\dfrac{5 \pm \sqrt{73}}{6}$ **17.** $-2 \pm \sqrt{10}$

19. $-1 \pm \sqrt{3}$ **21.** $4, \dfrac{2}{3}$ **23.** No

real-number solution **25.** No real solution
27. $-0.6, -3.4$ **29.** No real-number

solution **31.** $\dfrac{-1 \pm \sqrt{17}}{2}$ **33.** $\dfrac{2 \pm 2\sqrt{13}}{3}$

35. $\sqrt{6}, \dfrac{-\sqrt{6}}{3}$ **37.** From Exercise 36, $\dfrac{w}{l} \approx$

0.618, where w and l are the width and length
of a golden rectangle. Thus, $w \approx 0.618l$. Since
$0.618 > 0.6$, it follows that $0.618l > 0.6l$, or
$w > 0.6l$.

Written Exercises, pages 550–551

1. ± 8 **3.** $\dfrac{-7 \pm \sqrt{13}}{6}$ **5.** $4, -\dfrac{3}{2}$ **7.** $7, -4$

9. $\dfrac{2}{3}, -\dfrac{5}{2}$ **11.** 4 **13.** $8 \pm \sqrt{17}$ **15.** $0, 3$

17. $\dfrac{3 \pm \sqrt{7}}{2}$ **19.** $-\dfrac{3}{2}$ **21.** $\dfrac{-1 \pm \sqrt{6}}{5}$

23. $6.7, 3.3$ **25.** $0.6, -4.6$ **27.** $2.3, -0.6$
29. 324 **31.** 10 **33.** 4 s **35.** 325
37. 20 **39.** 12 s **41.** Pellet reaches peak at
190 m above ground and then begins to fall.
43. $x^2 - 4x\sqrt{11} + 44 = 0$

Midchapter Review, page 552

1. $\pm\sqrt{34}$ **3.** $-2 \pm \sqrt{5}$ **5.** $(x + 12)^2$

7. $-3 \pm \sqrt{2}$ **9.** $\dfrac{1 \pm \sqrt{6}}{5}$ **11.** $2, -1$

13. $\dfrac{-3 \pm \sqrt{29}}{2}$ **15.** No real-number solution

17. $9, -5$ **19.** $0, -7$ **21.** $\dfrac{-3 \pm \sqrt{7}}{2}$

23. $\dfrac{5 \pm \sqrt{61}}{2}$

Written Exercises, pages 555–556

1. $l = 12$ ft, $w = 9$ ft **3.** $l = 10$ ft, $w = 9$ ft
5. $l = 23.4$ ft, $w = 8.8$ ft **7.** Sample answer:
In Exercise 1, the quadratic equation
$w^2 + 3w - 108 = 0$ has two solutions, 9 and
-12. Since the width of a rectangle cannot be
neg, -12 is rejected as a solution. **9.** 1.5 ft,
5.5 ft **11.** 1.6 m **13.** 12.1 in

Problem Solving Strategies, page 557

1. Both have the same area. **3.** 7

Written Exercises, pages 562–563

1.

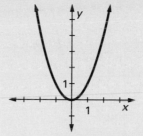

3.

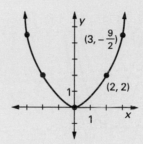

5.

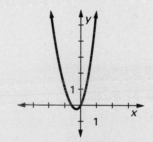

7. $(0, 2)$; $x = 0$; Min: 2

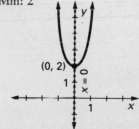

9. $(2, -1)$; $x = 2$
Min: -1

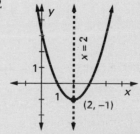

11. $\left(1, -\frac{5}{2}\right)$; $x = 1$; Min: $-\frac{5}{2}$

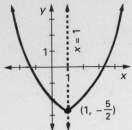

13. 6; $24   **15.** 3s; 144 ft   **17.** 100
19. a–c.

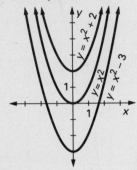

d. Parabolas move up as k increases.
e. $(0,k)$; k
21. a–c.

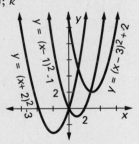

d. (h,k); k
23. $-\dfrac{b^2}{4a} + c$

25.

x	0	1	1	4	4	9	9
y	0	1	−1	2	−2	3	−3

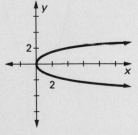

27. No; more than 1 y-value for a given x-value.

1. $(9,0)$, $(-2,0)$ **3.** $(3,0)$, $(-8,0)$ **5.** $\left(\frac{1}{3},0\right)$, $(-4,0)$ **7.** $\left(\frac{-7 + \sqrt{65}}{2},0\right)$, $\left(\frac{-7 - \sqrt{65}}{2},0\right)$
9. $\left(\frac{1 + \sqrt{19}}{3},0\right)$, $\left(\frac{1 - \sqrt{19}}{3},0\right)$ **11.** 1   **13.** 0
15. 2   **17.** 2   **19.** 0   **21.** 1   **23.** 2
25. $c = 81$ **27.** All real numbers I $c > 9$
29. Answers will vary.   **31.** To determine the number of real-number solutions of a quadratic equation, only the value of the discriminant, $b^2 - 4ac$, is needed. Since b is squared, the sign of b has no effect on the value of the discriminant. Hence the sign of b doesn't affect the number of solutions.   **33.** 2 x-intercepts

Chapter 15

1. 6   **3.** 3   **5.** 333.3   **7.** 14.7   **9.** $\angle S$
11. $\angle T$ **13.** 8 m   **15.** 10 m   **17.** 48 ft
19. 14.4 cm, 16.2 cm   **21.** Yes. In $\triangle ABC$, $m\angle C = 180 - (62 + 28) = 90$. In $\triangle XYZ$, $m\angle Y = 180 - (90 + 62) = 28$. Since the three pairs of corresponding angles have the same measure, the triangles are similar.

1. 0.385   **3.** 0.417   **5.** 0.385   **7.** 0.280
9. 0.292   **11.** 0.280   **13.** $\frac{4}{5}$ **15.** $\frac{4}{3}$ **17.** $\frac{4}{5}$
19. 48   **21.** 0.923   **23.** 0.923   **25.** $\sqrt{13}$
27. $\frac{6}{7}$ **29.** $\frac{\sqrt{13}}{7}$ **31.** $\frac{\sqrt{14}}{7}$ **33.** $\frac{\sqrt{10}}{5}$
35. $\frac{\sqrt{14}}{7}$ **37.** 15 cm   **39.** 0.600
41. $\frac{\sqrt{2}}{2}$, $\frac{\sqrt{2}}{2}$, 1

1. 0.5878   **3.** 3.271   **5.** 0.6009   **7.** 0.2126
9. 0.9325   **11.** 0.0699   **13.** 0.9336   **15.** 0.0698
17. 29   **19.** 5   **21.** 60   **23.** 66   **25.** 29
27. 40   **29.** 2   **31.** 1   **33.** 0.8452   **35.** 1

37. 45   **39.** Answers will vary. Sample answers: sin 45 = 0.7071 = cos 45 = cos (90 − 45); sin 30 = 0.5000 = cos 60 = cos (90 − 30); sin 14 = 0.2419 = cos 76 = cos (90 − 14).

Midchapter Review, page 585

1. 9   **3.** 6   **5.** 0.280   **7.** 0.292   **9.** 0.280   **11.** $\frac{1}{3}$ **13.** $\frac{\sqrt{2}}{4}$ **15.** 0.6157   **17.** 0.8693   **19.** 76   **21.** 9 m

Written Exercises, pages 588–589

1. 18.7   **3.** 49.5   **5.** 59   **7.** 8.1   **9.** 151.1   **11.** 41   **13.** 35   **15.** 34.4   **17.** 89.9   **19.** m∠S = 70, t = 17.5, s = 16.5   **21.** m∠A = 80, a = 56.7, f = 57.6   **23.** 15.2 cm   **25.** 9.5   **27.** 8.6   **29.** 4.0   **31.** 65   **33.** 9.5

Written Exercises, pages 591–592

1. 11 ft   **3.** 20 m   **5.** 180 m   **7.** 61 ft   **9.** 20,021 m   **11.** 158 mi   **13.** 79 ft

Mixed Problem Solving, page 593

1. 40%   **3.** $2,016   **5.** 22, 24, 26   **7.** 16 ft   **9.** 10 mi   **11.** 50 mm   **13.** $y = \frac{1}{2}x + 5$ **15.** Cashews: 4 kg; pecans: 7 kg

Chapter 16

Written Exercises, pages 601–602

1. $\frac{1}{6}$ **3.** $\frac{1}{2}$ **5.** $\frac{1}{6}$ **7.** $\frac{3}{8}$ **9.** $\frac{1}{8}$ **11.** $\frac{1}{2}$ **13.** $\frac{1}{2}$ **15.** 0   **17.** $\frac{1}{3}$ **19.** $\frac{1}{5}$ **21.** $\frac{3}{10}$ **23.** $\frac{4}{5}$ **25.** $\frac{7}{10}$ **27.** $\frac{7}{10}$ **29.** $\frac{4}{5}$ **31.** $\frac{1}{3}$ **33.** $\frac{7}{1}$ **35.** Let s = successful outcomes and t = total outcomes. Then t − s = the number of unsuccessful outcomes.

$$\frac{P(E)}{P\,(\text{not } E)} = \frac{\frac{s}{t}}{\frac{t-s}{t}} = \frac{s}{t-s} = \frac{\text{successful outcomes}}{\text{unsuccessful outcomes}}$$

Written Exercises, pages 606–607

1. {(H,1), (H,2), (H,3), (H,4), (T,1), (T,2), (T,3), (T,4)}   **3.** 0   **5.** $\frac{1}{64}$ **7.** $\frac{1}{16}$ **9.** $\frac{3}{32}$ **11.** $\frac{2}{3}$ **13.** $\frac{5}{9}$ **15.** $\frac{5}{9}$ **17.** 0   **19.** $\frac{2}{3}$ **21.** $\frac{1}{5}$ **23.** $\frac{3}{10}$ **25.** $\frac{3}{10}$ **27.** {(GGG), (GGB), (GBG), (GBB), (BGG), (BGB), (BBG), (BBB)}; 8   **29.** $\frac{3}{8}$

Written Exercises, pages 612–613

1. 15   **3.** 26   **5.** 72.2   **7.** $80\frac{1}{6}$ **9.** 97   **11.** 104   **13.** 91   **15.** 91   **17.** 48, 50   **19.** 98

21.

Test Scores (s)	Tally	Frequency (f)	f · s
70	III	3	210
75	IIII	4	300
80	II	2	160
85	IIII	4	340
90	⊬⊬ I	6	540
95	⊬⊬	5	475
100	⊬⊬ I	6	600
		30	2,625

23. 90   **25.** 46.56   **27.** 290   **29.** x + 3   **31.** 4, 2   **33.** 104

Midchapter Review, page 613

1. $\frac{4}{9}$ **3.** 1   **5.** $\frac{1}{8}$ **7.** 0   **9.** $\frac{1}{6}$ **11.** $\frac{1}{16}$ **13.** $\frac{5}{6}$ **15.** 13

Written Exercises, pages 617–618

1. About 40   **3.** 95   **5.** 5   **7.** 20   **9.** 140   **11.** 20   **13.** 8   **15.** Answers will vary. Sample answer: A scatter plot provides a visual means for quickly determining whether a relationship, such as a linear relationship, exists among the data.   **17.** $\frac{3}{8}$

Written Exercises, pages 620–621

1. 11   **3.** 30   **5.** 1.41   **7.** 6.71   **9.** 7.73   **11.** 5.75   **13.** 9 g   **15.** 0.7 ft   **17.** R:4.0 cm; M: x + 0.9 cm; SD:1.46 cm   **19.** 68.2%   **21.** 15.9%

Index

Boldfaced numerals indicate the pages that contain definitions.

Abscissa, **374**
Absolute value, **46**, 53–54,
  62–63, 190–191
  equations with, 190–191
  graphs of, 192
  inequalities with, 192–193
Acute angle(s), **579**
  cosine of, 579–581
  sine of, 579–581
  tangent of, 579–581
Addition
  applications, 55–56
  calculator activities for, 54
  method for solving a system
    of equations, 460–461
  of integers, 53–54
  of like terms, 26–27
  of polynomials, 222–223
  of radicals, 516–517
  of rational expressions,
    306–313
  of real numbers, 53–55
  on a number line, 49–51
Addition method for systems of
  equations, 460–461
Addition Property
  for equations, **89–91**
  for inequalities, **166–168**
Additive Identity Property,
  50, 115–116
Additive Inverse Property, **51**,
  115–116
Age problems, 472–473
Algebraic expression(s), **1–3**
  equivalent, **19**
  evaluating, 1, 2, 10, 72–73
  simplifying, 75–76
Altitude of a triangle, **13**
Angle(s)
  acute, 579, 586–587
  of depression, 590
  of elevation, 590
  of triangles, 140–141
  right, 508, 579
  supplementary, 346
Application(s), (*see also*
  Problem Solving)

automobile rental rates, 66
boiling point of water, 271
commission sales, 266
compound interest, 225
cost and profit formulas, 29
direct variation, 348
earth's hydrosphere, 217
fixed and variable costs, 391
gas mileage, 255
gear depths, 143
heat transfer, 21
linear programming,
  486–487
shock wave, 114
stopping distance, 552
temperature and altitude, 423
temperature humidity index
  (THI), 8
thunder and lightning, 109
triangle inequality, 189
typing and mathematics, 93
using electricity, 507
wind chill, 61
Approximation of square roots,
  504–505
Area, **13**
  of a circle, 16
  of a square, 15
  of a trapezoid, 13
  of a triangle, 13
Arithmetic mean, **69**, 145, 608
Associative Property
  for Addition, **17–19**, 115
  for Multiplication, **17–19**,
  115
Average, **69**, 145, 608
Axis (axes)
  in the coordinate plane, 373
  of symmetry, 559
    equation of, 560

Base
  of a power, **9**
  of a triangle, **13**, 140
  of a trapezoid, 13
Base angle(s), 140
Binomials, **218**

FOIL method of multiplying,
  229–230
  product of, 229–230
  square of, 232–234
Brainteaser(s), 78, 134, 184,
  235, 251, 276, 353, 567,
  589, 607
Business problem(s), 29,
  154–155, 266

Calculator applications
  addition, 54
  compound interest, 225
  exponents, 10
  function keys, 381
  literal equations, 350
  multiplication, 14
  percent problems, 150–151
  prime factorization, 244
  proportions, 345
  quadratic equations and
    geometry, 554
  rational expressions, 289
  reciprocals of positive
    numbers, 71
  scientific notation, 215, 217
  square roots, 501, 545
Central tendency
  measures of, 608–611
Circumference, **16**
Closure Property
  for Addition, **54**, 115
  for Multiplication, **63**, 115
Coefficient(s), **26**
Coin problem(s), 475
College Prep Test, 39, 85, 123,
  161, 199, 239, 287,
  333, 371, 409, 443, 491,
  533, 571, 597, 625
Commission sales, 155, 266
Common denominator, 144,
  311
Common factor(s), 244
Commutative Property
  for Addition, **17–19**, 115
  for Multiplication, **17–19**,
  115

Completing the square,
539–542
Complex rational expression(s),
326–329
Composite number(s), **243**
Compound event(s), 603–605
Compound interest, 225
Compound sentences, 175–181
with absolute value, 192–193
Computer Investigations, 628
Slope-Intercept Form
of a Line, 629
Graphing $y = |Ax + B|$, 631
Graphing $y = |Ax + B| + C$, 633
Graphing Systems of
Equations, 635
Graphing Quadratic
Functions, 637
Maximum and Minimum,
638
Using Statistics: Predicting,
641
Conditional statement(s), **116**
Conjugate(s), 523
Conjunction(s), **175**
graphing, 179–182
truth of, 175–178
Consecutive integer(s),
135–136, 277–278
Constant(s), **26**
of variation, 397–398,
401–402
Constraint(s), 486
Consumer Applications
automobile rental rates, 66
commission sales, 266
compound interest, 225
cost or profit formulas, 29
discount, 155
gas mileage, 255
heat transfer, 21
sale price, **155**
sales tax, 154
Conversion fraction(s),
364–365
Coordinate(s)
of point, 373–375
of points on line, 41–43
Corresponding angles
of triangles, 575
Corresponding sides

of triangles, 575
Cosine, 580–585
applications, 590
Counting number(s), 41
Cubic equation(s), 269

Decimal(s)
equations with, 147–148
nonrepeating, 497
nonterminating, 495–497
repeating, 495–497
terminating, 495–496
Deductive reasoning, 116–118
Difference of two squares,
259–260
Digit problem(s), 468–469
Dimensional analysis, 364–365
Direct Proof, 116–117
Direct variation(s), 348,
397–398
Discount, 155
Discriminant, **545**
of quadratic function(s),
564–565
Disjunction, **176–177**
graphing, 179–182
Distance/Rate/Time, 111, 479
applications, 109, 479–480
Distributive Property, 22–24,
26, 75, 79, 106, 115, 248
Division, **68**
Property of Equality, 95
of monomials, 207–208
of polynomials, 320–322
of radicals, 522–524
of rational expressions,
302–303
of real numbers, 67–69
Division Property
for equations, 95
for inequalities, 171–173
Domain, 378–379

Empty set(s), **31**
Equation(s), **30**
absolute value, 190–191
addition property, 89–91
cubic, 269
division property, 95
equivalent, **89**, 447
linear, 418–420, 424–426

graph, 392–394
with two variables, (See
equations, systems of)
literal, 349–351
multiplication property for,
94–96
of a function, 383–384
point–slope form, 418–420
quadratic, 267–269
radical, 526–527
rational, 337–340
subtraction property, 90–91
systems of, 445–448,
452–453, 460–461,
464–465
using factoring to solve,
267–269
using two properties of
equality, 98–99
with absolute value, 190–191
with decimals, 147–148
with fractions, 144–145
with parentheses, 106–107
with rational expressions,
337–340
with two variables, 386–388
with variable on both sides,
102–103
Estimation and graphs,
614–616
Even integer(s), **135**
Event(s), 603–605
compound, **605**
independent, **604**
mutually exclusive, **605**
probability of, 599–601
Exponent(s), **9–10**
calculator activities, 10
division properties, 207–208
multiplication properties,
201–202
negative, 210–212
power properties, 204–205
zero, 210
Exponential form, 9
Expression(s)
algebraic, 1–3
mixed, 72–73
numerical, 1
rational, 289–291
Extraneous solution(s), 338, 526
Extremes of a proportion, 343

Factor(s), 9, 243
  common, 244
  greatest common, 244–245
  greatest common monomial,
    245–246, 248–249
  prime, 243
Factoring, 243–246
  by grouping, 264
  completely, 263–264
  difference of two squares,
    259–260
  integers, 243–245
  perfect square trinomial, 260
  polynomials, 248–249
  prime factorization, 244
  to solve equations, 267–269
  trinomials, 252–257
FOIL method of multiplying
  binomials, 229–230
Formula(s), 9–10, 13–14
  angles in a triangle, 140
  area of a circle, 16
  area of a square, 14–15
  area of a trapezoid, 13
  area of a triangle, 13
  business, 29
  calculator application, 14
  circumference, 16
  compound interest, 225
  cost or profit, 29
  distance/rate/time, 111
  exponents, 9
  perimeter of a rectangle, 13,
    139
  perimeter of a square, 14
  perimeter of a triangle, 140
  quadratic, 543–549
  solving for a variable,
    349–351
  surface area of a rectangular
    solid, 111
  volume
    of a rectangular solid,
      14–15
Fraction(s)
  cancellation property of, 207
  complex, 325–327
  conversion, 364–365
  equations with, 144–145
Frequency table, **610**
Function(s), **378–379**
  constant linear, 393

domain, 378
equation, 383–384
linear graph, 392–394
quadratic, 558–565
range, 378
values of, 382–384
vertical line test, 394

Geometry
  angle(s)
    acute, 579, 586–587
    of a triangle, 140–141
    right, 508, 579, 586–587
    supplementary, 346
  area, 13
    of a rectangle, 15
    of a square, 15
    of a triangle, 13–15
    of a trapezoid, 13–15
  parallel lines, 429–430
  perimeter, 13–16, 75
    of a rectangle, 13, 139
    of a triangle, 140
  Pythagorean theorem,
    508–510
  similar triangles, 575–576
  square,
    area, 15
  surface area, 111
  triangle(s)
    altitude, 13
    isosceles, 140
    right, 586–587
    similar, 575–576
    sum of the angles, 140
  volume
    of a rectangular solid,
      14–15
Graph(s)
  in problem solving, 390
  of absolute value, 394–396
  of conjunctions, 179–182
  of disjunctions, 179–182
  of functions, 558–561
  of inequalities, 167–168,
    179–182, 192–193
  of linear equations
    (functions), 392–394,
    425–426
  of linear inequalities,
    433–436

of numbers, 41
of ordered pairs, 373–375
of quadratic equations,
  558–561
of relations, 378–379
of systems
  of equations, 445–448
  of inequalities, 483–484,
    487
statistical, 614–616
Greatest common factor (GCF),
  244–245
Grouping symbol(s), 5–6
Guide for problem solving, 35,
  101, 157, 185, 282, 324, 390,
  405, 438, 451, 557
Guess and check, 157, 252–253

Half–plane(s), 433–434
  boundary(edge), 433
  closed, 433
  open, 433
Histogram(s), 615–616
Horizontal line, 393
Hypotenuse, 579
Hypothesis, 116

Identity Property
  for Addition, 50–51
  for Multiplication, 27
Independent event(s), **604**
Inequalities, **30**
  addition property for,
    166–168
  multiplication, division
    properties of, 171–173
  equivalent, 166
  graphs, 165–167, 192–193
  in problem solving, 186–187
  linear, 433–436, 483–484
  multiplication property for,
    170–173
  open, 165–168
  subtraction property for,
    166–168
  systems of, 483–484, 487
  triangle, 189
  with absolute value, 192–193
Infinite repeating decimal,

495–497
Integer(s), 41, 497–498
  consecutive, 135–136,
    277–278
  even, 135
  factoring, 243–245
  odd, 136
Intercepts of a graph, 424–426
Inverse(s)
  additive, 51
  multiplicative, 68
Inverse variation, 401–402
Irrational number(s), 497–498,
  501
Irreducible polynomial(s), 257

Least common denominator
  (LCD), 144–145, 311–313
Least common multiple,
  144, 311
Leg(s), of triangles, 140
Like term(s), 218
  combining, 26–27
  in addition of polynomials,
    222–223
  in multiplication of
    polynomials, 229–230
  in subtraction of
    polynomials, 222–223
  real number coefficients,
    75–76
Line(s)
  parallel, 429–430
  perpendicular, 430
  slope of, 413–416
Linear combination
  method for solving systems of
    equations, 464–465
Linear equation(s), 418–420,
  424–426
  graphing, 392–393
  in two variables, 392
  standard form of, 392
  systems of, 445–448,
    452–453, 464–465
  using two points to write,
    419–420
  using slope to write, 418,
    424–426
Linear function, 392–394
Linear inequalities, 165

graphing, 165–167, 433–436
systems of, 483–484
Linear programming, 486–487

Mathematical sentence, 30
Maximum Values, 559–561
Mean(s), 69, 145, 608–609, 619
  of proportion, 343
Measure(s) of central tendency,
  608–611
Median, 609
Mixture problems, 476–477
Mode, 609–610
Monomial(s), 201, 218
  degree of, 219
  dividing, 207–208
  divisor of polynomials, 320
  multiplying, 201–202
  powers of, 204–205
Motion problem(s), 354–356,
  479–480
Multiplication. (See also
  Product(s))
  Associative Property, 17–19,
    115
  Closure Property for, 63, 115
  Commutative Property for,
    17–19, 115
  Distributive Property of
    Multiplication
    over addition, 22–23, 115
    over subtraction, 23–24
  Identity Property for, 27
  of binomials, 229–230
  of monomials, 201–202
  of polynomials, 226,
    229–234
  or radicals, 519–520
  of rational expressions,
    297–299
  of real numbers, 62–64
  property of equality, 94–96
  property for equations,
    94–96
  property for inequalities,
    170–173
  property for −1, 76
  property for zero, 62, 267
Multiplication/addition method
  for solving a system of
  equations, 464–465

Multiplicative Identity
  Property, 27, 115
  Property for Rational
    Expressions, 311
Multiplicative inverse, 68
  Property, 68, 115

Natural number(s), 41
Negation of a mathematical
  sentence, 178
Negative
  exponent, 210–212
  factor, 79–80
  integer, 41
  number(s), 41–43
Nonrepeating decimal, 497
Nonterminating decimal,
  495–497
Normal curve, 621
Null set (See empty set)
Number(s) (See also integer(s);
  real number(s))
  composite, 243
  counting, 41
  even, 135
  irrational, 497–498, 501
  natural, 41
  odd, 136
  prime, 243
  rational, 495–498
  whole, 41
Number line, 41–43
  addition on, 49–51
Numerical coefficient(s), 26
Numerical expression(s), 1
  order of operations, 5–6
  simplifying, 5–6, 72–73
  value of, 1–2

Open half plane, 433
Open inequality, 165
Open sentence(s), 30–32
Opposite(s), 45–46
Order of magnitude, 217
Order of operations, 5–6, 9, 72
  calculator applications, 8
Ordered pair, 373
Ordinate(s), 374
Origin, 373

Parabola(s), 559
  axis of symmetry, 559
  maximum point, 559
  minimum point, 559
  vertex, 559
Parallel lines, 429–430
Parentheses
  as grouping symbols, 5–6
  equations with, 106–107
Percent, 150–155
  calculator application, 150–151
  discount, 155
  decrease, 151
  increase, 151
  solving equations with, 150–151
Perfect square, 501
  trinomial, 260, 539
Perimeter, 13–16
  of rectangle, 15, 139
  of triangle, 140
Perpendicular lines, 430
Point–slope form of a linear equation, 418–420
Polynomial(s), 218
  addition of, 222–223
  degree of, 219
  descending order of, 219
  division of, 320–322
  factoring, 248, 264
  irreducible, 257
  multiplication of, 226–233
  opposite, 223
  simplifying, 218–219
  subtraction of, 222–223
Power(s), 9
  of monomials, 204–205
  of a power, 204
  of a product, 204–205
  product of, 201–202
  quotient of, 207–208
Prime factorization, 244–245
Prime numbers(s), 243
Probability, 599–600
  compound events, 603–605
  independent events, 604
Problem solving (See also Applications)
  age, 472–473
  angle measurement of

triangles, 140–141
business, 154–155
coin, 475
compound interest, 225
conditions and inequalities, 186–187
consecutive integer, 135–136
digit, 468–469
dimensional analysis, 364–365
distance/rate/time, 479–480
drawing a diagram, 479–480
guess and check/making a table, 157, 282
inequalities, 186–187
mixture, 476–477
motion, 354–356, 479–480
organizing data: distance/rate/time, 479–480
organizing data: mixture problems, 476–477
organizing data: motion problems, 354–356, 479–480
percent problems, 150–155
perimeter, 139–140
probability, 599–605
quadratic equations, 274, 277–279, 553–554
  and geometry, 553–554
restating the problem, 405
solving word problems, 125–141
statistical graphs, 614–616
surface area: 111
systems of equations, 456–457
testing to find conditions, 324
translation: words to symbols, 125–126
trigonometric ratios, 590
two or more numbers, 129–131
using addition, 55
using approximations of square roots, 505
using direct variation, 348, 397–398
using geometry formulas,

139–141
using graphs, 390
using inverse variation, 401–402
using opposites, 55
using percent, 150–155
using the Pythagorean Theorem, 508–510
using quadratic equations, 274
using radical equations, 528
using ratio and proportions, 255, 345–346
using scientific notation, 217
using similar triangles, 576
using the sine, cosine, and tangent ratios, 590
using subtraction, 58
using systems of equations, 456–457
using two variables, 456–457
  digit problems, 468–469
words to symbols, 125–126
work problems, 359–361
Problem–solving strategy(ies)
  checking assumptions, 557
  choosing a strategy, 593
  developing a plan, 101
  drawing a diagram, 195, 278–279, 354–355, 479–480, 529, 553–554, 590
  estimating before solving, 283
  guess and check, 157
  looking back, 185
  making a graph, 390, 486–487, 614–615
  making a table, 354–355, 360–361, 439, 479–480
  restating the problem, 405
  testing conditions, 324
  understanding the problem, 35, 119
  using a formula, 8, 10, 13–14, 21, 29, 65, 66, 93, 109, 110, 111, 139–140, 143, 225, 255, 266, 350–351, 391, 507, 549
  working backwards, 451
  writing an equation, 105,

107, 129–131, 135–136, 274, 277–279, 345, 348, 403–404, 456–457, 465

Product(s) (*See also* Multiplication)
  of powers, 201–202
  power of, 204–205
  property for square roots, 500
  sum and difference of two terms, 233–234

Proof
  conclusion, 116
  hypothesis, 116

Property
  addition, for equations, 89–91
  addition, for inequalities, 166–168
  additive identity, 50, 115
  additive inverse, 51, 115
  associative, 17–19, 115
  cancellation for fractions, 207
  closure, for addition, 54, 115
  closure, for multiplication, 63 64, 115
  commutative, 17–19, 115
  comparison, 186
  distributive, 22–24, 79–80, 106–107, 115
  division, for equations, 95–96
  division, for inequalities, 171–173
  identity, for addition, 50
  identity, for multiplication, 27
  multiplication, for equations, 94–96
  multiplication, for inequalities, 170–171
  multiplicative identity, 27, 115
  multiplicative identity for rational expessions, 311
  multiplicative inverse, 68, 115
  negative one for multiplication, 76
  of equality, 115
  of the power of a power, 204

of the power of a product, 204–205
of the product of powers, 201–202
of proportions, 343
quotient, of powers, 207–208
quotient, of square roots, 522
reflexive, 115
square root, of even powers, 513
square root, of odd powers, 513
substitution, 115
subtraction, for equations, 90–91
subtraction, for inequalities, 166
symmetric, 115
transitive, 115
trichotomy, 186
zero, for multiplication, 62, 267

Proportion(s), **343–346**
  extremes, 343
  means, 343
  property of, 343
  solutions of, 343–348

Pythagorean Theorem, 508–510

Quadrant, 374

Quadratic equations,
  applications, 274, 277–279, 533–554
  double root of, 268–269
  graphing, 558–560
  number of solutions, 268–269, 565
  roots, 268–269
  solving by completing the square, 539–541
  solving by factoring, 267–269, 548
  solving by the quadratic formula, 543–549
  solving by using square roots, 535–537, 548
  standard form, 272–274

Quadratic formula, 543–546
  discriminant, 545

Quadratic functions, 558–561
  discriminant, 564–565
  graph of, 558–561
    maximum point, 559
    minimum point, 559

Radical(s), 500
  addition of, 516–517
  conjugates, 523
  division of, 522–524
  equations with, 526–527
  like, 516–517
  multiplication of, 519–520
  product property of, 500–501
  rationalizing the denominator, 522–524
  simplifying, 513–514
  simplest form, 513–514, 522–524
  subtraction of, 516–517

Radicand, **500**

Range, 619
  of relation, 378

Ratio, **343**, 345–346
  trigonometric, 579–581

Rational expressions, **289**
  addition of, 306–318
  complex rational, 325–327
  division of, 302–303
  equations with, 337–340
  least common denominator, 311–313
  multiplication of, 297–299
  multiplicative identity property, 311
  simplest form, 289–295
  subtraction of, 306–318

Rational numbers, 495–497

Reading mathematics, 11, 33, 64, 73, 104, 137, 182, 220, 230, 234, 264, 269, 295, 313, 346, 375, 395, 399, 465, 502, 550, 576, 611

Real number(s), 41–43, 495–498

Reciprocal(s), **68**

Reflexive Property, 115

Relation(s), **378**

Replacement set, 30, 387–388

Right angle, 508, 579

Roots (*See* Solution.)

Index

Index

Sample space, 603–605
Scatter plot, 614–615
Scientific notation, 214–215
Sentence
  compound, 175–177
  mathematical, 30–32
  open, 30–32
Set
  empty, 31–32
  of counting numbers, 41
  of integers, 41, 497–498
  of rational numbers,
    495–498
  of real numbers, 41–43,
    495–498
  of whole numbers, 41
  replacement, 30–32,
    387–388
  solution, 31–32, 387
Similar triangles, 575–576
Simplest form (of a rational
  expression), 208, 290–291
Sine, 580–584
Slope, 413–416
  used to write linear
    equations, 418–420
  slope-intercept form of a
    linear equation, 424–426
Solution(s)
  extraneous, 338, 526
  of an equation, 31–32, 386
  of an inequality, 165
  of a system of linear
    equations, 445–448
  of a system of inequalities,
    483–484
  set, 30–32, 386
Solving equations,
  addition property, 89–91
  multiplication property,
    94–96
  ratio and proportion,
    344–346
  for a variable, 89–91, 94–96
  more than one step, 98–99
  variable on both sides,
    102–103
Square,
  area, 15
Square root(s), **500**
  addition of, 516–517
  approximations of, 504–505

division of, 522–524
multiplication of, 519–520
perfect square, **501**
principal, **500**
product property for, 500
quotient property of, 522
simplifying, 500–502,
  513–514
Standard deviation, **619**
Standard form
  of linear equation in two
    variables, **392**
  of quadratic equation,
    272–274
Statistics
  frequency table, 610
  graphs, 614–616
  histogram, 615
  mean, 69, 145, 608, 611, 619
  median, **609**
  mode, 609–610
  scatter plot, 614–615
Subset(s), **498**
Substitution method, for solving
  a system of equations,
  452–453
Substitution property, 115
Subtraction, 57
  Distributive Property of
    Multiplication over
    23–24, 115
  of like terms, 26–27
  of polynomials, 222–223
  of radicals, 516–517
  of rational expressions,
    306–313
  of real numbers, 57–58
  property for equations,
    90–91
Supplementary angles, **346**
Symmetric Property, 115
System(s) of equations, **445**
  applications
    age problems, 472–473
    coin problems, 475
    digit problems, 468–469
    graph of, 445–448
    linear combination,
      464–465
    mixture problems,
      476–477
    motion problems, 479–480

solution set, 445
solved by addition,
  460–461
solved by graphing,
  445–448
solved by
  multiplication/addition,
  464–465
solved by substitution,
  452–453
Systems of inequalities,
  483–484, 487

Tangent, 580–584
Technology (*See* Calculator
  applications)
Terminating decimal(s),
  495–496
Theorem, **116**
  proof, 116–117
Transitive Property, 115
Tree diagram, 603–604
Triangle(s)
  altitude, 13
  angle measures, 140–141
  area, 13
  corresponding angles, 575
  corresponding sides, 575
  hypotenuse, 579
  isosceles, 140
  legs of, 579
  perimeter of, 140
  Pythagorean Theorem,
    508–510
  right, 508–510, 579–581,
    586–587
  similar, 575–576
  sum of the angles, 140–141
Triangle inequality, 189
Trichotomy Property, 186
Trigonometric ratios, 579–590
Trinomial(s), **218**
  factoring, 252–264
  perfect square, 260
Truth table(s), 176, 178

Value of the function, 382–384
Variable, 1
  equations with two variables,

386–387
  on each side of an equation, 102–103

Variation
  constant of, 397, 401
  direct, 397–398
  inverse, 401–402

Vertex
  angle, 140
  of a parabola, 559

Vertical line, 393–394
  test, 394

Volume
  formulas, 14–16
  of a cube, 301
  of a rectangular solid, 14

Whole number(s), 41

Word problems (*See* Problem Solving and Applications)

Work problems, 359–361

Writing math (partial listing), 8(WE 44, 49), 12(WE 50), 20(WE 46), 37(WE 28), 48(WE 79), 97(WE 37), 100(WE 56), 189(WE 21), 213(WE 34), 221(WE 37), 228(WE 36), 247(WE 68), 258(WE 46), 262(WE 48), 275(WE 25), 292(WE 42), 314(WE 33, 34), 353(WE 35), 377(WE 40), 380(WE 21), 407(WE 32), 422(WE 35), 463(WE 28), 555(WE 7), 618(WE 15)

x-axis, 373
x-coordinate, 374
x-intercept, **424**

y-axis, 373
y-coordinate, 374
y-intercept, **424**

Zero exponent(s), 210
Zero-Product Property, 267